ESSENTIALS OF BUSINESS STATISTICS

The McGraw Hill Series in Operations and Decision Sciences

ESSENTIALS OF BUSINESS STATISTICS
Using Excel

Sanjiv Jaggia

California Polytechnic State University

Alison Kelly

Suffolk University

ESSENTIALS OF BUSINESS STATISTICS

1 2 3 4 5 6 7 8 9 LWI 28 27 26 25 24 23

ISBN 978-1-266-29004-6
MHID 1-266-29004-4

Cover Image: *GLandStudio/Shutterstock*

mheducation.com/highered

Dedicated to our families.

Sanjiv Jaggia

Courtesy Sanjiv Jaggia

Sanjiv Jaggia is a professor of economics and finance at California Polytechnic State University in San Luis Obispo. Dr. Jaggia holds a Ph.D. from Indiana University and is a Chartered Financial Analyst (CFA®). He enjoys research in statistics and data analytics applied to a wide range of business disciplines. Dr. Jaggia has published numerous papers in leading academic journals and has co-authored three successful textbooks, two in business statistics and one in business analytics. His ability to communicate in the classroom has been acknowledged by several teaching awards. Dr. Jaggia resides in San Luis Obispo with his wife and daughter. In his spare time, he enjoys cooking, hiking, and listening to a wide range of music.

Alison Kelly

Courtesy Alison Kelly

Alison Kelly is a professor of economics at Suffolk University in Boston. Dr. Kelly holds a Ph.D. from Boston College and is a Chartered Financial Analyst (CFA®). Dr. Kelly has published in a wide variety of academic journals and has co-authored three successful textbooks, two in business statistics and one in business analytics. Her courses in applied statistics and econometrics are popular with students as well as working professionals. She has also served as a consultant for a number of companies; her most recent work focused on how large financial institutions satisfy requirements mandated by the Dodd-Frank Act. Dr. Kelly resides in Hamilton, Massachusetts, with her husband, daughter, and son. In her spare time, she enjoys exercising and gardening.

A Unique Emphasis on Communication Makes Business Statistics Relevant to Students

We wrote *Essentials of Business Statistics* because we saw a need for a contemporary, core statistics text that sparked student interest and bridged the gap between how statistics is taught and how practitioners think about and apply statistical methods. Throughout the text, the emphasis is on communicating with numbers rather than on number crunching. In every chapter, students are exposed to statistical information conveyed in written form. By incorporating the perspective of practitioners, it has been our goal to make the subject matter more relevant and the presentation of material more straightforward for students. Although the text is labeled as business statistics, the content is just as relevant in non-business fields in STEM and the social sciences.

From our years of experience in the classroom, we have found that an effective way to make statistics interesting is to use timely applications. For these reasons, examples in *Essentials of Business Statistics* come from all walks of life, including salaries, education, technology, sports, housing, public health, discrimination, environment, polling, and much more. By carefully matching examples with statistical methods, students learn to appreciate the relevance of statistics in our world today, and, perhaps, end up learning statistics without realizing they are doing so.

> *"The amount of material covered [. . .] and the examples and detailed solutions as well as illustrations were excellent. I thought the material was well covered and presented in a very basic but easily understandable fashion. It was engaging and easy to read and understand."*
>
> **—Christopher O'Byrne,** *San Diego State University*

> *"Very useful and well-written book. Student-friendly as far as readability and workload."*
>
> **—Michael Cervetti,** *University of Memphis*

Continuing Key Features

The third edition of *Essentials of Business Statistics* reinforces and expands six core features that were well-received in the second edition.

Integrated Introductory Cases. Each chapter begins with an interesting and relevant introductory case. The case is threaded throughout the chapter, and once the relevant statistical tools have been covered, a synopsis—a short summary of findings—is provided. The introductory case often serves as the basis of several examples in other chapters.

Writing with Data. Interpreting results and conveying information effectively are critical to effective decision making in virtually every field of employment. Students are taught how to take the data, apply them, and convey the information in a meaningful way.

Unique Coverage of Regression Analysis. Relevant and extensive coverage of regression without repetition is an important hallmark of this text.

Written as Taught. Topics are presented the way they are taught in class, beginning with the intuition and explanation, followed by solved examples, and concluding with nontechnical interpretations.

Integration of Microsoft Excel. Students are taught to develop an understanding of the concepts and how to derive any of the calculations; then Excel is used as a tool to perform the cumbersome calculations.

Connect. Connect is an online system that gives students the tools they need to be successful in the course. Through guided examples and LearnSmart adaptive study tools, students receive guidance and practice to help them master the topics.

"A very good textbook that is worth reviewing and considering for adoption."

–Dennis K. Agboh, *Morgan State University*

"Concise, at the right level of difficulty, and suitable for a one-semester business course."

–Yijun (Susan) He, *Washington State University*

Features New to the Third Edition

We have made substantial revisions that address the current needs of the market. These revisions are based on the feedback of countless reviewers and users of our earlier editions. In addition, we have incorporated many of the recommendations from the 2016 Guidelines for Assessment and Instruction in Statistics (GAISE) College Report that was endorsed and published by the American Statistical Association.

As the title suggests, this edition focuses exclusively on Microsoft Excel. Most problems are solved with Excel rather than using tedious calculations with formulas and/or statistical tables.

There are four major innovations in this edition.

More Emphasis on Data Preparation and Visualization

- We include new sections in Chapter 1 devoted to data preparation.
- We include new sections in Chapter 2 devoted to data visualization methods.
- We discuss subsetted means in Chapter 3.
- We use pivot tables to analyze empirical probabilities in Chapter 4.

More Reliance on Excel and Connect

- We remove the dependence on z-, t-, χ^2-, and F-tables in all relevant chapters.
- We use Excel to explore concepts and solve problems.
- We provide Excel instructions in several exercises in Connect.
- We have improved the Connect product to facilitate teaching in an online environment.

Significant Rewrite of Regression and Forecasting

- We streamline the discussion of goodness-of-fit measures in Chapter 12.
- We include a revised section on model assumptions and common violations in Chapter 12.
- We expand the coverage of regression with interaction variables in Chapter 13.
- We include a stand-alone discussion of forecasting models in Chapter 14.
- We have improved visualizations to explore regression and forecasting models in Chapters 12–14.

More Relevant Discussion

- We include numerous new examples, exercises, and case studies.
- We use updated data to make the applications more current.
- We use big data in the writing sections for Chapters 1, 2, 3, 12, and 13.
- We use one of the big data sets to create several Connect questions, spanning multiple chapters, that can serve as a capstone project.

We also include two new appendices in this edition. Appendix A is a data dictionary for the three big data sets that are used in Chapters 1, 2, 3, 12, and 13. Appendix B summarizes Excel formulas, references, and functions that are commonly used for calculations and data analysis.

Students Learn through Real-World Cases and Business Examples . . .

Integrated Introductory Cases

Each chapter opens with a real-life case study that forms the basis for several examples within the chapter. The questions included in the examples create a roadmap for mastering the most important learning outcomes within the chapter. A synopsis of each chapter's introductory case is presented when the last of these examples has been discussed.

INTRODUCTORY CASE

Investment Decision

Dorothy Brennan works as a financial advisor at a large investment firm. She meets with an inexperienced investor who has some questions regarding two approaches to mutual fund investing: growth investing versus value investing. The investor has heard that growth funds invest in companies whose stock prices are expected to grow at a faster rate, relative to the overall stock market. Value funds, on the other hand, invest in companies whose stock prices are below their true worth. The investor has also heard that the main component of investment return is through capital appreciation in growth funds and through dividend income in value funds.

The investor shows Dorothy the annual return data for Fidelity's Growth Index mutual fund (Growth) and Fidelity's Value Index mutual fund (Value). Table 3.1 shows a portion of the annual return (in %) for these two mutual funds from 1984 to 2019. It is difficult for the investor to draw any conclusions from the data in their present form. In addition to clarifying the style differences in growth investing versus value investing, the investor requests Dorothy to summarize the data.

SYNOPSIS OF INTRODUCTORY CASE

Growth and value are two fundamental styles in stock and mutual fund investing. Proponents of growth investing believe that companies that are growing faster than their peers are trendsetters and will be able to maintain their superior growth. By investing in the stocks of these companies, they expect their investment to grow at a rate faster than the overall stock market. By comparison, value investors focus on the stocks of companies that are trading at a discount relative to the overall market or a specific sector. Investors of value stocks believe that these stocks are undervalued and that their price will increase once their true value is recognized by other investors. The debate between growth and value investing is age-old, and which style dominates depends on the sample period used for the analysis.

Gladkikh/Getty Images

An analysis of annual return data for Fidelity's Growth Index mutual fund (Growth) and Fidelity's Value Index mutual fund (Value) for the years 1984 throuth 2019 provides important information for an investor trying to determine whether to invest in a growth mutual fund, a value mutual fund, or both types of mutual funds. Over this period, Growth's mean return of 15.755% is greater than Value's mean return of 12.005%. While the mean return typically represents the reward of investing, it does not incorporate the risk of investing.

Standard deviation tends to be the most common measure of risk with financial data. Because Growth's standard deviation (23.799%) is greater than Value's standard deviation (17.979%), Growth is likelier to have returns farther above and below its mean. Finally, given a risk-free rate of 1%, Growth's Sharpe ratio of 0.62 is slightly greater than Value's Sharpe ratio of 0.61, indicating that Growth provides more reward per unit of risk. Assuming that the behavior of these returns will continue, the investor will favor investing in Growth over Value. A commonly used disclaimer, however, states that past performance is no guarantee of future results.

"It has plenty of homework problems and case studies for the instructors to choose from. This is actually an important criteria for me to choose a textbook."

—Minghe Sun, *The University of Texas at San Antonio*

and Build Skills to Communicate Results

Writing with Data

One of our most important innovations is the inclusion of a sample report within every chapter. Our intent is to show students how to convey statistical information in written form to those who may not know detailed statistical methods. For example, such a report may be needed as input for managerial decision making in sales, marketing, or company planning. Several similar writing cases are provided at the end of every Writing with Data section. Each chapter also includes a synopsis that addresses questions raised from the introductory case. This serves as a shorter writing sample for students.

> *This is an excellent approach. . . . The ability to translate numerical information into words that others can understand is critical.*
> **Scott Bailey,**
> *Troy University*

6.4 WRITING WITH DATA

Case Study

Corbis / Image Source

Professor Lang is a professor of economics at Salem State University. She has been teaching a course in Principles of Economics for over 25 years. Professor Lang has never graded on a curve because she believes that relative grading may unduly penalize (benefit) a good (poor) student in an unusually strong (weak) class. She always uses an absolute scale for making grades, as shown in the two left columns of Table 6.1.

TABLE 6.1 Grading Scales with Absolute Grading versus Relative Grading

Absolute Grading		Relative Grading	
Grade	Score	Grade	Probability
A	92 and above	A	0.10
B	78 up to 92	B	0.35
C	64 up to 78	C	0.40
D	58 up to 64	D	0.10
F	Below 58	F	0.05

A colleague of Professor Lang's has convinced her to move to relative grading because it corrects for unanticipated problems. Professor Lang decides to experiment with grading based on the relative scale as shown in the two right columns of Table 6.1. Using this relative grading scheme, the top 10% of students will get A's, the next 35% B's, and so on. Based on her years of teaching experience, Professor Lang believes that the scores in her course follow a normal distribution with a mean of 78.6 and a standard deviation of 12.4.

> *Excellent. Students need to become better writers.*
> **Bob Nauss,**
> *University of Missouri, St. Louis*

Many teachers would confess that grading is one of the most difficult tasks of their profession. Two common grading systems used in higher education are relative and absolute. Relative grading systems are norm-referenced or curve-based, in which a grade is based on the student's relative position in the class. Absolute grading systems, on the other hand, are criterion-referenced, in which a grade is related to the student's absolute performance in class. In short, with absolute grading, the student's score is compared to a predetermined scale, whereas with relative grading, the score is compared to the scores of other students in the class.

Let X represent a grade in Professor Lang's class, which is normally distributed with a mean of 78.6 and a standard deviation of 12.4. This information is used to derive the grade probabilities based on the absolute scale. For instance, the probability of receiving an A is derived as $P(X \geq 92) = 0.14$. Other probabilities, derived similarly, are presented in Table 6.2.

Sample Report— Absolute Grading versus Relative Grading

TABLE 6.2 Probabilities Based on Absolute Scale and Relative Scale

Grade	Probability Based on Absolute Scale	Probability Based on Relative Scale
A	0.14	0.10
B	0.38	0.35
C	0.36	0.40
D	0.07	0.10
F	0.05	0.05

Unique Coverage and Presentation . . .

Unique Coverage of Regression Analysis

We combine simple and multiple regression in one chapter, which we believe is a seamless grouping and eliminates needless repetition. This grouping allows more coverage of regression analysis than the vast majority of *Essentials* texts. This focus reflects the topic's growing use in practice. However, for those instructors who prefer to cover only simple regression, doing so is still an option.

In addition, we have streamlined the discussion of goodness-of-fit measures, model assumptions, and common violations. We have also expanded coverage of regression with interaction variables and dedicated a chapter entirely to forecasting. A greater emphasis is placed on visualization in the context of regression and forecasting.

Written as Taught

We introduce topics just the way we teach them; that is, the relevant tools follow the opening application. Our roadmap for solving problems is

1. Start with intuition
2. Use Excel to make cumbersome calculations and/or to estimate the appropriate model, and
3. Interpret the results and communicate insights gained from a nontechnical standpoint.

We use worked examples and case studies throughout the text to illustrate how to apply concepts to solve real-world problems.

That Make the Content More Effective

Integration of Microsoft Excel®

Students are encouraged to develop an intuition for statistical concepts and how they are used in the business world before solving problems. As the title suggests, this edition focuses exclusively on Microsoft Excel for solving problems rather than using tedious calculations with formulas and/or statistical tables. All chapters, with the exception of Chapter 4, include hands-on tutorials and examples solved with Excel.

USING EXCEL TO OBTAIN BINOMIAL PROBABILITIES

We use Excel's **BINOM.DIST** function to calculate binomial probabilities. We enter =BINOM.DIST(x, n, p, TRUE or FALSE) where x is the number of successes, n is the number of trials, and p is the probability of success. For the last input, we enter TRUE if we want to find the cumulative probability $P(X \leq x)$ or FALSE if we want to find the probability $P(X = x)$.

a. In order to find the probability that exactly 70 American adults are Facebook users, $P(X = 70)$, we enter =BINOM.DIST(70, 100, 0.68, FALSE) and Excel returns 0.0791.

b. In order to find the probability that no more than 70 American adults are Facebook users, $P(X \leq 70)$, we enter =BINOM.DIST(70, 100, 0.68, TRUE) and Excel returns 0.7007.

c. In order to find the probability that at least 70 American adults are Facebook users, $P(X \geq 70) = 1 - P(X \leq 69)$, we enter =1 -BINOM.DIST(69, 100, 0.68, TRUE) and Excel returns 0.3784.

"I definitely like the use of Excel throughout the chapter."
−Richard Paulsen,
Bloomsburg University of Pennsylvania

Real-World Exercises and Case Studies That Reinforce the Material

Mechanical and Applied Exercises

In most chapters, exercises are a well-balanced blend of mechanical, computational-type problems followed by interpretive-type problems. We have found that simpler drill problems tend to build students' confidence prior to tackling more difficult applied problems. Moreover, we repeatedly use many data sets—including house prices, sales, personality types, demographics, health measures, stock returns, salaries, and debt—in various chapters of the text. For instance, students first use these real data to calculate summary measures, make statistical inferences with confidence intervals and hypothesis tests, and, finally, perform regression analysis.

EXERCISES 9.4

Mechanics

64. Consider the following hypotheses:

$$H_0: p \geq 0.38$$
$$H_A: p < 0.38$$

Calculate the p-value based on the following sample information.

a. $x = 22; n = 74$
b. $x = 110; n = 300$
c. $\bar{p} = 0.34; n = 50$
d. $\bar{p} = 0.34; n = 400$

65. Which sample information in the preceding question enables us to reject the null hypothesis at $\alpha = 0.01$ and at $\alpha = 0.10$?

66. Consider the following hypotheses

$$H_0: p = 0.32$$
$$H_A: p \neq 0.32$$

Calculate the p-value based on the following sample information

a. $x = 20; n = 66$
b. $x = 100; n = 264$
c. $\bar{p} = 0.40; n = 40$
d. $\bar{p} = 0.38; n = 180$

72. You would like to determine if more than 50% of the observations in a population are below 10. At $\alpha = 0.05$, conduct the test on the basis of the following 20 sample observations:

8	12	5	9	14	11	9	3	7	8
12	6	8	9	2	6	11	4	13	10

Applications

73. A study finds that 82% of employees will likely quit because of lack of progression at the job (msn.com, January 14, 2020). A human resources manager would like to determine whether the percentage has decreased due to uncertainty in the job market. The manager conducts an anonymous survey and finds that 150 out of 200 employees will likely quit because of lack of progression at the job.

a. State the null and the alternative hypotheses to test the manager's claim.
b. What is the value of the test statistic? What is the p-value?
c. At $\alpha = 0.05$, is the manager's claim supported by the data? Explain.

74. An economist is concerned that more than 20% of American

What Resources Are Available for Instructors?

Instructor Library

The Connect Instructor Library is your repository for additional resources to improve student engagement in and out of class. You can select and use any asset that enhances your lecture. The Connect Instructor Library includes:

- PowerPoint presentations
- Excel Data Files
- Test Bank
- Instructor's Solutions Manual
- Digital Image Library

Tegrity Campus: Lectures 24/7

Tegrity Campus is integrated in Connect to help make your class time available 24/7. With *Tegrity,* you can capture each one of your lectures in a searchable format for students to review when they study and complete assignments using Connect. With a simple one-click start-and-stop process, you can capture everything that is presented to students during your lecture from your computer, including audio. Students can replay any part of any class with easy-to-use browser-based viewing on a PC or Mac.

Educators know that the more students can see, hear, and experience class resources, the better they learn. In fact, studies prove it. With *Tegrity Campus,* students quickly recall key moments by using *Tegrity Campus*'s unique search feature. This search helps students efficiently find what they need, when they need it, across an entire semester of class recordings. Help turn all your students' study time into learning moments immediately supported by your lecture. To learn more about *Tegrity,* watch a two-minute Flash demo at http://tegritycampus.mhhe.com.

ALEKS

ALEKS is an assessment and learning program that provides individualized instruction in Business Statistics, Business Math, and Accounting. Available online in partnership with McGraw Hill Education, ALEKS interacts with students much like a skilled human tutor, with the ability to assess precisely a student's knowledge and provide instruction on the exact topics the student is most ready to learn. By providing topics to meet individual students' needs, allowing students to move between explanation and practice, correcting and analyzing errors, and defining terms, ALEKS helps students to master course content quickly and easily.

ALEKS also includes an instructor module with powerful, assignment-driven features and extensive content flexibility. ALEKS simplifies course management and allows instructors to spend less time with administrative tasks and more time directing student learning. To learn more about ALEKS, visit www.aleks.com.

MegaStat® for Microsoft Excel®

MegaStat by J. B. Orris of Butler University is a full-featured Excel add-in that is available online through the *MegaStat* website at www.mhhe.com/megastat or through an access card packaged with the text. It works with Excel 2016, 2013, and 2010 (and Excel: Mac 2016). On the website, students have 10 days to successfully download and install *MegaStat* on their local computer. Once installed, *MegaStat* will remain active in Excel with no expiration date or time limitations. The software performs statistical analyses within an Excel workbook. It does basic functions, such as descriptive statistics, frequency distributions, and probability calculations, as well as hypothesis testing, ANOVA, and regression. *MegaStat* output is carefully formatted, and its ease-of-use features include Auto Expand for quick data selection and Auto Label detect. Because *MegaStat* is easy to use, students can focus on learning statistics without being distracted by the software. *MegaStat* is always available from Excel's main menu. Selecting a menu item pops up a dialog box. Screencam tutorials are included that provide a walkthrough of major business statistics topics. Help files are built in, and an introductory user's manual is also included.

Instructors
Student Success Starts with You

Tools to enhance your unique voice

Want to build your own course? No problem. Prefer to use an OLC-aligned, prebuilt course? Easy. Want to make changes throughout the semester? Sure. And you'll save time with Connect's auto-grading, too.

65%
Less Time Grading

A unique path for each student

In Connect, instructors can assign an adaptive reading experience with SmartBook® 2.0. Rooted in advanced learning science principles, SmartBook 2.0 delivers each student a personalized experience, focusing students on their learning gaps, ensuring that the time they spend studying is time well-spent.
mheducation.com/highered/connect/smartbook

Affordable solutions, added value

Make technology work for you with LMS integration for single sign-on access, mobile access to the digital textbook, and reports to quickly show you how each of your students is doing. And with our Inclusive Access program, you can provide all these tools at at the lowest available market price to your students. Ask your McGraw Hill representative for more information.

Solutions for your challenges

A product isn't a solution. Real solutions are affordable, reliable, and come with training and ongoing support when you need it and how you want it. Visit **supportateverystep.com** for videos and resources both you and your students can use throughout the term.

Students
Get Learning that Fits You

Effective tools for efficient studying

Connect is designed to help you be more productive with simple, flexible, intuitive tools that maximize your study time and meet your individual learning needs. Get learning that works for you with Connect.

Study anytime, anywhere

Download the free ReadAnywhere® app and access your online eBook, SmartBook® 2.0, or Adaptive Learning Assignments when it's convenient, even if you're offline. And since the app automatically syncs with your Connect account, all of your work is available every time you open it. Find out more at **mheducation.com/readanywhere**

"I really liked this app—it made it easy to study when you don't have your text-book in front of you."

- Jordan Cunningham,
  Eastern Washington University

iPhone: Getty Images

Everything you need in one place

Your Connect course has everything you need—whether reading your digital eBook or completing assignments for class, Connect makes it easy to get your work done.

Learning for everyone

McGraw Hill works directly with Accessibility Services Departments and faculty to meet the learning needs of all students. Please contact your Accessibility Services Office and ask them to email accessibility@mheducation.com, or visit **mheducation.com/about/accessibility** for more information.

What Resources Are Available for Students?

29. **FILE** *Highway.* Many environmental groups and politicians are suggesting a return to the federal 55 miles-per-hour (mph) speed limit on America's highways. They argue that not only will a lower national speed limit reduce greenhouse emissions, it will also increase traffic safety. A researcher believes that a lower speed limit will not increase traffic safety because he feels that traffic safety is based on the variability of the speeds at which people are driving, rather than the average speed. The researcher gathers the speeds of 40 cars from a highway with a speed limit of 55 mph (Highway_1) and the speeds of 40 cars from a highway with a speed limit of 65 mph (Highway_2). The accompanying file contains the relevant data.

   a. Calculate the mean and the median for each highway.

   b. Calculate the standard deviation for each highway.

   c. Do the data support the researcher's belief? Explain.

30. **FILE** *Census.* The accompanying data file contains, among other variables, median household income and median house value for the 50 states.

   a. Calculate and discuss the range of household income and house value.

   b. Calculate the sample MAD and the sample standard deviation of household income and house value.

   c. Discuss why we cannot directly compare the sample MAD and the standard deviations of the two variables.

31. **FILE** *Franchise.* The accompanying data file contains the net profit (Net_Profit), counter sales (Counter_Sales), and drive-through sales (Drive_Sales) for a chain of 100 fast-food restaurants. All variables are measured in millions of dollars.

   a. Calculate the sample standard deviation for counter sales and drive-through sales. According to this measure of dispersion, which variable exhibited higher variability?

   b. Calculate the mean absolute deviation (MAD) for counter sales and drive-through sales. According to this measure of dispersion, which variable exhibited higher variability?

Integration of Excel Data Sets.

A convenient feature is the inclusion of an Excel data file link in many problems using data files in their calculation. The link allows students to easily launch into Excel, work the problem, and return to Connect to key in the answer and receive feedback on their results.

---

47. **FILE** *Prime.* Amazon Prime is a $139-per-year service that gives the company's customers free two-day shipping and discounted rates on overnight delivery. Prime customers also get other perks, such as free e-books. An analyst believes that Prime customers spend more than $1,200 per year on this service. The accompanying data file shows the annual expenditures (Expenditures in $) of 100 Prime customers.

   a. Specify the null and alternative hypotheses to test the analyst's claim.

   b. Calculate the value of the test statistic and the *p*-value.

   c. At the 5% significance level, what is the conclusion to the hypothesis test? Is the analyst's claim supported by the sample data?

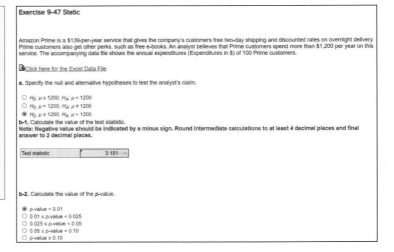

Guided Examples.

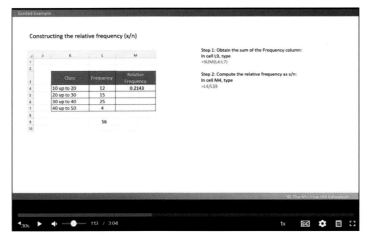

These narrated video walkthroughs provide students with step-by-step guidelines for solving selected exercises similar to those contained in the text. The student is given personalized instruction on how to solve a problem by applying the concepts presented in the chapter. The video shows the steps to take to work through an exercise. Students can go through each example multiple times if needed.

The Connect Student Resource page is the place for students to access additional resources. The Student Resource page offers students quick access to the recommended study tools, data files, and helpful tutorials on statistical programs.

McGraw Hill Customer Care Contact Information

At McGraw Hill, we understand that getting the most from new technology can be challenging. That's why our services don't stop after you purchase our products. You can email our product specialists 24 hours a day to get product training online. Or you can search our knowledge bank of frequently asked questions on our support website.

For customer support, call **800-331-5094** or visit **www.mhhe.com/support**. One of our technical support analysts will be able to assist you in a timely fashion.

ACKNOWLEDGMENTS

We would like to acknowledge the following people for providing useful comments and suggestions for past and present editions of all aspects of *Business Statistics*.

John Affisco
Hofstra University

Mehdi Afiat
College of Southern Nevada

Dennis K. Agboh
Morgan State University

Mohammad Ahmadi
University of Tennessee–Chattanooga

Sung Ahn
Washington State University

Fred Ahrens
University of Toledo

Mohammad Ahsanullah
Rider University

Imam Alam
University of Northern Iowa

Mostafa Aminzadeh
Towson University

Ardavan Asef-Vaziri
California State University

Antenah Ayanso
Brock University

Scott Bailey
Troy University

Jayanta Bandyopadhyay
Central Michigan University

Samir Barman
University of Oklahoma

Douglas Barrett
University of North Alabama

John Beyers
University of Maryland

Arnab Bisi
Purdue University–West Lafayette

Gary Black
University of Southern Indiana

Randy Boan
Aims Community College

Matthew Bognar
University of Iowa

Juan Cabrera
Ramapo College of New Jersey

Scott Callan
Bentley University

Gregory Cameron
Brigham Young University

Kathleen Campbell
St. Joseph's University

Alan Cannon
University of Texas–Arlington

Michael Cervetti
University of Memphis

Samathy Chandrashekar
Salisbury University

Xioahui Chang
Oregon State University

Gary Huaite Chao
University of Pennsylvania–Kutztown

Sangit Chatterjee
Northeastern University

Leida Chen
California Polytechnic State University

Anna Chernobai
Syracuse University

Alan Chesen
Wright State University

Juyan Cho
Colorado State University–Pueblo

Alan Chow
University of South Alabama

Bruce Christensen
Weber State University

Howard Clayton
Auburn University

Robert Collins
Marquette University

M. Halim Dalgin
Kutztown University

Tom Davis
University of Dayton

Matthew Dean
University of Maine

Jason Delaney
University of Arkansas–Little Rock

Mitra Devkota
University of North Georgia

Ferdinand DiFurio
Tennessee Tech University

Matt Dobra
UMUC

Luca Donno
University of Miami

Joan Donohue
University of South Carolina

David Doorn
University of Minnesota

James Dunne
University of Dayton

Mike Easley
University of New Orleans

Erick Elder
University of Arkansas–Little Rock

Ashraf El-Houbi
Lamar University

Moh El-Saidi
Utah Valley University

Roman Erenshteyn
Goldey-Beacom College

Grace Esimai
University of Texas–Arlington

Soheila Fardanesh
Towson University

Carol Flannery
University of Texas–Dallas

Sydney Fletcher
Mississippi Gulf Coast Community College

Andrew Flight
Portland State University

Samuel Frame
California Polytechnic State University–San Luis Obispo

Priya Francisco
Purdue University

Vickie Fry
Westmoreland County Community College

Ed Gallo
Sinclair Community College

Glenn Gilbreath
Virginia Commonwealth University

Robert Gillette
University of Kentucky

Xiaoning Gilliam
Texas Tech University

Mark Gius
Quinnipiac University

Malcolm Gold
Saint Mary's University of Minnesota

Michael Gordinier
Washington University

Deborah Gougeon
University of Scranton

Don Gren
Salt Lake Community College

Thomas G. Groleau
Carthage College

Babita Gupta
CSU Monterey Bay

Robert Hammond
North Carolina State University

Jim Han
Florida Atlantic University

Elizabeth Haran
Salem State University

Jack Harshbarger
Montreat College

Edward Hartono
University of Alabama–Huntsville

Clifford Hawley
West Virginia University

Santhi Heejebu
Cornell College

Natalie Hegwood
Sam Houston State University

Paul Hong
University of Toledo

Ping-Hung Hsieh
Oregon State University

Marc Isaacson
Augsburg College

Mohammad Jamal
Northern Virginia Community College

Dr. Robin James
William Rainey Harper College

Robin James
Harper College

Molly Jensen
University of Arkansas

Craig Johnson
Brigham Young University–Idaho

Janine Sanders Jones
University of St. Thomas

Vivian Jones
Bethune–Cookman University

Jerzy Kamburowski
University of Toledo

Howard Kaplon
Towson University

Krishna Kasibhatla
North Carolina A&T State University

Mohammad Kazemi
University of North Carolina–Charlotte

Ken Kelley
University of Notre Dame

Lara Khansa
Virginia Tech

Esther C. Klein
St. Francis College

Ronald Klimberg
St. Joseph's University

Andrew Koch
James Madison University

Subhash Kochar
Portland State University

Brandon Koford
Weber University

Randy Kolb
St. Cloud State University

Nastassia Krukava
Indiana University

Vadim Kutsyy
San Jose State University

Francis Laatsch
University of Southern Mississippi

David Larson
University of South Alabama

John Lawrence
California State University–Fullerton

Shari Lawrence
Nicholls State University

Radu Lazar
University of Maryland

David Leupp
University of Colorado–Colorado Springs

Carel Ligeon
Auburn University–Montgomery

Carin Lightner
North Carolina A&T State University

Constance Lightner
Fayetteville State University

Scott Lindsey
Dixie State College of Utah

Ken Linna
Auburn University–Montgomery

Andy Litteral
University of Richmond

Jun Liu
Georgia Southern University

Chung-Ping Loh
University of North Florida

Salvador Lopez
University of West Georgia

John Loucks
St. Edward's University

Cecilia Maldonado
Georgia Southwestern State University

Farooq Malik
University of Southern Mississippi

Ken Mayer
University of Nebraska–Omaha

Bradley McDonald
Northern Illinois University

Elaine McGivern
Duquesne University

John McKenzie
Babson University

Norbert Michel
Nicholls State University

John Miller
Sam Houston State University

Virginia Miori
St. Joseph's University

Prakash Mirchandani
University of Pittsburgh

Elizabeth Moliski
University of Texas–Austin

Jason Molitierno
Sacred Heart University

Joseph Mollick
Texas A&M University–Corpus Christi

James Moran
Oregon State University

Khosrow Moshirvaziri
California State University–Long Beach

Tariq Mughal
University of Utah

Patricia Mullins
University of Wisconsin–Madison

Kusum Mundra
Rutgers University–Newark

Anthony Narsing
Macon State College

Robert Nauss
University of Missouri–St. Louis

Satish Nayak
University of Missouri–St. Louis

Thang Nguyen
California State University–Long Beach

Justin S. Nobles
Blinn College
Christopher O'Byrne
San Diego State University
Mohammad Oskoorouchi
California State University–San Marcos
Barb Osyk
University of Akron
Bhavik Pathak
Indiana University South Bend
Richard Paulsen
Bloomsburg University of Pennsylvania
Scott Paulsen
Illinois Central College
James Payne
Calhoun Community College
Norman Pence
Metropolitan State College of Denver
Dane Peterson
Missouri State University
Joseph Petry
University of Illinois–Urbana/Champaign
Courtney Pham
Missouri State University
Martha Pilcher
University of Washington
Cathy Poliak
University of Wisconsin–Milwaukee
Simcha Pollack
St. John's University
Hamid Pourmohammadi
California State University–Dominguez Hills
Tammy Prater
Alabama State University
Zbigniew H. Przasnyski
Loyola Marymount University
Manying Qiu
Virginia State University
Troy Quast
Sam Houston State University
Michael Racer
University of Memphis
Srikant Raghavan
Lawrence Technological University
Bharatendra Rai
University of Massachusetts–Dartmouth
Michael Aaron Ratajczyk
Saint Mary's University of Minnesota

Tony Ratcliffe
James Madison University
David Ravetch
University of California
Bruce Reinig
San Diego State University
Darlene Riedemann
Eastern Illinois University
David Roach
Arkansas Tech University
Carolyn Rochelle
East Tennessee State University
Alfredo Romero
North Carolina A&T State University
Ann Rothermel
University of Akron
Jeff Rummel
Emory University
Deborah Rumsey
The Ohio State University
Stephen Russell
Weber State University
William Rybolt
Babson College
Fati Salimian
Salisbury University
Fatollah Salimian
Perdue School of Business
Samuel Sarri
College of Southern Nevada
Jim Schmidt
University of Nebraska–Lincoln
Patrick Scholten
Bentley University
Bonnie Schroeder
The Ohio State University
Pali Sen
University of North Florida
Donald Sexton
Columbia University
Vijay Shah
West Virginia University–Parkersburg
Dmitriy Shaltayev
Christopher Newport University
Soheil Sibdari
University of Massachusetts–Dartmouth
Prodosh Simlai
University of North Dakota
Harvey Singer
George Mason University
Harry Sink
North Carolina A&T State University

Don Skousen
Salt Lake Community College
Robert Smidt
California Polytechnic State University
Gary Smith
Florida State University
Antoinette Somers
Wayne State University
Ryan Songstad
Augustana College
Erland Sorensen
Bentley University
Arun Kumar Srinivasan
Indiana University–Southeast
Scott Stevens
James Madison University
Alicia Strandberg
Temple University
Linda Sturges
SUNY Maritime College
Wendi Sun
Rockland Trust
Minghe Sun
The University of Texas at San Antonio
Bedassa Tadesse
University of Minnesota
Pandu Tadikamalta
University of Pittsburgh
Roberto Duncan Tarabay
University of Wisconsin–Madison
Faye Teer
James Madison University
Rafael Teixeira
College of Charleston
Deborah Tesch
Xavier University
Patrick Thompson
University of Florida
Satish Thosar
University of Redlands
Ricardo Tovar-Silos
Lamar University
Quoc Hung Tran
Bridgewater State University
Elzbieta Trybus
California State University–Northridge
Fan Tseng
University of Alabama–Huntsville
Silvanus Udoka
North Carolina A&T State University

Shawn Ulrick
Georgetown University
Bulent Uyar
University of Northern Iowa
Ahmad Vakil
Tobin College of Business
Tim Vaughan
*University of Wisconsin–
Eau Claire*
Raja Velu
Syracuse University
Holly Verhasselt
*University of
Houston–Victoria*
Zhaowei Wang
Citizens Bank
Rachel Webb
Portland State University
Kyle Wells
Dixie State College
Alan Wheeler
*University of Missouri–
St. Louis*

Mary Whiteside
*University of Texas–
Arlington*
Blake Whitten
University of Iowa
Rick Wing
*San Francisco State
University*
Jan Wolcott
*Wichita State
University*
Rongning Wu
Baruch College
John Yarber
*Northeast Mississippi
Community College*
John C. Yi
St. Joseph's University
Kanghyun Yoon
*University of Central
Oklahoma*
Mark Zaporowski
Canisius College

Ali Zargar
San Jose State University
Dewit Zerom
California State University
Eugene Zhang
Midwestern State University
Ye Zhang
*Indiana University–Purdue
University–Indianapolis*
Yi Zhang
*California State
University–Fullerton*
Yulin Zhang
San Jose State University
Wencang Zhou
Baruch College
Zhen Zhu
*University of Central
Oklahoma*

The editorial staff of McGraw Hill Education are deserving of our gratitude for their guidance throughout this project, especially Eric Weber, Pat Frederickson, Ryan McAndrews, Harper Christopher, Kelsy Darin, and Matt Diamond. We would also like to thank Gregory John Larmour and Noah Hebert for their outstanding research assistance.

BRIEF CONTENTS

The Glossary is available in Connect.

CONTENTS

1

Data and Data Preparation

In just about any contemporary human activity, we use statistics to analyze large amounts of data for making better decisions. Managers, consumers, sports enthusiasts, politicians, and medical professionals are increasingly turning to data to boost a company's revenue, deepen customer engagement, find better options on consumer products, prevent threats and fraud, succeed in sports and elections, provide better diagnoses and cures for diseases, and so on. In this chapter, we will describe various types of data and measurement scales of variables that are used in statistics.

It is important to note that after obtaining relevant data, we often spend a considerable amount of time inspecting and preparing the data for subsequent analysis. In this chapter, we will discuss a few important data preparation tasks. We will use counting and sorting of relevant variables to inspect and explore data. Finally, we will discuss a commonly used technique called subsetting, where only a portion (subset) of the data is used for the analysis.

Yuliia Mazurkevych/Shutterstoick

INTRODUCTORY CASE

Gaining Insights into Retail Customer Data

Organic Food Superstore is an online grocery store that specializes in providing organic food products to health-conscious consumers. The company offers a membership-based service that ships fresh ingredients for a wide range of chef-designed meals to its members' homes. Catherine Hill is a marketing manager at Organic Food Superstore. She has been assigned to market the company's new line of Asian-inspired meals. Research has shown that the most likely customers for healthy ethnic cuisines are college-educated millennials (born on or after January 1, 1982, and before January 1, 2000).

In order to spend the company's marketing dollars efficiently, Catherine wants to focus on this target demographic when designing the marketing campaign. With the help of the information technology (IT) group, Catherine has acquired a representative sample that includes each customer's identification number (CustID), gender (Gender), race (Race), birthdate (BirthDate), whether the customer has a college degree (College), household size (HHSize), annual income (Income), total spending (Spending), total number of orders during the past 24 months (Orders), and the channel through which the customer was originally acquired (Channel). There are no non-binary customers in this data set. Table 1.1 shows a portion of the data set.

TABLE 1.1 A Sample of Organic Food Superstore Customers

CustID	Gender	Race	BirthDate	...	Channel
1530016	Female	Black	12/16/1986	...	SM
1531136	Male	White	5/9/1993	...	TV
⋮	⋮	⋮	⋮	⋮	⋮
1579979	Male	White	7/5/1999	...	SM

Customers

Catherine wants to use the **Customers** data set to:

1. Identify Organic Food Superstore's college-educated millennial customers.

2. Compare the profiles of female and male college-educated millennial customers.

A synopsis of this case is provided at the end of Section 1.3.

In general, data are compilations of facts, figures, or other contents, both numerical and nonnumerical. Data of all types and formats are generated from multiple sources. Insights from all of these data improve a company's bottom line and enhance consumer experience. In particular, companies benefit by developing better marketing strategies, deepening customer engagement, enhancing efficiency in procurement, uncovering ways to reduce expenses, identifying emerging market trends, mitigating risk and fraud, etc. We often find a large amount of data at our disposal. However, we also derive insights from relatively small data sets, such as from consumer focus groups, marketing surveys, or reports from government agencies.

Every day, consumers and businesses use data from various sources to help make decisions. In order to make intelligent decisions in a world full of uncertainty, we have to understand statistics—the language of data. In the broadest sense, statistics is the science of extracting useful information from data. Three steps are essential for performing a good statistical analysis. An important first step for making decisions is to find the right data, which are both complete and lacking any misrepresentation, and prepare them for the analysis. Second, we must use the appropriate statistical tools, depending on the data at hand. Finally, an important ingredient of a well-executed statistical analysis is to clearly communicate information into verbal and written language. It is important to note that numerical results are not very useful unless they are accompanied with clearly stated actionable business insights.

> ### DATA AND STATISTICS
> Data are compilations of facts, figures, or other contents, both numerical and nonnumerical. Statistics is the science that deals with the collection, preparation, analysis, interpretation, and presentation of data.

In the introductory case, Catherine wants to target college-educated millennials when designing the marketing campaign so that she spends the company's marketing dollars efficiently. Before we analyze the information that Catherine has gathered, it is important to understand the various types of data and measurement scales of variables. In this section, we focus on the various types of data.

Sample and Population Data

We generally divide the study of statistics into two branches: descriptive statistics and inferential statistics. **Descriptive statistics** refers to the summary of important aspects of a data set. This includes collecting, organizing, and presenting the data in the form of charts and tables. In addition, we often calculate numerical measures that summarize the data by providing, for example, the typical value and the variability of the item of interest. Today, the techniques encountered in descriptive statistics account for the most visible application of statistics—the abundance of quantitative information that is collected and published in our society every day. The unemployment rate, the president's approval rating, the Dow Jones Industrial Average, batting averages, the crime rate, and the divorce rate are but a few of the many "statistics" that can be found in a reputable publication on a frequent, if not daily, basis. Yet, despite the familiarity of descriptive statistics, these methods represent only a minor portion of the body of statistical applications.

The phenomenal growth in statistics is mainly in the field called inferential statistics. Generally, **inferential statistics** refers to drawing conclusions about a large set of data—called a **population**—based on a smaller set of **sample** data. A population is defined as all members of a specified group (not necessarily people), whereas a sample is a subset of that particular population. In most statistical applications, we must rely on sample data in order to make inferences about various characteristics of the population.

Figure 1.1 depicts the flow of information between a population and a sample. Consider, for example, a 2016 Gallup survey that found that 50% of millennials plan to stay at their current job for more than a year. We use this sample result, called a **sample statistic,** in an attempt to estimate the corresponding unknown **population parameter.** The parameter of interest is the percentage of *all* millennials, and not just those sampled for the survey, who plan to be with their current job for more than a year.

FIGURE 1.1 Population versus Sample

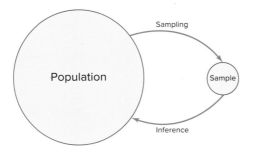

POPULATION VERSUS SAMPLE

A population consists of all items of interest in a statistical study. A sample is a subset of the population. We analyze sample data and calculate a sample statistic to make inferences about the unknown population parameter.

It is generally not feasible to obtain population data due to prohibitive costs and/or practicality. We rely on sampling because we are unable to use population data for two main reasons.

- **Obtaining information on the entire population is expensive.** Consider how the monthly unemployment rate in the United States is calculated by the Bureau of Labor Statistics (BLS). Is it reasonable to assume that the BLS counts every unemployed person each month? The answer is a resounding NO! In order to do this, every home in the country would have to be contacted. Given that there are approximately 160 million individuals in the labor force, not only would this process cost too much, it would take an inordinate amount of time. Instead, the BLS conducts a monthly sample survey of about 60,000 households to measure the extent of unemployment in the United States.

- **It is impractical to examine every member of the population.** Suppose we are interested in the average length of life of a Duracell AAA battery. If we tested the duration of each Duracell AAA battery, then in the end, all batteries would be dead and the answer to the original question would be useless.

Cross-Sectional and Time Series Data

Sample data are generally collected in one of two ways. **Cross-sectional data** refer to data collected by recording a characteristic of many subjects at the same point in time, or without regard to differences in time. Subjects might include individuals, households, firms, industries, regions, and countries.

Table 1.2 is an example of a cross-sectional data set. It lists the top eight teams in the Eastern Conference of the National Basketball Association (NBA) at the end of the 2020–2021 regular season. The eight teams may not have ended the season precisely on the same day and time, but the differences in time are of no relevance in this example. Other examples of cross-sectional data include the recorded grades of students in a class, the sale prices of single-family homes sold last month, the current price of gasoline in different cities in the United States, and the starting salaries of recent business graduates from the University of Connecticut.

TABLE 1.2 2020–2021 NBA Eastern Conference Standings

Team name	Wins	Losses	Winning percentage
Philadelphia 76ers	49	23	0.681
Brooklyn Nets	48	24	0.667
Milwaukee Bucks*	46	26	0.639
New York Knicks	41	31	0.569
Atlanta Hawks	41	31	0.569
Miami Heat	40	32	0.556
Boston Celtics	36	36	0.500
Washington Wizards	34	38	0.472

*The Milwaukee Bucks won the 2021 NBA championship.

Time series data refer to data collected over several time periods focusing on certain groups of people, specific events, or objects. Time series data can include hourly, daily, weekly, monthly, quarterly, or annual observations. Examples of time series data include the hourly body temperature of a patient in a hospital's intensive care unit, the daily price of General Electric stock in the first quarter of 2020, the weekly exchange rate between the U.S. dollar and the euro over the past six months, the monthly sales of cars at a dealership in 2020, and the annual population growth rate of India in the last decade. In these examples, temporal ordering is relevant and meaningful.

Figure 1.2 shows a plot of the quarterly median sales price of houses sold in the United States from the first quarter of 2012 through the second quarter of 2021. As shown, house prices have generally risen over this period. Interestingly, despite the severe pandemic-induced economic downturn in 2020, house prices rose dramatically. The increased demand for houses coupled with lower mortgage rates led to this steep rise, especially in areas with a shortage of homes.

FIGURE 1.2

Quarterly sales price of houses from First Quarter 2012 through Second Quarter 2021

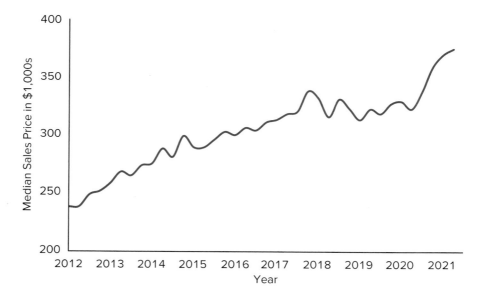

Structured and Unstructured Data

When you think of data, the first image that probably pops in your head is lots of numbers and perhaps some charts and graphs. In reality, data can come in multiple forms. For example, information exchange in social networking websites such as Facebook, LinkedIn, and Twitter also constitute data. In order to better understand the various forms of data, we make a distinction between structured and unstructured data.

Generally, **structured data** reside in a predefined, row-column format. We use spreadsheet or database applications to enter, store, query, and analyze structured data. Examples of structured data include numbers, dates, and groups of words and numbers, typically stored in a tabular format. Structured data often consist of numerical information that is objective and is not open to interpretation.

Point-of-sale and financial data are examples of structured data that are usually designed to capture a business process or transaction. Examples include the sale of retail products, a money transfer between bank accounts, and the student enrollment in a university course. When individual consumers buy products from a retail store, each transaction is captured into a record of structured data.

Consider the sales invoice shown in Figure 1.3. Whenever a customer places an order like this, there is a predefined set of data to be collected, such as the transaction date, shipping address, and the units of product being purchased. Even though a receipt or an invoice may not always be presented in rows and columns, the predefined structure allows businesses and organizations to translate the data on the document into a row-column format.

FIGURE 1.3 A sample invoice from a retail transaction

Tranquility Home and Garden

2 Harmony Drive
San Francisco, CA 94126
Phone: (415) SOL-SAVE

| Date: | July, 20, 2022 |
| Invoice number: | A9239145-W |

Customer Name:	Kevin Lau	Account Number:	KL0927
Street Address:	123 Solstice Circle	City:	San Francisco
State/Province:	California	Postal Code:	94126
Telephone:	(415) 234-4550		

Product code	Product description	Units ordered	Price per unit	Extended Price
421-L	8W LED light bulbs	27	$7.59	$204.93
389-P	Chlorine removing shower filter	6	$19.99	$119.94
682-K	Compostable cutlery (box sets)	5	$14.99	$74.95

	Total amount:	$399.82
	Sales Tax:	$31.99
	Shipping fee:	$6.99
	Grand total:	$438.80

Unlike structured data, **unstructured data** (or unmodeled data) do not conform to a predefined, row-column format. They tend to be textual (e.g., written reports, email messages, doctor's notes, or open-ended survey responses) or have multimedia contents (e.g., photographs, videos, and audio data). Even though these data may have some implied structure (e.g., a report title, email's subject line, or a time stamp on a photograph), they are still considered unstructured as they do not conform to a row-column model required in most database systems. Social media data such as Twitter, YouTube, Facebook, and blogs are examples of unstructured data.

For decades, companies and organizations relied mostly on structured data to run their businesses and operations. Today, with the advent of the digital age, both structured and unstructured data are used for making business decisions.

STRUCTURED AND UNSTRUCTURED DATA

- Structured data reside in a predefined, row-column format.
- Unstructured data do not conform to a predefined, row-column format.

Big Data

Nowadays, businesses and organizations generate and gather more and more data at an increasing pace. The term **big data** is a catch-phrase, meaning a massive amount of both structured and unstructured data that are extremely difficult to manage, process, and analyze using traditional data-processing tools. Despite the challenges, big data present great opportunities to gain knowledge and business intelligence with potential game-changing impacts on company revenues, competitive advantage, and organizational efficiency.

More formally, a widely accepted definition of big data is "high-volume, high-velocity and/or high-variety information assets that demand cost-effective, innovative forms of information processing that enable enhanced insight, decision making, and process automation" (www.gartner.com). The three characteristics (the three Vs) of big data are:

- Volume: An immense amount of data is compiled from a single source or a wide range of sources, including business transactions, household and personal devices, manufacturing equipment, social media, and other online portals.
- Velocity: In addition to volume, data from a variety of sources get generated at a rapid speed. Managing these data streams can become a critical issue for many organizations.
- Variety: Data also come in all types, forms, and granularity, both structured and unstructured. These data may include numbers, text, and figures as well as audio, video, emails, and other multimedia elements.

In addition to the three defining characteristics of big data, we also need to pay close attention to the veracity of the data and the business value that they can generate. Veracity refers to the credibility and quality of data. One must verify the reliability and accuracy of the data content prior to relying on the data to make decisions. This becomes increasingly challenging with the rapid growth of data volume fueled by social media and automatic data collection. Value derived from big data is perhaps the most important aspect of any statistical project. Having a plethora of data does not guarantee that useful insights or measurable improvements will be generated. Organizations must develop a methodical plan for formulating business questions, curating the right data, and unlocking the hidden potential in big data.

Big data, however, do not necessarily imply complete (population) data. Take, for example, the analysis of all Facebook users. It certainly involves big data, but if we consider all Internet users in the world, Facebook users are only a very large sample. There are many Internet users who do not use Facebook, so the data on Facebook do not represent the population. Even if we define the population as pertaining to those who use Facebook, the relevant information may include only active Facebook users rather than all Facebook users. Therefore, Facebook data may simply represent a very large sample.

In addition, we may choose not to use big data in its entirety even when they are available. Sometimes it is just inconvenient to analyze a very large data set as it is computationally burdensome, even with a modern, high-capacity computer system. Other times, the additional benefits of working with big data may not justify the associated costs. In sum, we often choose to work with relatively smaller data sets drawn from big data.

BIG DATA

Big data is a term used to describe both structured and unstructured data. The following Vs summarize the characteristics of big data as well as provide guidelines for using big data when making decisions.

- Volume: Big data imply an immense amount of data.
- Velocity: Big data are generated at a rapid speed.
- Variety: Big data come in all forms.
- Veracity: Businesses must verify the reliability and veracity of the big data before making decisions.
- Value: Businesses must develop a methodical plan for formulating questions in order to unlock the hidden potential in big data.

Interestingly, big data do not necessarily imply complete (population) data.

Note: In this text, we focus on traditional statistical methods applied to structured data. Sophisticated tools to analyze unstructured data are beyond the scope of this text.

Data on the Web

The explosion in the field of statistics and data analytics is partly due to the growing availability of vast amounts of data and improved computational power. Many experts believe that 90 percent of the data in the world today were created in the last two years alone. These days, it has become easy to access data by simply using a search engine like Google. These search engines direct us to data-providing websites. For instance, searching for economic data may lead you to the Bureau of Economic Analysis (www.bea.gov), the Bureau of Labor Statistics (www.bls.gov/data), the Federal Reserve Economic Data (htpp://research.stlouisfed.org), and the U.S. Census Bureau (www.census.gov/data.html). These websites provide data on inflation, unemployment, GDP, and much more, including useful international data.

Comstock Images/Jupiterimages

The National Centers for Environmental Information (www.ncei.noaa.gov/products) provides a large collection of environmental, meteorological, and climate data. Similarly, transportation data can be found at www.its-rde.net. The University of Michigan has compiled sentiment data found at www.sca.isr.umich.edu. Several cities in the United States have publicly available data in categories such as finance, community and economic development, education, and crime. For example, the Chicago data portal (http://data.cityofchicago.org) provides a large volume of city-specific data. Excellent world development indicator data are available at http://data.worldbank.org. The happiness index data for most countries are available at http://happyplanetindex.org/countries.

Private corporations also make data available on their websites. For example, Yahoo Finance (www.finance.yahoo.com) and Google Finance (www.google.com/finance) list data such as stock prices, mutual fund performance, and international market data. Zillow (www.zillow.com/) supplies data for recent home sales, monthly rent, mortgage rates, and so forth. Similarly, www.espn.go.com offers comprehensive sports data on both professional and college teams. Finally, *The Wall Street Journal, The New York Times, USA Today, The Economist, Business Week, Forbes,* and *Fortune* are all reputable publications that provide all sorts of data. We would like to point out that all of the above data sources represent only a fraction of publicly available data.

EXERCISES 1.1

Applications

1. According to recent estimates, annually, the average American spends $583 on alcohol and $1,100 on coffee.
   a. Describe the relevant population.
   b. Are the estimates based on sample or population data?

2. Many people regard video games as a hobby of younger people, but, in fact, the average age of a video game player is 35 years old. Is the value 35 likely the actual or the estimated average age of the population? Explain.

3. An accounting professor wants to know the average GPA of the students enrolled in her class. She looks up information on Blackboard about the students enrolled in her class and computes the average GPA as 3.29. Describe the relevant population.

4. Recent college graduates with an engineering degree continue to earn high salaries. An online search revealed that the average annual salary for an entry-level position in engineering is $80,000.

   a. What is the relevant population?
   b. Do you think the average salary of $80,000 is computed from the population? Explain.

5. Research suggests that depression significantly increases the risk of developing dementia later in life. Suppose that in a study involving 949 older adults, it was found that 22 percent of those who had depression went on to develop dementia, compared to only 17 percent of those who did not have depression.
   a. Describe the relevant population and the sample.
   b. Are the numbers 22 percent and 17 percent associated with the population or a sample?

6. According to Statistica.com, the average life expectancies in the United States for those born in 2019 is 76 years for males and 81 years for females. Data on non-binary individuals are not available.
   a. Describe the relevant population for the average life expectancy estimates.
   b. Are the average life expectancies computed from sample or population data?

7. Ask students in your class whether they live in a dormitory, a rental unit, or other form of accommodation. Also find out their approximate monthly lodging expenses. Create a table that uses this information. Are the data considered structured or unstructured? Are they cross-sectional or time series data?

8. Go to www.zillow.com and find the sale price of 20 single-family homes sold in Las Vegas, Nevada, in the last 30 days. Structure the data in a tabular format and include the sale price, the number of bedrooms, the square footage, and the age of the house. Do these data represent cross-sectional or time series data?

9. Go to www.finance.yahoo.com to get the current stock quote for Home Depot (ticker symbol = HD). Use the ticker symbol to search for historical prices and create a table that includes the monthly adjusted close price of Home Depot stock for the last 12 months. Do these data represent cross-sectional or time series data?

10. Go to *The New York Times* website at www.nytimes.com and review the front page. Would you consider the data on the page to be structured or unstructured? Explain.

11. Conduct an online search to compare small hybrid vehicles (e.g., Toyota Prius, Ford Fusion, Chevrolet Volt) on price, fuel economy, and other specifications. Do you consider the search results structured or unstructured data? Explain.

12. Find Under Armour's annual revenue from the past 10 years. Are the data considered structured or unstructured? Explain. Are they cross-sectional or time series data?

13. Ask 20 of your friends about their online social media usage, specifically whether or not they use Facebook, Instagram, and Snapchat; how often they use each social media portal; and their overall satisfaction of each of these portals. Create a table that presents this information. Are the data considered structured or unstructured? Are they cross-sectional or time series data?

1.2 VARIABLES AND SCALES OF MEASUREMENT

Describe variables and types of measurement scales.

For any statistical analysis, we invariably focus on people, firms, or events with particular characteristics. When a characteristic of interest differs in kind or degree among various observations (records), then the characteristic can be termed a **variable.** Marital status and income are examples of variables because a person's marital status and income vary from person to person. Variables are further classified as either **categorical** (qualitative) or **numerical** (quantitative). The observations of a categorical variable represent categories, whereas the observations of a numerical variable represent meaningful numbers. For example, marital status is a categorical variable, whereas income is a numerical variable.

For a categorical variable, we use labels or names to identify the distinguishing characteristic of each observation. For instance, a university may identify each student's status as either at the undergraduate or the graduate level, where the education level is a categorical variable representing two categories. Categorical variables can also be defined by more than two categories. Examples include marital status (single, married, widowed, divorced, separated), IT firm (hardware, software, cloud), and course grade (A, B, C, D, F). It is important to note that categories are often converted into numerical codes for purposes of data processing, which we will discuss in later chapters.

For a numerical variable, we use numbers to identify the distinguishing characteristic of each observation. Numerical variables, in turn, are either discrete or continuous. A **discrete variable** assumes a countable number of values. Consider the number of children in a family or the number of points scored in a basketball game. We may observe values such as 3 children in a family or 90 points being scored in a basketball game, but we will not observe fractions such as 1.3127 children or 92.4724 scored points. The values that a discrete variable assumes need not be whole numbers. For example, the price of a stock for a particular firm is a discrete variable. The stock price may take on a value of $20.37 or $20.38, but it cannot take on a value between these two points.

A **continuous variable** is characterized by uncountable values within an interval. Weight, height, time, and investment return are all examples of continuous variables. For example, an unlimited number of values occur between the weights of 100 and 101 pounds, such as 100.3, 100.625, 100.8342, and so on. In practice, however, continuous variables are often measured in discrete values. We may report a newborn's weight (a continuous variable) in discrete terms as 6 pounds 10 ounces and another newborn's weight in similar discrete terms as 6 pounds 11 ounces.

> ### CATEGORICAL AND NUMERICAL VARIABLES
>
> A variable is a general characteristic being observed on a set of people, objects, or events, where each observation varies in kind or degree.
>
> - The observations of a categorical variable assume names or labels.
> - The observations of a numerical variable assume meaningful numerical values. A numerical variable can be further categorized as either discrete or continuous. A discrete variable assumes a countable number of values, whereas a continuous variable is characterized by uncountable values within an interval.

EXAMPLE 1.1

In the introductory case, Catherine Hill has been assigned to help market Organic Food Superstore's new line of Asian-inspired meals. With the help of the IT group, she has acquired a representative sample of customers at her store. Determine which of the variables in the sample are categorical or numerical and, if numerical, determine if they are discrete or continuous.

SOLUTION:

The variables Gender, Race, College, and Channel are categorical, merely representing labels. We also treat Birthdate as a categorical variable, with numerous categories, even though it contains numbers. Note that we can easily convert date of birth to a numerical variable age by simply subtracting it from the current date. On the other hand, HHSize, Income, Spending, and Orders are numerical variables because the observations are all meaningful numbers. Note that all of the numerical variables in this example are discrete because they can only assume a countable number of values; in other words, they are not characterized by uncountable values within an interval.

The Measurement Scales

In order to choose the appropriate techniques for summarizing and analyzing variables, we need to distinguish between the different measurement scales. The observations for any variable can be classified into one of four major measurement scales: nominal, ordinal, interval, or ratio. Nominal and ordinal scales are used for categorical variables, whereas interval and ratio scales are used for numerical variables. We discuss these scales in ascending order of sophistication.

The Nominal Scale

The **nominal scale** represents the least sophisticated level of measurement. If we are presented with nominal observations, all we can do is categorize or group them. The observations differ merely by name or label. Table 1.3 lists the 30 publicly owned companies, as of February 2019, that comprise the Dow Jones Industrial Average (DJIA). The DJIA is a stock market index that shows how these large U.S.-based companies have traded during a standard trading session in the stock market. Table 1.3 also indicates where stocks of these companies are traded: on either the National Association of Securities Dealers Automated Quotations (Nasdaq) or the New York Stock Exchange (NYSE). These observations are classified as nominal scale because we are simply able to group or categorize them. Specifically, only five stocks are traded on the Nasdaq, whereas the remaining 25 are traded on the NYSE.

Often, we substitute numbers for the particular categorical characteristic or trait that we are grouping. For instance, we might use the number 0 to show that a company's stock is traded on the Nasdaq and the number 1 to show that a company's stock is traded on the NYSE. One reason why we do this is for ease of exposition; always referring to the National Association of Securities Dealers Automated Quotations, or even the Nasdaq, can be awkward and unwieldy.

TABLE 1.3 Companies of the DJIA and Exchange Where Stock Is Traded

Company	Exchange	Company	Exchange
3M (MMM)	NYSE	Johnson & Johnson (JNJ)	NYSE
American Express (AXP)	NYSE	JPMorgan Chase (JPM)	NYSE
Apple (AAPL)	Nasdaq	McDonald's (MCD)	NYSE
Boeing (BA)	NYSE	Merck (MRK)	NYSE
Caterpillar (CAT)	NYSE	Microsoft (MFST)	Nasdaq
Chevron (CVX)	NYSE	Nike (NKE)	NYSE
Cisco (CSCO)	Nasdaq	Pfizer (PFE)	NYSE
Coca-Cola (KO)	NYSE	Procter & Gamble (PG)	NYSE
Disney (DIS)	NYSE	Travelers (TRV)	NYSE
DowDupont (DWDP)	NYSE	United Health (UNH)	NYSE
ExxonMobil (XOM)	NYSE	United Technologies (UTX)	NYSE
Goldman Sachs (GS)	NYSE	Verizon (VZ)	NYSE
Home Depot (HD)	NYSE	Visa (V)	NYSE
IBM (IBM)	NYSE	Wal-Mart (WMT)	NYSE
Intel (INTC)	Nasdaq	Walgreen (WBA)	Nasdaq

The Ordinal Scale

Compared to the nominal scale, the **ordinal scale** reflects a stronger level of measurement. With ordinal observations, we are able to both categorize and rank them with respect to some characteristic or trait. The weakness associated with ordinal observations is that we cannot interpret the difference between the ranked observations because the actual numbers used are arbitrary. Consider, for example, hotel reviews where consumers are asked to classify the service at a particular hotel as excellent (5 stars), very good (4 stars), good (3 stars), fair (2 stars), or poor (1 star). We summarize the categories and their respective ratings in Table 1.4.

TABLE 1.4 Hotel Survey Categories with Ratings

Category	Rating
Excellent	5
Very good	4
Good	3
Fair	2
Poor	1

In Table 1.4, the number attached to excellent (5 stars) is higher than the number attached to good (3 stars), indicating that the response of excellent is preferred to good. However, we can easily redefine the ratings, as we show in Table 1.5.

TABLE 1.5 Hotel Survey Categories with Redefined Ratings

Category	Rating
Excellent	100
Very good	80
Good	70
Fair	50
Poor	40

In Table 1.5, excellent still receives a higher number than good, but now the difference between the two categories is 30 points (100 − 70), as compared to a difference of 2 points (5 − 3) when we use the first classification. In other words, differences between categories are meaningless with ordinal observations. (We also should note that we could reverse the ordering so that, for instance, excellent equals 40 and poor equals 100; this renumbering would not change the nature of the observations.)

As mentioned earlier, observations of a categorical variable are typically expressed in words but are coded into numbers for purposes of data processing. When summarizing the results of a categorical variable, we typically count the number of observations that fall into each category or calculate the percentage of observations that fall into each category. However, with a categorical variable, we are unable to perform meaningful arithmetic operations, such as addition and subtraction.

The Interval Scale

With observations that are measured on the **interval scale,** we are able to categorize and rank them as well as find meaningful differences between them. The Fahrenheit scale for temperatures is an example of interval-scaled variable. Not only is 60 degrees Fahrenheit hotter than 50 degrees Fahrenheit, the same difference of 10 degrees also exists between 90 and 80 degrees Fahrenheit.

The main drawback of an interval-scaled variable is that the value of zero is arbitrarily chosen; the zero point of an interval-scaled variable does not reflect a complete absence of what is being measured. No specific meaning is attached to 0 degrees Fahrenheit other than to say it is 10 degrees colder than 10 degrees Fahrenheit. With an arbitrary zero point, meaningful ratios cannot be constructed. For instance, it is senseless to say that 80 degrees is twice as hot as 40 degrees; in other words, the ratio 80/40 has no meaning.

The Ratio Scale

The **ratio scale** represents the strongest level of measurement. The ratio scale has all the characteristics of the interval scale as well as a true zero point, which allows us to interpret the ratios between observations. The ratio scale is used in many business applications. Variables such as sales, profits, and inventory levels are expressed on the ratio scale. A meaningful zero point allows us to state, for example, that profits for firm A are double those of firm B. Variables such as weight, time, and distance are also measured on a ratio scale because zero is meaningful.

Unlike nominal- and ordinal-scaled variables (categorical variables), arithmetic operations are valid on interval- and ratio-scaled variables (numerical variables). In later chapters, we will calculate summary measures, such as the mean, the median, and the variance, for numerical variables; we cannot calculate these measures for categorical variables.

MEASUREMENT SCALES

The observations for any variable can be classified into one of four major measurement scales: nominal, ordinal, interval, or ratio.

- Nominal: Observations differ merely by name or label.
- Ordinal: Observations can be categorized and ranked; however, differences between the ranked observations are meaningless.
- Interval: Observations can be categorized and ranked, and differences between observations are meaningful. The main drawback of the interval scale is that the value of zero is arbitrarily chosen.
- Ratio: Observations have all the characteristics of an interval-scaled variable as well as a true zero point; thus, meaningful ratios can be calculated.

Nominal and ordinal scales are used for categorical variables, whereas interval and ratio scales are used for numerical variables.

Survey

EXAMPLE 1.2

The owner of a ski resort two hours outside Boston, Massachusetts, is interested in serving the needs of the pre-teen population (children aged 8 to 12 years old). He believes that pre-teen spending power has grown over the past few years, and he wants their skiing experience to be memorable so that they want to return. At the end of last year's ski season, he asked 20 pre-teens the following four questions.

- Question 1. On your car drive to the resort, which music streaming service was playing?
- Question 2. On a scale of 1 to 4, rate the quality of the food at the resort (where 1 is poor, 2 is fair, 3 is good, and 4 is excellent).
- Question 3. Presently, the main dining area closes at 3:00 pm. What time do you think it should close?
- Question 4. How much of your own money did you spend at the lodge today?

A portion of their responses is shown in Table 1.6. Identify the scale of measurement for each variable used in the survey. Given the pre-teen responses, provide suggestions to the owner for improvement.

TABLE 1.6 Pre-teen Responses to Resort Survey

Pre-teen	Question 1	Question 2	Question 3	Question 4
1	Apple Music	4	5:00 pm	20
2	Pandora	2	5:00 pm	10
⋮	⋮	⋮	⋮	⋮
20	Spotify	2	4:30 pm	10

SOLUTION:

- Question 1. Responses for music streaming service are nominal because the observations differ merely in label. Twelve of the 20 pre-teens, or 60%, listened to Spotify. If the resort wishes to contact pre-teens using this means, then it may want to direct its advertising dollars to this streaming service.
- Question 2. Food quality responses are on an ordinal scale because we can both categorize and rank the observations. Eleven of the 20 pre-teens, or 55%, felt that the food quality was, at best, fair. Perhaps a more extensive survey that focuses solely on food quality would reveal the reason for their apparent dissatisfaction.
- Question 3. Closing time responses are on an interval scale. We can say that 3:30 pm is 30 minutes later than 3:00 pm, and 6:00 pm is 30 minutes later than 5:30 pm; that is, differences between observations are meaningful. The closing time responses, however, have no apparent zero point. We could arbitrarily define the zero point at 12:00 am, but ratios are still meaningless. In other words, it makes no sense to form the ratio 6:00 pm/3:00 pm and conclude that 6:00 pm is twice as long a time period as 3:00 pm. A review of the closing time responses shows that the vast majority (19 out of 20) would like the dining area to remain open later.
- Question 4. The pre-teens' responses with respect to their own money spent at the resort are on a ratio scale. We can categorize and rank observations as well as calculate meaningful differences. Moreover, because there is a natural zero point, valid ratios can also be calculated. Seventeen of the 20 pre-teens spent their own money at the lodge. It appears that the discretionary spending of this age group is significant. The owner would be wise to cater to some of their preferences.

EXERCISES 1.2

Applications

14. Which of the following variables are categorical and which are numerical? If the variable is numerical, then specify whether the variable is discrete or continuous.
    a. Points scored in a football game.
    b. Ethnic groups in a high school classroom.
    c. Heights of 15-year-olds.

15. Which of the following variables are categorical and which are numerical? If the variable is numerical, then specify whether the variable is discrete or continuous.
    a. Colors of cars in a mall parking lot.
    b. Time it takes each student to complete a final exam.
    c. The number of patrons who frequent a restaurant.

16. In each of the following scenarios, define the type of measurement scale.
    a. An animal shelter worker marks down whether a puppy is a labrador, poodle, or terrier.
    b. A ski resort records the daily temperature during the month of January.
    c. A restaurant surveys its customers about the quality of its waiting staff on a scale of 1 to 4, where 1 is poor and 4 is excellent.

17. In each of the following scenarios, define the type of measurement scale.
    a. An investor collects data on the weekly closing price of gold throughout the year.
    b. An analyst assigns a sample of bond issues to one of the following credit ratings, given in descending order of credit quality (increasing probability of default): AAA, AA, BBB, BB, CC, D.
    c. The dean of the business school at a local university categorizes students by major (i.e., accounting, finance, marketing, etc.) to help in determining class offerings in the future.

18. In each of the following scenarios, define the type of measurement scale.
    a. A meteorologist records the amount of monthly rainfall over the past year.
    b. A sociologist notes the birth year of 50 individuals.
    c. An investor monitors the daily stock price of BP following the 2010 oil disaster in the Gulf of Mexico.

19. **FILE** *Major.* A professor records the majors of her 30 students. The accompanying file contains the data.
    a. What is the measurement scale of the Major variable?
    b. Summarize the results in tabular form.
    c. What information can be extracted from the data?

20. **FILE** *DOW.* The accompanying file contains data for the 30 companies that comprise the Dow Jones Industrial Average (DJIA). For each company, the data set lists the year that it joined the DJIA, its industry, and its stock price (in $) as of February 15, 2019.
    a. What is the measurement scale of the Industry variable?
    b. What is the measurement scale of the Year variable? What are the strengths of this type of measurement scale? What are its weaknesses?
    c. What is the measurement scale of the Price variable? What are the strengths of this type of measurement scale?

21. **FILE** *Retailer.* An online retail company is trying to predict customer spending in the first three months of the year. Brian Duffy, the marketing analyst of the company, has compiled a data set on 200 existing customers that includes purchase type (Purchase; Apparel, Non-apparel), annual income (Income, in $1,000), age (Age, in years), and total spending in the first three months of the year (Spending). The accompanying file contains relevant data.
    a. Which of the above variables are categorical and which are numerical?
    b. What is the measurement scale of each of the above variables?

22. **FILE** *Vacation.* Vacation destinations often run on a seasonal basis, depending on the primary activities in that location. Cynthia Olowe is the owner of a travel agency in Cincinnati, Ohio. She has compiled a data set of the number of vacation packages (Vacation) that she has sold over the last 12 years. The accompanying file contains relevant data.
    a. What is the measurement scale of the Year variable? What are the strengths of this type of measurement scale? What are its weaknesses?
    b. What is the measurement scale of the Quarter variable? What is a weakness of this type of measurement scale?
    c. What is the measurement scale of the Vacation variable? What are the strengths of this type of measurement scale?

1.3 DATA PREPARATION

As noted earlier, after obtaining relevant data, we often spend a considerable amount of time inspecting and preparing the data for subsequent analysis. In this section, we will discuss a few important data preparation tasks. We first count and sort the observations of relevant variables in order to inspect and explore the data. We also discuss a commonly used technique called subsetting where only a portion (subset) of the data is used for the statistical analysis.

LO 1.3

Inspect and explore data.

Counting and Sorting

In addition to visually reviewing data, counting and sorting are among the very first tasks most data analysts perform to gain a better understanding and insights into the data. Counting and sorting data help us verify that the data set is complete or that it may have missing values, especially for important variables. Sorting data also allows us to review the range of values for each variable. We can sort data based on a single variable or multiple variables.

In Example 1.3, we demonstrate how to use counting and sorting features in Excel to inspect and gain insights into the data.

FILE

Gig

EXAMPLE 1.3

BalanceGig is a company that matches independent workers for short-term engagements with businesses in the construction, automotive, and high-tech industries. The 'gig' employees work only for a short period of time, often on a particular project or a specific task. A manager at BalanceGig extracts the employee data from their most recent work engagement, including the hourly wage (Wage), the client's industry (Industry), and the employee's job classification (Job). A portion of the *Gig* data set is shown in Table 1.7.

TABLE 1.7 Gig Employee Data

EmployeeID	Wage	Industry	Job
1	32.81	Construction	Analyst
2	46.00	Automotive	Engineer
⋮	⋮	⋮	⋮
604	26.09	Construction	Other

The manager suspects that data about the gig employees are sometimes incomplete, perhaps due to the short engagement and the transient nature of the employees. She would like to find the number of missing observations for the Wage, Industry, and Job variables. In addition, she would like information on the number of employees who (1) worked in the automotive industry, (2) earned more than $30 per hour, and (3) worked in the automotive industry and earned more than $30 per hour. Finally, the manager would like to know the hourly wage of the lowest- and the highest-paid employees at the company as a whole and the hourly wage of the lowest- and the highest-paid accountants who worked in the automotive and the tech industries.

Use counting and sorting functions in Excel to find the relevant information requested by the manager, and then summarize the results.

Important: Due to different fonts and type settings, copying and pasting Excel functions from this text directly into Excel may cause errors. When such errors occur, you may need to replace special characters such as quotation marks and parentheses or delete extra spaces in the functions.

SOLUTION:

a. Open the *Gig* data file. Note that the employee data are currently sorted by their employee ID in column A. Scroll to the end of the data set and note that the last record is in row 605. With the column heading in row 1, the data set has a total of 604 records.

b. We use two Excel functions, **COUNT** and **COUNTA,** to inspect the number of observations in each column. The **COUNT** function counts the number of cells that contain numeric observations and, therefore, can only apply to the EmployeeID and Wage variables. The **COUNTA** function counts the number of cells that are not empty and is applicable to all four variables. Because Wage is a numerical variable, we can enter either =COUNT(B2:B605) or =COUNTA(B2:B605) in an empty cell to count the number of observations for Wage. We get 604, implying that there are no missing observations. We enter =COUNTA(C2:C605) and =COUNTA(D2:D605) in empty cells to count the number of observations for the Industry (column C) and Job (column D) variables. Because these two variables are non-numerical, we use **COUNTA** instead of **COUNT.** Verify that the number of observations for Industry and Job are 594 and 588, respectively, indicating that there are 10 (= 604 − 594) and 16 (= 604 − 588) blank or missing observations, respectively, for these two variables.

c. To count the number of employees in each industry, we use the **COUNTIF** function. Entering =COUNTIF(C2:C605,"=Automotive") in an empty cell will show that 190 of the 604 employees worked in the automotive industry. Similarly, entering =COUNTIF(B2:B605,">30") in an empty cell will show that 536 employees earned more than $30 per hour. Note that the first parameter in the **COUNTIF** function is the range of cells to be counted, and the second parameter specifies the selection criterion. Other logical operators such as >=, <, <=, and <> (not equal to) can also be used in the **COUNTIF** function.

d. To count the number of employees with multiple selection criteria, we use the **COUNTIFS** function. For example, entering =COUNTIFS(C2:C605, "=Automotive", B2:B605,">30") in an empty cell will show that 181 employees worked in the automotive industry and earned more than $30 per hour. Additional data ranges and selection criteria can be added in corresponding pairs. The >=, <, <=, and <> operators can also be used in the **COUNTIFS** function.

e. To sort all employees by their hourly wage, highlight cells A1 through D605. From the menu, click **Data > Sort** (in the Sort & Filter group). Make sure that the *My data has headers* checkbox is checked. Select Wage for the *Sort by* option and choose the *Smallest to Largest* (or ascending) order. Click **OK.**

At the top of the sorted list, verify that there are three employees with the lowest hourly wage of $24.28. To sort data in descending order, repeat step e but choose the *Largest to Smallest* (or descending) order. Verify that the highest hourly wage is $51.00.

f. To sort the data based on multiple variables, again highlight cells A1:D605 and go to **Data > Sort.** Choose Industry in the *Sort by* option and the *A to Z* (or ascending) order. Click the *Add Level* button and choose Job in the *Then by* option and the *A to Z* order. Click the *Add Level* button again and choose Wage in the second *Then by* option and the *Smallest to Largest* order. Click **OK.** We see that the lowest- and the highest-paid accountants who worked in the automotive industry made $28.74 and $49.32 per hour, respectively.

Similarly, sorting the data by industry in descending order (*Z to A*) and then by job classification and hourly wage in ascending order reveals that the lowest- and the highest-paid accountants in the Tech industry made $36.13 and $49.49 per hour, respectively.

g. To resort the data set to its original order, highlight cells A1:D605 and go to **Data > Sort.** Select each of the *Then by* rows and click the *Delete Level* button. Choose EmployeeID in the *Sort by* option and the *Smallest to Largest* order.

Summary

- There are a total of 604 records in the data set. There are no missing values in the Wage variable. The Industry and Job variables have 10 and 16 missing values, respectively.
- 190 employees worked in the automotive industry, 536 employees earned more than $30 per hour, and 181 employees worked in the automotive industry and earned more than $30 per hour.
- The lowest and the highest hourly wages in the data set are $24.28 and $51.00, respectively. The three employees who had the lowest hourly wage of $24.28 all worked in the construction industry and were hired as Engineer, Sales Rep, and Accountant, respectively. Interestingly, the employee with the highest hourly wage of $51.00 also worked in the construction industry in a job type classified as Other.
- The lowest- and the highest-paid accountants who worked in the automotive industry made $28.74 and $49.32 per hour, respectively. In the technology industry, the lowest- and the highest-paid accountants made $36.13 and $49.49 per hour, respectively. Note that the lowest hourly wage for an accountant is considerably higher in the technology industry compared to the automotive industry ($36.13 > $28.74).

A Note on Handling Missing Values

There are two common strategies for dealing with missing values. The **omission** strategy recommends that observations with missing values be excluded from subsequent analysis. The **imputation** strategy recommends that the missing values be replaced with some reasonable imputed values. For numerical variables, it is common to replace the missing values with the average values of the relevant variables. For categorical variables, it is common to impute the most predominant category of the relevant variables. Further details regarding the imputation strategy are beyond the scope of this text.

Apply data subsetting.

Subsetting

The process of extracting portions of a data set that are relevant to the analysis is called **subsetting.** For example, a multinational company has sales data for its global operations, and it creates a subset of sales data by country and performs analysis accordingly. For time series data, which are data indexed in time order, we may choose to create subsets of recent observations and observations from the distant past in order to analyze them separately. Subsetting can also be used to eliminate observations that contain missing values, low-quality data, or outliers. Sometimes, subsetting involves excluding variables that contain redundant information, or variables with excessive amounts of missing values.

> **SUBSETTING**
>
> Subsetting is the process of extracting a portion of a data set that is relevant for subsequent statistical analysis or when the objective of the analysis is to compare two subsets of the data.

In Example 1.4, we demonstrate how to use subsetting functions in Excel to select or exclude variables and/or observations from the original data set.

EXAMPLE 1.4

In the introductory case, Catherine Hill wants to gain a better understanding of Organic Food Superstore's customers who are college-educated millennials, born on or after January 1, 1982, and before January 1, 2000. She feels that gender, household size, annual income, total spending, total number of orders, and channel through which the customer was acquired are useful for her to create a profile of these customers. Recall that there are no non-binary customers in this data set. Use Excel to first identify college-educated millenial customers in the ***Customers*** data file. Then, create subsets of female and male college-educated millenial customers and provide a summary of the results.

SOLUTION:

a. Open the ***Customers*** data file.

b. We first filter the data set to include only college-educated millennials. Select the data range A1:J201. From the menu choose **Home > Sort & Filter > Filter.** The column headings (A1 through J1) will turn into drop-down boxes.

c. Click on the drop-down box in E1 (College). Uncheck *(Select all),* then check the box next to *Yes.* Click **OK.** This step shows only those customers who have a college degree (Yes) by hiding those who don't (No) in the data set.

d. Click on the drop-down box in D1 (BirthDate). Select **Date filters > Between.** See Figure 1.4. In the *Custom AutoFilter* dialog box, enter 1/1/1982 next to the *is after or equal to* box or select the date from the calendar object. Select *And* and enter 12/31/1999 next to the is *before or equal to* box or select the date from the calendar object. Click **OK.** The data set now only displays college-educated millennials who were born between 1982 and 2000.

FIGURE 1.4 Excel's AutoFilter dialog box

Microsoft Corporation

e. Select the entire filtered data that are left in the worksheet. Copy and paste the filtered data to a new worksheet. Verify that the new worksheet contains 59 observations of college-educated millennials. Rename the new worksheet as *College-Educated Millennials.*

f. We now exclude the variables that are not relevant to the current analysis. In the *College-Educated Millennials* worksheet, select cell A1 (CustID). From the menu choose **Home > Delete > Delete Sheet Columns** to remove the CustID column. Repeat this step for the Race, BirthDate, and College columns from the data set.

g. To subset the college-educated millennials data by gender, select column A. From the menu choose **Home > Sort & Filter > Sort A to Z.** If prompted, select *Expand the selection* in the *Sort Warning* dialog box and click *Sort.* The observations are now sorted by gender in alphabetic order. The female customer observations are followed by male customer observations.

h. Create two new worksheets and assign the worksheet names *Female* and *Male*. Copy and paste the female and male customer observations, including the column headings, to the new *Female* and *Male* worksheets, respectively. Table 1.8 shows a portion of the results. Verify that there are 21 female college-educated millennials and 38 male college-educated millennials.

TABLE 1.8 College-Educated Millennial Customers

a) Female College-Educated Millennials

Gender	HHSize	Income	Spending	Orders	Channel
Female	5	53000	241	3	SM
Female	3	84000	153	2	Web
⋮	⋮	⋮	⋮	⋮	⋮
Female	1	52000	586	13	Referral

b) Male College-Educated Millennials

Gender	HHSize	Income	Spending	Orders	Channel
Male	5	94000	843	12	TV
Male	1	97000	1028	17	Web
⋮	⋮	⋮	⋮	⋮	⋮
Male	5	102000	926	10	SM

SYNOPSIS OF INTRODUCTORY CASE

Catherine Hill has been assigned to help market Organic Food Superstore's new line of Asian-inspired meals. In order to understand the potential target market for this product, Catherine subsetted the data that contain a representative sample of the company's customers to include only college-educated millennials. She also partitioned the data set into two subsets based on gender to compare the profiles of female and male college-educated millennials. There are no non-binary customers in this data set.

The data show that an overwhelming portion of the male customers were acquired through social media ads, while female customers tend to be enticed by web ads or referrals. Catherine plans to use these results to design and run a series of social media ads about the new product line with content

mackoflower/123RF

that targets male customers. For female customers, she plans to focus her marketing efforts on web banner ads and the company's referral program.

Furthermore, as the male customers seem to place more frequent but smaller orders than female customers do, Catherine plans to work with her marketing team to develop some cross-sell and upsell strategies that target male customers. Given the fact that the company's male college-educated millennial customers tend to be high-income earners, Catherine is confident that with the right message and product offerings, her marketing team will be able to develop strategies for increasing the total spending of these customers.

EXERCISES 1.3

Mechanics

23. **FILE** *Exercise*_**1.23.** The accompanying data set contains two numerical variables, x_1 and x_2.
    a. For x_2, how many of the observations are equal to 2?
    b. Sort x_1 and then x_2, both in ascending order. After the variables have been sorted, what is the first observation for x_1 and x_2?
    c. Sort x_1 and then x_2, both in descending order. After the variables have been sorted, what is the first observation for x_1 and x_2?
    d. Sort x_1 in ascending order and x_2 in descending order. After the variables have been sorted, what is the first observation for x_1 and x_2?
    e. How many missing values are there in x_1 and x_2?

24. **FILE** *Exercise*_**1.24.** The accompanying data set contains three numerical variables, x_1, x_2, and x_3.
    a. For x_1, how many of the observations are greater than 30?
    b. Sort x_1, x_2, and then x_3 all in ascending order. After the variables have been sorted, what is the first observation for x_1, x_2, and x_3?
    c. Sort x_1 and x_2 in descending order and then x_3 in ascending order. After the variables have been sorted, what is the first observation for x_1, x_2, and x_3?
    d. How many missing values are there in x_1, x_2, and x_3?

25. **FILE** *Exercise*_**1.25.** The accompanying data set contains three numerical variables, x_1, x_2, and x_3, and one categorical variable, x_4.
    a. For x_4, how many of the observations are less than three?
    b. Sort x_1, x_2, x_3, and then x_4 all in ascending order. After the variables have been sorted, what is the first observation for x_1, x_2, x_3, and x_4?
    c. Sort x_1, x_2, x_3, and then x_4 all in descending order. After the variables have been sorted, what is the first observation for x_1, x_2, x_3, and x_4?
    d. How many missing values are there in x_1, x_2, x_3, and x_4?
    e. How many observations are there in each category in x_4?

26. **FILE** *Exercise*_**1.26.** The accompanying data set contains four variables, x_1, x_2, x_3, and x_4.
    a. Subset the data set to include only observations that have a date on or after May 1, 1975, for x_3. How many observations are in the subset data?
    b. Subset the original data set based on the binary 1/0 values for x_4. How many observations are in each of the two subsets?

27. **FILE** *Exercise*_**1.27.** The accompanying data set contains five variables, x_1, x_2, x_3, x_4, and x_5.
    a. Subset the data set to include only x_2, x_3, and x_4. How many missing values are there in these three variables?

b. Remove all observations that have "Own" as the value for x_2. Then remove all observations that have values lower than 150 for x_3. How many observations remain in the data set?

28. **FILE** *Exercise*_**1.28.** The accompanying data set contains five variables, x_1, x_2, x_3, x_4, and x_5. There are missing values in the data set.
    a. Which variables have missing values?
    b. Which observations have missing values?
    c. Omit all observations (rows) that have missing values. How many observations remain in the data set?

Applications

29. **FILE** *SAT.* The accompanying data file contains the average writing and math SAT scores for the 50 states as well as the District of Columbia, Puerto Rico, and the U.S. Virgin Islands for the year 2017 as reported by the College Board.
    a. Sort the data by writing scores in descending order. Which state has the highest average writing score? What is the average math score of that state?
    b. Sort the data by math scores in ascending order. Which state has the lowest average math score? What is the average writing score of that state?
    c. How many states reported an average math score higher than 600?
    d. How many states reported an average writing score lower than 550?

30. **FILE** *Fitness.* A social science study conducts a survey of 418 individuals about how often they exercise, marital status, and annual income. The accompanying file contains relevant data.
    a. Sort the data by annual income. Of the 10 highest income earners, how many of them are married and always exercise?
    b. Sort the data by marital status and exercise, both in descending order. How many of the individuals who are married and exercise sometimes earn more than $110,000 per year?
    c. How many missing values are there in each variable?
    d. How many individuals are married and unmarried?
    e. How many married individuals always exercise? How many unmarried individuals never exercise?

31. **FILE** *Demographics.* The accompanying file contains the data for an individual's income (Income in $1,000s), age, gender (Male or Non-male), and marital status (Married; Y = yes, N = no).
    a. Count the number of males and non-males in the data.
    b. What percentages of males and non-males are married?
    c. Of the 10 individuals with the highest income, how many are married males.

d. What are the highest and the lowest incomes of males and non-males?

e. What are the highest and lowest incomes of married and unmarried males?

32. **FILE** *Travel_Plan.* Juan Sánchez is the manager of a travel agency. He wants to build a model that can predict whether or not a customer will travel within the next year. He has compiled a data set that contains the following variables: whether the individual has a college degree (College), annual household spending on food (FoodSpend in $), annual income (Income in $), and whether the customer has plans to travel within the next year (TravelPlan; 1 = have travel plans, 0 = do not have travel plans). The accompanying file contains relevant data.

a. Which variables have missing values?

b. Omit all observations (rows) that have missing values. How many observations are removed due to missing values?

c. In order to better understand his customers with high incomes, Jerry wants to create a subset of the data that only includes customers with annual incomes higher than $75,000 and who plan to travel within the next year. Subset the data to build the list of customers who meet these criteria. How many observations are in this subset?

33. **FILE** *Population.* The U.S. Census Bureau records the population for the 50 states each year. The accompanying file shows these data for the years 2010 to 2018.

a. Create two subsets of the state population data: one with 2018 population greater than or equal to 5 million and one with 2018 population less than 5 million. How many observations are in each subset?

b. In the subset of states with 5 million or more people, remove the states with over 10 million people. How many states were removed?

34. **FILE** *Spend.* A company conducts a consumer survey with questions about home ownership (OwnHome: Yes/No), car ownership (OwnCar: Yes/No), annual household spending on food (Food), and annual household spending on travel (Travel). The accompanying file contains relevant data.

a. Sort the data by home ownership, car ownership, and the travel spending all in descending order. How much did the first customer on the ordered list spend on food?

b. Sort the data only by the travel spending amount in descending order. Of the 10 customers who spend the most on traveling, how many of them are homeowners? How many of them are both homeowners and car owners?

c. How many missing values are there in each variable?

d. How many customers are homeowners? How many customers are homeowners but do not own a car?

35. **FILE** *Salaries.* Deon Williams is a human resource analyst working for the city of Seattle. He is performing a compensation analysis of city employees. The accompanying file contains the data for three variables: Department,

Job Title, and Hourly Rate (in $). A few hourly rates are missing in the data.

a. Split the data set into a number of subsets based on Department. How many subsets are created?

b. Which subset contains missing values? How many missing values are in that data set?

36. **FILE** *Admission.* College admission is a competitive process where, among other things, the SAT and high school GPA scores of students are evaluated to make an admission decision. The accompanying data set contains the admission decision (Decision; Admit/Deny), SAT score, Female (Yes/No), and high school GPA (HSGPA) for 1,230 students. The accompanying file contains relevant data.

a. Count the number of female and non-female students.

b. What percentages of female and non-female students are admitted?

c. Of the 10 students with the highest HSGPA, how many are not females?

d. Of the 10 students with the lowest SAT, how many are females?

e. What are the highest and the lowest SAT scores of admitted female and non-female students?

37. **FILE** *Longitudinal.* The accompanying file contains a portion of data from the National Longitudinal Survey (NLS), which follows over 12,000 individuals in the United States over time. Variables in this analysis include the following information on individuals: Urban (1 if lives in urban area, 0 otherwise), Siblings (number of siblings), White (1 if white, 0 otherwise), FamilySize, Height, Weight (in pounds), and Income (in $).

a. Are there any missing values in the data set? If there are, which variables have missing values? Which observations have missing values?

b. Omit all observations (rows) that have missing values. How many observations are removed due to missing values?

38. **FILE** *Stocks.* Investors usually consider a variety of information to make investment decisions. The accompanying file contains a sample of large publicly traded corporations and their financial information. Relevant information includes stock price (Price), dividend as a percentage of share price (Dividend), price to earnings ratio (PE), earnings per share (EPS), and lowest and highest share prices within the past 52 weeks (Lowest and Highest).

a. Are there any missing values in the data set? If there are, which variables have missing values?

b. Omit all observations (rows) that have missing values. How many complete observations are in the subset?

c. The financial analyst is most interested in companies with a price to earnings ratio less than 15. Remove all observations from the subset in part b for which PE equals 15 or more. How many observations are left in the data set?

1.4 WRITING WITH DATA

Case Study

Cassius Weatherby is a human resources manager at a major technology firm that produces software and hardware products. He would like to analyze the net promoter score (NPS) of sales professionals at the company. The NPS measures customer satisfaction and loyalty by asking customers how likely they are to recommend the company to others on a scale of 0 (unlikely) to 10 (very likely). This measure is an especially important indicator for the company's software business as a large percentage of the sales leads come from customer referrals. Cassius wants to identify relevant factors that are linked with the NPS that a sales professional receives. These insights can help the company make better hiring decisions and develop a more effective training program.

With the help of the company's IT group, a data set with over 20,000 observations of sales professionals is extracted from the enterprise data warehouse. The relevant variables for this report include the product line to which the sales professional is assigned, personality type based on the Myers-Briggs personality assessment, the number of professional certificates acquired, and the average NPS received. Cassius is tasked with inspecting and reviewing the data to prepare a report for the company's top management team.

FILE

TechSales_Reps

Sample Report– Evaluation of Net Promoter Scores

The net promoter score (NPS) is a key indicator of customer satisfaction and loyalty. It measures how likely a customer would recommend a product or company to others. Because our software line for business relies heavily on customer referrals to generate sales leads, the NPS that our sales professionals receive is a key indicator of our company's future success.

dizain/Shutterstock

From a total of about 20,000 records of sales professionals, we select only the sales professionals in the software product group and divide them into two categories: those with an average NPS below nine and those with an average NPS of nine or ten. When a customer gives a sales professional an NPS of nine or ten, the customer is considered "enthusiastically loyal," meaning that they are very likely to continue purchasing from us and refer their colleagues to our company. Based on the NPS categorization, we then divide the sales professionals into two categories: those with zero to three professional certificates and those with four or more professional certificates. Table 1.9 shows the results. Of the 12,130 sales professionals in the software product group, we find that 65.57% have earned less than four professional certificates, whereas 34.43% have earned four or more. However, there appears to be a link between those with four or more professional certificates and NPS values. For those who received an NPS of nine or ten, we find that 62.60% have earned at least four professional certificates. Similarly, for those who received an NPS of below nine, we find that 73.00% earned less than four professional certificates.

TABLE 1.9 Sales Professionals by the Number of Certificates and NPS Value

Number of certificates	Full Sample (n = 12,130)	NPS < 9 (n = 9,598)	NPS ≥ 9 (n = 2,532)
0 to 3	65.57%	73.00%	37.40%
4 or more	34.43%	27.00%	62.60%

Although this might simply suggest that high-achieving employees tend to be self-motivated to earn professional certificates, we also believe that sales professionals with sufficient technical knowledge can effectively communicate and assist their customers in finding technology solutions, which will lead to increased customer satisfaction and loyalty. Our training and development program must place a greater emphasis on helping the employees earn relevant certifications and acquire necessary technical knowledge.

Based on NPS categorization, we then divide the sales professionals into categories based on personality type. Table 1.10 shows the results. In addition to professional certification, we find that personality types are linked with NPS values. Among the four personality types, Diplomats and Explorers account for 72.69% of all the sales professionals in the software group. However, when we divide the employees based on the NPS values, these two personality types account for 91.63% of the group with an average NPS of nine or ten, whereas they account for only 67.69% for the below-nine NPS group.

TABLE 1.10 Sales Professionals by Personality Type and NPS Value

Myers-Briggs Personality Type	Full Sample (n = 12,130)	NPS < 9 (n = 9,598)	NPS ≥ 9 (n = 2,532)
Analyst	12.13%	14.47%	3.24%
Diplomat	35.62%	33.07%	45.30%
Explorer	37.07%	34.62%	46.33%
Sentinel	15.19%	17.84%	5.13%

We also examined NPS variations by other variables such as age, gender, education attainment, sales, and commission, but did not find considerable differences in NPS categorization. Other variables such as salary and the tenure of the employee with the company are not included in our initial analysis.

Based on the insights from this analysis, we request that the company appoint an analytics task force to conduct a more comprehensive analysis of sales professionals. We strongly suggest that the analysis focus on professional certification and personality, among relevant factors for determining the NPS value. At a minimum, two goals of the task force should include making recommendations on (1) a redesign of our training and development program to focus on helping employees acquire relevant professional certificates and (2) the efficacy of using personality types as part of the hiring decision.

Suggested Case Studies

As discussed in the chapter, data from an endless number of online sources are available for us to explore and investigate. Here are some suggested case studies using online as well as the big data that accompany the text.

Report 1.1 Finland is the happiest country in the world, according to the 2018 Happiness Index Report by the United Nations (www.worldhappiness.report). In fact, several Scandinavian countries have consistently held the top spots among the 156 countries, included in the annual Happiness Index Report in the past several years. Visit the Happiness Index website, download and explore online data, and write a report on your choice of countries, focusing on variables such as social support, healthy life expectancy at birth, freedom to make life choices, and generosity.

Report 1.2 `FILE` *House_Price.* Choose any two campus towns and focus on variables representing the sale price, beds, baths, square footage, lot size, and the house type. Describe the variable type and scales of measurement for each variable. Further, make a comparison between the two campus towns.

Report 1.3 `FILE` *College_Admissions.* Choose any college and focus on variables representing parents' education, race (white, Asian, or other), high school GPA, SAT/Act scores, and admission decision. Describe the variable type and scales of measurement for each variable. Further, subset the data by race to report any patterns that you observe for these selected variables.

Report 1.4 `FILE` *TechSales_Reps.* Use data on employees in the software product group with a college degree for variables representing feedback, personality type, salary, and net promoter score. Describe the variable type and scales of measurement for each variable. Further, subset the data by personality type to report any patterns that you observe for these selected variables.

2 Data Visualization

People often have difficulty processing information provided by data in its raw form. A useful way of interpreting data effectively is through data visualization. In this chapter, we present several tabular and graphical tools that help us organize and present data.

We first construct a frequency distribution for a categorical variable. A frequency distribution is a tabular method for condensing and summarizing data. For visual representations of a categorical variable, we construct a bar chart and a pie chart.

For a numerical variable, we again construct a frequency distribution. In addition to giving us an overall picture of where the data tend to cluster, a frequency distribution for a numerical variable also shows us how the data are spread out from the minimum value to the maximum value. For visual representations of a numerical variable, we construct a histogram.

Finally, we examine the relationship between two variables. For two categorical variables, we construct a contingency table, a stacked column chart, and a clustered column chart. For two numerical variables, we construct a scatterplot and a line chart.

INTRODUCTORY CASE

Construction Clothing

ReliableWorkWear.com is an online company that offers a large selection of construction clothing and gear that keep workers safe and comfortable on the job. The rugged workwear has also become wildly popular by fans outside of the construction industry because of their protection, warmth, and style.

Brendan Navarro is the marketing analyst for ReliableWorkWear.com. He has compiled data on 200 recent transactions that include the following information: the purchase amount (Purchase in $), the customer's annual income (Income in $1,000s), the customer's satisfaction with the purchase (Satisfaction = Rating_1 through Rating_5, with Rating_1 being very dissatisfied and Rating_5 being very satisfied), whether the customer is a repeat customer (Repeat = Yes or No), and whether the customer is male or female (Sex = Male or Female). [Note that for the Sex variable, there are no non-binary observations in this data set.]

Table 2.1 shows a portion of the **Transactions** data file.

TABLE 2.1 Information on 200 Customer Transactions

FILE

Transactions

Customer	Purchase	Income	Satisfaction	Repeat	Sex
1	241	53	Rating_1	No	Male
2	843	94	Rating_3	Yes	Male
⋮	⋮	⋮	⋮	⋮	⋮
200	926	102	Rating_4	Yes	Male

Brendan will use the sample information to:

1. Convey the information from the variables in tabular form.
2. Convey the information from the variables in graphical form.
3. Discuss findings and provide strategies that may help increase sales.

A synopsis of this case is provided at the end of Section 2.4.

2.1 METHODS TO VISUALIZE A CATEGORICAL VARIABLE

In this section, we present several tabular and graphical tools that help us organize and present data for a categorical variable. Recall from Chapter 1 that a categorical variable consists of observations that represent labels or names. For example, participants in a survey are often asked to indicate their gender or race, or provide ratings of a product. When presented with a categorical variable, it is often useful to summarize the variable with a frequency distribution, a bar chart, and/or a pie chart. We first discuss the construction of a frequency distribution. Consider the following example.

A Frequency Distribution for a Categorical Variable

Recall the online construction clothing company ReliableWorkWear.com from the introductory case. Brendan Navarro, the company's marketing analyst, has information on 200 recent purchases stored in the **Transactions** data file. The Satisfaction variable records a customer's satisfaction with the purchase. It is a categorical variable of ordinal scale, ranging from 1 (very dissatisfied) to 5 (very satisfied).

Data presented in this format—that is, in raw form—are very difficult to interpret. Converting the raw data into a **frequency distribution** is often a first step in making the data more manageable and easier to assess.

As shown in Table 2.2, the categories of the Satisfaction variable form the first column of a frequency distribution where the categories represent ratings 1 through 5. We then record the number of responses that fall into each category in an adjacent column labeled Frequency. We can readily see from Table 2.2 that the rating of 4 occurs with the most frequency, while the rating of 1 occurs with the least frequency.

In some applications, especially when comparing data sets of differing sizes, our needs may be better served by focusing on the **relative frequency** for each category rather than its frequency. The relative frequency for each category is calculated by dividing the frequency by the sample size. The third column of Table 2.2 shows the relative frequency for each category. We can easily convert relative frequencies into percentages by multiplying by 100, as shown in the fourth column. From Table 2.2 we can conclude that 46% of the transactions result in a rating of 4 for the Satisfaction variable.

Transactions

TABLE 2.2 Frequency Distribution for the Satisfaction Variable

Satisfaction	Frequency	Relative frequency	Percent frequency
Rating_1	12	0.06	6
Rating_2	18	0.09	9
Rating_3	36	0.18	18
Rating_4	92	0.46	46
Rating_5	42	0.21	21

A FREQUENCY DISTRIBUTION FOR A CATEGORICAL VARIABLE

A frequency distribution for a categorical variable groups the observations into categories and records the number of observations that fall into each category. The relative frequency for each category equals the proportion of observations in each category. The percent frequency for each category is the relative frequency multiplied by 100.

We can visualize the information found in the frequency distribution by constructing various graphs. A graphical representation often portrays the variable more dramatically, as well as simplifies interpretation. A bar chart and a pie chart are two widely used graphical representations for a categorical variable.

A Bar Chart

We first construct a vertical **bar chart,** sometimes referred to as a column chart. The height of each bar is equal to the frequency or the relative frequency of the corresponding category. Figure 2.1 shows the bar chart for the Satisfaction variable.

FIGURE 2.1 Bar chart for the Satisfaction variable

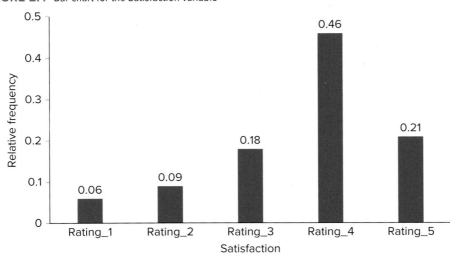

A BAR CHART
A bar chart depicts the frequency or the relative frequency for each category of the categorical variable as a series of horizontal or vertical bars.

A Pie Chart

A **pie chart** is a circle that is cut into slices, or sectors, such that each sector is proportional to the size of the category we wish to display. For instance, for the Satisfaction variable, we found that the relative frequency for a rating of 4 is 0.46. Because a circle contains 360 degrees, the portion of the circle representing a rating of 4 encompasses $0.46 \times 360 = 165.6$ degrees. Calculations for the other categories are obtained in a similar manner.

Figure 2.2 shows the pie chart for the Satisfaction variable. We see that Figure 2.1 and Figure 2.2 reveal the same information in different ways; that is, the most common rating is 4 and the least common rating is 1.

FIGURE 2.2   A pie chart for the Satisfaction variable

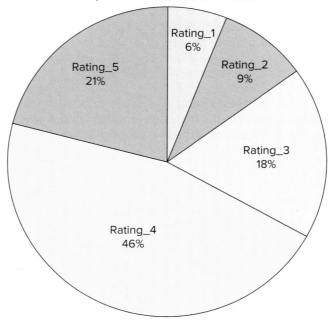

> ### A PIE CHART
>
> A pie chart is a segmented circle whose segments portray the relative frequency of each category for a categorical variable.

EXAMPLE 2.1

Transactions

Recall the online construction clothing company ReliableWorkWear.com from the introductory case. The ***Transactions*** data file contains information on 200 recent customer purchases. In addition to the Satisfaction variable, there are two other categorical variables. The Repeat variable records whether or not the customer made a prior purchase (Repeat = Yes if prior purchase, No otherwise). The Sex variable records whether the customer is male or female. For each variable, use Excel to construct its frequency distribution, relative frequency distribution, bar chart, and pie chart; summarize the results.

Important: Due to different fonts and type settings, copying and pasting Excel functions from this text directly into Excel may cause errors. When such errors occur, you may need to replace special characters such as quotation marks and parentheses or delete extra spaces in the functions.

SOLUTION:

a. Open the ***Transactions*** data file.

b. We first construct frequency and relative frequency distributions for the Repeat variable. Enter the column headings Repeat, Frequency, and Relative Frequency in cells H1, I1, and J1 respectively. Enter the column headings Yes and No in cells H2 and H3, respectively. We use the **COUNTIF** function to find the frequency for each category. This function requires two inputs. The first input is the range of observations for the Repeat variable, and the second input states one of the categories. In general, if the category is represented as text, then we need to enclose the text with double quotations. If the category is numeric, then double quotations are not necessary. Enter the formula =COUNTIF(D2:D201, "Yes") in cell I2. Enter the formula =COUNTIF(D2:D201, "No") in cell I3.

In order to calculate the relative frequency for each category, select cell J2 and enter =I2/200. Copy and paste the formula from cell J2 to cell J3. Table 2.3(a) shows the frequency and the relative frequency distributions for the Repeat variable.

We follow the same steps for the Sex variable, but now the relevant observations are in cells E2 through E201 and the categories are Male and Female. Verify that the frequency and the relative frequency distributions match those that appear in Table 2.3(b).

TABLE 2.3 Frequency and Relative Frequency Distributions

(a) The Repeat Variable		
Repeat	Frequency	Relative frequency
Yes	140	0.70
No	60	0.30

(b) The Sex Variable		
Sex	Frequency	Relative frequency
Male	150	0.75
Female	50	0.25

c. We first construct a bar chart for the Repeat variable. Select cells H2:I4. From the menu, select **Insert,** and in the Charts group, expand the selection by clicking on the arrow at the bottom right. Select the **All Charts** tab and then select **Column.** Then select the option at the top left. Figure 2.3(a) shows the bar chart for the Repeat variable. Note that in this instance we have constructed a vertical bar chart. If you wish to construct a horizontal bar chart, then you would select **Bar** instead of **Column** under the **All Charts** tab. Repeat these steps to obtain the bar chart for the Sex variable. Verify that the bar chart is similar to the one that appears in Figure 2.3(b).

Formatting (regarding axis titles, gridlines, etc.) can be done by selecting the '+' sign at the top right of the chart or by selecting **Add Chart Elements** from the menu. For example, go to **Add Chart Elements > Data Labels > Outside End** to add the frequency values above the bars of the bar chart.

FIGURE 2.3 Bar charts

(a) The Repeat variable

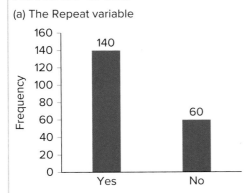

(b) The Sex variable

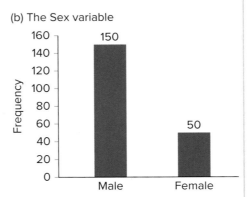

d. We will now construct a pie chart, starting with the Repeat variable. Select cells H2:I4. From the menu, select **Insert,** and in the Charts group, expand the selection by clicking on the arrow at the bottom right. Select the **All Charts** tab and then select **Pie.** Then select the option at the top left. Figure 2.4(a) shows the pie chart for the Repeat variable. See Step c for formatting. Repeat these steps to obtain the pie chart for the Sex variable and verify that it is similar to the one that appears in Figure 2.4(b).

FIGURE 2.4 Pie charts

(a) The repeat variable

No
30%

Yes
70%

(b) The sex variable

Female
25%

Male
75%

Summary
Table 2.3, Figure 2.3, and Figure 2.4 reveal that 140 of the 200 purchases (70%) came from customers who made prior purchases. It appears that ReliableWork-Wear.com has a loyal base. In addition, 50 of the 200 purchases (25%) were made by females. This is an interesting finding because, of all people working in the construction industry, females comprise only about 10% (*Women in Construction: The State of the Industry in 2021,* January 19, 2021). This likely implies that women in construction tend to purchase from ReliableWorkWear.com more frequently or that females who do not work in the construction industry are purchasing the rugged workwear because of its protection, warmth, and style.

Cautionary Comments When Constructing Graphs

As with many of the analytical methods that we examine throughout this text, the possibility exists for unintentional, as well as purposeful, distortions of graphical information. As a careful researcher, you should follow these basic guidelines:

- The simplest graph should be used for a given set of data. Strive for clarity and avoid unnecessary adornments.

- Axes should be clearly marked with the numbers of their respective scales; each axis should be labeled.

- When creating a bar chart or a histogram (discussed in Section 2.2), each bar/rectangle should be of the same width. Differing widths create distortions. Figure 2.5(a) shows a bar chart for the number and the sizes of sweatshirts sold over the past month at an online retailer. Because the width of the Medium sweatshirt is far wider than the other categories, it is given undue importance. Figure 2.5(b) shows a bar chart where all widths of the categories are the same. It is now much clearer that the Large sweatshirt was the best seller.

FIGURE 2.5
Misleading bar chart: Unequal bar widths

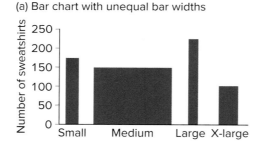

(a) Bar chart with unequal bar widths

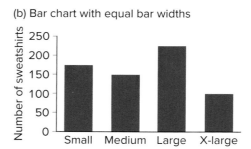

(b) Bar chart with equal bar widths

EXERCISES 2.1

Applications

1. Fifty pro-football rookies were rated on a scale of 1 to 5, based on performance at a training camp as well as on past performance. A ranking of 1 indicated a poor prospect, whereas a ranking of 5 indicated an excellent prospect. The following frequency distribution was constructed.

Rating	Frequency
1	4
2	10
3	14
4	18
5	4

   a. How many of the rookies received a rating of 4 or better? How many of the rookies received a rating of 2 or worse?
   b. Construct the relative frequency distribution. What proportion received a rating of 5?
   c. Construct a bar chart. Comment on the findings.

2. The following frequency distribution shows the counts of sales of T-shirts at an online retailer over the weekend.

Size	Frequency
Small	80
Medium	175
Large	210
X-Large	115

   a. Construct the relative frequency distribution. What proportion of sales were for a medium-sized shirt?
   b. Construct a bar chart. Comment on the findings.

3. The following frequency distribution summarizes the counts of purchases by day of the week for a major domestic retailer.

Day	Frequency
Mon	2,504
Tue	2,880
Wed	3,402
Thur	3,566
Fri	4,576
Sat	5,550
Sun	5,022

   a. Construct the relative frequency distribution. What proportion of the purchases occurred on Wednesday?
   b. Construct a bar chart using relative frequencies. Comment on the findings.

4. In 2018, the U.S. Census Bureau provided the following frequency distribution for the number of people (in 1,000s) who live below the poverty level by region.

Region	Number of People
Northeast	6,373
Midwest	7,647
South	16,609
West	9,069

   a. Construct the relative frequency distribution. What proportion of people who live below the poverty level live in the Midwest?
   b. Construct a bar chart. Comment on the findings.

5. A recent poll of 3,057 individuals asked: "What's the longest vacation you plan to take this summer?" The following relative frequency distribution summarizes the results.

Response	Relative Frequency
A few days	0.21
A few long weekends	0.18
One week	0.36
Two weeks	0.25

   a. Construct the frequency distribution. How many people are going to take a one-week vacation this summer?
   b. Construct a bar chart. Comment on the findings.

6. **FILE** *Dining.* A local restaurant is committed to providing its patrons with the best dining experience possible. On a recent survey, the restaurant asked patrons to rate the quality of their entrées. The responses ranged from 1 to 5, where 1 indicated a disappointing entrée and 5 indicated an exceptional entrée. The responses are shown in the accompanying data file.

   a. Construct the frequency distribution that summarizes the results from the survey. Which rating appeared with the most frequency?
   b. Construct a bar chart. Are the patrons generally satisfied with the quality of their entrées? Explain.

7. **FILE** *Health.* Patients at North Shore Family Practice are required to fill out a questionnaire that gives the doctor an overall idea of each patient's health. The first question is: "In general, what is the quality of your health?" The patient chooses Excellent, Good, Fair, or Poor. The responses are shown in the accompanying data file.

   a. Construct the frequency distribution that summarizes the results from the questionnaire. What is the most common response to the questionnaire?
   b. Construct a bar chart for the results from the questionnaire. How would you characterize the health of patients at this medical practice? Explain.

8. **FILE** *Millennials.* A few years ago, a study found that 35% of millennials (Americans born between 1981 and 1996) identified themselves as not religious. A researcher wonders if this finding is consistent today. She surveys 600 millennials

and asks them to rate their faith. Possible responses were Very Religious, Somewhat Religious, Slightly Religious, and Not Religious. The responses are shown in the accompanying data file.

a. Construct the frequency distribution that summarizes the results from the survey. What is the most common response to the survey?

b. Construct a pie chart. Do the researcher's results appear consistent with those found by the earlier study? Explain.

9. **FILE** *Classification.* A statistics instructor is interested in the academic classification of her students, which is defined as freshman, sophomore, junior, or senior. Her roster is shown in the accompanying data file.

a. Construct the frequency and relative frequency distributions. How many freshmen are in her class? What percentage of the class are sophomores?

b. Construct the pie chart. Summarize the findings.

10. **FILE** *AdultChild.* A recent survey of 400 Americans asked whether or not parents do too much for their young adult children. The results of the survey are shown in the accompanying data file.

a. Construct the frequency and the relative frequency distributions. How many respondents felt that parents do too much for their adult children? What proportion of respondents felt that parents do too little for their adult children?

b. Construct the pie chart. Summarize the findings.

11. **FILE** *CEO.* The accompanying data file shows the highest degrees earned by a sample of 200 chief executive officers (CEOs) in the United States.

a. Construct the frequency and the relative frequency distributions. Do most CEOs in the United States have advanced degrees, such as a Master's degree or a PhD? What percentage of CEOs do not have at least a Bachelor's degree?

b. Construct the bar chart. Summarize the findings.

2.2 METHODS TO VISUALIZE A NUMERICAL VARIABLE

Visualize a numerical variable.

With a numerical variable, each observation represents a meaningful amount or count. The number of patents held by pharmaceutical firms (count) and household incomes (amount) are examples of numerical variables. Although different in nature from a categorical variable, we still use a frequency distribution to summarize a numerical variable.

A Frequency Distribution for a Numerical Variable

When we constructed a frequency distribution for a categorical variable, we simply counted the number of observations in each category. For a numerical variable, instead of categories, we construct a series of intervals (sometimes called classes or bins). We must make certain decisions about the number of intervals, as well as the width of each interval. When making these decisions, we consider the following guidelines.

- *The total number of intervals in a frequency distribution usually ranges from 5 to 20.* Smaller data sets tend to have fewer intervals than larger data sets. Recall that the goal of constructing a frequency distribution is to summarize the data in a form that accurately depicts the group as a whole. If we have too many intervals, then this advantage of the frequency distribution is lost. Similarly, if the frequency distribution has too few classes, then considerable accuracy and detail are lost.

- *Intervals are exhaustive.* The total number of intervals covers the entire sample (or population). In order to ensure that all observations are included when constructing a frequency distribution, a common first step is to identify the minimum and maximum values of the variable.

- *Intervals are mutually exclusive.* For example, suppose the first two intervals of a frequency distribution are defined as $300 < x \leq 400$ and $400 < x \leq 500$, where x is an observation of the variable. The values 300 and 400 are defined as the lower limit and upper limit, respectively, of the first interval. Similarly, the values 400 and 500 are the lower limit and upper limit, respectively, of the second interval. If $x = 400$, then it would fall into the first interval, but not the second interval because of how the intervals have been defined. In other words, intervals do not overlap, and each observation falls into one, and only one, interval. It is also important to note that Excel defines its intervals in this manner; that is, if an observation equals the upper limit of an interval, then it is included in that interval.

- *Interval limits are easy to recognize and interpret.* As a starting point for approximating the width of each interval, we often use the formula (Maximum Value − Minimum Value)/Number of Intervals. Suppose that we decide to have 6 intervals and the minimum and maximum values of the variable are 9 and 291, respectively. We calculate $(291 − 9)/6 = 47$. We could use an interval width of 47 with a lower limit of 8 and define the intervals as $8 < x \leq 55$, $55 < x \leq 102$, etc. However, intervals with these lower and upper limits are not easily recognizable. It would be preferable to use an interval width of 50 with a lower limit of 0 and define the intervals as $0 < x \leq 50$, $50 < x \leq 100$, etc.

Recall the online construction clothing company ReliableWorkWear.com from the introductory case. The Purchase variable in the *Transactions* data file is a numerical variable. Each observation reflects the amount (in $) that a customer spent on construction clothing and gear. Here we will create a frequency distribution with five intervals. The minimum and maximum values for the Purchase variable are 55 and 996, respectively. Using the approximation formula to find the width of each interval, we calculate $(996 − 55)/5 = 188.2$. However, intervals with a width of 188.2 would not have limits that are easily recognizable. For this reason, we define the lower limit of the first interval as 0, and we make each interval of width 200; that is, $0 < x \leq 200$, $200 < x \leq 400$, etc., where x is the amount of each purchase.

The first two columns of Table 2.4 show the frequency distribution for the Purchase variable. Even though some detail is lost because we no longer see the actual observations, we can now readily observe that the most likely amount for the Purchase variable is between $200 and $400; there are 63 observations in this interval. We also note that only 25 of the purchases are less than $200. Summing the values in the frequency column shows that the sample size (or n) is 200. The relative frequency for each interval is again calculated by dividing the frequency by the sample size. The third column of Table 2.4 shows the relative frequency for each interval. As before, a relative frequency can be converted into a percentage by multiplying by 100. The last column of Table 2.4 shows that 31.5% of the purchases fall between $200 and $400.

TABLE 2.4 Frequency Distribution for the Purchase variable

Interval (in $)	Frequency	Relative frequency	Percent frequency
$0 < x \leq 200$	25	0.125	12.5
$200 < x \leq 400$	63	0.315	31.5
$400 < x \leq 600$	49	0.245	24.5
$600 < x \leq 800$	33	0.165	16.5
$800 < x \leq 1,000$	30	0.150	15.0

For a numerical variable, we can modify the frequency distribution by constructing a **cumulative frequency distribution.** For the cumulative frequency distribution, we use the same number of intervals, interval widths, and interval limits that we developed when constructing the frequency distribution. However, rather than showing the frequency of each interval, the cumulative frequency distribution shows the number of observations that fall below the upper limit of a particular interval. The first two columns of Table 2.5 show the cumulative frequency distribution for the Purchase variable. The cumulative frequency of the first interval is the same as the frequency of the first interval from Table 2.4—here, that value is 25. To obtain the cumulative frequency for the second interval, we add its frequency, 63, with the preceding frequency, 25, and obtain 88, meaning that 88 of the purchases are for $400 or less. We find the cumulative frequencies of the remaining intervals in a like manner. Note that the cumulative frequency of the last interval is equal to the sample size of 200. This indicates that all 200 purchases are for $1,000 or less.

TABLE 2.5 Cumulative Frequency Distribution for the Purchase variable

Interval (in $)	Cumulative frequency	Cumulative relative frequency	Cumulative percent frequency
$0 < x \leq 200$	25	0.125	12.5
$200 < x \leq 400$	88	0.440	44.0
$400 < x \leq 600$	137	0.685	68.5
$600 < x \leq 800$	170	0.850	85.0
$800 < x \leq 1,000$	200	1.000	100.0

The **cumulative relative frequency** for an interval indicates the proportion (fraction) of the observations that falls below the upper limit of that interval. We can calculate the cumulative relative frequency of each interval in one of two ways: (1) We can sum successive relative frequencies from Table 2.4 or (2) we can divide each interval's cumulative frequency by the sample size. The third column of Table 2.5 shows the cumulative relative frequency for each interval. A cumulative relative frequency can be converted into a cumulative percent frequency by multiplying by 100—these values are shown in the last column of Table 2.5. We can conclude, for instance, that 68.5% of the purchases are for $600 or less.

A FREQUENCY DISTRIBUTION FOR A NUMERICAL VARIABLE

For a numerical variable, a frequency distribution groups the observations into intervals and records the number of observations that falls into each interval. The relative frequency for each interval equals the proportion of observations in each interval. The percent frequency for each interval is the relative frequency multiplied by 100.

A Histogram

Next, we show a graphical representation of a frequency distribution. For a numerical variable, a **histogram** is essentially the counterpart to the vertical bar chart that we use for a categorical variable.

When constructing a histogram, we typically mark off the interval limits along the horizontal axis. The height of each bar represents either the frequency or the relative frequency for each interval. No gaps appear between the interval limits.

Figure 2.6 shows a histogram for the Purchase variable. The advantage of a visual display is that we can quickly see where most of the observations tend to cluster, as well as the spread and shape of the variable. From Figure 2.6 we can see that purchases ranged from $0 up to $1,000. Purchases between $200 and $400 were the most frequent, whereas purchases less than $200 were the least frequent.

FIGURE 2.6 Histogram for the Purchase variable

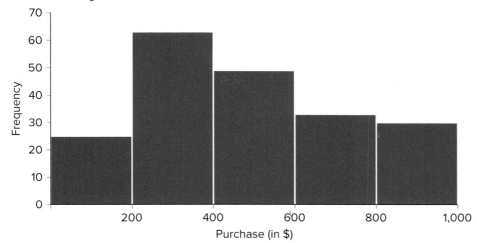

A histogram also provides information on the shape of the distribution. In general, the shape of most distributions can be categorized as either **symmetric** or **skewed**. A symmetric distribution is one that is a mirror image of itself on both sides of its center. That is, the location of values below the center correspond to those above the center. As we will see in Chapter 6, the smoothed histogram for many variables approximates a bell-shaped curve, which is indicative of the well-known normal distribution. Figure 2.7(a) shows a histogram with a symmetric distribution. If the edges were smoothed, this histogram would look somewhat bell-shaped.

In general, if the distribution is not symmetric, then it is either **positively skewed** or **negatively skewed.** Figure 2.7(b) shows a histogram with a positively skewed, or skewed to the right, distribution. The long tail that extends to the right reflects the presence of a small number of relatively large observations. The histogram for the Purchase variable in Figure 2.6 shows that it is not a symmetric distribution; rather, it is positively skewed. Figure 2.7(c) shows a histogram with a negatively skewed, or skewed to the left, distribution because it has a long tail extending off to the left. A variable with a negatively skewed distribution has a small number of relatively small observations.

FIGURE 2.7 Histograms with differing shapes

(a) Symmetric distribution   (b) Positively skewed distribution   (c) Negatively skewed distribution

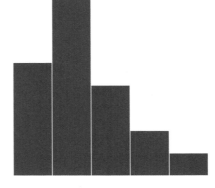

A HISTOGRAM

A histogram is a series of rectangles where the width and height of each rectangle represent the interval width and frequency (or relative frequency) of the respective interval.

EXAMPLE 2.2

Recall the online construction clothing company ReliableWorkWear.com from the introductory case. The Income variable in the **Transactions** data file shows the annual income (in $1,000s) for 200 customers. Construct a frequency distribution and a histogram using Excel, and then summarize the results.

SOLUTION

Before using Excel, we need to make some decisions about the number of intervals, as well the width of each interval. For a variable with 200 observations, it is reasonable to use five intervals. We then find the minimum and maximum values for the Income variable; they are 31 and 240, respectively. Using the formula to approximate the interval width, we calculate $(240 − 31)/5 = 41.8$. In order to have interval limits that are easy to recognize, we will construct a frequency distribution with a width of 50, instead of 41.8; also, we will set the lower limit of the first interval equal to 0 instead of 31.

Using Excel

a. Open the **Transactions** data file.

b. In cell H1 enter the heading Upper_Limit, and in cells H2 through H6 enter the upper limit of each interval, so 50, 100, 150, 200, and 250. The reason for these entries will be explained shortly.

c. From the menu choose **Data > Data Analysis > Histogram > OK.** (Note: If you do not see the **Data Analysis** option under **Data,** you must add in the **Analysis Toolpak** option. For PC users, choose **File > Options > Add-Ins** and choose **Go** at the bottom of the dialog box. Select **Analysis Toolpak** and then click **OK.** For Mac users, choose **Tools > Excel Add-ins.** In the **Add-Ins available** box, select **Analysis ToolPak,** and then click **OK.** If you have installed this option properly, you should now see **Data Analysis** under **Data.**)

d. See Figure 2.8. In the *Histogram* dialog box, next to *Input Range,* select the Income observations. We use *Bin Range* to define the interval limits. If we leave the *Bin Range* box empty, Excel creates evenly distributed intervals using the minimum and maximum values of the variable as end points. This approach is rarely satisfactory. In order to construct a histogram that is more informative, we use the upper limits of each interval as the bin values. Next to *Bin Range,* we select cells H1:H6 (the Upper_Limit observations). We check the *Labels* box because we have included the Income and Upper_Limit headings as part of the selection. Under *Output Options,* select *Output Range* and enter cell I1 and then select **Chart Output.** Click **OK.**

FIGURE 2.8 Excel's dialog box for a histogram

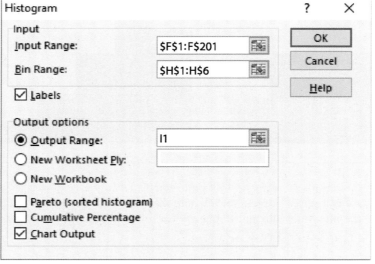

Source: Microsoft Office 2019

Table 2.6 shows the frequency distribution for the Income variable. We have edited the first column for exposition, but you should verify that you obtain the same frequencies for each interval. In the event that the given interval limits do not include all the observations, Excel automatically adds another interval labeled "More" to the resulting frequency distribution and histogram. Because we observe zero observations in this interval, we delete this interval. Also, as mentioned earlier, if an observation equals the upper limit of an interval, Excel accounts for that observation in that interval. For example, if the value 50 appeared in the data, Excel would account for this observation in the first interval.

In order to calculate the relative frequency and percent frequency for each interval, enter the column headings Relative frequency and Percent frequency in cells K1 and L1, respectively. Select cell K2 and enter = J2/200; then copy and paste the formula from cell K2 to cells K3 through K6. Select cell L2 and enter = K2*100; then copy and paste the formula from cell L2 to cells L3 through L6. The last two columns of Table 2.6 show the relative frequencies and the percent frequencies for each interval.

TABLE 2.6 Frequency Distribution for the Income Variable

Interval (in $1,000s)	Frequency	Relative frequency	Percent frequency
$0 < x \leq 50$	40	0.20	20
$50 < x \leq 100$	132	0.66	66
$100 < x \leq 150$	18	0.09	9
$150 < x \leq 200$	6	0.03	3
$200 < x \leq 250$	4	0.02	2

e. Because Excel leaves spaces between the rectangles in the histogram, we right-click on any of the rectangles, choose **Format Data Series,** change the *Gap Width* to 0, and then choose **Close.** Formatting (regarding axis titles, gridlines, etc.) can be done by selecting **Format > Add Chart Element** from the menu. Figure 2.9 shows the histogram for the Income variable.

Figure 2.9 Histogram for the Income variable

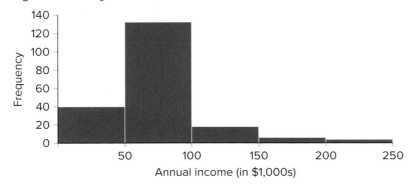

Note that you can construct a frequency distribution by using Excel's **COUNTIF** function that we used in Example 2.1. You can then use the resulting frequency distribution to plot a histogram. The Histogram option in Excel's Data Analysis Toolpak allows us to construct both the frequency distribution and the histogram with one command.

Summary

From Table 2.6, we see that the range of annual income for the 200 customers is between $0 and $250,000. The majority of customers (66%) earned between $50,000 and $100,000. Only 5% of the customers earned more than $150,000. From Figure 2.9, we see that the distribution for Income is not symmetric; it is positively skewed with a tail running off to the right.

EXERCISES 2.2

Mechanics

12. Consider the following frequency distribution:

Interval	Frequency
$1,000 < x \le 1,100$	22
$1,100 < x \le 1,200$	38
$1,200 < x \le 1,300$	44
$1,300 < x \le 1,400$	16

a. Construct the relative frequency distribution. What proportion of the observations is more than 1,100 but no more than 1,200?
b. Construct the cumulative frequency distribution. How many of the observations are 1,300 or less?
c. Construct the cumulative relative frequency distribution. What proportion of the observations is 1,300 or less? More than 1,300?

13. Consider the following frequency distribution:

Interval	Frequency
$10 < x \le 20$	12
$20 < x \le 30$	15
$30 < x \le 40$	25
$40 < x \le 50$	4

a. Construct the relative frequency distribution. What proportion of the observations is in the interval $20 < x \le 30$?
b. Construct the cumulative frequency distribution. How many of the observations are less than 40?
c. Construct the cumulative relative frequency distribution. What proportion of the observations is less than 30?

14. Consider the following cumulative frequency distribution:

Interval	Cumulative Frequency
$15 < x \le 25$	30
$25 < x \le 35$	50
$35 < x \le 45$	120
$45 < x \le 55$	130

a. Construct the frequency distribution. How many observations are more than 35 but no more than 45?
b. Construct the cumulative relative frequency distribution. What proportion of the observations is 45 or less?
c. Graph the histogram. Is the distribution symmetric?

15. Consider the following relative frequency distribution:

Interval	Relative Frequency
$-20 < x \le -10$	0.04
$-10 < x \le 0$	0.28
$0 < x \le 10$	0.26
$10 < x \le 20$	0.22
$20 < x \le 30$	0.20

a. Suppose this relative frequency distribution is based on a sample of 50 observations. Construct the frequency distribution. How many of the observations are more than −10 but no more than 0?
b. Construct the cumulative frequency distribution. How many of the observations are 20 or less?

16. Consider the following cumulative relative frequency distribution.

Interval	Cumulative Relative Frequency
$150 < x \le 200$	0.10
$200 < x \le 250$	0.35
$250 < x \le 300$	0.70
$300 < x \le 350$	1

a. What proportion of observations is less than 300?
b. Construct the relative frequency distribution. What proportion of the observations is more than 250 but no more than 300?

17. **FILE** *Exercise_2.17.* The accompanying data file shows 100 observations for Variable *X*.
a. Construct the frequency distribution using 6 intervals with widths of $3 < x \le 5$, $5 < x \le 7$, etc. How many of the observations are greater than 7 but less than or equal to 9?

b. Construct the relative frequency distribution. What proportion of the observations is greater than 5 but less than or equal to 7?

c. Construct the histogram. Is the distribution symmetric?

18. **FILE** *Exercise_2.18.* The accompanying data file shows 100 observations for Variable *X*.

a. Construct the frequency distribution using 5 intervals with widths of $-10 < x \leq 0, 0 < x \leq 10$, etc. How many of the observations are greater than 0 but less than or equal to 10?

b. Construct the relative frequency and the cumulative relative frequency distributions. What proportion of the observations is greater than 10 but less than or equal to 20? What proportion of the observations is greater than 20?

Applications

19. A researcher conducts a mileage economy test involving 80 cars. The frequency distribution describing average miles per gallon (mpg) appears in the following table.

Average mpg	Frequency
$15 \leq x < 20$	15
$20 \leq x < 25$	30
$25 \leq x < 30$	15
$30 \leq x < 35$	10
$35 \leq x < 40$	7
$40 \leq x < 45$	3

a. Construct the relative frequency distribution. What proportion of the cars got at least 20 mpg but less than 25 mpg? What proportion of the cars got less than 35 mpg? What proportion of the cars got 35 mpg or more?

b. Construct a histogram. Comment on the shape of the distribution.

20. Consider the following relative frequency distribution that summarizes the returns (in %) for 500 small cap stocks.

Return (%)	Relative frequency
$-20 \leq x < -10$	0.04
$-10 \leq x < 0$	0.25
$0 \leq x < 10$	0.42
$10 \leq x < 20$	0.25
$20 \leq x < 30$	0.04

a. Construct the frequency distribution. How many of the stocks had a return of at least 10% but less than 20%?

b. Construct a histogram. Comment on the shape of the distribution.

21. The manager at a water park constructed the following frequency distribution to summarize attendance in July and August.

Attendance	Frequency
$1,000 \leq x < 1,250$	5
$1,250 \leq x < 1,500$	6
$1,500 \leq x < 1,750$	10
$1,750 \leq x < 2,000$	20
$2,000 \leq x < 2,250$	15
$2,250 \leq x < 2,500$	4

a. Construct the relative frequency distribution. What proportion of the time was attendance at least 1,750 but less than 2,000? What proportion of the time was attendance less than 1,750? What proportion of the time was attendance 1,750 or more?

b. Construct a histogram. Comment on the shape of the distribution.

22. Fifty cities provided information on vacancy rates (in %) in local apartments in the following relative frequency distribution.

Vacancy rate (%)	Relative frequency
$0 \leq x < 3$	0.10
$3 \leq x < 6$	0.20
$6 \leq x < 9$	0.40
$9 \leq x < 12$	0.20
$12 \leq x < 15$	0.10

a. Construct the frequency distribution. How many of the cities had a vacancy rate of at least 6% but less than 9%? How many of the cities had a vacancy rate of at least 9%?

b. Construct a histogram. Comment on the shape of the distribution.

23. The following relative frequency histogram summarizes the median household income for the 50 states as reported by the U.S. Census Bureau in 2010.

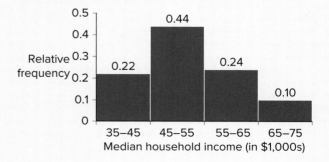

a. Is the distribution symmetric? If not, is it positively or negatively skewed?

b. What percentage of the states had median household income between $45,000 and $55,000?

c. What percentage of the states had median household income between $35,000 and $55,000?

24. The following histogram summarizes Apple Inc.'s monthly stock price for the years 2014 through 2018.

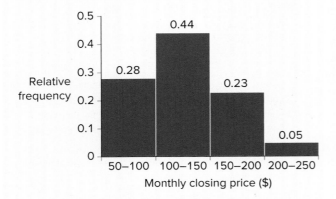

Monthly closing price ($)

a. Is the distribution symmetric? If not, is it positively or negatively skewed?

b. Over this five-year period, approximate the minimum monthly stock price and the maximum monthly stock price.

c. Over this five-year period, which interval had the highest relative frequency?

25. The following histogram summarizes the salaries (in $100,000s) for the 30 highest-paid portfolio managers at a large investment firm over the past year.

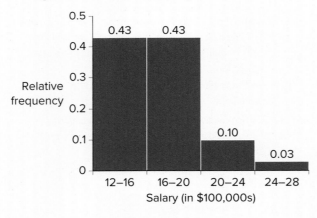

Salary (in $100,000s)

a. Is the distribution symmetric? If not, is it positively or negatively skewed?

b. How many of the portfolio managers earned between $2,000,000 and $2,400,000?

c. Approximately how many of the portfolio managers earned between $1,200,000 and $2,000,000?

26. **FILE** *Prime.* Amazon Prime is a $139-per-year service that gives the company's customers free two-day shipping and discounted rates on overnight delivery. Prime customers also get other perks, such as free e-books. The accompanying data file shows the annual expenditures (in $) for 100 Prime customers.

a. Construct the frequency distribution for Expenditures. Use six intervals with widths of $400 < x \le 700$, $700 < x \le 1,000$, etc. How many customers spent between $701 and $1,000?

b. What proportion of the customers spent $1,300 or less? What proportion of the customers spent more than $1,300?

27. **FILE** *Census.* The accompanying data file shows the median house values (in $) for the 50 states as reported by the U.S. Census Bureau in 2010.

a. Construct the frequency distribution and the histogram for the median house values. Use six intervals with widths of $0 < x \le 100,000$, $100,000 < x \le 200,000$, etc. Which interval had the highest frequency? How many of the states had median house values of $300,000 or less?

b. Is the distribution symmetric? If not, is it positively or negatively skewed?

28. **FILE** *DJIA_2019.* The accompanying data file shows the daily price index for the Dow Jones Industrial Average (DJIA) for the first half of 2019.

a. Construct the frequency distribution and the histogram for the DJIA. Use five intervals with widths of $22,000 < x \le 23,000$, $23,000 < x \le 24,000$, etc. On how many days during the first half of 2019 was the DJIA more than 26,000?

b. Is the distribution symmetric? If not, is it positively or negatively skewed?

29. **FILE** *Gas_Prices.* The accompanying data file shows the average price (in $) for a gallon of gas for the 50 states and the District of Columbia as reported by AAA Gas Prices on January 2, 2019.

a. Construct the frequency distribution and the histogram for the average price of gas. Use six intervals with widths of $1.70 < x \le 2.00$, $2.00 < x \le 2.30$, etc. Which interval had the highest frequency? How many of the states had average gas prices greater than $2.60?

b. Is the distribution symmetric? If not, is it positively or negatively skewed?

30. **FILE** *Work_Experience.* The accompanying data file shows the salary (in $) and work experience (in years) for 100 employees in a marketing firm.

a. Construct the frequency and the relative frequency distributions for the Salary variable. Use five intervals with widths of $0 < x \le 50,000$, $50,000 < x \le 100,000$, etc. How many employees earn between $100,000 and

$150,000? What proportion of the employees earns at most $200,000?

b. Construct the frequency and the relative frequency distributions for the Experience variable. Use five intervals with widths of $0 < x \leq 6$, $6 < x \leq 12$, etc. How many employees have between 6 and 12 years of experience? What proportion of the employees has more than 24 years of experience?

2.3 METHODS TO VISUALIZE THE RELATIONSHIP BETWEEN TWO CATEGORICAL VARIABLES

LO 2.3

All of the tabular and graphical tools presented thus far have focused on describing one variable. However, in many instances we are interested in the relationship between two variables. People in virtually every discipline examine how one variable may vary with another variable. Consider, for instance, how

- Incomes vary with education.
- Sales vary with advertising expenditures.
- Stock prices vary with corporate profits.
- Crop yields vary with the use of fertilizer.
- Cholesterol levels vary with dietary intake.
- Employee absences vary with work shift.

Visualize the relationship between two categorical variables.

In the next two sections, we examine the relationship between two variables. In this section, we focus on the relationship between two categorical variables, and in Section 2.4 we focus on the relationship between two numerical variables.

We first construct a contingency table, which is a tabular method that helps us summarize the relationship between two categorical variables. A contingency table is widely used in marketing as well as other business and nonbusiness applications. In order to graphically depict the information presented in a contingency table, we then construct a stacked column chart and a clustered column chart.

A Contingency Table

Recall the online construction clothing company ReliableWorkWear.com from the introductory case. The **Transactions** data file shows customer information on 200 recent purchases. The Satisfaction variable records the customer's satisfaction with the purchase (Satisfaction = Rating_1 (very dissatisfied) through Rating_5 (very satisfied)). The data file also contains information on whether the customer is female or male (Sex = Female or Male). Suppose we are interested in whether purchase ratings differ between females and males. A contingency table can help us summarize this potential relationship.

A **contingency table** shows the frequencies for two categorical variables. Table 2.7 shows the contingency table for the 200 purchases cross-classified by the satisfaction rating and whether the customer is female or male. From the contingency table, we see that 50 of the purchases were made by females and 150 of the purchases were made by males. The most frequent satisfaction rating is 4 and the least frequent satisfaction rating is 1. We also see, for example, that no females gave a purchase rating of 1, whereas 12 males fall into this category. While male customers made three times as many purchases as compared to female customers, they reported less than twice as many very satisfied (5) ratings as compared to female customers. The contingency table allows us to present and interpret the raw data in a much more manageable format.

TABLE 2.7 Contingency Table for Satisfaction and Sex Variables

Satisfaction	Sex Female	Sex Male	Total
Rating_1	0	12	12
Rating_2	4	14	18
Rating_3	7	29	36
Rating_4	23	69	92
Rating_5	16	26	42
Total	50	150	200

A CONTINGENCY TABLE

A contingency table shows the frequencies for two categorical variables, *x* and *y*, where each cell represents a mutually exclusive combination of the pair of *x* and *y* values.

Clustered and Stacked Column Charts

The information in a contingency table can be shown graphically using a **clustered column chart** or a **stacked column chart.** Both charts are advanced versions of the bar chart that we discussed in Section 2.1. They are designed to visualize more than one categorical variable, plus they allow for the comparison of composition within each category. In a clustered bar chart, we show each category as a separate bar. In a stacked bar chart, we show the categories as blocks lying on top of each other within a single bar.

Figure 2.10 shows the clustered column chart for the contingency table presented in Table 2.7. The female and male responses for each rating are shown as separate bars. Figure 2.11 shows the corresponding stacked column chart. Each bar in the stacked column chart represents the total number of responses for each rating, and the two boxes within each bar represent female and male responses.

FIGURE 2.10 A clustered column chart

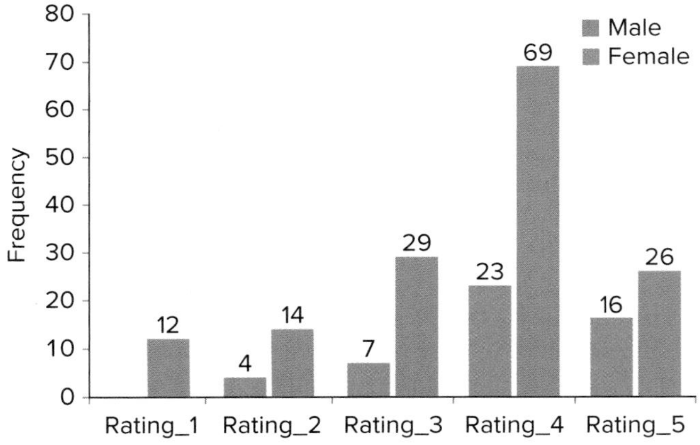

FIGURE 2.11 A stacked column chart

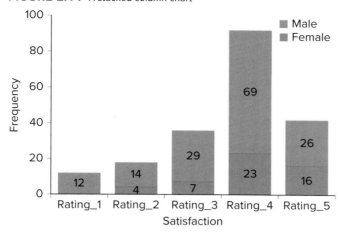

The clustered column chart and the stacked column chart highlight two major findings. The first finding is that most customers gave product ratings of 4 or more. The second finding is that no females gave a rating of 1; however, 12 males gave a rating of 1. In general, females appeared to be more satisfied with their purchases as compared to males.

CLUSTERED AND STACKED COLUMN CHARTS

Clustered and stacked column charts are designed to visualize more than one categorical variable. They allow for the comparison of composition within each category.

In order to illustrate the construction of a contingency table, a clustered column chart, and a stacked column chart using Excel, consider the following example.

EXAMPLE 2.3

An online retailer recently sent emails to customers that included a promotional discount. The retailer wonders whether there is any relationship between a customer's location in the United States (Midwest, Northeast, South, or West) and whether the customer made a purchase with the discount (Yes or No). Table 2.8 shows a portion of the results from 600 email accounts.

Promotion

TABLE 2.8 Location and Purchase Survey Responses

Email	Location	Purchase
1	West	Yes
2	Northeast	Yes
⋮	⋮	⋮
600	South	No

Construct a contingency table, a clustered column chart, and a stacked column chart using Excel, and then summarize the results.

SOLUTION:

a. Open the ***Promotion*** data file.

b. Click anywhere on the data (we choose cell A5). From the menu, select **Insert > Pivot Table.** Figure 2.12 shows the *Create PivotTable* dialog box. Because we clicked on the data before creating a pivot table, the default option in *Select a table or range* should already be populated. We choose to place the pivot table in the existing worksheet beginning in cell E1. Click **OK.**

FIGURE 2.12 Excel's *Create PivotTable* dialog box

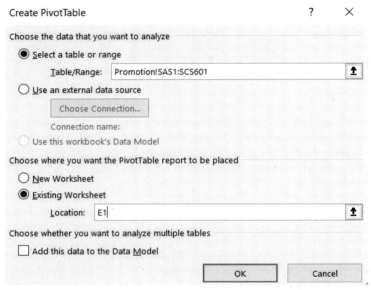

Source: Microsoft Office 2019

c. A menu will appear on the right side of the screen called *PivotTable Fields.* In the top of this menu you will see all of the variables in our data set. In the bottom part of the menu, there is a grid with four fields: Filters, Rows, Columns, and Values; see Figure 2.13. Drag the Location variable to the Rows field. Drag the Purchase variable to the Columns field. Drag the Email variable to the Values field. If the Email variable in the Values field is not presented as a count (for example, it may be presented as a sum), you will need to change it. Click the arrow below the Values field and select *Value Field Settings.* In the dialog box, select the *Summarize value field by* tab, and then, in the drop-down menu, select *Count.* Click **OK.**

FIGURE 2.13 Excel's Pivot Table Fields

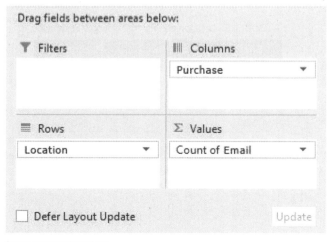

Source: Microsoft Office 2019

The resulting contingency table should be similar to Table 2.9.

TABLE 2.9 Contingency Table for the Location and Purchase Example

| | Purchase | | |
Location	No	Yes	Total
Midwest	107	77	**184**
Northeast	41	102	**143**
South	24	130	**154**
West	18	101	**119**
Total	**190**	**410**	**600**

Sometimes it is preferable to convert counts to percentages, as shown in Table 2.10. In order to make this change, go back to the *Value Field Settings* dialog box, select the *Show values as* tab, and in the drop-down menu select *% of Grand Total.*

TABLE 2.10 Percent Table for the Location and Purchase Example

| | Purchase | | |
Location	No	Yes	Total
Midwest	17.83%	12.83%	**30.67%**
Northeast	6.83%	17.00%	**23.83%**
South	4.00%	21.67%	**25.67%**
West	3.00%	16.83%	**19.83%**
Total	**31.67%**	**68.33%**	**100.00%**

d. We first illustrate how to create a clustered column chart using the contingency table. Make sure that the contingency table shows counts as in Table 2.9. Select the cells E2:G6. From the menu, select **Insert,** and in the Charts group, expand the selection by clicking on the arrow at the bottom right. Select the **All Charts** tab and then select **Column.** Then select the option at the top left. Choose **Insert > Insert Column or Bar Chart > 2-D Column > Clustered Column.**

Formatting (regarding axis titles, gridlines, etc.) can be done by selecting the "+" sign at the top right of the chart or by selecting **Add Chart Elements** from the menu. Check the box next to *Data Labels* in the *Chart Elements* pop-up box to display frequencies in the clustered column chart. The resulting clustered column chart is shown in Figure 2.14.

FIGURE 2.14 A clustered column chart for the Location and Purchase example

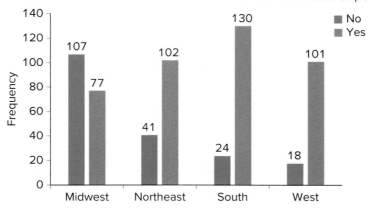

e. For a stacked column chart, select cells E2:G6. From the menu, select **Insert,** and in the Charts group, expand the selection by clicking on the arrow at the bottom right. Select the **All Charts** tab and then select **Column.** Then select the second option from the top left. Refer to part d for formatting. The resulting stacked column chart is shown in Figure 2.15.

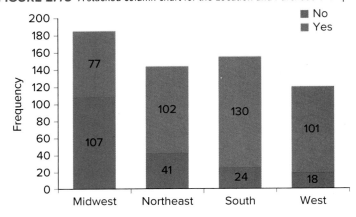

FIGURE 2.15 A stacked column chart for the Location and Purchase example

Summary
We can readily see from Table 2.9 that of the 600 email recipients, 410 of them made a purchase using the promotional discount. Or from Table 2.10, we see that this translates into a 68.33% positive response rate, suggesting that this marketing strategy was successful. However, there do appear to be some differences depending on location, and these differences are apparent from Figures 2.14 and 2.15. Recipients residing in the South and West were a lot more likely to make a purchase (130 out of 154 and 101 out of 119, respectively) compared to those residing in the Midwest (77 out of 184). It would be wise for the retailer to examine if there are other traits that the customers in the South and West share (age, sex, etc.). That way, in the next marketing campaign, the e-mails can be even more targeted.

EXERCISES 2.3

Applications

31. The following contingency table shows inspection records for 630 units of a particular product. The records have been cross-classified by the inspector's decision (Pass and Fail) and the inspector's experience (Low, Medium, and High).

Decision	Experience		
	Low	Medium	High
Pass	152	287	103
Fail	16	46	26

a. How many of the units passed inspection? How many of the units failed inspection?
b. How many of the units were inspected by inspectors with high experience?
c. What proportion of the units were inspected by inspectors with low experience?
d. What proportion of the units were inspected by inspectors with medium experience and failed inspection?

32. The following contingency table shows shipments received by a large firm. The shipments have been cross-classified by Vendor (I, II, and III) and Quality (Defective and Acceptable).

Vendor	Quality	
	Defective	Acceptable
I	14	112
II	10	70
III	22	150

a. How many shipments did the firm receive?
b. How many of the shipments were defective?
c. How many of the shipments were from Vendor II?
d. How many of the shipments were from Vendor I and were defective?

33. **FILE** *Myers_Briggs.* The Human Resources department of a large technology company maintains personnel information on each employee's personality type based on the Myers-Briggs assessment. The accompanying data file shows each employee's personality type (Analyst, Diplomat, Explorer, or Sentinel) as well as sex (Female or Male).

a. Construct a contingency table that cross-classifies these data by Personality and Sex. How many employees are female? What is the most frequent personality type?

b. What proportion of the employees are female Explorers? What proportion are male Diplomats?

34. **FILE** *Bar.* At a local bar in a small Midwestern town, beer and wine are the only two alcoholic options. The manager conducts a survey on the bar's customers over the past weekend. Customers are asked to identify their sex (defined as male or female) and their drink choice (beer, wine, or soft drink). The accompanying data file shows the responses from 270 customers.

a. Construct a contingency table that cross-classifies the data by Sex and Drink_Choice. How many of the customers were male? How many of the customers drank wine?

b. Given that a customer is male, what is the likelihood that he drank beer? Given that a customer is female, what is the likelihood that she drank beer?

c. Construct a clustered column chart. Comment on the findings.

35. **FILE** *Drug.* The accompanying data file contains information on 186 terminally ill patients who agreed to participate in a new drug trial. They were randomly assigned to either an experimental group or a control group. Patients in the experimental group were given the new drug that is being tested for this particular illness. Patients in the control group were kept on the medicine they had been receiving. After one year, it was noted whether or not the patient was still alive.

a. Construct a contingency table that cross-classifies the data by Experimental_Drug and Living. How many of the patients received the experimental drug? How many of the patients were still living after one year?

b. Of the patients in the control group, what proportion was still living after one year? Of the patients in the experimental group, what proportion was still living after one year?

c. Construct a stacked column chart. Does the experimental drug seem promising? Explain.

36. **FILE** *Shift.* Metalworks, a supplier of fabricated industrial parts, wonders if there is any connection between when a component is constructed (Shift is equal to 1, 2, or 3) and whether or not it is defective (Defective equals yes if the component is defective, no otherwise). The accompanying data file shows this information for 300 components.

a. Construct a contingency table that cross-classifies the data by shift and whether or not the component is defective. How many components constructed during Shift 1 were defective? How many components constructed during Shift 2 were not defective?

b. Given that the component was defective, what is the likelihood that it was constructed during Shift 2? Given that the component was defective, what is the likelihood that it was constructed during Shift 3? Does there seem to be any connection between when a component is constructed and whether or not it is defective? Explain.

c. Construct a clustered column chart. Are the defect rates consistent across all shifts?

37. **FILE** *Athletic.* A researcher at a marketing firm examines whether the age of a consumer matters when buying athletic clothing. Her initial feeling is that Brand A attracts a younger customer, whereas the more established companies (Brands B and C) draw an older clientele. She collects data on a customer's age (Age equals 1 if the customer is under 35, 0 otherwise) and the brand name of the athletic clothing (Brand equals A, B, or C). The accompanying data file shows the responses for 600 recent purchases.

a. Construct a contingency table that cross-classifies the data by Age and Brand. How many of the purchases were for Brand A? How many of the purchases were from customers under 35 years old?

b. Given that the purchase was made by a customer under 35 years old, what is the likelihood that the customer purchased Brand A? Brand B? Brand C? Do the data seem to support the researcher's belief? Explain.

c. Construct a stacked column chart. Does there appear to be a relationship between the age of the customer and the brand purchased?

38. **FILE** *Study.* A report suggests that business majors spend the least amount of time on course work compared to all other college students. A provost of a university conducts a similar survey. Students are asked their major (Major equals business or nonbusiness) and if they study hard (Study_Hard equals yes or no), where study hard is defined as spending at least 20 hours per week on course work. The accompanying data file shows the responses from 270 students.

a. Construct a contingency table that cross-classifies the data by Major and Study_Hard. How many of the students are business majors? How many of the students study hard?

b. Given that the student is a business major, what is the likelihood that the student studies hard? Given that the student is a nonbusiness major, what is the likelihood that the student studies hard? Do the data seem to support the findings in the report? Explain.

c. Construct a clustered column chart. Comment on the findings.

2.4 METHODS TO VISUALIZE THE RELATIONSHIP BETWEEN TWO NUMERICAL VARIABLES

Visualize the relationship between two numerical variables.

In this section we examine the relationship between two numerical variables. We discuss a scatterplot and a line chart.

A Scatterplot

A **scatterplot** is a common graphical method that allows us to determine whether two numerical variables are related in some systematic way.

Each point in a scatterplot represents a paired observation for the two variables. When constructing a scatterplot, we generally refer to one of the variables as x and represent it on the horizontal axis (x-axis) and the other variable as y and represent it on the vertical axis (y-axis). We then plot each pairing: (x_1, y_1), (x_2, y_2), and so on. Once the data are plotted, the graph may reveal that

- A linear relationship exists between the two variables;
- A nonlinear relationship exists between the two variables; or
- No relationship exists between the two variables.

For example, Figure 2.16(a) shows points on a scatterplot clustered together along a line with a negative slope; we infer that the two variables have a negative linear relationship. Figure 2.16(b) depicts a positive nonlinear relationship; as x increases, y tends to increase at an increasing rate. The points in Figure 2.16(c) are scattered with no apparent pattern; thus, there is no relationship between the two variables.

FIGURE 2.16 Scatterplots depicting various relationships between two variables

(a) Linear relationship   (b) Nonlinear relationship   (c) No relationship

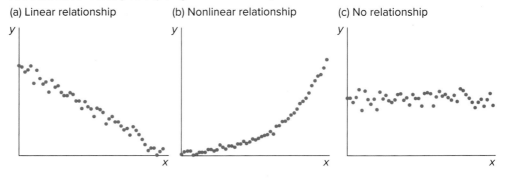

A SCATTERPLOT

A scatterplot is a graphical tool that helps in determining whether or not two numerical variables are related in some systematic way. Each point in a scatterplot represents a paired observation for the two variables.

In order to illustrate a scatterplot, consider the following example.

EXAMPLE 2.4

FILE
Transactions

Recall the online construction clothing company ReliableWorkWear.com from the introductory case. The *Transactions* data file shows each customer's purchase amount (Purchase in $) and the customer's annual income (Income in $1,000s) for 200 customers. Perhaps we are interested in whether or not a customer's annual income influences the purchase amount. Construct a scatterplot of Purchase against Income using Excel, and then summarize the results.

SOLUTION:

a. Open the *Transactions* data file.

b. The easiest way to construct a scatterplot in Excel is to place the observations for the two numerical variables in adjacent columns, with the observations for the variable that is to appear on the *x*-axis in the first column and the observations for the variable that is to appear on the *y*-axis in the second column. Because we want to plot Purchase against Income, we place the observations for Income in the first column and the observations for Purchase in the second column.

Simultaneously select the observations for the Income and Purchase variables. From the menu, select **Insert,** and in the Charts group, expand the selection by clicking on the arrow at the bottom right. Select the **All Charts** tab and then select **XY (Scatter).** Then select the first option from the top left. The resulting scatterplot should be similar to Figure 2.17.

c. Formatting (regarding axis titles, gridlines, etc.) can be done by selecting **Format > Add Chart Element** from the menu.

FIGURE 2.17 A scatterplot of Purchase against Income

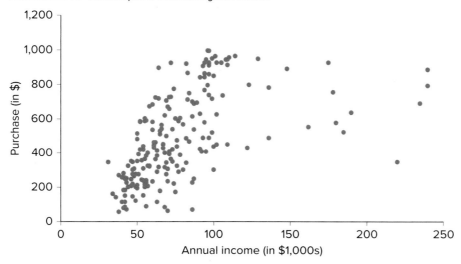

Summary
From Figure 2.17, we can infer that there seems to be a positive relationship between Purchase and Income; that is, those customers with higher incomes tend to make purchases of a higher amount. However, this relationship seems to level off as a customer's income grows.

A Line Chart

A **line chart** displays a numerical variable as a series of consecutive observations connected by a line. A line chart is especially useful for tracking changes or trends over time. For example, if we use a line chart to plot a firm's sales over time, then we can easily tell whether sales follow an upward, a downward, or a steady trend. It is also easy for us to identify any major changes that happened in the past on a line chart.

When multiple lines are plotted in the same chart, we can compare these observations on one or more dimensions. For example, if we simultaneously plot the historical sales of Firm A alongside its competitor Firm B, we would be able to compare the trends and the rates of change of the two firms. We may even detect interesting patterns such as whether a drop in the sales of Firm A coincides with a surge in the sales of Firm B.

> ### A LINE CHART
>
> A line chart connects the consecutive observations of a numerical variable with a line. It tends to be used to track changes of the variable over time.

We illustrate the use of a line chart in Example 2.5.

EXAMPLE 2.5

FILE

Apple_Merck

The *Apple_Merck* data file contains monthly stock prices for Apple, Inc. and Merck & Co. for the years 2016 through 2019. A portion of the data is shown in Table 2.11. Use Excel to construct line charts for the stock prices for Apple and Merck. Then, summarize the results.

TABLE 2.11 Monthly Stock Prices for Apple and Merck, 2016–2019

Date	Apple	Merck
1/1/2016	90.96	44.98
2/1/2016	90.35	44.57
⋮	⋮	⋮
12/1/2019	293.65	90.33

SOLUTION:

a. Open the *Apple_Merck* data file.

b. Select cells B1 through C49. From the menu, select **Insert,** and in the Charts group, expand the selection by clicking on the arrow at the bottom right. Select the **All Charts** tab and then select **Line.** Then select the first option from the top left.

c. For PC users, select **Design > Select Data** and click the *Edit* button under *Horizontal (Category) Axis Labels.* In the *Axis Labels* dialog box, select cells A2 through A49 in the *Axis label range* box. Click **OK.**
For Mac users, select **Select Data** and next to *Horizontal (Category) axis labels,* select cells A2 through A49. Click **OK.**

d. Formatting (regarding axis titles, gridlines, etc.) can be done by selecting **Format > Add Chart Element** from the menu. The resulting line chart should be similar to Figure 2.18.

FIGURE 2.18 Monthly stock prices for Apple and Merck

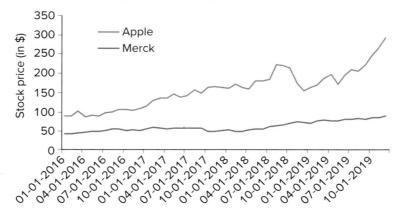

Summary

The line charts in Figure 2.18 show the monthly stock prices for Apple and Merck over the years 2016 through 2019. Both stocks rose over this period; however, the rise in Apple's stock price is far more dramatic as compared to the rise in Merck's stock price. There is also a lot more volatility in Apple's stock price. Specifically, we see a dramatic decline in Apple's stock at the end of 2018. This dip corresponded to news that the company would no longer offer unit sales data for its products. At the time, some wondered if this lack of transparency presaged weaker iPhone sales in the future. Fortunately for Apple, this prediction did not materialize.

More Cautionary Comments When Constructing Graphs

In Section 2.1, we outlined some basic guidelines to follow when constructing graphs. Here are a couple of more guidelines that are especially relevant with line charts.

- The relevant part of the vertical axis should not be compressed by using an unreasonably high upper limit. In these instances, the data may appear compressed so that an increase (or decrease) of the data is not as apparent as it perhaps should be. For example, Figure 2.19(a) plots the daily price for a barrel of crude oil for the first quarter in 2011 and gives the impression that prices have remained stable. Due to Middle East unrest, the price of crude oil rose from a low of $83.13 per barrel to a high of $106.19 per barrel, or approximately 28% $\left(= \frac{106.19 - 83.13}{83.13}\right)$. However, because Figure 2.19(a) compresses the vertical axis with an upper limit of 325, the rise in price appears dampened. Figure 2.19(b) shows a vertical axis with an upper limit of $110; this value better reflects the upper limit observed during this time period.

Crude_Oil

FIGURE 2.19 Misleading scale on vertical axis: compressed scale

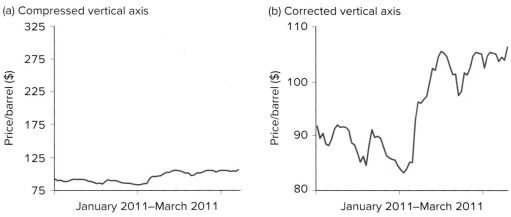

(a) Compressed vertical axis — Price/barrel ($), January 2011–March 2011

(b) Corrected vertical axis — Price/barrel ($), January 2011–March 2011

- The vertical axis should not be stretched so that an increase (or decrease) of the data appears more pronounced than warranted. For example, Figure 2.20(a) charts the daily closing stock price of a large retailer for the week of April 4. It is true that the stock price declined over the week from a high of $60.15 to a low of $59.46; this amounts to a $0.69 decrease, or an approximate 1% decline. However, because the vertical axis is stretched, the drop in stock price appears more dramatic. Figure 2.20(b) shows a vertical axis that has not been stretched.

Stock_Price

FIGURE 2.20 Misleading scale on vertical axis: stretched scale

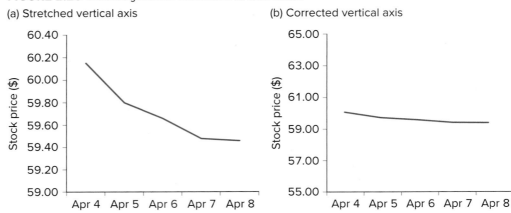

(a) Stretched vertical axis   (b) Corrected vertical axis

SYNOPSIS OF INTRODUCTORY CASE

ReliableWorkWear.com is an online retail company that offers rugged workwear primarily for workers in the construction industry. Brendan Navarro, the company's marketing analyst, provides some interesting findings based on 200 recent transactions.

First, females comprised 25% of these transactions. The company knows that 10% of the workers in the construction industry are female, so this suggests that females may be purchasing the rugged workwear for reasons that are not work-related; that is, for the product's warmth and style. The company would be wise to direct marketing funds to this segment of the population.

In addition, 70% of the transactions were from customers who had made a prior purchase. This finding supports the company's belief that it has a loyal customer base. Moreover, 134 of the 200

ljubaphoto/Getty Images

customers gave their purchase a rating of a 4 or 5; that is, they were satisfied or very satisfied with their purchase. However, 12 male customers gave their purchase a rating of a 1 (very dissatisfied); this potential troubling finding should be investigated. Overall, females tend to be more satisfied than males with their purchases.

Purchases ranged from $55 up to $996. Most purchases—68 of the 200, or 31.5%—fell in the $200 to $400 range. However, 30 purchases (or 15%) were in the $800 to $1,000 range, which is a promising trend for the company. Finally, there was also a moderate positive relationship between a customer's annual income and the amount of the purchase, but this relationship needs further investigation before any direct marketing action is undertaken.

EXERCISES 2.4

Applications

39. **FILE** *Test_Scores.* The accompanying data file shows the midterm and final grades for 32 students. Construct a scatterplot of Final against Midterm. Describe the relationship.

40. **FILE** *Life_Obesity.* The accompanying data file shows the life expectancies (in years) and obesity rates (in %) for the 50 states and the District of Columbia. Construct a scatterplot of Life_Expectancy against Obesity. Describe the relationship.

41. **FILE** *Consumption.* The accompanying data file shows quarterly data for U.S. consumption (Consumption in $) and disposable income (Income in $) for the years 2000–2016. Construct a scatterplot of Consumption against Income. Describe the relationship.

42. **FILE** *Return.* In order to diversify risk, investors are often encouraged to invest in assets whose returns have either a negative relationship or no relationship. The accompanying data file shows the annual return data (in %) on two assets

over the past 20 years. Construct a scatterplot of Return_B against Return_A. In order to diversify risk, would the investor be wise to include both of these assets in their portfolio? Explain.

43. **FILE** *Healthy_Living.* Healthy living has always been an important goal for any society. Most would agree that a diet that is rich in fruits and vegetables (FV) and regular exercise have a positive effect on health, while smoking has a negative effect on health. The accompanying data file shows the percentage of these variables observed in various states in the United States.
    a. Construct a scatterplot of Health against Exercise. Describe the relationship.
    b. Construct a scatterplot of Health against Smoking. Describe the relationship.

44. **FILE** *Car_Price.* The accompanying data file shows the price, the age, and the mileage for 20 used sedans.
    a. Construct a scatterplot of Price against Age. Describe the relationship.
    b. Construct a scatterplot of Price against Mileage. Describe the relationship.

45. **FILE** *InternetStocks.* A financial analyst wants to compare the performance of the stocks of two Internet companies, Amazon (AMZN) and Google (GOOG). The accompanying data file shows the monthly closing prices of the two stocks for the years 2016 through 2019. Construct a line chart that shows the movements of the two stocks over time using two lines, each with a unique color. Describe the overall trend of price movement for the two stocks. Which stock shows the greater trajectory of price appreciation?

46. **FILE** *India_China.* It is believed that India will overtake China to become the world's most populous nation much sooner than previously thought (*CNN,* June 19, 2019). The accompanying data file contains the population data, in millions, for India and China from 1960 to 2017. Construct a line chart that shows the changes in the two countries' populations over time using two lines, each with a unique color. Describe the overall trend of population growth in the two countries. Which country shows the faster population growth during the past 40 years?

47. **FILE** *Exchange_Rate.* The accompanying data file shows the exchange rates between the U.S. dollar and

the euro (Euro) and between the U.S. dollar and the British pound (Pound) from January 2018 to January 2020. Construct a line chart that shows the movements of the exchange rates over time using two lines, each with a unique color. Describe and interpret the overall trend of each currency against the U.S. dollar.

48. The accompanying figure plots the monthly stock price of a large construction company from July 2019 through March 2021. The stock has experienced tremendous growth over this time period, almost tripling in price. Does the figure reflect this growth? If not, why not?

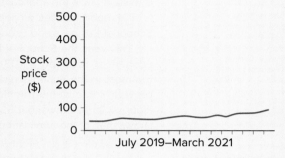

49. Annual sales at a small pharmaceutical firm have been rather stagnant over the most recent five-year period, exhibiting only 1.2% growth over this time frame. A research analyst prepares the accompanying graph for inclusion in a sales report.

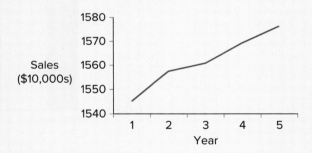

Does this graph accurately reflect what has happened to sales over the last five years? If not, why not?

2.5 WRITING WITH DATA

Case Study

College_Admissions

Camilla Jones works as data analyst in the Admissions office at a selective four-year university in North America. Every year, before making any important admissions decisions, the university reviews information on the applicant pool. Today, Camilla focuses on the School of Business and Economics. Camilla will use tabular and graphical methods to summarize the various demographic and academic variables.

Sample
Report—
Summary of
Applicant Pool
for College
Admission

As in previous years, the Admissions office strives to support and serve a diverse and talented array of prospective students while fulfilling institutional expectations and strategic priorities. Just as prospective students are anxious about receiving an acceptance letter, our office is concerned about meeting our enrollment target. One of the first steps in the acceptance process is to summarize the applicant pool. The following report focuses on applicants to the School of Business and Economics.

This year, the School of Business and Economics received 4,103 applications, the most in the School's history. First, we provide some demographic summaries.

Photographs in the Carol M. Highsmith Archive, Library of Congress, Prints & Photographs Division

Figure 2.21(a) shows that 59% of the applicants are male and 41% are female. Figure 2.21(b) shows that, of the applicant pool, 54% are white applicants, 20% are Asian applicants, and the remaining 26% of the applicants identified as other races.

FIGURE 2.21 Demographics of Applicant Pool

(a) Breakdown by sex

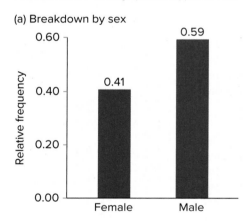

(b) Breakdown by race

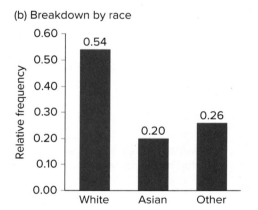

Two important factors that are considered for admission are a student's high school record and performance on standardized tests. Here we summarize the grade point averages (GPAs) and the SAT scores of the applicant pool. The left three columns of Table 2.12 show the frequency and relative frequency distributions for GPA. Notably, 55% of the GPAs are higher than 3.5, and only 14% are below a 3.0. The high school record of the applicant pool appears very strong.

TABLE 2.12 Frequency Distributions for GPA and SAT scores

GPA	Frequency	Relative frequency	SAT	Frequency	Relative frequency
$x \leq 2.5$	83	0.02	$x \leq 800$	74	0.02
$2.5 < x \leq 3.0$	490	0.12	$800 < x \leq 1000$	569	0.14
$3.0 < x \leq 3.5$	1258	0.31	$1000 < x \leq 1200$	1650	0.40
$3.5 < x \leq 4.0$	1693	0.41	$1200 < x \leq 1400$	1457	0.36
$4.0 < x \leq 4.5$	579	0.14	$1400 < x \leq 1600$	353	0.09

The right three columns of Table 2.12 show the frequency distribution for SAT scores. The national average SAT score is about 1060. In the applicant pool, 85% have SAT scores higher than 1000; moreover, 44% have SAT scores higher than 1200. These findings are similar to those found for GPA. However, as compared to GPA, the proportion of high SAT scores is lower and the proportion of low scores is a bit higher. This is not entirely surprising given the rise in grade inflation in both secondary and higher education.

Figure 2.22 shows the histograms for GPA and SAT scores. Both distributions are negatively skewed, reinforcing the findings from the frequency distributions; that is, the majority of GPA and SAT scores are clustered in the upper end of both distributions.

FIGURE 2.22 Histograms for GPA and SAT scores.

(a) Histogram for GPA

(b) Histogram for SAT scores

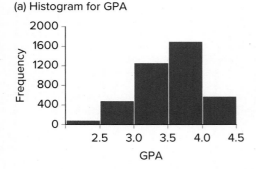
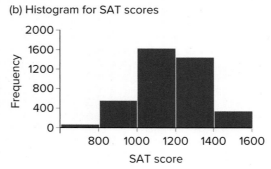

Not only is the applicant pool for the School of Business and Economics the largest ever, it also appears relatively diverse and very competitive. The School will face difficult decisions in the near future.

Suggested Case Studies

Here are some suggestions for analysis.

Report 2.1 FILE *College_Admissions.* Perform a similar analysis to the one conducted in this section, but choose another school.

Report 2.2 FILE *House_Price.* Choose a college town and use tabular and graphical methods to examine house prices along with other variables of interest.

Report 2.3 FILE *TechSales_Reps.* Use tabular and graphical methods to examine the salaries of sales representatives along with other variables of interest.

Report 2.4 COVID-19 necessitated that public health organizations gather and provide data to study the spread of the disease. Visit https://github.com/owid/covid-19-data to access data on variables such as cases, deaths, hospitalization, vaccination, demographics, etc. for all countries around the globe. For any two countries, use tabular and graphical methods to examine several variables of interest.

3

Summary Measures

LEARNING OBJECTIVES

After reading this chapter you should be able to:

LO 3.1   Calculate and interpret measures of location.

LO 3.2   Calculate and interpret measures of dispersion.

LO 3.3   Explain mean-variance analysis and the Sharpe ratio.

LO 3.4   Apply Chebyshev's theorem, the empirical rule, and z-scores.

LO 3.5   Construct and interpret a boxplot.

LO 3.6   Calculate and interpret measures of association.

In Chapter 2, we used tables and graphs in order to extract meaningful information from data. In this chapter, we focus on numerical descriptive measures. These measures provide precise, objectively determined values that are easy to calculate, interpret, and compare with one another. We first calculate several measures of location. When attempting to find a typical or central value for the variable, we often calculate measures of central location such as the mean, the median, or the mode. We then find a percentile, which is another measure of location—though not necessarily central location.

In addition to analyzing the typical value of a variable, we examine how the observations may vary from the typical value. Measures of dispersion gauge the underlying variability of the variable. We then use measures of central location and dispersion to introduce some popular applications, including the Sharpe ratio, Chebyshev's theorem, the empirical rule, and the z-score. We also summarize the distribution of a variable by constructing a boxplot.

Finally, we discuss measures of association that examine the linear relationship between two variables. These measures assess whether two variables have a positive linear relationship, a negative linear relationship, or no linear relationship.

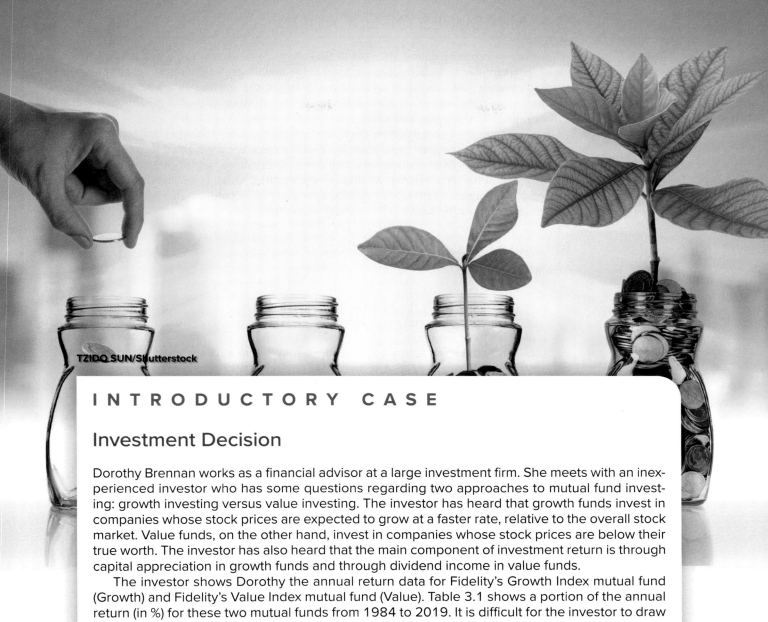

TZIDO SUN/Shutterstock

INTRODUCTORY CASE

Investment Decision

Dorothy Brennan works as a financial advisor at a large investment firm. She meets with an inexperienced investor who has some questions regarding two approaches to mutual fund investing: growth investing versus value investing. The investor has heard that growth funds invest in companies whose stock prices are expected to grow at a faster rate, relative to the overall stock market. Value funds, on the other hand, invest in companies whose stock prices are below their true worth. The investor has also heard that the main component of investment return is through capital appreciation in growth funds and through dividend income in value funds.

The investor shows Dorothy the annual return data for Fidelity's Growth Index mutual fund (Growth) and Fidelity's Value Index mutual fund (Value). Table 3.1 shows a portion of the annual return (in %) for these two mutual funds from 1984 to 2019. It is difficult for the investor to draw any conclusions from the data in their present form. In addition to clarifying the style differences in growth investing versus value investing, the investor requests Dorothy to summarize the data.

FILE

Growth_Value

TABLE 3.1 Annual Returns (in %) for Growth and Value

Year	Growth	Value
1984	−5.50	−8.59
1985	39.91	22.10
⋮	⋮	⋮
2019	38.42	31.62

Dorothy will use the sample information to:

1. Calculate and interpret the typical return for these two mutual funds.
2. Calculate and interpret the investment risk for these two mutual funds.
3. Determine which mutual fund provides the greater return relative to risk.

A synopsis of this case is provided at the end of Section 3.3.

3.1 MEASURES OF LOCATION

A measure of central location attempts to find a typical or central value that describes a variable. Examples include finding a typical value that describes the return on an investment, the number of defects in a production process, the starting salary of a business graduate, the rental price in a neighborhood, the number of monthly orders for a subscription-based service, and so on.

In this section, we first examine the three most widely used measures of central location: the mean, the median, and the mode. We then calculate a weighted mean. We also calculate the means from a subset of a variable's observations, which often reveal valuable insights in the data. Finally, we discuss a percentile, which is technically a measure of location (though not necessarily central location); a percentile is also used as a measure of relative position because it is so easy to interpret.

Measures of Central Location

The Mean

The arithmetic mean is the primary measure of central location. Generally, we refer to the arithmetic mean as simply the **mean** or the average. In order to calculate the mean of a variable, we simply add up all the observations and divide by the number of observations in the population or sample.

FILE
Growth_Value

Recall from the introductory case that the ***Growth_Value*** data file shows the annual returns (in %) for Growth and Value from 1984 through 2019. We can calculate the mean return for each variable as

$$\text{Growth: } \frac{(-5.50) + 39.91 + \cdots + 38.42}{36} = 15.755$$

$$\text{Value: } \frac{(-8.59) + 22.10 + \cdots + 31.62}{36} = 12.005$$

Over the 36-year period, the mean return for Growth was greater than the mean return for Value, or, equivalently, 15.755% > 12.005%. These means represent typical annual returns resulting from one-year investments. We will see throughout this chapter, however, that we would be ill-advised to invest in a mutual fund solely on the basis of its average return.

All of us have calculated a mean before. What might be new for you is the notation that we use to express the mean as a formula. If we let n represent the number of observations in a sample and x_i is the value of the ith observation (for $i = 1, \ldots, n$), then we can write the formula for the sample mean, referred to as $\bar{x}$ (pronounced as x-bar), as

$$\bar{x} = \frac{x_1 + x_2 + \ldots + x_n}{n} = \frac{\Sigma x_i}{n}.$$

If the observations come from a population, then we can write the formula for the population mean as

$$\mu = \frac{x_1 + x_2 + \cdots + x_N}{N} = \frac{\Sigma x_i}{N},$$

where μ is the Greek letter mu (pronounced as "mew") and N represents the number of observations in the population. The calculation method is identical for the sample mean and the population mean except that the sample mean uses n observations and the population mean uses N observations, where $n < N$.

The mean is used extensively in statistics. However, as we will see shortly, the mean can give a misleading description of the center of the distribution in the presence of extremely small or large values, also referred to as **outliers.**

The Median

The **median** is a measure of central location that is especially useful when outliers are present. It is the middle observation in a sample or a population. In other words, it divides the data in half; an equal number of observations lie above and below the median. In order to calculate the median, we first arrange the observations in ascending order (smallest to largest). We then find the middle observation if n (or N) is odd, or calculate the average of the two middle observations if n (or N) is even.

Many government publications and other data sources publish both the mean and the median in order to accurately portray a variable's typical value. For instance, in 2017 the U.S. Census Bureau found that the median income for American households was $61,372; however, the mean income was $86,220. It is well documented that a small number of households in the United States have income that is considerably higher than the typical American household income. As a result, these top-earning households influence the mean by pushing its value significantly above the value of the median. The median is the preferred measure of central location for money-related variables such as income, wealth, and house prices.

The Mode

The **mode** of a variable is the observation that occurs most frequently. A variable can have more than one mode, or even no mode. If a variable has one mode, then we say it is unimodal. If two or more modes exist, then the variable is multimodal; it is common to call it bimodal in the case of two modes. Generally, the mode's usefulness as a measure of central location tends to diminish with variables that have more than three modes.

EXAMPLE 3.1

Eight people work at Acetech, a small technology firm in Seattle. Their salaries (in $) over the past year are listed in Table 3.2. Compute the mean, the median, and the modal salary for this firm; then discuss which measure of central location best reflects the typical salary.

TABLE 3.2 Salaries of Employees at Acetech

Title	Salary
Administrative Assistant	40,000
Research Assistant	40,000
Data Analyst	65,000
Senior Research Associate	90,000
Senior Data Analyst	100,000
Senior Sales Associate	145,000
Chief Financial Officer	150,000
President (and owner)	550,000

SOLUTION:

The Mean Salary

We calculate the population mean salary as:

$$\mu = \frac{\Sigma x_i}{N} = \frac{40{,}000 + 40{,}000 + \cdots + 550{,}000}{8} = 147{,}500$$

Note that we find the population mean instead of the sample mean because we have all of the observations (the salaries) in the population (the firm).

The Median Salary

In Table 3.2, the data are already arranged in ascending order. We reproduce the salaries along with their relative positions.

Position:	1	2	3	4	5	6	7	8
Salary	40,000	40,000	65,000	90,000	100,000	145,000	150,000	550,000

Given eight salaries ($N = 8$), the median is the average of the observations occupying the 4th and 5th positions. Thus, the median salary is $95,000.

The Modal Salary

The salary $40,000 is earned by two employees. Every other salary occurs just once. So $40,000 is the modal salary.

Summary

The mean salary at Acetech is $147,500. However, six of the eight employees earn less than $147,500. The mean salary is very sensitive to the president's high salary of $550,000, which is considered an outlier. The modal salary at Acetech is $40,000, but most employees earn considerably more than this amount. Just because an observation occurs with the most frequency does not guarantee that it best reflects a typical value. The median salary is $95,000. Four employees earn less than $95,000 and four employees earn more than $95,000. As compared to the mean and the mode, the median better reflects the typical salary at Acetech.

In Example 3.1, we used measures of central location to describe a numerical variable. However, in many instances we want to summarize a categorical variable, where the mode is the only meaningful measure of central location. Consider the next example.

EXAMPLE 3.2

Aref Forbes is a manager at the University of Wisconsin campus bookstore. There has been a recent surge in the sale of sweatshirts, which are available in three sizes: Small (S), Medium (M), and Large (L). Aref notes that the campus bookstore sold 10 sweatshirts over the weekend in the following sizes:

Shutterstock/Natalia_Grabovskaya

S	L	L	M	S	L	M	L	L	M

Use the most appropriate measure of central location to find the typical size of a sweatshirt.

SOLUTION: The size of a sweatshirt is a categorical variable: S, M, or L. Here, the mode is the only relevant measure of central location. The modal size is L because it appears 5 times, as compared to S and M, which appear 2 and 3 times, respectively. Often, when examining issues relating to the demand for a product, such as replenishing stock, the mode tends to be the most relevant measure of central location.

MEASURES OF CENTRAL LOCATION

- The mean is the most commonly used measure of central location. The population mean is denoted as μ, and the sample mean is denoted as $\bar{x}$. One weakness of the mean is that it is unduly influenced by outliers.
- The median is the middle observation of a variable; that is, it divides the observations of a variable in half. The median is especially useful when outliers are present.
- The mode is the most frequently occurring value of a variable. A variable may have no mode or more than one mode. The mode is the only meaningful measure of central location for a categorical variable.

Using Excel to Calculate Measures of Central Location

In practice, we rarely calculate descriptive measures by hand. Excel offers a couple of ways to make most of these calculations. In the next example, we show how to use Excel to calculate measures of central location.

EXAMPLE 3.3

Using Excel, calculate the mean, the median, and the modal returns for the Growth and Value variables from the introductory case. Summarize the results.

FILE
Growth_Value

SOLUTION:

I. Excel's Formula Option   One way to find summary measures is to use Excel's formula option. We follow these steps to find measures of central location for Growth.

a. Open the *Growth_Value* data file.

b. In order to find the mean, find an empty cell and enter =AVERAGE(B2:B37). Verify that the output is 15.755.

c. In order to find the median, find an empty cell and enter =MEDIAN(B2:B37). Verify that the output is 15.245.

d. In order to find the mode, select three or four empty vertical cells because a variable can have more than one mode. With the cells highlighted, enter =MODE.MULT(B2:B37). You MUST hold down CTRL and SHIFT while pressing Enter. Verify that all cells now show #N/A, meaning that no observation appears more than once. If a variable has one or more modes, then these values would appear in the cells.

In order to calculate these measures of central location for Value, we simply replace B2:B37 with C2:C37 because the observations for Value occupy cells C2 through C37.

II. Excel's Data Analysis Toolpak Option   Another way to obtain summary measures is to use Excel's Data Analysis Toolpak option. One advantage of this option is that it provides numerous summary measures using a single command.

a. Open the *Growth_Value* data file.

b. From the menu, choose **Data > Data Analysis > Descriptive Statistics > OK.** (Note: As mentioned in Section 2.2, if you do not see **Data Analysis** under **Data,** you must add in the **Analysis Toolpak** option.)

c. See Figure 3.1. In the *Descriptive Statistics* dialog box, click on the box next to *Input Range,* then select the headings and the observations for the Growth and

Value variables. Select the options *Labels in First Row* and *Summary Statistics*. Select *Output Range* and enter cell E1, or any other blank cell. Then click **OK**.

FIGURE 3.1 Excel's *Descriptive Statistics* dialog box

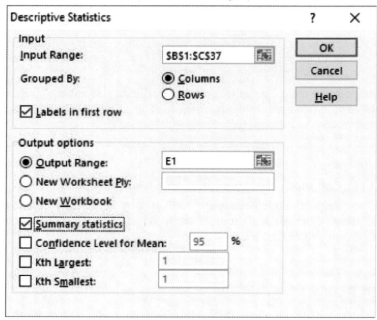

Source: Microsoft Office 2019

d. Table 3.3 presents the Excel output. If the output is difficult to read, highlight the output and choose **Home > Format > Column > Autofit Selection.** As noted earlier, Excel provides numerous summary measures; we have put the measures of central location in boldface.

TABLE 3.3 Excel's Output Using the Data Analysis Toolpak

Growth		Value	
Mean	**15.755**	**Mean**	**12.005**
Standard Error	3.966547567	Standard Error	2.996531209
Median	**15.245**	**Median**	**15.38**
Mode	**#N/A**	**Mode**	**#N/A**
Standard Deviation	23.7992854	Standard Deviation	17.97918725
Sample Variance	566.4059857	Sample Variance	323.2511743
Kurtosis	0.973702537	Kurtosis	1.853350762
Skewness	−0.028949752	Skewness	−1.023591081
Range	120.38	Range	90.6
Minimum	−40.9	Minimum	−46.52
Maximum	79.48	Maximum	44.08
Sum	567.18	Sum	432.18
Count	36	Count	36

Note: If a variable has more than one mode, this method will only report the first mode that it encounters.

Summary

From Table 3.3 we see that the average return for Growth is greater than the average return for Value, 15.76% > 12.01%. However, the median return for Value is greater than the median return for Growth, 15.38% > 15.25%. This example illustrates why it is useful to examine both the mean and the median when summarizing central location, especially when outliers may be present. Neither variable has a mode.

Note on Symmetry

In Chapter 2, we used histograms to discuss **symmetry** and **skewness.** Recall that the distribution is symmetric if one side of the histogram is a mirror image of the other side. For a symmetric and unimodal distribution, the mean, the median, and the mode are equal. In business applications, it is common to encounter distributions that are skewed. The mean is usually greater than the median when the distribution is positively skewed, and the mean is usually less than the median when the distribution is negatively skewed.

We would also like to comment on the numerical measure of skewness that Excel reports in Table 3.3, even though we will not discuss its calculation. A skewness coefficient of zero indicates the observations are evenly distributed on both sides of the mean. A positive skewness coefficient implies that extreme observations are concentrated in the right tail of the distribution, pulling the mean up, relative to the median, and the bulk of the observations lie to the left of the mean. Similarly, a negative skewness coefficient implies that extreme observations are concentrated in the left tail of the distribution, pulling the mean down, relative to the median, and the bulk of the observations lie to the right of the mean. For both Growth and Value, the skewness coefficient is negative; for Growth, however, the coefficient value of -0.0289 implies a very slight negative skew.

The Weighted Mean

So far we have focused on applications where each observation of a variable contributed equally to the mean. The **weighted mean** is relevant when some observations contribute more than others. For example, a student is often evaluated on the basis of the weighted mean because the score on the final exam is typically worth more than the score on the midterm.

We might also want to calculate the mean from a frequency distribution. Recall from Chapter 2 that a frequency distribution groups the observations into nonoverlapping intervals and records the number of observations in each interval. Because frequencies will likely differ for each interval, this difference will need to be incorporated into the mean.

THE WEIGHTED MEAN

Let $w_1, w_2, \ldots, w_n$ denote the weights of the sample observations $x_1, x_2, \ldots, x_n$ such that $w_1 + w_2 + \cdots + w_n = 1$. The weighted mean for the sample is computed as

$$\bar{x} = \Sigma\, w_i x_i, \text{ for } i = 1, \ldots, n.$$

For a frequency distribution, we substitute the relative frequency of the ith interval for w_i and the midpoint of the ith interval for x_i. The weighted mean for the population is computed similarly.

EXAMPLE 3.4

A student scores 60 on Exam 1, 70 on Exam 2, and 80 on Exam 3. What is the student's average score for the course if Exams 1, 2, and 3 are worth 25%, 25%, and 50% of the grade, respectively?

SOLUTION: We define the weights as $w_1 = 0.25$, $w_2 = 0.25$, and $w_3 = 0.50$. We compute the average score as $\bar{x} = \Sigma w_i x_i = 0.25 \times 60 + 0.25 \times 70 + 0.50 \times 80 = 72.50$. Note that the unweighted mean is only 70 because it does not incorporate the higher weight given to the score on Exam 3.

EXAMPLE 3.5

In Chapter 2, we constructed a frequency distribution to summarize the purchases (in $) for 200 customers. Table 3.4 shows this frequency distribution. Calculate the mean purchase.

TABLE 3.4 Frequency Distribution for Purchase

Interval (in $)	Frequency	Relative Frequency
$0 < x \leq 200$	25	0.125
$200 < x \leq 400$	63	0.315
$400 < x \leq 600$	49	0.245
$600 < x \leq 800$	33	0.165
$800 < x \leq 1,000$	30	0.150

SOLUTION: In order to calculate the mean from a frequency distribution, we first calculate the midpoint, m_i, for each interval. The first interval is $0 < x \leq 200$, so its midpoint, m_1, equals $\dfrac{0 + 200}{2} = 100$. The midpoints for the other intervals are found similarly as 300, 500, 700, and 900.

We then use the relative frequency for each interval as its respective weight. So, the weight for the first interval is defined as $w_1 = 0.125$. The weights for the other intervals are defined in a similar manner. We compute the mean purchase as

$$\bar{x} = \Sigma w_i m_i = 0.125 \times 100 + 0.315 \times 300 + \cdots + 0.150 \times 900 = 480.$$

Based on the frequency distribution for 200 customers, the mean purchase is $480.

Calculating the Means of Subgroups

As discussed in Chapter 1, sometimes it is useful to subset the observations in a sample or a population. This process often reveals important information that would not be uncovered if the variable is analyzed using all of the observations. For example, in addition to reporting its total sales over the past year, a multinational company often reports sales by region. This way the company easily identifies which region has the highest or lowest sales. Consider the following example.

FILE
Online

EXAMPLE 3.6

The marketing analyst of an online retail company is trying to understand spending behavior of customers during the holiday season. She has compiled information on 130 existing customers that includes the customer's sex (Sex = Female or Male) and spending (in $) in the following categories: clothing (Clothing), health and beauty (Health), technology (Tech), and miscellaneous items (Misc). [Note that for the Sex variable, there are no non-binary observations in this data set.] A portion of the data is shown in Table 3.5.

TABLE 3.5 Online Spending by Females versus Males

Customer	Sex	Clothing	Health	Tech	Misc
1	Female	246	185	64	75
2	Male	171	78	345	10
⋮	⋮	⋮	⋮	⋮	⋮
130	Male	52	73	542	58

Use Excel to find the average spending for each of the product categories for female customers and for male customers. Then, help the manager determine whether it seems appropriate to target females or males for the different product categories.

SOLUTION:

a. Open the *Online* data file.

b. We use the **AVERAGEIF** function. The inputs for the function are (1) the range of cells that are to meet a certain criterion, (2) the criterion, and (3) the cells that are to be averaged. For instance, to find the average amount that females spend on clothing, we enter =AVERAGEIF(B2:B131, "Female", C2:C131), and Excel returns 225.67. To find the average amount that males spend on clothing, we enter =AVERAGEIF(B2:B131, "Male", C2:C131), and Excel returns 97.93. The averages for the other categories can be found in a similar manner. Table 3.6 summarizes the results.

TABLE 3.6 Average Amount Spent (in $) by Females versus Males

Sex	Clothing	Health	Tech	Misc
Female	225.67	100.25	47.10	159.88
Male	97.93	100.64	310.97	85.84

Summary

Given the means for the two groups, the manager should target females for clothing and miscellaneous products and males for technology products. Because females and males spend approximately the same on health products, the manager need not differentiate this market.

Another Measure of Location

A Percentile

Recall that the median is the middle observation of a variable; that is, half of the observations fall below the median and half fall above it. The median is also called the 50th percentile. In many instances, we are interested in a **percentile** other than the 50th percentile. In general, the *p*th percentile divides a variable into two parts:

- Approximately *p* percent of the observations are less than the *p*th percentile.
- Approximately $(100 - p)$ percent of the observations are greater than the *p*th percentile.

A percentile is technically a measure of location; however, it is also used as a measure of relative position because it is so easy to interpret. For example, suppose you obtained a raw score of 650 on the math portion of the SAT, where scores range from 200 to 800. It may not be readily apparent how you performed relative to other students that took the same test. However, if you know that the raw score corresponds to the 75th percentile, then you know that approximately 75% of students had scores lower than your score and approximately 25% of students had scores higher than your score.

Earlier, we found that the median or the 50th percentile for the Growth variable was 15.245%. When we calculate the 25th, the 50th, and the 75th percentiles for a variable, we have effectively divided the data into four equal parts, or quarters. Thus, the 25th percentile is also referred to as the first quartile (Q1), the 50th percentile is referred to as the second quartile (Q2), and the 75th percentile is referred to as the third quartile (Q3). These **quartiles** are the most commonly used percentiles. A common way to report descriptive measures for a variable is to use a five-number summary. A five-number summary shows the minimum value, the quartiles, and the maximum value for a variable.

We should note that it only makes sense to calculate percentiles for larger data sets. For this reason, we tend to rely on software packages, like Excel, to make the calculations for us. Software packages often use different algorithms to calculate percentiles; however, with larger samples sizes, the differences, if any, tend to be negligible.

A PERCENTILE

In general, the *p*th percentile divides a data set into two parts:

- Approximately *p* percent of the observations have values less than the *p*th percentile.
- Approximately $(100 - p)$ percent of the observations have values greater than the *p*th percentile.

Growth_Value

EXAMPLE 3.7

Use Excel to find the five-number summary for the Growth and Value variables from the introductory case.

SOLUTION:

a. Open the ***Growth_Value*** data file.

b. We use the **MIN** and **MAX** functions to find the minimum and maximum values for a variable. For Growth, we enter =MIN(B2:B37) for the minimum value and =MAX(B2:B37) for the maximum value. Similar entries are made for Value, except we substitute C2:C37 for B2:B37.

c. We use Excel's **PERCENTILE.INC** function to find the *p*th percentile. The first input is the range of observations and the second input is the percentile entered as a proportion. For the 25th percentile for Growth, we enter =PERCENTILE.INC(B2:B37, 0.25). The 50th and the 75th percentiles are found by entering 0.50 and 0.75, respectively, for the second input. Similar entries are made for Value, except we substitute C2:C37 for B2:B37.

Table 3.7 reports the five-number summary for the Growth and Value variables.

TABLE 3.7 Five-Number Summary for Growth and Value

	Min	Q1	Q2	Q3	Max
Growth	−40.90	2.86	15.25	36.97	79.48
Value	−46.52	1.70	15.38	22.44	44.08

EXERCISES 3.1

Mechanics

1. Given the following observations from a sample, calculate the mean, the median, and the mode.

8	10	9	12	12

2. Given the following observations from a sample, calculate the mean, the median, and the mode.

−4	0	−6	1	−3	−4

3. Given the following observations from a population, calculate the mean, the median, and the mode.

150	257	55	110	110	43	201	125	55

4. Given the following observations from a population, calculate the mean, the median, and the mode.

20	15	25	20	10	15	25	20	15

68 | ESSENTIALS OF BUSINESS STATISTICS | 3.1   Measures of Location

5. **FILE** *Exercise_3.5.* The accompanying data file has three variables, x_1, x_2, x_3. Calculate the 25th, 50th, and 75th percentiles for x_1. [Note: Use Excel's **PERCENTILE.INC** function to find a percentile.]

6. **FILE** *Exercise_3.6.* The accompanying data file has three variables, x_1, x_2, x_3.
   a. Calculate the 25th, 50th, and 75th percentiles for x_2. [Note: Use Excel's **PERCENTILE.INC** function to find a percentile.]
   b. Calculate the 20th and 80th percentiles for x_3. [Note: Use Excel's **PERCENTILE.INC** function to find a percentile.]

Applications

7. **FILE** *Houses.* The accompanying data file contains the sale price (in $1,000s) for 36 homes sold in a suburb outside Chicago, Illinois. Find the mean and median sale price.

8. **FILE** *Gas_Prices.* The accompanying data file contains the average price of gas (in $ per gallon) for the 50 states in the United States. Find the mean and the median price.

9. **FILE** *Life_Expectancy.* The accompanying data file contains U.S. life expectancy (in years) for the 50 states. Find the mean and median life expectancy.

10. **FILE** *Prime.* Amazon Prime is a service that gives the company's customers free two-day shipping and discounted rates on overnight delivery. Prime customers also get other perks, such as free e-books. The accompanying data file contains the annual expenditures (in $) for 100 Prime customers. Find the mean and the median for annual expenditures.

11. **FILE** *Fitness.* A survey of 417 individuals asks questions about how often they exercise, marital status, and annual income. The accompanying data file contains their responses.
    a. Find the mean and the median for Income.
    b. Find the mean income for married individuals and the mean income for nonmarried individuals. Which subgroup earns more?
    c. Find the mean income for individuals who always exercise and the mean income for individuals who never exercise. Which subgroup earns more?

12. **FILE** *Spend.* A survey of 500 individuals asks questions about home ownership (OwnHome: Yes/No), car ownership (OwnCar: Yes/No), annual household spending on food (Food), and annual household spending on travel (Travel). The accompanying data file contains their responses.
    a. Find the mean for Food and Travel.
    b. Find the mean amount spent on food for homeowners versus nonhomeowners. Which subgroup spends more?
    c. Find the mean amount spent on travel for homeowners versus nonhomeowners. Which subgroup spends more?

13. You score 90 on the midterm, 60 on the final, and 80 on the class project. What is your average score if the midterm is worth 30%, the final is worth 50%, and the class project is worth 20%?

14. Over the past year, an investor bought common stock of Firm A on three occasions at the following prices.

Date	Price per Share
January	94.81
July	102.67
December	115.32

   a. What is the average price per share if the investor had bought 100 shares in January, 60 in July, and 40 in December?
   b. What is the average price per share if the investor had bought 40 shares in January, 60 in July, and 100 in December?

15. Over the past year, an investor bought common stock of Corporation A on three occasions at the following prices.

Date	Price per Share	Number of Shares
January	19.58	70
July	24.06	80
December	29.54	50

   Calculate the average price per share at which the investor bought these shares.

16. A local hospital provided the following relative frequency distribution summarizing the weights of babies (in pounds) delivered over the month of January. Calculate the average weight.

Weight (in pounds)	Relative Frequency
$2 < x \le 4$	0.04
$4 < x \le 6$	0.11
$6 < x \le 8$	0.36
$8 < x \le 10$	0.43
$10 < x \le 12$	0.06

17. Fifty cities provided information on vacancy rates (in %) for local apartments in the following relative frequency distribution. Calculate the average vacancy rate.

Vacancy Rate (in %)	Relative Frequency
$0 < x \le 3$	0.10
$3 < x \le 6$	0.10
$6 < x \le 9$	0.20
$9 < x \le 12$	0.40
$12 < x \le 15$	0.20

18. **FILE** *Franchise.* The accompanying data file shows the net profit (Net_Profit), counter sales (Counter_Sales), and drive-through sales (Drive_Sales) for a chain of 100 fastfood restaurants. All variables are measured in millions of dollars.
    a. Construct the five-number summary for each variable.
    b. Interpret the median for net profits.
    c. Interpret the 25th percentile for counter sales. Interpret the 75th percentile for drive-through sales.

19. **FILE** *Work_Experience.* The accompanying data file shows the salary (in $) and work experience (in years) of 100 employees in a marketing firm.

   a. Construct the five-number summary for each variable.

   b. What are the minimum and maximum salaries at this firm? Interpret the 25th percentile for salary.

   c. What are the minimum and maximum years of work experience at this firm? Interpret the 75th percentile for work experience.

20. **FILE** *IceCream.* The accompanying data file shows 35 observations for an ice cream truck driver's daily income

(Income in $), number of hours on the road (Hours), whether it was a hot day (Hot = 1 if the high temperature was above 85° F, 0 otherwise), and whether it was a holiday (Holiday = 1 if holiday, 0 otherwise).

   a. Calculate the mean Income and the mean Hours.

   b. Find the mean Income for a hot day and the mean Income for a non–hot day. Which subgroup has a higher Income?

   c. Find the mean Income for a holiday and the mean Income for a nonholiday. Which subgroup has a higher Income?

LO 3.2

3.2 MEASURES OF DISPERSION

Calculate and interpret measures of dispersion.

In Section 3.1, we focused on measures of central location in an attempt to find a typical or central value that describes a variable. It is also important to analyze how the observations vary around the center. Recall from the introductory case that the average returns for the Growth and Value mutual funds were 15.755% and 12.005%, respectively. As an investor, you might ask why anyone would put money in Value when, on average, this fund has a lower return. It turns out that the average is not sufficient when summarizing a variable. The average fails to describe the underlying variability of the variable.

We now discuss several measures of dispersion that gauge the variability of a variable. Each measure is a numerical value that equals zero if all observations are identical, and increases as the observations become more diverse. In addition to outlining how these measures of dispersion are calculated manually, we also provide instructions for obtaining these results in Excel.

The Range and the Interquartile Range

The **range** is the simplest measure of dispersion. It is the difference between the maximum value (Max) and the minimum value (Min) in a sample or a population, or, equivalently, Range = Max − Min. The range is not considered a good measure of dispersion because it focuses solely on the extreme values and ignores every other observation in the sample or the population.

The **interquartile range** (IQR) is the difference between the third quartile and the first quartile, or, equivalently, IQR = Q3 − Q1. We can think of IQR as the range of the middle 50% of the observations of the variable. Even though IQR does not depend on the extreme observations, it does not incorporate all the observations.

> **THE RANGE AND THE INTERQUARTILE RANGE**
>
> - The range is the difference between the maximum value (Max) and minimum value (Min) in a sample or a population; that is, Range = Max − Min.
> - The interquartile range (IQR) is the difference between the 75th percentile and the 25th percentile; that is, IQR = Q3 − Q1.

> **EXAMPLE 3.8**
>
> Find the range and the interquartile range (IQR) for Growth and Value. What do your answers suggest?

SOLUTION:

a. Open the *Growth_Value* data file.

b. We use the MIN and MAX functions to find the range. For Growth, we enter =MAX(B2:B37)-MIN(B2:B37), and Excel returns 120.38. For Value, we replace B2:B37 with C2:C37, and Excel returns 90.6.

   Note too that the Descriptive Statistics option in Excel's Analysis Toolpak also reports the range for a variable.

c. We use the **PERCENTILE.INC** function to find the IQR. For Growth, we enter =PERCENTILE.INC(B2:B37, 0.75)−PERCENTILE.INC(B2:B37, 0.25), and Excel returns 34.1125. For Value, we replace B2:B37 with C2:C37, and Excel returns 20.735.

Summary

Growth's range and IQR are greater than Value's range and IQR. As measures of dispersion, these results imply that the observations for Growth are more dispersed than the observations for Value.

The Mean Absolute Deviation

A good measure of dispersion should consider differences of all observations from the mean. If we simply average all differences from the mean, the positives and the negatives will cancel out, even though they both contribute to dispersion, and the resulting average will equal zero. The **mean absolute deviation** (MAD) is an average of the absolute differences between the observations and the mean.

THE MEAN ABSOLUTE DEVIATION (MAD)

For sample observations $x_1, x_2, \ldots, x_n$, the sample MAD is computed as

$$\text{Sample MAD} = \frac{\Sigma|x_i - \bar{x}|}{n}.$$

For population observations $x_1, x_2, \ldots, x_N$, the population MAD is computed as

$$\text{Population MAD} = \frac{\Sigma|x_i - \mu|}{N}.$$

EXAMPLE 3.9

Find the mean absolute deviation (MAD) for Growth and Value. What do your answers suggest?

SOLUTION: We first outline how to manually calculate MAD for Growth. Recall from Example 3.3 that the sample mean for Growth is $\bar{x} = 15.755$. We calculate MAD for Growth as

$$\text{MAD} = \frac{\Sigma|x_i - \bar{x}|}{n} = \frac{|-5.50 - 15.755| + |39.91 - 15.755| + \cdots + |38.42 - 15.755|}{36}$$

$$= \frac{629.66}{36} = 17.491$$

The Variance and the Standard Deviation

The **variance** and the **standard deviation** are the two most widely used measures of dispersion. Instead of calculating the average of the absolute differences from the mean, as in MAD, the variance is calculated as the average of the squared differences from the mean. The squaring of differences from the mean emphasizes larger differences more than smaller ones; MAD weighs large and small differences equally.

Due to the fact that the variance is a squared number, two practical issues arise when we try to apply it as a measure of dispersion. First, the variance tends to be a large number when compared to the original observations whose spread it is meant to describe. Second, it is not expressed in the same units as the original observations. For example, if the original observations are expressed in dollars, then the variance is expressed in squared dollars. Fortunately, there is an easy remedy to these issues: We simply take the positive square root of the variance, which gives us the standard deviation.

The formulas for the variance differ depending on whether we have a sample or a population. The following definition box elaborates on the formulas, as well as the notation, for the variance and the standard deviation.

THE VARIANCE AND THE STANDARD DEVIATION

For sample observations $x_1, x_2, \ldots, x_n$, the sample variance s^2 and the sample standard deviation s are computed as

$$s^2 = \frac{\Sigma(x_i - \bar{x})^2}{n - 1} \quad \text{and} \quad s = \sqrt{s^2}.$$

For population observations $x_1, x_2, \ldots, x_N$, the population variance σ^2 (the Greek letter sigma, squared) and the population standard deviation σ are computed as

$$\sigma^2 = \frac{\Sigma(x_i - \mu)^2}{N} \quad \text{and} \quad \sigma = \sqrt{\sigma^2}.$$

Note: The sample variance uses $n - 1$ rather than n in the denominator to ensure that the sample variance is an unbiased estimator for the population variance. Unbiased estimators are defined in Chapter 7.

EXAMPLE 3.10

Find the variance and the standard deviation for Growth and Value. What do your answers suggest?

SOLUTION: We first outline how to manually calculate the variance and the standard deviation for Growth. Recall from Example 3.3 that the sample mean for Growth is $\bar{x} = 15.755$. We calculate the variance and the standard deviation for Growth as

$$s^2 = \frac{\Sigma(x_i - \bar{x})^2}{n - 1} = \frac{(-5.50 - 15.755)^2 + (39.91 - 15.755)^2 + \cdots + (38.42 - 15.755)^2}{36 - 1}$$

$$= \frac{19{,}824.21}{35} = 566.406(\%^2)$$

$$s = \sqrt{s^2} = \sqrt{566.406} = 23.799(\%)$$

Using Excel

a. Open the *Growth_Value* data file.

b. We use the **VAR.S** function and the **STDEV.S** function to find a variable's sample variance and sample standard deviation, respectively. (We use the **VAR.P** function and the **STDEV.P** function to find a variable's population variance and population standard deviation, respectively.) For Growth, we enter =VAR.S(B2:B37) and =STDEV.S(B2:B37), and Excel returns 566.406 for the sample variance and 23.799 for the sample standard deviation. For Value, we replace B2:B37 with C2:C37, and Excel returns 323.251 for the sample variance and 17.979 for the sample standard deviation.

   Note: We can also use the **Descriptive Statistics** option in Excel's Analysis Toolpak to find the sample variance and the sample standard deviation. Verify that the values that you obtain using the **VAR.S** and **STDEV.S** functions match those that appear in Table 3.3.

Summary

Growth's variance and standard deviation are greater than Value's variance and standard deviation, which implies that the observations are more dispersed for Growth. Note that this finding is consistent with the findings for the range, interquartile range, and MAD. With financial data, standard deviation tends to be the most common measure of risk. Therefore, the investment risk of Growth is higher than that of Value over this time period.

The Coefficient of Variation

In some instances, analysis entails comparing the variability of two or more variables that have different means or units of measurement. The **coefficient of variation (CV)** serves as a relative measure of dispersion and adjusts for differences in the magnitudes of the means. Calculated by dividing a variable's standard deviation by its mean, CV is a unit-less measure that allows for direct comparisons of mean-adjusted dispersion across different variables.

THE COEFFICIENT OF VARIATION (CV)

The coefficient of variation (CV) for a variable is calculated by dividing its standard deviation by its mean.

- For a sample, $CV = s/\bar{x}$.
- For a population, $CV = \sigma/\mu$.

EXAMPLE 3.11

Use the information from Table 3.3 to calculate and interpret the coefficient of variation for Growth and Value.

SOLUTION: We use the sample means and the sample standard deviations to calculate CV for the two variables as

Growth: $CV = s/\bar{x} = 23.799/15.755 = 1.511$
Value: $CV = s/\bar{x} = 17.979/12.005 = 1.498$

The coefficient of variation indicates that the relative dispersion of the two variables is about the same.

EXERCISES 3.2

Mechanics

21. Consider the following population data:

34	42	12	10	22

   a. Calculate the range.
   b. Calculate MAD.
   c. Calculate the population variance.
   d. Calculate the population standard deviation.

22. Consider the following population data:

0	−4	2	−8	10

   a. Calculate the range.
   b. Calculate MAD.
   c. Calculate the population variance.
   d. Calculate the population standard deviation.

23. Consider the following sample data:

40	48	32	52	38	42

   a. Calculate the range.
   b. Calculate MAD.
   c. Calculate the sample variance.
   d. Calculate the sample standard deviation.

24. Consider the following sample data:

−10	12	−8	−2	−6	8

   a. Calculate the range.
   b. Calculate MAD.
   c. Calculate the sample variance and the sample standard deviation.

Applications

25. **FILE** *Prime.* The accompanying data file contains the annual expenditures (in $) for 100 Prime customers.
   a. What were minimum expenditures? What were maximum expenditures?
   b. Calculate the mean and the median expenditures.
   c. Calculate the variance and the standard devation.

26. **FILE** *StockPrices.* Monthly closing stock prices for Firm A and Firm B are collected for the past five years. The accompanying file contains relevant data.
   a. Calculate the sample variance and the sample standard deviation for each firm's stock price.
   b. Which firm's stock price had greater variability as measured by the standard deviation?
   c. Which firm's stock price had the greater relative dispersion?

27. **FILE** *Rental.* The accompanying data file shows monthly rent and the square footage for 40 apartments in a college town.
   a. Calculate the mean and the standard deviation for monthly rent.
   b. Calculate the mean and the standard deviation for square footage.
   c. Which variable exhibits greater relative dispersion?

28. **FILE** *Revenues.* The accompanying data file contains the annual revenues (in $ millions) for Corporation A and Corporation B for the past 13 years.
   a. Calculate the coefficient of variation for Corporation A.
   b. Calculate the coefficient of variation for Corporation B.
   c. Which variable exhibits greater relative dispersion?

29. **FILE** *Highway.* Many environmental groups and politicians are suggesting a return to the federal 55 miles-per-hour (mph) speed limit on America's highways. They argue that not only will a lower national speed limit reduce greenhouse emissions, it will also increase traffic safety. A researcher believes that a lower speed limit will not increase traffic safety because he feels that traffic safety is based on the variability of the speeds at which people are driving, rather than the average speed. The researcher gathers the speeds of 40 cars from a highway with a speed limit of 55 mph (Highway_1) and the speeds of 40 cars from a highway with a speed limit of 65 mph (Highway_2). The accompanying file contains the relevant data.

    a. Calculate the mean and the median for each highway.

    b. Calculate the standard deviation for each highway.

    c. Do the data support the researcher's belief? Explain.

30. **FILE** *Census.* The accompanying data file contains, among other variables, median household income and median house value for the 50 states.

    a. Calculate and discuss the range of household income and house value.

    b. Calculate the sample MAD and the sample standard deviation of household income and house value.

    c. Discuss why we cannot directly compare the sample MAD and the standard deviations of the two variables.

31. **FILE** *Franchise.* The accompanying data file contains the net profit (Net_Profit), counter sales (Counter_Sales), and drive-through sales (Drive_Sales) for a chain of 100 fast-food restaurants. All variables are measured in millions of dollars.

    a. Calculate the sample standard deviation for counter sales and drive-through sales. According to this measure of dispersion, which variable exhibited higher variability?

    b. Calculate the mean absolute deviation (MAD) for counter sales and drive-through sales. According to this measure of dispersion, which variable exhibited higher variability?

3.3 MEAN-VARIANCE ANALYSIS AND THE SHARPE RATIO

LO 3.3

In the introduction to Section 3.2, we asked why any rational investor would invest in Value over Growth since the average return for Value over the time period was 12.005%, whereas the average return for Growth was 15.755%. It turns out that, in general, investments with higher returns also carry higher risk. The average return represents an investor's reward, whereas variance, or equivalently standard deviation, corresponds to risk.

Explain mean-variance analysis and the Sharpe ratio.

    According to **mean-variance analysis,** we can measure performance of any risky asset solely on the basis of the average and the variance of its returns.

> **MEAN-VARIANCE ANALYSIS**
>
> Mean-variance analysis postulates that the performance of an asset is measured by its rate of return, and this rate of return is evaluated in terms of its reward (mean) and risk (variance). In general, investments with higher average returns are also associated with higher risk.

Consider Table 3.8, which summarizes the returns for Growth and Value. It is true that an investment in Growth rather than Value provided an investor with a higher reward over this time period, as measured by the mean return. However, this same investor encountered more risk, as measured by the variance or the standard deviation.

TABLE 3.8 Mean-Variance Analysis for Growth and Value

Mutual Fund	Mean Return %	Variance %²	Standard Deviation %
Growth	15.755	566.406	23.799
Value	12.005	323.251	17.979

A discussion of mean-variance analysis seems almost incomplete without mention of the **Sharpe ratio.** Nobel Laureate William Sharpe developed what he originally referred to as the "reward-to-variability" ratio. However, academics and finance professionals prefer to call it the "Sharpe ratio." The Sharpe ratio is used to characterize how well the return of an asset compensates for the risk that the investor takes. Investors are often advised to pick investments that have high Sharpe ratios.

The Sharpe ratio is defined with the reward specified in terms of the population mean and the variability specified in terms of the population standard deviation. However, we often compute the Sharpe ratio in terms of the sample mean and the sample standard deviation, where the return is usually expressed as a percent and not a decimal.

THE SHARPE RATIO

The Sharpe ratio measures the extra reward per unit of risk. The Sharpe ratio for an investment I is computed as

$$\frac{\bar{x}_I - \bar{R}_f}{s_I},$$

where $\bar{x}_I$ is the mean return for the investment, $\bar{R}_f$ is the mean return for a risk-free asset such as a Treasury bill (T-bill), and s_I is the standard deviation for the investment.

The numerator of the Sharpe ratio measures the extra reward that investors receive for the added risk taken—this difference is often called excess return. The higher the Sharpe ratio, the better the investment compensates its investors for risk.

EXAMPLE 3.12

Use the information in Table 3.8 to calculate and interpret the Sharpe ratios for Growth and Value given that the return on a 1-year T-bill is 1%.

SOLUTION: Because the return on a 1-year T-bill is 1%, $\bar{R}_f = 1$. Plugging in the values of the relevant means and standard deviations into the Sharpe ratio yields

Sharpe ratio for Growth: $\dfrac{\bar{x}_I - \bar{R}_f}{s_I} = \dfrac{15.755 - 1}{23.799} = 0.62.$

Sharpe ratio for Value: $\dfrac{\bar{x}_I - \bar{R}_f}{s_I} = \dfrac{12.005 - 1}{17.979} = 0.61.$

We had earlier shown that Growth had a higher return, which is good, along with a higher variance, which is bad. We can use the Sharpe ratio to make a valid comparison between the mutual funds. Growth provides a slightly higher Sharpe ratio than Value (0.62 > 0.61); therefore, Growth offered more reward per unit of risk compared to Value.

SYNOPSIS OF INTRODUCTORY CASE

Growth and value are two fundamental styles in stock and mutual fund investing. Proponents of growth investing believe that companies that are growing faster than their peers are trendsetters and will be able to maintain their superior growth. By investing in the stocks of these companies, they expect their investment to grow at a rate faster than the overall stock market. By comparison, value investors focus on the stocks of companies that are trading at a discount relative to the overall market or a specific sector. Investors of value stocks believe that these stocks are undervalued and that their price will increase once their true value is recognized by other investors. The debate between growth and value investing is age-old, and which style dominates depends on the sample period used for the analysis.

Gladkikh/Getty Images

An analysis of annual return data for Fidelity's Growth Index mutual fund (Growth) and Fidelity's Value Index mutual fund (Value) for the years 1984 throuth 2019 provides important information for an investor trying to determine whether to invest in a growth mutual fund, a value mutual fund, or both types of mutual funds. Over this period, Growth's mean return of 15.755% is greater than Value's mean return of 12.005%. While the mean return typically represents the reward of investing, it does not incorporate the risk of investing.

Standard deviation tends to be the most common measure of risk with financial data. Because Growth's standard deviation (23.799%) is greater than Value's standard deviation (17.979%), Growth is likelier to have returns farther above and below its mean. Finally, given a risk-free rate of 1%, Growth's Sharpe ratio of 0.62 is slightly greater than Value's Sharpe ratio of 0.61, indicating that Growth provides more reward per unit of risk. Assuming that the behavior of these returns will continue, the investor will favor investing in Growth over Value. A commonly used disclaimer, however, states that past performance is no guarantee of future results.

EXERCISES 3.3

Mechanics

32. Consider the following data for two investments, A and B:

| Investment A: | $\bar{x} = 10\%$ and $s = 5\%$ |
| Investment B: | $\bar{x} = 15\%$ and $s = 10\%$ |

a. Which investment provides the higher return? Which investment provides less risk? Explain.

b. Given a risk-free rate of 1.4%, calculate the Sharpe ratio for each investment. Which investment provides the higher reward per unit of risk? Explain.

33. Consider the following data for two investments, A and B:

| Investment A: | $\bar{x} = 8\%$ and $s = 5\%$ |
| Investment B: | $\bar{x} = 10\%$ and $s = 7\%$ |

a. Which investment provides the higher return? Which investment provides less risk? Explain.

b. Given a risk-free rate of 2%, calculate the Sharpe ratio for each investment. Which investment provides the higher reward per unit of risk? Explain.

34. Consider the following returns for two investments, A and B, over the past four years:

| Investment 1: | 2% | 8% | −4% | 6% |
| Investment 2: | 6% | 12% | −8% | 10% |

a. Which investment provides the higher return?

b. Which investment provides less risk?

c. Given a risk-free rate of 1.2%, calculate the Sharpe ratio for each investment. Which investment has performed better? Explain.

Applications

35. Consider the following summary measures for the annual returns for Stock 1 and Stock 2 over the past 13 years.

Stock 1: $\bar{x} = 9.62\%$ and $s = 23.58\%$

Stock 2: $\bar{x} = 12.38\%$ and $s = 15.45\%$

a. Which stock had the higher average return?

b. Which stock was riskier over this time period? Given your answer in part (a), is this result surprising? Explain.

c. Given a risk-free rate of 3%, which stock has the higher Sharpe ratio? What does this ratio imply?

36. **FILE** *MutualFunds1.* The accompanying data file shows the annual returns (in %) for Mutual Fund 1 and Mutual Fund 2 over the past 17 years.
    a. Compare the sample means and the sample standard deviations of the two funds.
    b. Use a risk-free rate of 2% to compare the Sharpe ratios of the two funds.

37. **FILE** *MutualFunds2.* The accompanying data file shows the annual returns (in %) for Mutual Fund 1 and Mutual Fund 2 over the past 18 years.
    a. Which fund had the higher average return?
    b. Which fund was riskier over this time period?
    c. Given a risk-free rate of 3%, which fund has the higher Sharpe ratio? What does this ratio imply?

3.4 ANALYSIS OF RELATIVE LOCATION

The mean and the standard deviation are the most extensively used measures of central location and dispersion, respectively. Unlike the mean, it is not easy to interpret the standard deviation intuitively. All we can say is that a low value for the standard deviation indicates that the observations are close to the mean, while a high value for the standard deviation indicates that the observations are spread out.

In this section, we will first use Chebyshev's theorem and the empirical rule to make precise statements regarding the percentage of observations that fall within a specified number of standard deviations from the mean. We then use the mean and the standard deviation to compute a z-score that measures the relative location of a particular observation; z-scores are also used to detect outliers.

Finally, we construct a boxplot. A boxplot is a convenient way to graphically depict the five-number summary of a variable. It is also an effective tool for identifying outliers. A series of boxplots are useful when comparing variables or similar information for a variable gathered at another place or time.

LO 3.4

Apply Chebyshev's theorem, the empirical rule, and z-scores.

Chebyshev's Theorem

As we will see in more detail in later chapters, it is important to be able to use the standard deviation to make statements about the proportion of observations that fall within certain intervals. Fortunately, a Russian mathematician named Pavroty **Chebyshev** (1821–1894) found bounds for the proportion of the observations that lie within a specified number of standard deviations from the mean.

> **CHEBYSHEV'S THEOREM**
>
> For any variable, the proportion of observations that lie within k standard deviations from the mean is at least $1 - 1/k^2$, where k is any number greater than 1.

EXAMPLE 3.13

A large lecture class has 280 students. The professor has announced that the mean score on an exam is 74 with a standard deviation of 8. At least how many students scored within 58 and 90?

SOLUTION: A score of 58 is two standard deviations below the mean ($\bar{x} - 2s = 74 - (2 \times 8) = 58$), while a score of 90 is two standard deviations above the mean ($\bar{x} + 2s = 74 + (2 \times 8) = 90$). Using Chebyshev's theorem and $k = 2$, we have $1 - 1/2^2 = 0.75$. In other words, Chebyshev's theorem asserts that at least 75% of the scores will fall within 58 and 90. Therefore, at least 75% of 280 students, or $0.75 \times 280 = 210$ students, scored within 58 and 90.

This theorem holds both for a sample and for a population. For example, it implies that at least 0.75, or 75%, of the observations fall within $k = 2$ standard deviations from the mean. Similarly, at least 0.89, or 89%, of the observations fall within $k = 3$ standard deviations from the mean. The main advantage of Chebyshev's theorem is that it applies to all variables, regardless of the shape of the distribution. However, it results in conservative bounds for the percentage of observations falling in a particular interval. The actual percentage of observations lying in the interval may in fact be much larger.

The Empirical Rule

If we know that the observations are drawn from a relatively symmetric and bell-shaped distribution—perhaps by a visual inspection of the variable's histogram—then we can make more precise statements about the percentage of observations that fall within certain intervals. Symmetry and bell-shape are characteristics of the normal distribution, a topic that we discuss in Chapter 6. The normal distribution is often used as an approximation for many real-world applications. The **empirical rule** is illustrated in Figure 3.2. It provides the approximate percentage of observations that fall within 1, 2, or 3 standard deviations from the mean.

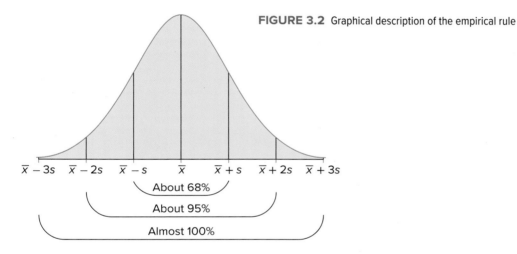

FIGURE 3.2 Graphical description of the empirical rule

THE EMPIRICAL RULE

Given a sample mean $\bar{x}$, a sample standard deviation s, and a relatively symmetric and bell-shaped distribution:

- Approximately 68% of all observations fall in the interval $\bar{x} \pm s$,
- Approximately 95% of all observations fall in the interval $\bar{x} \pm 2s$, and
- Almost all observations fall in the interval $\bar{x} \pm 3s$.

EXAMPLE 3.14

Let's revisit Example 3.13 regarding a large lecture class with 280 students with a mean score of 74 and a standard deviation of 8. Assume that the distribution is symmetric and bell-shaped.

a. Approximately how many students scored within 58 and 90?

b. Approximately how many students scored more than 90?

SOLUTION:

a. As shown in Example 3.13, a score of 58 is two standard deviations below the mean, while a score of 90 is two standard deviations above the mean. For a bell-shaped distribution, the empirical rule states that approximately 95% of the observations fall within two standard deviations of the mean. Therefore, about 95% of 280 students, or $0.95 \times 280 = 266$ students, scored within 58 and 90.

b. We found that approximately 95% of the scores fall between 58 and 90, which implies that 5% of the scores fall outside the interval. Given the symmetry of the distribution, about half of 5%, or 2.5%, of 280 students scored above 90. Equivalently, about seven students (0.025×280) scored above 90 on the exam. If the professor uses a cutoff score above 90 for an A, then only seven students in the class are expected to get an A.

The main difference between Chebyshev's theorem and the empirical rule is that Chebyshev's theorem applies to all variables, whereas the empirical rule is appropriate when the distribution of a variable is symmetric and bell-shaped. In the preceding two examples, while Chebyshev's theorem asserts that at least 75% of the students scored between 58 and 90, we are able to make a more precise statement with the empirical rule that suggests that about 95% of the students scored between 58 and 90. It is preferable to use the empirical rule if the histogram or other visual and numerical measures suggest a symmetric and bell-shaped distribution.

A z-Score

It is often instructive to use the mean and the standard deviation to find the relative location of an observation within a distribution. Suppose a student gets a score of 90 on her accounting exam and 90 on her marketing exam. While the student's scores are identical in both classes, her relative position in these classes may be quite different. What if the mean scores were different in the classes? Even with the same mean scores, what if the standard deviations were different in the classes? Both the mean and the standard deviation are needed to find the relative position of this student in both classes.

We use a **z-score** to find the relative position of an observation within a distribution by dividing the difference of the observation from the mean by the standard deviation.

A z-SCORE

For a sample, the z-score for a given value x is computed as

$$z = \frac{x - \bar{x}}{s},$$

where $\bar{x}$ and s are the sample mean and the sample standard deviation, respectively. For a population, the z-score for a given value x is computed as

$$z = \frac{(x - \mu)}{\sigma},$$

where μ and σ are the population mean and the population standard deviation, respectively.

A z-score is a unitless measure since its numerator and the denominator have the same units, which cancel out with each other. It measures the distance of a given observation from the mean in terms of standard deviations. For example, a z-score of 2 implies that the given observation is 2 standard deviations above the mean. Similarly, a z-score of -1.5 implies that the given observation is 1.5 standard deviations below the mean. Converting observations into z-scores is also called standardizing the observations.

EXAMPLE 3.15

The mean and the standard deviation of scores on an accounting exam are 74 and 8, respectively. The mean and standard deviation of scores on a marketing exam are 78 and 10, respectively. Find the z-scores for a student who scores 90 in both classes.

SOLUTION: The z-score in the accounting class is $z = \frac{90 - 74}{8} = 2$. Similarly, the z-score in the marketing class is $z = \frac{90 - 78}{10} = 1.2$. Therefore, the student has fared relatively better in accounting because she is two standard deviations above the mean, as compared to marketing where she is only 1.2 standard deviations above the mean.

If the distribution of a variable is relatively symmetric and bell-shaped, we can also use z-scores to detect outliers. Because almost all observations fall within three standard deviations of the mean, it is common to treat an observation as an outlier if its z-score is more than 3 or less than -3. Such observations must be reviewed to determine if they should remain in the data set.

EXAMPLE 3.16

Consider the information presented in the introductory case of this chapter. Use z-scores to determine if there are outliers for Growth.

FILE
Growth_Value

SOLUTION: The smallest and the largest observations for Growth are -40.90 and 79.48, respectively. The z-score for the smallest observation is $z = \frac{-40.90 - 15.775}{23.799} = -2.38$ and the z-score for the largest observation is $z = \frac{79.48 - 15.775}{23.799} = 2.68$. Because the absolute value of both z-scores is less than 3, it would suggest that there are no outliers for Growth.

A Boxplot

Recall from Section 3.1 that a common way to describe a variable is to use a five-number summary; this summary shows the minimum value, the quartiles (Q1, Q2, and Q3), and the maximum value of the variable. A **boxplot**, also referred to as a box-and-whiskers plot, is a convenient way to graphically display the five-number summary of a variable. Manually, we sketch a boxplot as follows:

LO 3.5

Construct and interpret a boxplot.

- Plot the five-number summary values in ascending order on the horizontal axis. (The current version of Excel uses a vertical boxplot, where five-number summary values are plotted on the vertical axis.)
- Draw a box encompassing the first and third quartiles, and draw a dashed vertical line in the box at the median.

- Calculate Q1 − (1.5 × IQR), where IQR = Q3 − Q1. This value is the end of the lower fence. The left whisker is a line that extends from Q1 to the smallest observation that is within the lower fence. Calculate Q3 + (1.5 × IQR). This value is the end of the upper fence. The right whisker is a line that extends from Q3 to the largest observation that is within the upper fence.
- Any observations that are less than the end of the lower fence or greater than the end of the upper fence are considered outliers. Use an asterisk (Excel uses a circle) to identify these observations.

Consider the boxplot in Figure 3.3. The left whisker extends from Q1 to the minimum value (Min) because Min is not farther than 1.5 × IQR from Q1. The right whisker, on the other hand, does not extend from Q3 to the maximum value because there is an observation that is farther than 1.5 × IQR from Q3. The asterisk indicates that this observation is considered an outlier.

A boxplot is also used to informally gauge the shape of the distribution. Symmetry is implied if the median is in the center of the box and the left and right whiskers are equidistant from their respective quartiles. If the median is left of center and the right whisker is longer than the left whisker, then the distribution is positively skewed. Similarly, if the median is right of center and the left whisker is longer than the right whisker, then the distribution is negatively skewed. If outliers exist, we need to include them when comparing the lengths of the left and right whiskers.

From Figure 3.3, we note that the median is located to the left of center and that an outlier exists on the right side. Here the right whisker is longer than the left whisker, and if the outlier is included, then the right whisker becomes even longer. This indicates that the underlying distribution is positively skewed.

FIGURE 3.3 An example of a boxplot

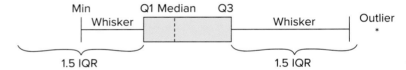

A BOXPLOT

A boxplot is a convenient way to graphically display the five-number summary of a variable. If outliers are present, then they are indicated as asterisks (or another symbol) that are farther than 1.5 × IQR from the box. A boxplot can also be used to informally gauge the shape of the distribution.

Generally, we use software to construct a boxplot. Consider the following example, where we use Excel to construct a vertical boxplot.

EXAMPLE 3.17

Use Excel to construct boxplots for the Growth and Value variables from the introductory case. Interpret the results.

SOLUTION:

Growth_Value

a. Open the ***Growth_Value*** data file.

b. Select cells B1:C37. From the menu, select Insert, and in the Charts group, expand the selection by clicking on the arrow at the bottom right. Select the All Charts tab and then select **Box & Whisker.** Formatting (regarding axis titles, gridlines, etc.) can be done by selecting the "+" sign at the top right of the chart. Figure 3.4 shows the resulting boxplots.

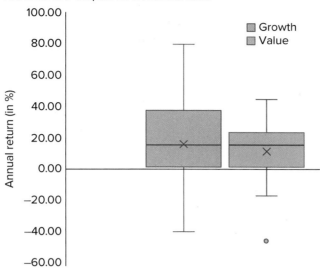

FIGURE 3.4 Boxplots for Growth and Value

Summary

From Figure 3.4, we can see that the median returns for the two funds are similar, as indicated by the horizontal lines within the IQR boxes. Excel also reports the mean for each variable, shown with an X. We see that the mean and the median for Growth are nearly identical, but the mean for Value is less than its median.

The median for Growth is below the center in the IQR box. The top and bottom whiskers appear to be of similar length, so we cannot determine skewness from the boxplot. In Section 3.1, we found that the skewness coefficient for Growth was −0.029, implying that the distribution is slightly negatively skewed. Growth does not have any outliers.

For Value, the outlier at the bottom of the distribution, shown as a circle, coupled with a median that lies above the center in the IQR box suggests that this distribution is negatively skewed. This is consistent with the negative skewness coefficient that was calculated for this variable in Section 3.1.

EXERCISES 3.4

Mechanics

38. A variable has a mean of 80 and a standard deviation of 5.
    a. Using Chebyshev's theorem, approximately what percentage of the observations fall between 70 and 90?
    b. Using Chebyshev's theorem, approximately what percentage of the observations fall between 65 and 95?

39. A variable has a mean of 1,500 and a standard deviation of 100.
    a. Using Chebyshev's theorem, approximately what percentage of the observations fall between 1,300 and 1,700?
    b. Using Chebyshev's theorem, approximately what percentage of the observations fall between 1,100 and 1,900?

40. A variable has a mean of 500 and a standard deviation of 25.
    a. Using Chebyshev's theorem, find the interval that encompasses at least 75% of the data.
    b. Using Chebyshev's theorem, find the interval that encompasses at least 89% of the data.

41. Observations are drawn from a bell-shaped distribution with a mean of 20 and a standard deviation of 2.
    a. Approximately what percentage of the observations fall between 18 and 22?
    b. Approximately what percentage of the observations fall between 16 and 24?
    c. Approximately what percentage of the observations are less than 16?

42. Consider a bell-shaped distribution with a mean of 750 and a standard deviation of 50. There are 500 observations in the data set.
    a. Approximately what percentage of the observations are less than 700?
    b. Approximately how many observations are less than 700?

43. Observations are drawn from a bell-shaped distribution with a mean of 25 and a standard deviation of 4. There are 1,000 observations in the data set.
    a. Approximately what percentage of the observations are less than 33?
    b. Approximately how many observations are less than 33?

44. Observations are drawn from a bell-shaped distribution with a mean of 5 and a standard deviation of 2.5.
    a. Approximately what percentage of the observations are positive?
    b. Approximately what percentage of the observations are not positive?

45. Data are drawn from a bell-shaped distribution with a mean of 50 and a standard deviation of 12. There are 250 observations in the data set. Approximately how many observations are more than 74?

46. Consider a sample with six observations of 6, 9, 12, 10, 9, and 8. Compute the z-score for each observation.

47. Consider a sample with 10 observations of −3, 8, 4, 2, −4, 15, 6, 0, −4, and 5. Use z-scores to determine if there are any outliers in the data; assume a bell-shaped distribution.

48. Consider the following horizontal boxplot.

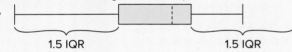

1.5 IQR   1.5 IQR

    a. Does the boxplot indicate possible outliers in the data?
    b. Comment on the skewness of the underlying distribution.

49. Consider the following horizontal boxplot.

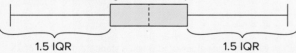

1.5 IQR   1.5 IQR

    a. Does the boxplot indicate possible outliers in the data?
    b. Comment on the skewness of the underlying distribution.

50. Using 500 observations, the following five-point summary was obtained for a variable.

Min	Q1	Median	Q3	Max
125	200	300	550	1300

    a. Interpret Q1 and Q3.
    b. Calculate the interquartile range. Determine whether any outliers exist.
    c. Is the distribution symmetric? If not, comment on its skewness.

51. Using 200 observations, the following five-point summary was obtained for a variable.

Min	Q1	Median	Q3	Max
34	54	66	78	98

    a. Interpret Q1 and Q3.
    b. Calculate the interquartile range. Determine whether any outliers exist.
    c. Is the distribution symmetric? If not, comment on its skewness.

Applications

52. A sample of the salaries of assistant professors on the business faculty at a local university revealed a mean income of $72,000 with a standard deviation of $3,000.
    a. Using Chebyshev's theorem, approximately what percentage of the faculty earns at least $66,000 but no more than $78,000?
    b. Using Chebyshev's theorem, approximately what percentage of the faculty earns at least $63,000 but no more than $81,000?

53. The historical returns on a portfolio had an average return of 8% and a standard deviation of 12%. Assume that returns on this portfolio follow a bell-shaped distribution.
    a. Approximately what percentage of returns were greater than 20%?
    b. Approximately what percentage of returns were below −16%?

54. It is often assumed that IQ scores follow a bell-shaped distribution with a mean of 100 and a standard deviation of 16.
    a. Approximately what percentage of scores are between 84 and 116?
    b. Approximately what percentage of scores are less than 68?
    c. Approximately what percentage of scores are more than 116?

55. An investment strategy has an expected return of 8% and a standard deviation of 6%. Assume investment returns are bell-shaped.
    a. How likely is it to earn a return between 2% and 14%?
    b. How likely is it to earn a return greater than 14%?
    c. How likely is it to earn a return below −4%?

56. On average, an American professional football game lasts about three hours, even though the ball is actually in play only 11 minutes. Let the standard deviation be 0.4 hour.
    a. Use Chebyshev's theorem to approximate the proportion of games that last between 2.2 hours and 3.8 hours.
    b. Assume a bell-shaped distribution to approximate the proportion of games that last between 2.2 hours and 3.8 hours.

57. **FILE** *Prime.* The accompanying data file shows the annual expenditures (Expenditures in $) for 100 Amazon Prime customers.
   a. Construct a boxplot for the Expenditures variable. Does the boxplot suggest that outliers exist?
   b. Use z-scores to determine if there are any outliers for the Expenditures variable. Are your results consistent with part a? Explain why or why not.

58. **FILE** *Debt.* The accompanying data file shows the average monthly debt payments (Debt in $) for residents of 26 metropolitan areas.
   a. Construct a boxplot for the Debt variable. Does the boxplot suggest that outliers exist?
   b. Use z-scores to determine if there are any outliers for the Debt variable. Are your results consistent with part a? Explain why or why not.

3.5 MEASURES OF ASSOCIATION

LO 3.6

Calculate and interpret measures of association.

In Chapter 2, we introduced a scatterplot to visually assess whether two variables are related in some systematic way. In this section, we present two numerical measures of association that quantify the direction and strength of the linear relationship between two variables, x and y. It is important to point out that these measures may not be appropriate when the underlying relationship between the variables is nonlinear.

A numerical measure that reveals the direction of the linear relationship between two variables is called the **covariance.** We use s_{xy} to refer to the sample covariance, and σ_{xy} to refer to the population covariance.

THE COVARIANCE

The covariance shows the direction of the linear relationship between two variables. For observations $(x_1, y_1), (x_2, y_2), \ldots, (x_n, y_n)$, the sample covariance is computed as

$$s_{xy} = \frac{\Sigma(x_i - \bar{x})(y_i - \bar{y})}{n - 1}.$$

For observations $(x_1, y_1), (x_2, y_2), \ldots, (x_N, y_N)$, the population covariance is computed as

$$\sigma_{xy} = \frac{\Sigma(x_i - \mu_x)(y_i - \mu_y)}{N}.$$

Note: As in the case of the sample variance, the sample covariance uses $n - 1$ rather than n in the denominator.

The covariance can assume a negative value, a positive value, or a value of zero.

- A negative value for covariance indicates a negative linear relationship between the two variables; on average, if x is above its mean, then y tends to be below its mean, and vice versa.

- A positive value for covariance indicates a positive linear relationship between the two variables; on average, if x is above its mean, then y tends to be above its mean, and vice versa.

- The covariance is zero if x and y have no linear relationship.

The covariance is difficult to interpret because it is sensitive to the units of measurement. That is, the covariance between two variables might be 100 and the covariance between two other variables might be 100,000, yet all we can conclude is that both sets of variables are positively related. We cannot comment on the strength of the relationships. An easier measure to interpret is the **correlation coefficient;** it describes both the direction and the strength of the linear relationship between x and y. We use r_{xy} to refer to the sample correlation coefficient and ρ_{xy} (the Greek letter rho) to refer to the population correlation coefficient.

THE CORRELATION COEFFICIENT

The correlation coefficient shows the direction and the strength of the linear relationship between two variables.

- The sample correlation coefficient is computed as $r_{xy} = \frac{s_{xy}}{s_x s_y}$.
- The population correlation coefficient is computed as $\rho_{xy} = \frac{\sigma_{xy}}{\sigma_x \sigma_y}$.

The correlation coefficient is unit-free because the units in the numerator cancel with those in the denominator. The value of the correlation coefficient falls between -1 and 1. If the correlation coefficient equals 1, then a perfect positive linear relationship exists between x and y; if it equals -1, then a perfect negative linear relationship exists between x and y. There is no linear relationship between the two variables if the correlation coefficient equals 0. Other values for the correlation coefficient must be interpreted with reference to -1, 0, or 1. For instance, a correlation coefficient equal to -0.80 indicates a strong negative linear relationship, whereas a correlation coefficient equal to 0.12 indicates a weak positive linear relationship.

EXAMPLE 3.18

Growth_Value

Find the covariance and the correlation coefficient for Growth and Value. Summarize the results.

SOLUTION: As a first step, it is useful to construct a scatterplot for the two variables. Figure 3.5 shows a scatterplot of Value (y) against Growth (x), and it appears that there is a positive linear relationship between the two variables.

FIGURE 3.5 Scatterplot of Value against Growth

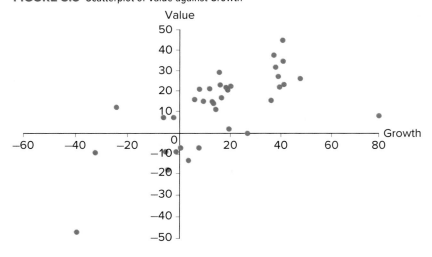

We first outline how to manually calculate the sample covariance and the sample correlation coefficient. Recall from Example 3.3 that the sample mean for Growth is $\bar{x} = 15.755$ and the sample mean for Value is $\bar{y} = 12.005$. We calculate the sample covariance as

$$s_{xy} = \frac{\Sigma(x_i - \bar{x})(y_i - \bar{y})}{n - 1}$$

$$= \frac{(-5.50 - 15.755)(-8.59 - 12.055) + \cdots + (38.42 - 15.755)(31.62 - 12.005)}{36 - 1}$$

$$= \frac{9,996.19}{35} = 285.605$$

Recall from Example 3.10 that the sample standard deviation for Growth is $s_x = 23.799$ and the sample standard deviation for Value is $s_y = 17.979$. We calculate the sample correlation coefficient as

$$r_{xy} = \frac{s_{xy}}{s_x s_y} = \frac{285.605}{23.799 \times 17.979} = 0.667$$

Using Excel

a. Open the *Growth_Value* data file.

b. We use the **COVARIANCE.S** and **CORREL** functions to find the sample covariance and the sample correlation coefficient, respectively. (We use the **COVARIANCE.P** and **CORREL** functions to find the population covariance and the population correlation coefficient, respectively.) For the sample covariance, we enter =COVARIANCE.S(B2:B37, C2:C37), and for the sample correlation coefficient, we enter =CORREL(B2:B37, C2:C37). Verify that you obtain the same values that were obtained manually.

Summary
The covariance of 285.605 indicates that the variables have a positive linear relationship. The correlation coefficient of 0.667 indicates a moderate to strong, positive linear relationship between the two variables. In order to diversify the risk in an investor's portfolio, an investor is often advised to invest in assets (such as stocks, bonds, and mutual funds) whose returns are not strongly correlated. If asset returns do not have a strong positive correlation, then if one investment does poorly, the other may still do well.

EXERCISES 3.5

Mechanics

59. Consider the following sample data:

x	12	18	20	22	25
y	15	20	25	22	27

   a. Calculate the covariance.
   b. Calculate and interpret the correlation coefficient.

60. Consider the following sample data:

x	−2	0	3	4	7
y	−2	−3	−8	−9	−10

   a. Calculate the covariance.
   b. Calculate and interpret the correlation coefficient.

Applications

61. **FILE** *MutualFunds2.* The accompanying data file shows the annual returns (in percent) for Mutual Fund 1 and Mutual Fund 2 over the past 17 years.

   a. Calculate and interpret the sample covariance between the returns.

   b. Calculate and interpret the correlation coefficient.

62. **FILE** *PriceDays.* The accompanying data file shows the price of a house (Price in $1,000s) and the number of days it takes to sell the house (Days) for a sample of eight recent transactions.

   a. Calculate the sample covariance. What kind of linear relationship exists?

   b. Calculate and interpret the correlation coefficient.

63. **FILE** *GPA.* The director of graduate admissions at a local university is analyzing the relationship between scores on the math portion of the Graduate Record Examination (GRE) and subsequent performance in graduate school, as measured by a student's grade point average (GPA). The accompanying data file contains the results for 24 students who graduated within the past five years.
   a. Calculate and interpret the sample covariance.
   b. Calculate and interpret the correlation coefficient. Does an applicant's GRE score seem to be a good indicator of subsequent performance in graduate school?

64. **FILE** *Education.* A social scientist would like to analyze the relationship between educational attainment (in years of higher education) and salary (in $1,000s). The accompanying data file contains the results for 20 individuals.
   a. Calculate and interpret the sample covariance.
   b. Calculate and interpret the correlation coefficient.

65. **FILE** *Happiness_Age.* Many attempts have been made to relate happiness with various factors. One such study relates happiness with age and finds that holding everything else constant, people are least happy when they are in their mid-40s. Data are collected on a respondent's age and their perception of well-being on a scale from 0 to 100. The accompanying data file contains the results for 24 respondents.

   a. Calculate and interpret the correlation coefficient between age and happiness.
   b. Construct a scatterplot to point out a flaw with the correlation analysis conducted in part a.

66. **FILE** *Census.* The accompanying data file shows demographic information for the 50 states.
   a. Calculate and interpret the correlation coefficient for household income and house value.
   b. Calculate and interpret the correlation coefficient for household income and the percentage of the residents who are foreign born.
   c. Calculate and interpret the correlation coefficient for household income and the percentage of the residents who are without a high school diploma.

67. **FILE** *Car_Prices.* The accompanying data file shows the price, the age, and the mileage for 20 used sedans.
   a. Calculate the mean price, the mean age, and the mean mileage.
   b. Calculate the standard deviation for price, the standard deviation for age, and the standard deviation for mileage.
   c. Calculate and interpret the correlation coefficient between price and age.
   d. Calculate and interpret the correlation coefficient between price and mileage.

3.6 WRITING WITH DATA

When confronted with raw data, a necessary first step for any analysis is to convert them into a more meaningful form. Summary measures prove very useful. Consider the following case.

Case Study

FILE
House_Price

An investor currently owns real estate in the college town of Blacksburg, Virginia—home to the Virginia Tech Hokies. He would like to expand his holdings by purchasing similar rental property in either Athens, Georgia, or Chapel Hill, North Carolina. As a preliminary step, he would like information on house prices in these two areas. He is interested in properties that have at least two bedrooms and that are listed for less than $1,000,000. The following report will summarize previous sales that have satisfied these criteria.

Sample
Report—
Investing in
College Town
Real Estate

There are a number of reasons why you might consider investing in a rental property near a university. First, there's a large pool of renters, including students, faculty, and staff. Second, because many universities are unable to house their students beyond freshman year, students offer a steady stream of rental demand. Finally, university towns tend to be filled with restaurants, shopping, and nightlife. All of these factors can make it easier for you to market your property.

The following report examines house prices in Athens, Georgia—home to the University of Georgia Bulldogs—and Chapel Hill, North Carolina—home to the University of North Carolina Tar Heels. The sample consists of 293 house sales in Athens and 351 house sales in Chapel Hill. In addition, all houses in the sample had at least two bedrooms and sold for less than $1,000,000. Table 3.9 provides the most relevant summary measures for the analysis.

kali9/Getty Images

TABLE 3.9 Summary Measures for House Prices (in $) in Athens and Chapel Hill

Summary Measure	Athens, GA	Chapel Hill, NC
Mean	219,671	429,152
Median	177,500	395,000
Minimum	41,125	105,000
Maximum	910,000	950,000
Standard deviation	147,648	186,762
Coefficient of variation	0.67	0.44
Number of houses	293	351

The average house price in Athens is $219,671, as opposed to $429,152 in Chapel Hill, a difference of almost $210,000. In Athens, the median house price is $177,500, suggesting that half of the house prices are below this value and half are above this value. The corresponding value in Chapel Hill is $395,000. The difference in medians between these two cities is close to $218,000. In both cities, the median is quite a bit less than the mean, which implies that outliers, some extremely high house prices, are likely present.

While the mean and the median represent where house prices tend to cluster, they do not relay information about the variability in house prices. Generally, standard deviation is used as a measure of variability. The standard deviation for house prices in Chapel Hill is greater than the standard deviation for house prices in Athens ($186,762 > $147,648), suggesting that, compared to Athens, house prices in Chapel Hill are more dispersed from the mean.

Finally, Figure 3.6 shows the boxplots of house prices for each city. The boxplots reveal two more major points with respect to house prices in these two cities:

- In each boxplot, the median is off-center within the box, being located below the center.

- In each boxplot, there are outliers at the top of the distribution, suggesting that a few very expensive houses have pushed up the means above the medians. However, there are far fewer outliers in the Chapel Hill distribution as compared to the Athens distribution.

FIGURE 3.6 Boxplots of house prices in Athens, Georgia, and Chapel Hill, North Carolina

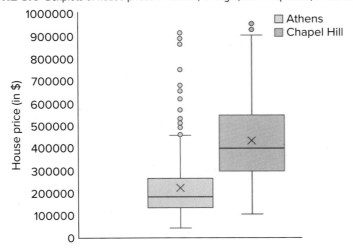

These two observations suggest that both distributions are positively skewed. This implies that the bulk of the house prices falls in the lower end of the distribution, and there are relatively few high-priced houses.

This report summarizes house prices in Athens, Georgia, and Chapel Hill, North Carolina. On average, houses in Chapel Hill are almost twice as expensive as those in Athens. Moreover, if outliers are removed from the analysis, house prices in Athens are less variable than house prices in Chapel Hill. However, before any investor purchases property in either city, many other factors should be considered, such as the size of the houses and their distance from campus.

Suggested Case Studies

Summary measures prove very useful when analyzing the big data that accompanies this text. Here are some suggestions for analysis.

Report 3.1 `FILE` *House_Price.* Perform a similar analysis to the one conducted in this section, but choose two other college towns.

Report 3.2 `FILE` *College_Admissions.* Use summary measures to examine the high school GPA and the SAT scores of those students who were admitted to the School of Business & Economics versus those students who were admitted to the School of Arts & Letters.

Report 3.3 `FILE` *TechSales_Reps.* Use summary measures to examine the salaries and the net promoter score (NPS) of sales representatives depending on their personality types and gender in the software group.

4 Introduction to Probability

Every day we make choices about issues in the presence of uncertainty. By figuring out the chances of various events, we are better prepared to make more desirable choices. For example, given the weather forecast, we determine whether we should wear a jacket or carry an umbrella. Similarly, retailers tweak their sales force in anticipation of an increase or decrease in shoppers, and the Federal Reserve adjusts interest rates based on its anticipation of growth and inflation. Probability is simply the likelihood that something will happen under uncertainty.

This chapter presents the essential probability tools needed to frame and address many real-world issues involving uncertainty. Probability theory turns out to be the very foundation for statistical inference, and numerous concepts introduced in this chapter are essential for understanding advanced topics in later chapters.

Halfpoint/Shutterstock

INTRODUCTORY CASE

24/7 Fitness Center Annual Membership

24/7 Fitness Center is a high-end, full-service gym and recruits its members through advertisements and monthly open house events. Each open house attendee is given a tour and a one-day pass. Potential members register for the open house event by answering a few questions about themselves and their exercise routine. The fitness center staff places a follow-up phone call with the potential member and sends information to open house attendees by mail in the hopes of signing the potential member up for an annual membership.

Janet Mwangi, a manager at 24/7 Fitness Center, wants to develop a data-driven strategy for selecting which open house attendees to contact. From 400 past open house attendees, she knows the outcome (Enroll or Not Enroll) of a follow-up phone call regarding a club membership. In addition, she has information on the age of each attendee, where age is binned into groups Under 30, Between 30 and 50, and Over 50. Table 4.1 shows a portion of the data.

TABLE 4.1 24/7 Fitness Center Enrollment and Age Data ($n = 400$)

Attendee	Age Group	Outcome
1	Between 30 and 50	Not Enroll
2	Over 50	Enroll
⋮	⋮	⋮
400	Between 30 and 50	Enroll

FILE
Gym

Janet wants to use the sample information to

a. Construct a contingency table and use it to calculate and interpret relevant empirical probabilities concerning age and enrollment.

b. Use the empirical probabilities to develop a data-driven strategy for selecting open house attendees.

A synopsis of this case is provided at the end of Section 4.3.

Describe fundamental
probability concepts.

We are better prepared to deal with uncertainty if we know the probabilities that describe which events are likely and which are unlikely. A **probability** is defined as follows.

> ### PROBABILITY
>
> A probability is a numerical value that measures the likelihood that an event occurs. This value is between zero and one, where a value of zero indicates an *impossible* event and a value of one indicates a *definite* event.

In order to define an event and assign the appropriate probability to it, it is useful to first establish some terminology and impose some structure on the situation.

An **experiment** is a process that leads to one of several possible outcomes. The diversity of the outcomes of an experiment is due to the uncertainty of the real world. When you purchase a new computer, there is no guarantee as to how long it will last before any repair work is needed. It may need repair in the first year, in the second year, or after two years. You can think of this as an experiment because the actual outcome will be determined only over time. Outcomes of other examples of an experiment include whether a customer will default on a loan or not; whether an email is legitimate or spam; and whether a ball game will end in a win, loss, or tie.

A **sample space,** denoted by S, of an experiment contains all possible outcomes of the experiment. For example, suppose the sample space representing the letter grade in a course is given by $S = \{A, B, C, D, F\}$. The sample space for an experiment does not need to be unique. For example, in the above experiment, we can also define the sample space with just P (pass) and F (fail) outcomes; that is, $S = \{P, F\}$. Note that if the teacher also gives out an I (incomplete) grade, then neither of these sample spaces is valid because they do not contain all possible outcomes of the experiment.

> ### EXAMPLE 4.1
>
> A snowboarder competing in the Winter Olympic Games is trying to assess her probability of earning a medal in her event, the ladies' halfpipe. Construct the appropriate sample space.
>
> **SOLUTION:** The athlete's assessment of earning a medal is based on an experiment because, until the Winter Games occur, the outcome is unknown. We formalize an experiment by constructing its sample space. The athlete's competition has four possible outcomes: gold medal, silver medal, bronze medal, and no medal. We formally write the sample space as $S = \{$gold, silver, bronze, no medal$\}$.

Events

An **event** is a subset of the sample space. A **simple event** consists of just one of the possible outcomes of an experiment. Getting an A in a course is an example of a simple event. An event may also contain several outcomes of an experiment. For example, we can define an event as getting a passing grade in a course; this event is formed by the subset of outcomes A, B, C, and D.

Let us define two events from Example 4.1, where one event represents "earning a medal" and the other denotes "failing to earn a medal." These events are **exhaustive** because they include all outcomes in the sample space. In the grade-distribution example, if we define two simple events as "an A grade" and "a B grade," then these events are not exhaustive because they do not include all feasible grades in the sample space. However, the events P and F, defined as "pass" and "fail," respectively, are exhaustive.

Another important probability concept concerns **mutually exclusive** events. For two mutually exclusive events, the occurrence of one event precludes the occurrence of the other. Referring back to Example 4.1, suppose that we define two events as "at least earning a silver medal" (outcomes of gold and silver) and "at most earning a silver medal" (outcomes of silver, bronze, no medal). These two events are exhaustive because no outcome of the experiment is omitted. However, the events are not mutually exclusive because the outcome "silver" appears in both events. In the grade-distribution example, while the simple events of getting grades A and B are not exhaustive, they are mutually exclusive because you cannot possibly get an A as well as a B in the same course. However, getting grades P and F are mutually exclusive and exhaustive. Similarly, the events defined as "at least earning a silver medal" and "at most earning a bronze medal" are mutually exclusive and exhaustive.

EXPERIMENTS AND EVENTS

- An experiment is a process that leads to one of several possible outcomes. A sample space, denoted *S,* of an experiment contains all possible outcomes of the experiment.

- An event is any subset of outcomes of the experiment. It is called a simple event if it contains a single outcome.

- Events are exhaustive if they include all possible outcomes of an experiment.

- Events are mutually exclusive if they do not share any common outcome of an experiment.

For any experiment, we can define events based on one or more outcomes of the experiment and also combine events to form new events. The **union** of two events, denoted $A \cup B$, is the event consisting of all outcomes in A or B. A useful way to illustrate these concepts is through the use of a Venn diagram, named after the British mathematician John Venn (1834–1923). Figure 4.1 shows a Venn diagram where the rectangle represents the sample space S and the two circles represent events A and B. The union $A \cup B$ is the portion in the Venn diagram that is included in either A or B.

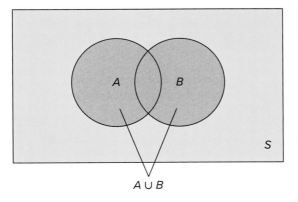

FIGURE 4.1
The union of two events, $A \cup B$

The **intersection** of two events, denoted $A \cap B$, is the event consisting of all outcomes in A and B. Figure 4.2 depicts the intersection of two events A and B. The intersection $A \cap B$ is the portion in the Venn diagram that is included in both A and B.

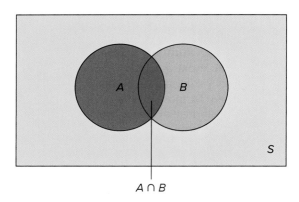

FIGURE 4.2
The intersection of two events, $A \cap B$

$A \cap B$

The **complement** of event A, denoted A^c, is the event consisting of all outcomes in the sample space S that are not in A. In Figure 4.3, A^c is shown as everything in S that is not included in A.

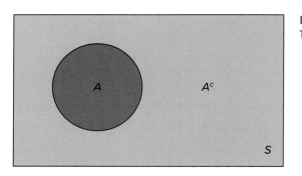

FIGURE 4.3
The complement of an event, A^c

COMBINING EVENTS

- The union of two events, denoted $A \cup B$, is the event consisting of all outcomes in A or B.
- The intersection of two events, denoted $A \cap B$, is the event consisting of all outcomes in A and B.
- The complement of event A, denoted A^c, is the event consisting of all outcomes in the sample space S that are not in A.

EXAMPLE 4.2

Recall that the snowboarder's sample space from Example 4.1 is defined as $S = \{gold, silver, bronze, no medal\}$. Now suppose the snowboarder defines the following three events:

- $A = \{gold, silver, bronze\}$; that is, event A denotes earning a medal;
- $B = \{silver, bronze, no medal\}$; that is, event B denotes earning at most a silver medal; and
- $C = \{no medal\}$; that is, event C denotes failing to earn a medal.

a. Find $A \cup B$ and $B \cup C$.
b. Find $A \cap B$ and $A \cap C$.
c. Find B^c.

SOLUTION:

a. The union of A and B denotes all outcomes common to A or B; here, the event $A \cup B = \{\text{gold, silver, bronze, no medal}\}$. Note that there is no double counting of the outcomes "silver" or "bronze" in $A \cup B$. Similarly, we have the event $B \cup C = \{\text{silver, bronze, no medal}\}$.

b. The intersection of A and B denotes all outcomes common to A and B; here, the event $A \cap B = \{\text{silver, bronze}\}$. The event $A \cap C = \emptyset$, where $\emptyset$ denotes the null (empty) set; no common outcomes appear in both A and C.

c. The complement of B denotes all outcomes in S that are not in B; here, the event $B^c = \{\text{gold}\}$.

Assigning Probabilities

Now that we have described a valid sample space and the various ways in which we can define events from that sample space, we are ready to assign probabilities. When we arrive at a probability, we are generally able to categorize the probability as a subjective probability, an empirical probability, or a classical probability. Regardless of the method used, there are two defining properties of probability.

THE TWO DEFINING PROPERTIES OF PROBABILITY

1. The probability of any event A is a value between 0 and 1; that is, $0 \leq P(A) \leq 1$.

2. The sum of the probabilities of any list of mutually exclusive and exhaustive events equals 1.

Suppose the snowboarder from Example 4.1 believes that there is a 10% chance that she will earn a gold medal, a 15% chance that she will earn a silver medal, a 20% chance that she will earn a bronze medal, and a 55% chance that she will fail to earn a medal. She has assigned a **subjective probability** to each of the simple events. She made a personal assessment of these probabilities without referencing any data. Subjective probabilities differ from person to person and may contain a high degree of personal bias.

The snowboarder believes that the most likely outcome is failing to earn a medal because she gives that outcome the greatest chance of occurring at 55%. When formally writing out the probability that an event occurs, we generally construct a probability statement. Here, the probability statement might take the form: $P(\{\text{no medal}\}) = 0.55$, where $P(\text{"event"})$ represents the probability that a given event occurs. Table 4.2 summarizes these events and their respective subjective probabilities. Note that the events are mutually exclusive and exhaustive.

TABLE 4.2 Snowboarder's Subjective Probabilities

Event	Probability
Gold	0.10
Silver	0.15
Bronze	0.20
No medal	0.55

Reading from the table we can readily see, for instance, that she assesses that there is a 15% chance that she will earn a silver medal, or $P(\{\text{silver}\}) = 0.15$. We should note that all the probabilities are between the values of zero and one, and they add up to one, thus meeting the defining properties of probability.

Suppose the snowboarder wants to calculate the probability of earning a medal. In Example 4.2, we defined "earning a medal" as event A, so the probability statement takes the form $P(A)$. We calculate this probability by summing the probabilities of the outcomes in A, or equivalently,

$$P(A) = P(\{\text{gold}\}) + P(\{\text{silver}\}) + P(\{\text{bronze}\}) = 0.10 + 0.15 + 0.20 = 0.45.$$

EXAMPLE 4.3

Given the events in Example 4.2 and the probabilities in Table 4.2, calculate the following probabilities.

a. $P(B \cup C)$

b. $P(A \cap C)$

c. $P(B^c)$

SOLUTION:

a. The probability that event B or event C occurs is

$$P(B \cup C) = P(\{\text{silver}\}) + P(\{\text{bronze}\}) + P(\{\text{no medal}\})$$
$$= 0.15 + 0.20 + 0.55 = 0.90.$$

b. The probability that event A and event C occur is

$$P(A \cap C) = 0; \text{recall that there are no common outcomes in } A \text{ and } C.$$

c. The probability that the complement of B occurs is

$$P(B^c) = P(\{\text{gold}\}) = 0.10.$$

In many instances, we calculate probabilities by referencing data based on the observed outcomes of an experiment. An **empirical probability** of an event is the observed relative frequency with which an event occurs. The experiment must be repeated a large number of times for empirical probabilities to be accurate. For example, it may be misleading to report a default rate of 0.40 if payments are delinquent in two out of five new loans. The probability would be reliable if the default is based on a much larger number of new loans.

EXAMPLE 4.4

The frequency distribution in Table 4.3 summarizes the ages of the richest 400 Americans. Suppose we randomly select one of these individuals.

a. What is the probability that the individual is at least 50 but less than 60 years old?

b. What is the probability that the individual is younger than 60 years old?

c. What is the probability that the individual is at least 80 years old?

TABLE 4.3 Frequency Distribution of Ages of 400 Richest Americans

Ages	Frequency
$x < 40$	13
$40 \leq x < 50$	24
$50 \leq x < 60$	67
$60 \leq x < 70$	113
$70 \leq x < 80$	117
$80 \leq x < 90$	55
$x \geq 90$	11

SOLUTION: In Table 4.4, we first label each outcome with letter notation; for instance, the outcome "x < 40" is denoted as event A. Next we calculate the relative frequency of each event and use the relative frequency to denote the probability of the event.

TABLE 4.4 Relative Frequency Distribution of Ages of 400 Richest Americans

Ages	Event	Frequency	Relative Frequency
x < 40	A	13	13/400 = 0.0325
40 ≤ x < 50	B	24	0.0600
50 ≤ x < 60	C	67	0.1675
60 ≤ x < 70	D	113	0.2825
70 ≤ x < 80	E	117	0.2925
80 ≤ x < 90	F	55	0.1375
x ≥ 90	G	11	0.0275

a. The probability that an individual is at least 50 but less than 60 years old is

$$P(C) = \frac{67}{400} = 0.1675.$$

b. The probability that an individual is younger than 60 years old is

$$P(A \cup B \cup C) = \frac{13 + 24 + 67}{400} = 0.260.$$

c. The probability that an individual is at least 80 years old is

$$P(F \cup G) = \frac{55 + 11}{400} = 0.165.$$

In a more narrow range of well-defined experiments, we can sometimes deduce probabilities by reasoning about the experiment. The resulting probability is a **classical probability.** Classical probabilities are often used in games of chance. They are based on the assumption that all outcomes of an experiment are equally likely. Therefore, the classical probability of an event is computed as the number of outcomes belonging to the event divided by the total number of outcomes.

EXAMPLE 4.5

Suppose our experiment consists of rolling a six-sided die. Then we can define the appropriate sample space as $S = \{1, 2, 3, 4, 5, 6\}$.

a. What is the probability that we roll a 2?

b. What is the probability that we roll a 2 or 5?

c. What is the probability that we roll an even number?

SOLUTION: Here we recognize that each outcome is equally likely. So with 6 possible outcomes, each outcome has a 1/6 chance of occurring.

a. The probability that we roll a 2, $P(\{2\})$, is thus 1/6 or 0.1667.

b. The probability that we roll a 2 or 5, $P(\{2\}) + P(\{5\})$, is 1/6 + 1/6 = 1/3 or 0.3333.

c. The probability that we roll an even number, $P(\{2\}) + P(\{4\}) + P(\{6\})$, is 1/6 + 1/6 + 1/6 = 1/2 or 0.50.

> ## CATEGORIZING PROBABILITIES
>
> - A subjective probability is calculated by drawing on personal and subjective judgment.
> - An empirical probability is calculated as a relative frequency of occurrence.
> - A classical probability is based on logical analysis rather than on personal judgment or observation.
>
> Because empirical and classical probabilities generally do not vary from person to person, they are often grouped as objective probabilities.

According to the famous **law of large numbers,** the empirical probability approaches the classical probability if the experiment is run a very large number of times. Consider, for example, flipping a fair coin 10 times. It is possible that heads may not show up exactly 5 times and, therefore, the relative frequency may not be 0.50. However, if we flip the fair coin a very large number of times, heads will show up approximately half of the time. This would make the empirical probability equal to the classical probability of 0.50.

EXERCISES 4.1

Mechanics

1. Determine whether the following probabilities are best categorized as subjective, empirical, or classical probabilities.
   a. Before flipping a fair coin, Sunil assesses that he has a 50% chance of obtaining tails.
   b. At the beginning of the semester, John believes he has a 90% chance of receiving straight A's.
   c. A political reporter announces that there is a 40% chance that the next person to come out of the conference room will be a Republican because there are 60 Republicans and 90 Democrats in the room.

2. A sample space S yields five equally likely events, $A, B, C, D,$ and E.
   a. Find $P(D)$.
   b. Find $P(B^c)$.
   c. Find $P(A \cup C \cup E)$.

3. You roll a die with the sample space $S = \{1, 2, 3, 4, 5, 6\}$. You define A as $\{1, 2, 3\}$, B as $\{1, 2, 3, 5, 6\}$, C as $\{4, 6\}$, and D as $\{4, 5, 6\}$. Determine which of the following events are exhaustive and/or mutually exclusive.
   a. A and B
   b. A and C
   c. A and D
   d. B and C

4. A sample space, S, yields four simple events, $A, B, C,$ and D, such that $P(A) = 0.35$, $P(B) = 0.10$, and $P(C) = 0.25$.
   a. Find $P(D)$.
   b. Find $P(C^c)$.
   c. Find $P(A \cup B)$.

Applications

5. Satish Bajaj has taken Amtrak to travel from New York to Washington, DC, on six occasions, of which three times the train was late. Therefore, Satish tells her friends that the probability that this train will arrive on time is 0.50. Would you label this probability as empirical or classical? Why would this probability not be accurate?

6. Consider the following scenarios to determine if the mentioned combination of attributes represents a union or an intersection.
   a. There are two courses that seem interesting to you, and you would be happy if you can take at least one of them.
   b. There are two courses that seem interesting to you, and you would be happy if you can take both of them.

7. Consider the following scenarios to determine if the mentioned combination of attributes represents a union or an intersection.
   a. A marketing firm is looking for a candidate with a business degree and at least five years of work experience.
   b. A family has decided to purchase a Toyota minivan or a Honda minivan.

8. You apply for a position at two firms. Let event A represent the outcome of getting an offer from the first firm and event B represent the outcome of getting an offer from the second firm.
   a. Explain why events A and B are not exhaustive.
   b. Explain why events A and B are not mutually exclusive.

9. According to a study based on the body mass index (BMI), a significant number of U.S. adults are either overweight or obese. An adult is considered overweight if the BMI is 25 or more but less than 30. An obese adult will have a BMI of 30 or greater. It is reported that 33.1% of the adult population in

the United States is overweight and 35.7% is obese. Use this information to answer the following questions.

a. What is the probability that a randomly selected adult is either overweight or obese?

b. What is the probability that a randomly selected adult is neither overweight nor obese?

c. Are the events "overweight" and "obese" exhaustive?

d. Are the events "overweight" and "obese" mutually exclusive?

10. At four community health centers on Cape Cod, Massachusetts, 15,164 patients were asked to respond to questions designed to detect depression. The survey produced the following results.

Diagnosis	Number
Mild	3,257
Moderate	1,546
Moderately Severe	975
Severe	773
No Depression	8,613

a. What is the probability that a randomly selected patient has experienced mild depression?

b. What is the probability that a randomly selected patient has not experienced depression?

c. What is the probability that a randomly selected patient has experienced moderately severe to severe depression?

d. Given that the national figure for moderately severe to severe depression is approximately 6.7%, does it appear that there is a higher rate of depression in this summer resort community? Explain.

11. The following frequency distribution shows the ages of India's 40 richest individuals. One of these individuals is selected at random.

Ages	Frequency
$30 \leq x < 40$	3
$40 \leq x < 50$	8
$50 \leq x < 60$	15
$60 \leq x < 70$	9
$70 \leq x < 80$	5

a. What is the probability that the individual is at least 50 years of age but less than 60 years of age?

b. What is the probability that the individual is younger than 50 years of age?

c. What is the probability that the individual is at least 60 years of age?

12. The Easy Credit Company reports the following table representing a breakdown of customers according to the amount they owe and whether a cash advance has been made. An auditor randomly selects one of the accounts.

Amounts owed by customers	Cash Advance?	
	Yes	No
$0–199.99	245	2,890
$200–399.99	380	1,700
$400–599.99	500	1,425
$600–799.99	415	940
$800–999.99	260	480
$1,000 or more	290	475
Total Customers	2,090	7,910

a. What is the probability that a customer received a cash advance?

b. What is the probability that a customer owed less than $200 and received a cash advance?

c. What is the probability that a customer owed less than $200 or received a cash advance?

d. Are the events "receiving a cash advance" and "owing $1,000 or more" mutually exclusive? Explain using probabilities.

4.2 RULES OF PROBABILITY

LO 4.2

In the previous section, we discussed how the probability of an event is assigned. Here we present various rules that are used to combine the probabilities of events.

Apply the rules of probability.

The **complement rule** follows from one of the defining properties of probability: The sum of probabilities assigned to simple events in a sample space must equal one. Therefore, for an event A and its complement A^c, we get $P(A) + P(A^c) = 1$. Rearranging this equation, we obtain the complement rule.

> ### THE COMPLEMENT RULE
> The probability of the complement of event A is derived as
> $$P(A^c) = 1 - P(A).$$

The complement rule is quite straightforward, but it is widely used and powerful.

EXAMPLE 4.6

A manager at Moksha Yoga Center believes that 37% of 30 to 50 year old and 30% of over 50 year old open house attendees will purchase a membership.

a. What is the probability that a randomly selected 30 to 50 year old open house attendee will not purchase a membership?

b. What is the probability that a randomly selected over 50 year old open house attendee will not purchase a membership?

SOLUTION:

a. Let's define A as the event that a randomly selected 30 to 50 year old open house attendee will purchase a membership; thus, $P(A) = 0.37$. In this example, we are interested in the complement of A. So $P(A^c) = 1 - P(A) = 1 - 0.37 = 0.63$.

b. Similarly, we define B as the event that a randomly selected over 50 year old open house attendee will purchase a membership, so $P(B) = 0.30$. Thus, $P(B^c) = 1 - P(B) = 1 - 0.30 = 0.70$.

The **addition rule** allows us to find the probability of the union of two events. Suppose we want to find the probability that either event A occurs or event B occurs, so in probability terms, $P(A \cup B)$. Recall from Figures 4.1 and 4.2 that the union, $A \cup B$, is the portion in the Venn diagram that is included in A or B, whereas the intersection, $A \cap B$, is the portion in the Venn diagram that is included in both A and B.

If we try to obtain $P(A \cup B)$ by simply summing $P(A)$ with $P(B)$, then we overstate the probability because we double-count the probability of the intersection of A and B, $P(A \cap B)$. It is common to refer to $P(A \cap B)$ as the **joint probability** of events A and B. When implementing the addition rule, we sum $P(A)$ and $P(B)$ and then subtract $P(A \cap B)$ from this sum.

> ### THE ADDITION RULE
> The probability that event A or event B occurs is derived as
> $$P(A \cup B) = P(A) + P(B) - P(A \cap B).$$

EXAMPLE 4.7

Anthony feels that he has a 75% chance of getting an A in Statistics and a 55% chance of getting an A in Managerial Economics. He also believes he has a 40% chance of getting an A in both classes.

a. What is the probability that he gets an A in at least one of these courses?

b. What is the probability that he does not get an A in either of these courses?

SOLUTION:

a. Let $P(A_S)$ correspond to the probability of getting an A in Statistics and $P(A_M)$ correspond to the probability of getting an A in Managerial Economics. Thus, $P(A_S) = 0.75$ and $P(A_M) = 0.55$. In addition, the joint probability that Anthony gets an A in both classes, $P(A_S \cap A_M) = 0.40$. In order to find the probability that he receives an A in at least one of these courses, we use the addition rule and calculate:

$$P(A_S \cup A_M) = P(A_S) + P(A_M) - P(A_S \cap A_M) = 0.75 + 0.55 - 0.40 = 0.90.$$

b. The probability that he does not receive an A in either of these two courses is actually the complement of the union of the two events; that is, $P((A_S \cup A_M)^c)$. We use the complement rule as well as the information from part a and calculate:

$$P((A_S \cup A_M)^c) = 1 - P(A_S \cup A_M) = 1 - 0.90 = 0.10$$

An alternative expression that correctly captures the required probability is $P(A_S^c \cap A_M^c)$, which is the probability that he does not get an A in Statistics and he does not get an A in Managerial Economics. A common mistake is to calculate the probability as $1 - P(A_S \cap A_M) = 1 - 0.40 = 0.60$, which simply indicates that there is a 60% chance that Anthony will not get an A in both courses. This is clearly not the required probability that Anthony does not get an A in either course.

Note that for mutually exclusive events A and B, the joint probability is zero; that is, $P(A \cap B) = 0$. We need not concern ourselves with double-counting, and, therefore, the probability of the union is simply the sum of the two probabilities.

In business applications, a probability of interest is often a **conditional probability.** Examples include the probability that a customer will make an online purchase conditional on receiving an email with a discount offer; the probability of making a six-figure salary conditional on getting an MBA; and the probability that sales will improve conditional on the firm launching a new marketing campaign.

Let's use an example to illustrate the concept of conditional probability. Suppose the probability that a recent business college graduate finds a suitable job is 0.80. The probability of finding a suitable job is 0.90 if the recent business college graduate has prior work experience. Here, the probability of an event is conditional on the occurrence of another event. If A represents "finding a job" and B represents "prior work experience," then $P(A) = 0.80$ and the conditional probability is denoted as $P(A|B) = 0.90$, where the vertical line stands for "given." In this example, the probability of finding a suitable job increases from 0.80 to 0.90 when conditioned on prior work experience. In general, the conditional probability, $P(A|B)$, is greater than the **unconditional probability,** $P(A)$, if B exerts a positive influence on A. Similarly, $P(A|B)$ is less than $P(A)$ if B exerts a negative influence on A. Finally, if B exerts no influence on A, then $P(A|B)$ equals $P(A)$. It is common to refer to an unconditional probability simply as a probability.

We rely on the Venn diagram in Figure 4.2 to explain the conditional probability. Because $P(A|B)$ represents the probability of A conditional on B (B has occurred), the original sample space S reduces to B. The conditional probability $P(A|B)$ is based on the portion of A that is included in B. It is derived as the ratio of the probability of the intersection of A and B to the probability of B.

CONDITIONAL PROBABILITY

The probability that event A occurs given that event B has occurred is derived as

$$P(A|B) = \frac{P(A \cap B)}{P(B)}.$$

EXAMPLE 4.8

Economic globalization is defined as the integration of national economies into the international economy through trade, foreign direct investment, capital flows, migration, and the spread of technology. Although economic globalization is often viewed favorably, it also increases the vulnerability of a country to economic conditions of other countries. An economist predicts a 60% chance that country A will perform poorly and a 25% chance that country B will perform poorly. There is also a 16% chance that both countries will perform poorly.

a. What is the probability that country A performs poorly given that country B performs poorly?

b. What is the probability that country B performs poorly given that country A performs poorly?

c. Interpret your findings.

SOLUTION: We first write down the available information in probability terms. Defining event A as "country A performing poorly" and event B as "country B performing poorly," we have the following information: $P(A) = 0.60$, $P(B) = 0.25$, and $P(A \cap B) = 0.16$.

a. $P(A|B) = \dfrac{P(A \cap B)}{P(B)} = \dfrac{0.16}{0.25} = 0.64$

b. $P(B|A) = \dfrac{P(A \cap B)}{P(A)} = \dfrac{0.16}{0.60} = 0.27$

c. It appears that globalization has definitely made these countries vulnerable to the economic conditions of the other country. The probability that country A performs poorly increases from 60% to 64% when country B has performed poorly. Similarly, the probability that country B performs poorly increases from 25% to 27% when conditioned on country A performing poorly.

In some situations, we are interested in finding the joint probability $P(A \cap B)$. Using the conditional probability formula $P(A|B) = \frac{P(A \cap B)}{P(B)}$, we can easily derive $P(A \cap B) = P(A|B)P(B)$. Because we calculate the product of two probabilities to find $P(A \cap B)$, we refer to it as the **multiplication rule** for probabilities.

THE MULTIPLICATION RULE

The joint probability of events A and B is derived as

$$P(A \cap B) = P(A|B)P(B).$$

EXAMPLE 4.9

A manager believes that 14% of consumers will respond positively to the firm's social media campaign. Also, 24% of those who respond positively will become loyal customers. Find the probability that the next recipient of the firm's social media campaign will react positively and will become a loyal customer.

SOLUTION: Let the event R represent a consumer who responds positively to a social media campaign and the event L represent a loyal customer. Therefore, $P(R) = 0.14$ and $P(L|R) = 0.24$. We calculate the probability that the next recipient of a social media campaign will react positively and become a loyal customer as $P(R \cap L) = P(L|R)P(R) = 0.24 \times 0.14 = 0.0336$.

Of particular interest to researchers is whether or not two events influence one another. Two events are **independent** if the occurrence of one event does not affect the probability of the occurrence of the other event. Similarly, events are considered **dependent** if the occurrence of one is related to the probability of the occurrence of the other. We generally determine the independence of two events by comparing the conditional probability of one event, for instance $P(A|B)$, to the probability, $P(A)$. If these two probabilities are the same, we say that the two events, A and B, are independent; if the probabilities differ, the two events are dependent.

> **INDEPENDENT VERSUS DEPENDENT EVENTS**
>
> Two events, A and B, are independent if $P(A|B) = P(A)$ or, equivalently, $P(A \cap B) = P(A|B)P(B) = P(A)P(B)$. Otherwise, the events are dependent.

EXAMPLE 4.10

Suppose that for a given year there is a 2% chance that your desktop computer will crash and a 6% chance that your laptop computer will crash. Moreover, there is a 0.12% chance that both computers will crash. Is the reliability of the two computers independent of each other?

SOLUTION: Let event D represent the outcome that your desktop crashes and event L represent the outcome that your laptop crashes. Therefore, $P(D) = 0.02$, $P(L) = 0.06$, and $P(D \cap L) = 0.0012$. The reliability of the two computers is independent because

$$P(D|L) = \frac{P(D \cap L)}{P(L)} = \frac{0.0012}{0.06} = 0.02 = P(D).$$

In other words, if your laptop crashes, it does not alter the probability that your desktop also crashes. Equivalently, we show that the events are independent because $P(D \cap L) = P(D)P(L) = 0.0012$.

EXERCISES 4.2

Mechanics

13. Let $P(A) = 0.65$, $P(B) = 0.30$, and $P(A|B) = 0.45$.
    a. Calculate $P(A \cap B)$.
    b. Calculate $P(A \cup B)$.
    c. Calculate $P(B|A)$.

14. Let $P(A) = 0.55$, $P(B) = 0.30$, and $P(A \cap B) = 0.10$.
    a. Calculate $P(A|B)$.
    b. Calculate $P(A \cup B)$.
    c. Calculate $P((A \cup B)^c)$.

15. Let A and B be mutually exclusive events with $P(A) = 0.25$ and $P(B) = 0.30$.
    a. Calculate $P(A \cap B)$.
    b. Calculate $P(A \cup B)$.
    c. Calculate $P(A|B)$.

16. Let A and B be independent events with $P(A) = 0.40$ and $P(B) = 0.50$.
    a. Calculate $P(A \cap B)$.
    b. Calculate $P((A \cup B)^c)$.
    c. Calculate $P(A|B)$.

17. Let $P(A) = 0.15$, $P(B) = 0.10$, and $P(A \cap B) = 0.05$.
    a. Are A and B independent events? Explain.
    b. Are A and B mutually exclusive events? Explain.
    c. What is the probability that neither A nor B takes place?

18. Consider the following probabilities: $P(A) = 0.40$, $P(B) = 0.50$, and $P(A^c \cap B^c) = 0.24$. Find:
    a. $P(A^c|B^c)$
    b. $P(A^c \cup B^c)$
    c. $P(A \cup B)$

19. Consider the following probabilities: $P(A^c) = 0.30$, $P(B) = 0.60$, and $P(A \cap B^c) = 0.24$. Find:
    a. $P(A|B^c)$
    b. $P(B^c|A)$
    c. Are A and B independent events? Explain.

Applications

20. Only 20% of students in a college ever go to their professor during office hours. Of those who go, 30% seek minor clarification and 70% seek major clarification.
    a. What is the probability that a student goes to the professor during their office hours for a minor clarification?
    b. What is the probability that a student goes to the professor during their office hours for a major clarification?

21. The probabilities that stock A will rise in price is 0.40 and that stock B will rise in price is 0.60. Further, if stock B rises in price, the probability that stock A will also rise in price is 0.50.
    a. What is the probability that at least one of the stocks will rise in price?
    b. Are events A and B mutually exclusive? Explain.
    c. Are events A and B independent? Explain.

22. Fraud detection has become an indispensable tool for banks and credit card companies to combat fraudulent credit card transactions. A fraud detection firm raises an alarm on 5% of all transactions and on 80% of fraudulent transactions. What is the probability that the transaction is fraudulent if the firm raises an alarm? Assume that 1% of all transactions are fraudulent.

23. Dr. Miriam Johnson has been teaching accounting for over 20 years. From her experience, she knows that 60% of her students do homework regularly. Moreover, 95% of the students who do their homework regularly pass the course. She also knows that 85% of her students pass the course.
    a. What is the probability that a student will do homework regularly and also pass the course?
    b. What is the probability that a student will neither do homework regularly nor will pass the course?
    c. Are the events "pass the course" and "do homework regularly" mutually exclusive? Explain.
    d. Are the events "pass the course" and "do homework regularly" independent? Explain.

24. An analysis of a recent labor union vote on a new contract shows the following results: In the Northeast, 4,000 of 10,000 members voted yes; in the Southeast, 5,000 of 20,000 members voted yes; in the Southwest, 8,000 of 15,000 members voted yes; and in the Northwest, 4,000 of 12,000 members voted yes. There were no abstentions.
    a. What is the probability that a member voted yes?
    b. What is the probability that a member from the Northeast or Southeast voted yes?
    c. What is the probability that a member who voted no was from the Northwest?
    d. What is the probability that a member was from the Southwest and voted no?

25. An analyst estimates that the probability of default on a seven-year AA-rated bond is 0.06, while that on a seven-year A-rated bond is 0.13. The probability that they will both default is 0.04.
    a. What is the probability that at least one of the bonds defaults?
    b. What is the probability that neither the seven-year AA-rated bond nor the seven-year A-rated bond defaults?
    c. Given that the seven-year AA-rated bond defaults, what is the probability that the seven-year A-rated bond also defaults?

26. Mike Danes finds out that there are only 20 shirts left at a clearance event of which 8 are in size M, 10 in size L, and 2 in size XL. Also, 9 of the shirts are white, 5 are blue, and the remaining are of mixed colors. Mike is interested in getting a white or a blue shirt in size L. Define the events A = Getting a white or a blue shirt and B = Getting a shirt in size L.
    a. Find $P(A)$, $P(A^c)$, and $P(B)$.
    b. Are the events A and B mutually exclusive? Explain.
    c. Would you describe Mike's preference by the events $A \cup B$ or $A \cap B$?

27. In general, shopping online is supposed to be more convenient than going to stores. However, according to a poll, 87% of people have experienced problems with an online transaction. Forty-two percent of people who experienced problems

abandoned the transaction or switched to a competitor's website. Fifty-three percent of people who experienced problems contacted customer-service representatives.

a. What proportion of people did not experience problems with an online transaction?

b. What proportion of people experienced problems with an online transaction and abandoned the transaction or switched to a competitor's website?

c. What proportion of people experienced problems with an online transaction and contacted customer-service representatives?

28. A manufacturing firm just received a shipment of 20 assembly parts, of slightly varied sizes, from a vendor. The manager knows that there are only 15 parts in the shipment that would be suitable. He examines these parts one at a time.

a. Find the probability that the first part is suitable.

b. If the first part is suitable, find the probability that the second part is also suitable.

c. If the first part is suitable, find the probability that the second part is not suitable.

29. Apple products have become a household name in America. Suppose that the likelihood of owning an Apple product is 61% for households with kids and 48% for households without kids. Suppose there are 1,200 households in a representative community, of which 820 are with kids and the rest are without kids.

a. Are the events "household with kids" and "household without kids" mutually exclusive and exhaustive? Explain.

b. What is the probability that a household is without kids?

c. What is the probability that a household is with kids and owns an Apple product?

d. What is the probability that a household is without kids and does not own an Apple product?

30. Bank regulators are renewing efforts to require Wall Street executives to cut back on bonuses. Despite that, it is believed that 10 out of 15 members of the board of directors of a company are in favor of bonuses. Suppose two members are randomly selected by the media.

a. What is the probability that both of them are in favor of bonuses?

b. What is the probability that neither of them is in favor of bonuses?

31. Christine has asked Dave and Mike to help her move into a new apartment on Sunday morning. She has asked them both, in case one of them does not show up. From past experience, Christine knows that there is a 40% chance that Dave will not show up and a 30% chance that Mike will not show up. Dave and Mike do not know each other and their decisions can be assumed to be independent.

a. What is the probability that both Dave and Mike will show up?

b. What is the probability that at least one of them will show up?

c. What is the probability that neither Dave nor Mike will show up?

32. According to results from the Spine Patient Outcomes Research Trial, or SPORT, surgery for a painful, common back condition resulted in significantly reduced back pain and better physical function than treatment with drugs and physical therapy. SPORT followed 803 patients, of whom 398 ended up getting surgery. After two years, of those who had surgery, 63% said they had a major improvement in their condition, compared with 29% among those who received nonsurgical treatment.

a. What is the probability that a patient had surgery? What is the probability that a patient did not have surgery?

b. What is the probability that a patient had surgery and experienced a major improvement in their condition?

c. What is the probability that a patient received nonsurgical treatment and experienced a major improvement in their condition?

33. Henry Chow is a stockbroker working for Merrill Lynch. He knows from past experience that there is a 70% chance that his new client will want to include U.S. equity in her portfolio and a 50% chance that she will want to include foreign equity. There is also a 40% chance that she will want to include both U.S. equity and foreign equity in her portfolio.

a. What is the probability that the client will want to include U.S. equity if she already has foreign equity in her portfolio?

b. What is the probability that the client decides to include neither U.S. equity nor foreign equity in her portfolio?

34. The subscription e-commerce market has grown substantially including subscription boxes that provide a recurring delivery of niche products. E-commerce firms pay attention to the churn rate, defined as the percentage of subscribers who discontinue their subscriptions. It is estimated that the monthly churn rate for subscription boxes is 12% for younger customers and 9% for older customers. It is also found that 62% of all subscription box customers are younger customers. Find the probability that a randomly selected customer will be an older customer who churns within a month.

35. Anthony Papantonis, owner of Nauset Construction, is bidding on two projects, A and B. The probability that he wins project A is 0.40 and the probability that he wins project B is 0.25. Winning Project A and winning Project B are independent events.

a. What is the probability that he wins project A or project B?

b. What is the probability that he does not win either project?

36. How much you smile in your younger days can predict your later success in marriage. The analysis is based on the success rate in marriage of people over age 65 and their smiles when they were only 10 years old. Researchers found that only 11% of the biggest smilers had been divorced, while 31% of the biggest frowners had experienced a broken marriage.

    a. Suppose it is known that 2% of the people are the biggest smilers at age 10 and divorced in later years. What percent of people are the biggest smilers?

    b. If 25% of people are considered to be the biggest frowners, calculate the probability that a person is the biggest frowner at age 10 and divorced later in life.

37. A study shows that unemployment does not impact males and females in the same way. Non-binary individuals were not polled in this study. According to a Bureau of Labor Statistics report, 8.5% of those who are eligible to work are unemployed. The unemployment rate is 8.8% for eligible males and only 7.0% for eligible females. Suppose 52% of the eligible workforce in the United States consists of males.

    a. You have just heard that another worker in a large firm has been laid off. What is the probability that this worker is a male?

    b. You have just heard that another worker in a large firm has been laid off. What is the probability that this worker is a female?

38. Wooden boxes are commonly used for the packaging and transportation of mangoes. A convenience store in Morganville, New Jersey, regularly buys mangoes from a wholesale dealer. For every shipment, the manager randomly inspects two mangoes from a box containing 20 mangoes for damages due to transportation. Suppose the chosen box contains exactly three damaged mangoes.

    a. Find the probability that the first mango is not damaged.

    b. Find the probability that neither of the mangoes is damaged.

    c. Find the probability that both mangoes are damaged.

39. A professor of management has heard that eight students in his class of 40 have landed an internship for the summer. Suppose he runs into two of his students in the corridor.

    a. Find the probability that neither of these students has landed an internship.

    b. Find the probability that both of these students have landed an internship.

40. According to the CGMA Economic Index, which measures executive sentiment across the world, 18% of all respondents expressed optimism about the global economy. Moreover, 22% of the respondents from the United States and 9% from Asia felt optimistic about the global economy.

    a. What is the probability that an Asian respondent is not optimistic about the global economy?

    b. If 28% of all respondents are from the United States, what is the probability that a respondent is from the United States and is optimistic about the global economy?

    c. Suppose 22% of all respondents are from Asia. If a respondent feels optimistic about the global economy, what is the probability that the respondent is from Asia?

4.3 CONTINGENCY TABLES AND PROBABILITIES

Calculate and interpret probabilities from a contingency table.

As discussed in Chapter 2, a **contingency table** proves very useful when examining the relationship between two categorical variables. It shows the frequencies for two categorical variables, x and y, where each cell represents a mutually exclusive combination of the pair of x and y observations. In this section, we will use contingency tables to calculate empirical probabilities of relevant events.

In the introductory case, Janet would like to use the information on age groups and enrollment outcome to develop a data-driven strategy for selecting which new open house attendees to contact. She uses the *Gym* data to construct a contingency table displayed in Table 4.5 (refer to Section 2.3 in Chapter 2 for the construction method). The table shows the frequencies for age groups and enrollment outcome for 400 past open house attendees.

TABLE 4.5 Enrollment and Age Frequencies of Past Open House Attendees

FILE
Gym

Outcome	Age Group			Total
	Under 30 (*U*)	Between 30 and 50 (*B*)	Over 50 (*O*)	
Enroll (*E*)	24	72	44	140
Not Enroll (*N*)	84	88	88	260
Total	108	160	132	400

As you can see, there are two outcomes regarding club membership (Enroll and Not Enroll) and three age groups of open house attendees (Under 30, Between 30 and 50, and Over 50). There are 400 open house attendees, of which 108 are under 30 years old, 160 are between 30 and 50 years old, and 132 are over 50 years old. Furthermore, 140 open house attendees enrolled and 260 did not enroll in the fitness center.

Recall that we can estimate an empirical probability by calculating the relative frequency of the occurrence of the event. To make calculating these probabilities less cumbersome, it is often useful to denote each event with letter notation. In Table 4.5, we let the letters E and N denote the events "Enroll" and "Not Enroll," respectively. Similarly, we use the letters U, B, and O to denote the events "Under 30," "Between 30 and 50," and "Over 50," respectively.

The following example illustrates how to calculate empirical probabilities when the data are presented in the form of a contingency table.

EXAMPLE 4.11

Use the contingency table in Table 4.5 to answer the following questions.

a. What is the probability that a randomly selected attendee enrolls in the fitness center?

b. What is the probability that a randomly selected attendee is over 50 years old?

c. What is the probability that a randomly selected attendee enrolls in the fitness center and is over 50 years old?

d. What is the probability that a randomly selected attendee enrolls in the fitness center or is over 50 years old?

e. What is the probability that an attendee enrolls in the fitness center, given that the attendee is over 50 years old?

SOLUTION:

a. $P(E) = \frac{140}{400} = 0.35$; there is a 35% chance that a randomly selected attendee enrolls in the fitness center.

b. $P(O) = \frac{132}{400} = 0.33$; there is a 33% chance that a randomly selected attendee is over 50 years old.

c. $P(E \cap O) = \frac{44}{400} = 0.11$; there is an 11% chance that a randomly selected attendee enrolls in the fitness center and is over 50 years old.

d. $P(E \cup O) = \frac{24 + 72 + 44 + 88}{400} = 0.57$; there is a 57% chance that a randomly selected attendee enrolls in the fitness center or is over 50 years old. Alternatively, we can use the addition rule to compute this probability as $P(E \cup O) = P(E) + P(O) - P(E \cap O) = 0.35 + 0.33 - 0.11 = 0.57$.

e. We wish to calculate the conditional probability $P(E|O)$. When the information is in the form of a contingency table, calculating a conditional probability is rather straightforward. We are given the information that the attendee is over 50 years old, so the relevant sample size shrinks from 400 attendees to 132 attendees. We can ignore all attendees who are under 30 years old or between 30 and 50 years old. Thus, of the 132 attendees who are over 50 years old, 44 of them enroll in the fitness center. Therefore, the probability that an attendee enrolls in the fitness center, given that they are over 50 years old is calculated as $P(E|O) = \frac{44}{132} = 0.33$. Alternatively, we can use the conditional probability formula to compute this probability as $P(E|O) = \frac{P(E \cap O)}{P(O)} = \frac{0.11}{0.33} = 0.33$.

Sometimes, a more convenient way of expressing relevant probabilities is to convert the contingency table to a joint probability table. The frequency in each cell is divided by the number of outcomes in the sample space, which in Example 4.11 is 400. Table 4.6 shows the joint probability table.

TABLE 4.6 Converting a Contingency Table to a Joint Probability Table

Outcome	Age Group			Total
	Under 30 (*U*)	Between 30 and 50 (*B*)	Over 50 (*O*)	
Enroll (*E*)	0.06	0.18	0.11	0.35
Not Enroll (*N*)	0.21	0.22	0.22	0.65
Total	0.27	0.40	0.33	1.00

The values in the interior of the table represent the probabilities of the intersection of two events, which as noted earlier are also referred to as **joint probabilities.** For instance, the probability that an attendee enrolls in the fitness center and is over 50 years old, denoted $P(E \cap O)$, is 0.11. Similarly, we can readily read from Table 4.6 that there is a 22% chance that an attendee does not enroll in the fitness center and is between 30 and 50 years old, or $P(N \cap B) = 0.22$.

The values in the margins of Table 4.6 represent unconditional probabilities, also referred to as **marginal probabilities.** For example, the probability that a randomly selected attendee is over 50 years old is $P(O) = 0.33$. Similarly, the probability that an attendee enrolls in the fitness center is $P(E) = 0.35$.

Note that the conditional probability is basically the ratio of a joint probability to a marginal probability. Take for example the conditional probability $P(E|O) = \frac{P(E \cap O)}{P(O)}$ where the numerator is the joint probability, $P(E \cap O)$, and the denominator is the marginal probability, $P(O)$. Using joint and marginal probabilities, we can calculate, for example, $P(E|O) = \frac{0.11}{0.33} = 0.33$.

EXAMPLE 4.12

Use the joint probability table in Table 4.6 to answer the following questions.

a. Calculate the conditional probabilities of enrolling in the fitness center for the different age groups.

b. Is age related to enrollment? Explain using probabilities.

SOLUTION:

a. For the event "Under 30," the conditional probability of enrolling is calculated as $P(E|U) = \frac{P(E \cap U)}{P(U)} = \frac{0.06}{0.27} = 0.22$. Similarly, for the other age groups, we compute $P(E|B) = \frac{P(E \cap B)}{P(B)} = \frac{0.18}{0.40} = 0.45$ and $P(E|O) = \frac{P(E \cap O)}{P(O)} = \frac{0.11}{0.33} = 0.33$.

b. If age and enrollment were independent, then $P(E|U) = P(E|B) = P(E|O) = P(E)$. In other words, the probability of enrollment will not be impacted by the age of attendees. Earlier, we found the unconditional probability of enrolling as $P(E) = 0.35$. Because the conditional probabilities of enrolling found in part a differ from $P(E)$, we can conclude that age and enrollment are not independent. The manager should focus on the attendees in the age group "Between 30 and 50" because they have the highest probability of buying a gym membership.

Note: It is important to note that the conclusions about independence, such as the one made in Example 4.12, are informal because they are based on empirical probabilities computed from given sample information. In Example 4.12, these empirical probabilities are likely to change if a different sample of 400 attendees is used. Formal tests of independence are discussed in Chapter 11.

SYNOPSIS OF INTRODUCTORY CASE

Gyms and exercise facilities usually have a high turnover rate among their members. Like other gyms, 24/7 Fitness Center relies on recruiting new members on a regular basis in order to sustain its business and financial well-being. Janet Mwangi, a manager at 24/7 Fitness Center, analyzes data from the gym's past open houses. She wants to gain a better insight into which attendees are likely to purchase a gym membership after attending an open house.

NDAB Creativity/Shutterstock

After careful analysis of the contingency table representing frequencies for age groups and enrollment outcome of attendees, several interesting observations are made. From a sample of 400 past attendees, 27% are younger than 30 years old, 40% are between 30 and 50 years old, and 33% are over 50 years old. It is also determined that 35% of all attendees enroll in 24/7 Fitness Center. Further inspection of the contingency table reveals that the probability of enrollment depends on the age of the attendees. In particular, the attendees who are between 30 and 50 years old have a 45% likelihood of enrolling in the fitness center, which is the highest of all age groups. The corresponding likelihood of enrollment is 22% for under 30 years old and 33% for over 50 years old.

Overall, with a simple analysis of the contingency table, Janet is able to identify individual open house attendees who are likely to purchase a gym membership. With this insight, she can train her staff to regularly analyze the monthly open house data in order to help 24/7 Fitness Center grow its membership base.

EXERCISES 4.3

Mechanics

41. Consider the following contingency table.

	B	B^c
A	26	34
A^c	14	26

a. Convert the contingency table into a joint probability table.
b. What is the probability that A occurs?
c. What is the probability that A and B occur?
d. Given that B has occurred, what is the probability that A occurs?
e. Given that A^c has occurred, what is the probability that B occurs?
f. Are A and B mutually exclusive events? Explain.
g. Are A and B independent events? Explain.

42. Consider the following joint probability table.

	B_1	B_2	B_3	B_4
A	0.09	0.22	0.15	0.20
A^c	0.03	0.10	0.09	0.12

a. What is the probability that A occurs?
b. What is the probability that B_2 occurs?
c. What is the probability that A^c and B_4 occur?
d. What is the probability that A or B_3 occurs?
e. Given that B_2 has occurred, what is the probability that A occurs?
f. Given that A has occurred, what is the probability that B_4 occurs?

Applications

43. An online retailer recently sent emails to customers that included a promotional discount. The retailer wonders whether there is any relationship between a customer's location in the United States (Midwest, Northeast, South, or West) and whether the customer made a purchase with the discount (Yes or No). The results are shown in the following contingency table.

Purchase	Location			
	Midwest	Northeast	South	West
Yes	77	102	130	101
No	107	41	24	18

a. What is the probability that a randomly selected customer made a purchase?

b. What is the probability that a randomly selected customer is from the northeast?

c. Given that a customer made a purchase, what is the probability that the customer is from the northeast?

d. Given that a customer is from the northeast, what is the probability that the customer made a purchase?

e. Are the events "Yes" and "Northeast" independent? Explain using probabilities.

44. A report suggests that business majors spend the least amount of time on course work than all other college students. A provost of a university decides to conduct a survey where students are asked if they study hard, defined by spending at least 20 hours per week on course work. Of 120 business majors included in the survey, 20 said that they studied hard, as compared to 48 out of 150 nonbusiness majors who said that they studied hard.

a. Construct a contingency table that shows the frequencies for the variables Major (business or nonbusiness) and Study Hard (yes or no).

b. Find the probability that a business major spends less than 20 hours per week on course work.

c. What is the probability that a student studies hard?

d. If a student spends at least 20 hours on course work, what is the probability that they are a business major? What is the corresponding probability that they are a nonbusiness major?

45. Research suggests that Americans are becoming increasingly polarized on issues pertaining to the environment. It is reported that 70% of Democrats see signs of global warming as compared to only 30% of Republicans who feel the same. Suppose the survey was based on 400 Democrats and 400 Republicans.

a. Construct a contingency table that shows frequencies for the variables Political Affiliation (Democrat or Republican) and Global Warming (yes or no).

b. Find the probability that a Republican sees signs of global warming.

c. Find the probability that a person does not see signs of global warming.

d. If a person sees signs of global warming, what is the probability that this person is a Democrat?

46. **FILE** *Happiness.* There have been numerous attempts that relate happiness with income. In a recent survey, 290 individuals were asked to evaluate happiness (Yes or No) and income (Low, Medium, or High). The accompanying data file shows the survey results.

a. Use the data to construct a contingency table.

b. Find the probability that a randomly selected individual feels happy.

c. Find the probability that a low-income individual feels happy. Find the corresponding probabilities for medium-income and high-income individuals.

d. Is income related to happiness? Explain using probabilities.

47. **FILE** *Crash.* The California Highway Patrol (CHP) routinely compiles car crash data in California. The accompanying data file shows information on the type of car crash (Head-On or Not Head-On) and light (Daylight or Not Daylight).

a. Use the data to construct a contingency table.

b. Find the probability that a randomly selected car crash is a head-on.

c. Find the probability that a randomly selected car crash is at daylight.

d. Find the probability that the car crash is a head-on, given daylight. Find the corresponding probability given not daylight.

e. Is crash related to light? Explain using probabilities.

48. The research team at a leading perfume company is trying to test the market for its newly introduced perfume. In particular the team wishes to look for gender and international differences in the preference for this perfume. They sample 2,500 people internationally and each person in the sample is asked to try the new perfume and list their preference. The following table reports the results.

Preference	Gender	America	Europe	Asia
Like it	Male	210	150	120
	Female	370	310	180
Don't like it	Male	290	150	80
	Female	330	190	120

a. What is the probability that a randomly selected male likes the perfume?

b. What is the probability that a randomly selected Asian likes the perfume?

c. What is the probability that a randomly selected European female does not like the perfume?

d. What is the probability that a randomly selected American male does not like the perfume?

e. Are the events "Male" and "Like Perfume" independent in (i) America, (ii) Europe, and (iii) Asia? Explain using probabilities.

f. Internationally, are the events "Male" and "Like Perfume" independent? Explain using probabilities.

49. More and more households are struggling to pay utility bills given high heating costs. Particularly hard hit are households with homes heated with propane or heating oil. Many of these households are spending twice as much to stay warm this winter compared to those who heat with natural gas or electricity. A representative sample of 500 households was taken to investigate if the type of heating influences whether or not a household is delinquent in paying its utility bill. The following table reports the results.

| Delinquent in Payment? | Type of Heating | | | |
	Natural Gas	Electricity	Heating Oil	Propane
Yes	50	20	15	10
No	240	130	20	15

a. What is the probability that a randomly selected household uses heating oil?

b. What is the probability that a randomly selected household is delinquent in paying its utility bill?

c. What is the probability that a randomly selected household uses heating oil and is delinquent in paying its utility bill?

d. Given that a household uses heating oil, what is the probability that it is delinquent in paying its utility bill?

e. Given that a household is delinquent in paying its utility bill, what is the probability that the household uses electricity?

f. Are the events "Heating Oil" and "Delinquent in Payment" independent? Explain using probabilities.

50. **FILE** *Machine.* Being able to predict machine failures before they happen can save millions of dollars for manufacturing companies. Manufacturers want to be able to perform preventive maintenance or repairs in advance to minimize machine downtime and often install electronic sensors to monitor the machines and their surrounding environment. A manager of a firm wants to explore the effect of percentage humidity (Low, Medium, or High) on machine failure (Yes or No). The accompanying data file shows the results.

a. Use the data to construct a contingency table.

b. Find the probability that a randomly selected machine fails.

c. Find the probability that a randomly selected machine operates in high humidity.

d. Find the probability that a machine fails, given high humidity. Find the corresponding probabilities given low and medium humidity.

e. Is machine failure related to humidity? Explain using probabilities.

51. At a local bar in a small Midwestern town, beer and wine are the only two alcoholic options. The manager noted that of all male customers who visited over the weekend, 150 ordered beer, 40 ordered wine, and 20 asked for soft drinks. Of female customers, 38 ordered beer, 20 ordered wine, and 12 asked for soft drinks.

a. Construct a contingency table that shows frequencies for the categorical variables Gender (male or female) and Drink Choice (beer, wine, or soft drink).

b. Find the probability that a customer orders wine.

c. What is the probability that a male customer orders wine?

d. Are the events "Wine" and "Male" independent? Explain using probabilities.

4.4 THE TOTAL PROBABILITY RULE AND BAYES' THEOREM

In this section, we present two important rules in probability theory: the total probability rule and Bayes' theorem. The **total probability rule** is a useful tool for breaking the computation of a probability into distinct cases. **Bayes' theorem** uses this rule to update the probability of an event that has been affected by a new piece of evidence.

Often, the probability of an event is not readily available from the given information. The total probability rule expresses the probability of an event in terms of joint or conditional probabilities. Let $P(A)$ denote the probability of an event of interest. We can express $P(A)$ as the sum of probabilities of the intersections of A with some mutually exclusive and exhaustive events corresponding to an experiment. For instance, consider event B and its complement B^c. Figure 4.4 shows the sample space partitioned into these two mutually exclusive and exhaustive events. The circle, representing event $A,$ consists entirely of its intersections with B and B^c. According to the total probability rule, $P(A)$ equals the sum of $P(A \cap B)$ and $P(A \cap B^c)$.

Apply the total probability rule and Bayes' theorem.

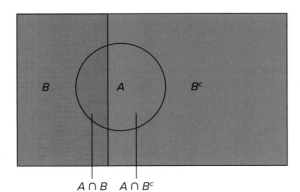

$A \cap B \quad A \cap B^c$

FIGURE 4.4
The total probability rule:
$P(A) = P(A \cap B) + P(A \cap B^c)$

Oftentimes the joint probabilities needed to compute the total probability are not explicitly specified. Therefore, we use the multiplication rule to derive these probabilities from the conditional probabilities as $P(A \cap B) = P(A|B)P(B)$ and $P(A \cap B^c) = P(A|B^c)P(B^c)$.

The total probability rule is also needed to derive Bayes' theorem. Bayes' theorem is a procedure for updating probabilities based on new information. The original probability is an unconditional probability called a **prior probability,** in the sense that it reflects only what we know now before the arrival of any new information. On the basis of new information, we update the prior probability to arrive at a conditional probability called a **posterior probability.**

Suppose we know that 99% of the individuals who take a lie detector test tell the truth. Therefore, the prior probability of telling the truth is 0.99. Suppose an individual takes the lie detector test and the results indicate that the individual lied. Bayes' theorem updates a prior probability to compute a posterior probability, which in this example is essentially a conditional probability based on the information that the lie detector has detected a lie.

Let $P(B)$ denote the prior probability and $P(B|A)$ the posterior probability. Note that the posterior probability is conditional on event A, representing new information. Recall the conditional probability formula from Section 4.2:

$$P(B|A) = \frac{P(A \cap B)}{P(A)}.$$

In some instances, we may have to evaluate $P(B|A)$, but we do not have explicit information on $P(A \cap B)$ or $P(A)$. However, given information on $P(B)$, $P(A|B)$, and $P(A|B^c)$, we can use the total probability rule to find $P(B|A)$, as shown in the following definition box.

THE TOTAL PROBABILITY RULE AND BAYES' THEOREM

The total probability rule expresses the probability of event A in terms of joint or conditional probabilities. If the sample space is partitioned into events B and B^c, the probability of event A can be found as

$$P(A) = P(A \cap B) + P(A \cap B^C) = P(A|B)P(B) + P(A|B^C)P(B^C).$$

Bayes' Theorem is a method for updating a prior probability, $P(B)$, to a posterior probability, $P(B|A)$. The posterior probability can be found as

$$P(B|A) = \frac{P(A \cap B)}{P(A \cap B) + P(A \cap B^c)} = \frac{P(A|B)P(B)}{P(A|B)P(B) + P(A|B^c)P(B^c)}.$$

Note: In the formula for Bayes' Theorem, we show how to update the prior probability $P(B)$ to the posterior probability $P(B|A)$. Equivalently, we can update the prior probability $P(A)$ to derive the posterior probability $P(A|B)$ by interchanging the events A and B in the formula for Bayes' Theorem.

EXAMPLE 4.13

In a lie-detector test, an individual is asked to answer a series of questions while connected to a polygraph (lie detector). This instrument measures and records several physiological responses of the individual on the basis that false answers will produce distinctive measurements. Assume that 99% of the individuals who go in for a polygraph test tell the truth. These tests are considered to be 95% reliable in that there is a 95% chance that the test will detect a lie if an individual lies. Let there also be a 0.5% chance that the test erroneously detects a lie even when the individual is telling the truth.

a. What is the probability that the polygraph test detects a lie?

b. What is the probability that the individual is telling the truth if the polygraph test has detected a lie?

SOLUTION: First we define some events and their associated probabilities. Let L and T correspond to the events that the polygraph detects a lie and that an individual is telling the truth, respectively. We are given that $P(T) = 0.99$, implying that $P(T^c) = 1 - 0.99 = 0.01$. In addition, we formulate $P(L|T^c) = 0.95$ and $P(L|T) = 0.005$. We need to find $P(L)$ in part a and $P(T|L)$ in part b when the corresponding joint probabilities are not explicitly given.

Although we can use the total probability rule and Bayes' Theorem to solve this example directly, we use Table 4.7 to help solve this example systematically.

TABLE 4.7 Computing Posterior Probabilities for Example 4.13

Prior Probability	Conditional Probability	Joint Probability	Posterior Probability
$P(T) = 0.99$	$P(L|T) = 0.005$	$P(L \cap T) = 0.00495$	$P(T|L) = 0.3426$
$P(T^c) = 0.01$	$P(L|T^c) = 0.95$	$P(L \cap T^c) = 0.00950$	
$P(T) + P(T^c) = 1$		$P(L) = 0.01445$	

a. We first use the total probability rule to compute $P(L) = P(L \cap T) + P(L \cap T^c)$. Joint probabilities are calculated as products of conditional probabilities with their corresponding prior probabilities. For instance, in Table 4.7, in order to obtain $P(L \cap T)$, we multiply $P(L|T)$ with $P(T)$, which yields $P(L \cap T) = 0.005 \times 0.99 = 0.00495$. Similarly, we find $P(L \cap T^c) = 0.95 \times 0.01 = 0.00950$. Thus, according to the total probability rule, $P(L) = 0.00495 + 0.00950 = 0.01445$.

b. We now use Bayes' theorem to compute $P(T|D) = \frac{P(L \cap T)}{P(L \cap T) + P(L \cap T^c)} = \frac{0.00495}{0.01445} = 0.3426$. The prior probability of an individual telling the truth is 0.99. However, given the new information that the polygraph detected the individual telling a lie, the posterior probability of this individual telling the truth is now revised downward to 0.3426.

Extensions of the Total Probability Rule and Bayes' Theorem

So far we have used the total probability rule as well as Bayes' theorem based on two mutually exclusive and exhaustive events, namely, B and B^c. We can easily extend the analysis to include n mutually exclusive and exhaustive events, $B_1, B_2, \ldots, B_n$.

> **EXTENSIONS OF THE TOTAL PROBABILITY RULE AND BAYES' THEOREM**
>
> Let the sample spaced be partitioned into $B_1, B_2, \ldots, B_n$, representing n mutually exclusive and exhaustive events for $i = 1, 2, \ldots, n$. The total probability rule extends to
>
> $$P(A) = P(A \cap B_1) + P(A \cap B_2) + \cdots + P(A \cap B_n) = P(A|B_1)P(B_1) + P(A|B_2)P(B_2) + \cdots + P(A|B_n)P(B_n).$$
>
> We can use Bayes' Theorem to update a prior probability, $P(B_i)$, to a posterior probability, $P(B_i|A)$, as
>
> $$P(B_i|A) = \frac{P(A \cap B_i)}{P(A \cap B_1) + P(A \cap B_2) + \cdots + P(A \cap B_n)} = \frac{P(A|B_i)P(B_i)}{P(A|B_1)P(B_1) + P(A|B_2)P(B_2) + \cdots + P(A|B_n)P(B_n)}.$$

EXAMPLE 4.14

Scott Myers is a security analyst for a telecommunications firm called Webtalk. Although he is optimistic about the firm's future, he is concerned that its stock price will be considerably affected by the condition of credit flow in the economy. He believes that the probability is 0.20 that credit flow will improve significantly, 0.50 that it will improve only marginally, and 0.30 that it will not improve at all. He also estimates that the probability that the stock price of Webtalk will go up is 0.90 with significant improvement in credit flow in the economy, 0.40 with marginal improvement in credit flow in the economy, and 0.10 with no improvement in credit flow in the economy.

a. Based on Scott's estimates, what is the probability that the stock price of Webtalk goes up?

b. If we know that the stock price of Webtalk has gone up, what is the probability that credit flow in the economy has improved significantly?

SOLUTION: As always, we first define the relevant events and their associated probabilities. Let S, M, and N denote significant, marginal, and no improvement in credit flow, respectively. Then $P(S) = 0.20$, $P(M) = 0.50$, and $P(N) = 0.30$. In addition, if we allow G to denote an increase in stock price, we formulate $P(G|S) = 0.90$, $P(G|M) = 0.40$, and $P(G|N) = 0.10$. We need to calculate $P(G)$ in part a and $P(S|G)$ in part b. Table 4.8 aids in assigning probabilities.

TABLE 4.8 Computing Posterior Probabilities for Example 4.14

Prior Probability	Conditional Probability	Joint Probability	Posterior Probability
$P(S) = 0.20$	$P(G|S) = 0.90$	$P(G \cap S) = 0.18$	$P(S|G) = 0.4390$
$P(M) = 0.50$	$P(G|M) = 0.40$	$P(G \cap M) = 0.20$	
$P(N) = 0.30$	$P(G|N) = 0.10$	$P(G \cap N) = 0.03$	
$P(S) + P(M) + P(N) = 1$		$P(G) = 0.41$	

a. In order to calculate $P(G)$, we use the total probability rule, $P(G) = P(G \cap S) + P(G \cap M) + P(G \cap N)$. The joint probabilities are calculated as products of conditional probabilities with their corresponding prior probabilities. For instance, in Table 4.8, $P(G \cap S) = P(G|S)P(S) = 0.90 \times 0.20 = 0.18$. Therefore, the probability that the stock price of Webtalk goes up equals $P(G) = 0.18 + 0.20 + 0.03 = 0.41$.

b. According to Bayes' theorem, $P(S|G) = \frac{P(G \cap S)}{P(G)} = \frac{P(G \cap S)}{P(G \cap S) + P(G \cap M) + P(G \cap N)}$. In part a, we used the total probability rule to find $P(G) = 0.18 + 0.20 + 0.03 = 0.41$. Therefore, $P(S|G) = \frac{P(G \cap S)}{P(G)} = \frac{0.18}{0.41} = 0.4390$. Note that the prior probability of a significant improvement in credit flow is revised upward from 0.20 to a posterior probability of 0.4390.

EXERCISES 4.4

Mechanics

52. Let $P(A) = 0.70$, $P(B|A) = 0.55$, and $P(B|A^c) = 0.10$. Find the following probabilities:

a. $P(A^c)$

b. $P(A \cap B)$ and $P(A^c \cap B)$

c. $P(B)$

d. $P(A|B)$

53. Complete the following probability table.

Prior Probability	Conditional Probability	Joint Probability	Posterior Probability
$P(B) = 0.85$	$P(A\|B) = 0.05$	$P(A \cap B) =$	$P(B\|A) =$
$P(B^c) =$	$P(A\|B^c) = 0.80$	$P(A \cap B^c) =$	$P(B^c\|A) =$
Total =		$P(A) =$	Total =

54. Let a sample space be partitioned into three mutually exclusive and exhaustive events, B_1, B_2, and B_3. Complete the following probability table.

Prior Probabilities	Conditional Probabilities	Joint Probabilities	Posterior Probabilities
$P(B_1) = 0.10$	$P(A\|B_1) = 0.40$	$P(A \cap B_1) =$	$P(B_1\|A) =$
$P(B_2) =$	$P(A\|B_2) = 0.60$	$P(A \cap B_2) =$	$P(B_2\|A) =$
$P(B_3) = 0.30$	$P(A\|B_3) = 0.80$	$P(A \cap B_3) =$	$P(B_3\|A) =$
Total =		$P(A) =$	Total =

Applications

55. Christine has always been weak in mathematics. Based on her performance prior to the final exam in Calculus, there is a 40% chance that she will fail the course if she does not have a tutor. With a tutor, her probability of failing decreases to 10%. There is only a 50% chance that she will find a tutor at such short notice.
    a. What is the probability that Christine fails the course?
    b. Christine ends up failing the course. What is the probability that she had found a tutor?

56. An analyst expects that 20% of all publicly traded companies will experience a decline in earnings next year. The analyst has developed a ratio to help forecast this decline. If the company is headed for a decline, there is a 70% chance that this ratio will be negative. If the company is not headed for a decline, there is a 15% chance that the ratio will be negative. The analyst randomly selects a company and its ratio is negative. What is the posterior probability that the company will experience a decline?

57. The State Police are trying to crack down on speeding on a particular portion of the Massachusetts Turnpike. To aid in this pursuit, they have purchased a new radar gun that promises greater consistency and reliability. Specifically, the gun advertises ± one-mile-per-hour accuracy 98% of the time; that is, there is a 0.98 probability that the gun will detect a speeder, if the driver is actually speeding. Assume there is a 1% chance that the gun erroneously detects a speeder even when the driver is below the speed limit. Suppose that 95% of the drivers drive below the speed limit on this stretch of the Massachusetts Turnpike.
    a. What is the probability that the gun detects speeding and the driver was speeding?
    b. What is the probability that the gun detects speeding and the driver was not speeding?
    c. Suppose the police stop a driver because the gun detects speeding. What is the probability that the driver was actually driving below the speed limit?

58. A crucial game of the Los Angeles Lakers basketball team depends on the health of their key player. According to his doctor's report, there is a 40% chance that he will be fully fit to play, a 30% chance that he will be somewhat fit to play, and a 30% chance that he will not be able to play at all. The coach has estimated the chances of winning at 80% if the player is fully fit, 60% if he is somewhat fit, and 40% if he is unable to play.
    a. What is the probability that the Lakers will win the game?
    b. You have just heard that the Lakers won the game. What is the probability that the key player had been fully fit to play in the game?

59. An analyst thinks that next year there is a 20% chance that the world economy will be good, a 50% chance that it will be neutral, and a 30% chance that it will be poor. They also predict probabilities that the performance of a start-up firm, Creative Ideas, will be good, neutral, or poor for each of the economic states of the world economy. The following table presents probabilities for three states of the world economy and the corresponding conditional probabilities for Creative Ideas.

State of the World Economy	Probability of Economic State	Performance of Creative Ideas	Conditional Probability of Creative Ideas
Good	0.20	Good	0.60
		Neutral	0.30
		Poor	0.10
Neutral	0.50	Good	0.40
		Neutral	0.30
		Poor	0.30
Poor	0.30	Good	0.20
		Neutral	0.30
		Poor	0.50

    a. What is the probability that the performance of the world economy will be neutral and that of Creative Ideas will be poor?
    b. What is the probability that the performance of Creative Ideas will be poor?
    c. The performance of Creative Ideas was poor. What is the probability that the performance of the world economy had also been poor?

60. An analyst predicts that there is a 40% chance that the U.S. economy will perform well. If the U.S. economy performs well, then there is an 80% chance that Asian countries will also perform well. On the other hand, if the U.S. economy performs poorly, the probability of Asian countries performing well goes down to 0.30.
    a. What is the probability that both the U.S. economy and the Asian countries will perform well?
    b. What is the probability that the Asian countries will perform well?
    c. What is the probability that the U.S. economy will perform well, given that the Asian countries perform well?

61. Apparently, depression significantly increases the risk of developing dementia later in life. In a study, it was reported that 22% of those who had depression went on to develop dementia, compared to only 17% of those who had not experienced depression. Suppose 10% of all people have experienced depression.
    a. What is the probability of a person developing dementia?
    b. If a person has developed dementia, what is the probability that the person has experienced depression?

62. According to data from the *National Health and Nutrition Examination Survey*, 36.5% of adult females and 26.6% of adult males are at a healthy weight. Non-binary individuals were not included in this report. Suppose 50.52% of the adult population consists of females.
    a. What proportion of adults is at a healthy weight?
    b. If an adult is at a healthy weight, what is the probability that the adult is a female?
    c. If an adult is at a healthy weight, what is the probability that the adult is a male?

63. Suppose that 60% of students do homework regularly. It is also known that 80% of students who had been doing homework regularly end up doing well in the course (get a grade of A or B). Only 20% of students who had not been doing homework regularly end up doing well in the course.
    a. What is the probability that a student does well in the course?
    b. Given that a student did well in the course, what is the probability that the student had been doing homework regularly?

64. There is a growing public support for marijuana law reform, with polls showing that more than half of the country is in favor of some form of marijuana legalization. However, opinions on marijuana are divided starkly along political party lines. The results of a survey are shown in the accompanying table. In addition, assume that 27% of Americans identify as Republicans, 30% as Democrats, and 43% as independents.

Political Party	Support
Republican	41%
Democrat	66%
Independent	63%

    a. Calculate the probability that a randomly selected American adult supports marijuana legalization and is a Republican.
    b. Calculate the probability that a randomly selected American adult supports marijuana legalization and is a Democrat.
    c. Calculate the probability that a randomly selected American adult supports marijuana legalization and is an independent.
    d. What percentage of American adults support marijuana legalization?
    e. If a randomly selected American adult supports marijuana legalization, what is the probability that this adult is a Republican?

4.4 WRITING WITH DATA

Case Study

Support for marijuana legalization in the United States has grown remarkably over the past few decades. In 1969, when the question was first presented, only 12% of Americans were in favor of its legalization. This support had increased to over 25% by the late 1970s. While support was stagnant from 1981 to 1997, the turn of the century brought a renewed interest in its legalization, with the percentage of Americans in favor exceeding 30% by 2000 and 40% by 2009.

Alexis Lewis works for a drug policy institute that focuses on science, health, and human rights. She is analyzing the demographic breakdown of marijuana supporters. Using results from a 2016 survey, she has found that support for marijuana legalization varies considerably depending on a person's age group. Alexis compiles information on support based on age group as shown in Table 4.9.

SEASTOCK/Shutterstock

TABLE 4.9 Percentage Support for Legalizing Marijuana by Age Group

Age Group	Support
Millennial (18–35)	71%
Generation X (36–51)	57%
Baby Boomer (52–70)	56%
Silent (71 and older)	33%

Alexis finds that another important factor determining the fate of marijuana legalization concerns each age group's ability to sway the vote. For adults eligible to vote as of 2016, she breaks down each age group's voting power. The Millennial, Generation X, Baby Boomer, and Silent generations account for 31%, 25%, 31%, and 13% of the voting population, respectively.

Alexis wants to use this information to calculate and interpret relevant probabilities to better understand the support for the legalization of marijuana in the United States.

Sample Report— Linking Support for Legalizing Marijuana with Age Group

Driven by growing public support, the legalization of marijuana in America has been moving at a breakneck speed in recent years. As of 2016, marijuana is now legal in some form in 28 states and in Washington, DC. Even recreational marijuana is gaining support, becoming legal in Alaska, California, Colorado, Maine, Massachusetts, Nevada, Oregon, Washington, and Washington, DC. Changing demographics can help explain how the tide has turned in marijuana's favor, especially because Millennials (those between the ages of 18 and 35) are on the verge of becoming the nation's largest living generation.

A 2016 survey provides interesting data regarding support for marijuana legalization. Two factors seem to drive support for the issue: generation (or age group) and the relative size of a generation's voting bloc. For ease of interpretation, let M, G, B, and S denote "Millennial," "Generation X," "Baby Boomer," and "Silent" generations, respectively. Based on data from the survey, the following probability statements can be formulated with respect to the relative size of each generation's voting bloc: $P(M) = 0.31$, $P(G) = 0.25$, $P(B) = 0.31$, $P(S) = 0.13$. In other words, Millennials and Baby Boomers have the most voting power, each comprising 31% of the voting population; the Generation X and Silent generations represent 25% and 13% of the voting population, respectively.

Now let L denote "support for legalizing marijuana." Again, based on data from the survey, conditional probabilities can be specified as $P(L|M) = 0.71$, $P(L|G) = 0.57$, $P(L|B) = 0.56$, and $P(L|S) = 0.33$. Therefore, the probability that a randomly selected adult supports legal marijuana and is in the Millennial generation is determined as $P(L \cap M) = 0.71 \times 0.31 = 0.2201$. Similarly, $P(L \cap G) = 0.1425$, $P(L \cap B) = 0.1736$, and $P(L \cap S) = 0.0429$. By combining all generations, we deduce the total probability of support for legalizing marijuana as $P(L) = 0.2201 + 0.1425 + 0.1736 + 0.0429 = 0.5791$; in 2016, a staggering 58% of Americans support the legalization of marijuana. Table 4.10 is the joint probability table that summarizes unconditional and joint probabilities.

TABLE 4.10 Joint Probability Table for the Support for Legalizing Marijuana by Age Group

Age Group	Legalizing Marijuana		Total
	Support	Do not Support	
Millennial (18–35)	0.2201	0.0899	0.31
Generation X (36–51)	0.1425	0.1075	0.25
Baby Boomer (52–70)	0.1736	0.1364	0.31
Silent (71 and older)	0.0429	0.0871	0.13
Total	0.5791	0.4209	1.00

To put it in perspective, suppose that there are 1,000 randomly selected adult attendees at a conference. The results imply that there would be about 310 Millennial, 250 Generation X, 310 Baby Boomer, and 130 Silent attendees. Further, the supporters of marijuana legalization would include about 220 Millennial, 143 Generation X, 174 Baby Boomer, and 43 Silent attendees.

Suggested Case Studies

Report 4.1 It is not uncommon to ignore the thyroid gland of females during pregnancy. This gland makes hormones that govern metabolism, helping to regulate body weight, heart rate, and a host of other factors. If the thyroid malfunctions, it can produce too little or too much of these hormones. Hypothyroidism, caused by an untreated underactive thyroid in pregnant females, carries the risk of impaired intelligence in the child. According to one research study, 62 out of 25,216 pregnant females were identified with hypothyroidism. Nineteen percent of the children born to females with an untreated underactive thyroid had an I.Q. of 85 or lower, compared with only 5% of those whose mothers had a healthy thyroid. It was also reported that if mothers have their hypothyroidism treated, their children's intelligence would not be impaired. In a report, calculate and discuss (a) the likelihood that a female suffers from hypothyroidism during pregnancy and later has a child with an I.Q. of 85 or lower and (b) the number of children in a sample of 100,000 who are likely to have an I.Q. of 85 or lower if the thyroid gland of pregnant females is ignored. Compare and comment on your answer to part b with the corresponding number if all pregnant females are tested and treated for hypothyroidism.

Report 4.2 Consider 600 terminally ill patients who agreed to participate in a new drug trial. They were randomly assigned to either an experimental group or a control group. There were 276 patients in the experimental group who were given the new drug, whereas the remaining patients were in the control group who were kept on the medicine they had been receiving. After one year, 348 of the patients were still alive, of which 190 were in the experimental group. Use these results to compute relevant probabilities to examine the effectiveness of the new drug.

Report 4.3 It is reported that rising gas prices have made California residents less resistant to offshore drilling. A Field Poll survey shows that a higher proportion of Californians supported the idea of drilling for oil or natural gas along the state's coast than a decade ago. Assume that random drilling for oil only succeeds 5% of the time. An oil company has just announced that it has discovered new technology for detecting oil. The technology is 80% reliable. That is, if there is oil, the technology will signal "oil" 80% of the time. Let there also be a 1% chance that the technology erroneously detects oil, when in fact no oil exists. In a report, use this information to compute and interpret the probability that, on a recent expedition, oil existed, but the technology detected "no oil" in the area.

Report 4.4 **FILE** *College_Admissions.* Explore the data on two categorical variables denoting admission decision (Admitted) and the college that a student applies to (College). Construct a contingency table and calculate and interpret relevant probabilities to examine the relative independence of the three colleges.

5 Discrete Probability Distributions

In this chapter, we extend our discussion about probability by introducing the concept of a random variable. A random variable summarizes the results of an experiment in terms of numerical values. It can be classified as discrete or continuous depending on the range of values that it assumes.

A discrete random variable assumes a countable number of distinct values. Examples of a discrete random variable include the number of refinancing applications in a sample of 100 homeowners and the number of cars lined up at a toll booth. A continuous random variable, on the other hand, is characterized by uncountable values within an interval. Examples of a continuous random variable include the investment return on a mutual fund and the completion time of a task.

In this chapter, we focus on a discrete random variable and its associated probability distribution. We calculate summary measures for a discrete random variable, including its mean, variance, and standard deviation. Finally, we discuss three widely used discrete probability distributions: the binomial, the Poisson, and the hypergeometric distributions.

INTRODUCTORY CASE

Available Staff for Probable Customers

Starbucks is facing stiff competition, and it is not coming from other coffee chains. Trendy coffee shops, emerging all over the country, are now competing with Starbucks clientele. The growth of daily consumption of gourmet coffee coupled with low capital investment has prompted entrepreneurs to start their own specialty coffee shops aimed at a younger, more affluent demographic.

Anne Jones, a manager at a local Starbucks, is concerned about how the stiff competition from trendy coffee shops might affect business at her store. Anne knows that a typical Starbucks customer visits the chain between 15 and 18 times a month, making it among the nation's most frequented retailers. She believes that her loyal Starbucks customers will average 18 visits to the store over a 30-day month. To decide staffing needs, Anne knows that she needs a solid understanding about the probability distribution of customer arrivals. If too many employees are ready to serve customers, some employees will be idle, which is costly to the store. However, if not enough employees are available to meet demand, this could result in losing angry customers who choose not to wait for service.

Anne wants to use the above information to

1. Calculate the expected number of visits from a typical Starbucks customer in a specified time period.

2. Calculate the probability that a typical Starbucks customer visits the chain a certain number of times in a specified time period.

A synopsis of this case is provided in Section 5.4.

5.1 RANDOM VARIABLES AND DISCRETE PROBABILITY DISTRIBUTIONS

We often have to make important decisions in the face of uncertainty. For example, a car dealership has to determine the number of cars to hold on its lot when the actual demand for cars is unknown. Similarly, an investor has to select a portfolio when the actual outcomes of investment returns are not known. This uncertainty is captured by what we call a **random variable.** A random variable summarizes the outcomes of an experiment with numerical values.

We generally use the uppercase letter X to denote a random variable and a lowercase letter x to denote the value that X may assume. A **discrete random variable** assumes a countable number of distinct values such as x_1, x_2, x_3, and so on. A **continuous random variable,** on the other hand, is characterized by uncountable values within an interval. Unlike the case of a discrete random variable, we cannot describe the possible values of a continuous random variable X with a list $x_1, x_2, \ldots$ because the value $(x_1 + x_2)/2$, which is not in the list, might also be possible.

DISCRETE VERSUS CONTINUOUS RANDOM VARIABLES

- A random variable is a function that assigns numerical values to the outcomes of an experiment.
- A discrete random variable assumes a countable number of distinct values.
- A continuous random variable is characterized by uncountable values in an interval.

Examples of discrete random variables include the number of salespeople who hit their target for the quarter, the number of employees leaving a firm in a given year, or the number of firms filing for bankruptcy in a given month. Similarly, the return on a mutual fund, the completion time of a task, and the volume of beer sold as 16 ounces are examples of continuous random variables. In this chapter, we focus on discrete random variables. We turn our attention to continuous random variables in Chapter 6.

The Discrete Probability Distribution

Every discrete random variable is associated with a **probability distribution,** also called the **probability mass function,** that provides the probability that the random variable X assumes a particular value x, or, equivalently, $P(X = x)$. We can also define the random variable in terms of its **cumulative distribution function,** or, equivalently, $P(X \leq x)$. There are two defining properties of all discrete probability distributions.

TWO KEY PROPERTIES OF DISCRETE PROBABILITY DISTRIBUTIONS

- The probability of each value x is a value between 0 and 1, or, equivalently, $0 \leq P(X = x) \leq 1$.
- The sum of the probabilities equals 1. In other words, $\Sigma P(X = x_i) = 1$, where the sum extends over all values x of X.

We can view a discrete probability distribution in several ways, including tabular, algebraic, and graphical forms.

EXAMPLE 5.1

Suppose we roll a regular six-sided die and define the number rolled as the random variable. Present the probability distribution in a tabular form.

SOLUTION: When we roll a regular six-sided die, the possible values that X assumes are $x = 1, 2, 3, 4, 5,$ or 6. Because each of the outcomes is equally likely, the probability that X assumes any of the six possible values is $1/6 = 0.1667$. Table 5.1 shows the probability distribution for rolling a regular six-sided die. With the given probability distribution, we can easily deduce, for instance, that $P(X = 5) = 0.1667$.

TABLE 5.1 Probability Distribution for Rolling a Die

x	1	2	3	4	5	6
P(X = x)	0.1667	0.1667	0.1667	0.1667	0.1667	0.1667

We would like to point out that the probability distribution for rolling a die in Example 5.1 represents a **discrete uniform distribution,** which has the following characteristics:

- The distribution has a finite number of specified values.
- Each value is equally likely.
- The distribution is symmetric.

There are two tabular ways to represent a discrete probability distribution. We can specify the probability that the random variable assumes a specific value, as shown in Table 5.1. Alternatively, we can represent by its cumulative distribution function. The cumulative distribution function is convenient when we are interested in finding the probability that the random variable assumes a range of values rather than a specific value. For the random variable defined in Example 5.1, the cumulative distribution is shown in Table 5.2. Note that $P(X \leq 2) = P(X = 1) + P(X = 2) = 1/6 + 1/6 = 0.3333$; other cumulative probabilities are found similarly.

TABLE 5.2 Cumulative Distribution for Rolling a Die

x	1	2	3	4	5	6
P(X ≤ x)	0.1667	0.3333	0.5000	0.6667	0.8333	1

If we are interested in finding the probability of rolling a four or less, $P(X \leq 4)$, we see from the cumulative distribution that this probability is 0.6667. At the same time, we can use the cumulative distribution to find the probability that the random variable assumes a specific value. For example, $P(X = 3)$ can be found as $P(X \leq 3) - P(X \leq 2) = 0.5000 - 0.3333 = 0.1667$.

In many instances, we can express a probability distribution by applying an algebraic formula. A formula representation of the probability distribution for rolling a six-sided die is expressed as

$$P(X = x) = \begin{cases} 0.1667 & \text{if } x = 1, 2, 3, 4, 5, 6 \\ 0 & \text{otherwise} \end{cases}$$

Thus, from the formula we find that $P(X = 5) = 0.1667$ and $P(X = 7) = 0$.

In order to graphically depict a probability distribution, we place all values x of X on the horizontal axis and the associated probabilities $P(X = x)$ on the vertical axis. We then draw a line segment that emerges from each x and ends where its height equals $P(X = x)$. Figure 5.1 graphically illustrates the probability distribution for rolling a six-sided die.

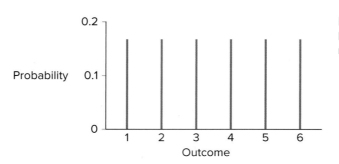

FIGURE 5.1
Probability distribution for
rolling a six-sided die

EXAMPLE 5.2

The number of homes that a Realtor sells over a one-month period has the probability distribution shown in Table 5.3.

TABLE 5.3 Probability Distribution for the Number of Houses Sold

Number of Houses Sold	Probability
0	0.30
1	0.50
2	0.15
3	0.05

a. Is this a valid probability distribution?

b. What is the probability that the Realtor does not sell any houses in a one-month period?

c. What is the probability that the Realtor sells at most one house in a one-month period?

d. What is the probability that the Realtor sells at least two houses in a one-month period?

e. Graphically depict the probability distribution and comment on its symmetry/skewness.

SOLUTION:

a. We first note that the random variable X denotes the number of houses that the Realtor sells over a one-month period, and the possible values of X are 0, 1, 2, or 3. The probability distribution is valid because it satisfies the following two conditions: (1) all probabilities fall between 0 and 1 and (2) the probabilities sum to 1 $(0.30 + 0.50 + 0.15 + 0.05 = 1)$.

b. We find the probability that the Realtor does not sell any houses as $P(X = 0) = 0.30$.

c. We find the probability that the Realtor sells at most one house as $P(X \leq 1) = P(X = 0) + P(X = 1) = 0.30 + 0.50 = 0.80$.

d. We find the probability that the Realtor sells at least two houses as $P(X \geq 2) = P(X = 2) + P(X = 3) = 0.15 + 0.05 = 0.20$. Note that because the sum of the probabilities over all values of X equals 1, we can also find the probability as $P(X \geq 2) = 1 - P(X \leq 1) = 1 - 0.80 = 0.20$.

e. The graph in Figure 5.2 shows that the distribution is not symmetric; rather, it is positively skewed. There are small chances of selling two or three houses in a one-month period. The most likely outcome by far is selling one house over a one-month period, with a probability of 0.50.

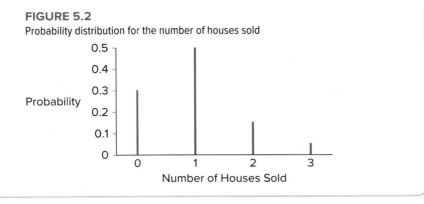

FIGURE 5.2
Probability distribution for the number of houses sold

EXERCISES 5.1

Mechanics

1. Consider the following discrete probability distribution.

x	15	22	34	40
P(X = x)	0.14	0.40	0.26	0.20

   a. Is this a valid probability distribution? Explain.
   b. Graphically depict this probability distribution.
   c. What is the probability that the random variable X is less than 40?
   d. What is the probability that the random variable X is between 10 and 30?
   e. What is the probability that the random variable X is greater than 20?

2. Consider the following discrete probability distribution.

x	−25	−15	10	20
P(X = x)	0.35	0.10		0.10

   a. Complete the probability distribution.
   b. Graphically depict the probability distribution and comment on the symmetry of the distribution.
   c. What is the probability that the random variable X is negative?
   d. What is the probability that the random variable X is greater than −20?
   e. What is the probability that the random variable X is less than 20?

3. Consider the following cumulative probability distribution.

x	0	1	2	3	4	5
P(X ≤ x)	0.15	0.35	0.52	0.78	0.84	1

   a. Calculate $P(X \leq 3)$.
   b. Calculate $P(X = 3)$.
   c. Calculate $P(2 \leq X \leq 4)$.

4. Consider the following cumulative probability distribution.

x	−25	0	25	50
P(X ≤ x)	0.25	0.50	0.75	1

   a. Calculate $P(X \leq 0)$.
   b. Calculate $P(X = 50)$.
   c. Is this a discrete uniform distribution? Explain.

Applications

5. Identify the possible values of the following random variables. Which of the random variables are discrete?
   a. The numerical grade a student receives in a course.
   b. The grade point average of a student.
   c. The salary of an employee, defined in figures (four-figure, five-figure, etc.).
   d. The salary of an employee defined in dollars.

6. Identify the possible values of the following random variables. Which of the random variables are discrete?
   a. The advertised size of a round Domino's pizza.
   b. The actual size of a round Domino's pizza.
   c. The number of daily visitors to Yosemite National Park.
   d. The age of a visitor to Yosemite National Park.

7. India is the second most populous country in the world, with a population of over 1 billion people. Some argue that the birth rate, especially in rural India, is still too high to be sustainable. A demographer assumes the following probability distribution for the household size in India.

Household Size	Probability
1	0.05
2	0.09
3	0.12
4	0.24
5	0.25
6	0.12
7	0.07
8	0.06

a. What is the probability that there are fewer than 5 members in a household in India?

b. What is the probability that there are 5 or more members in a household in India?

c. What is the probability that the number of members in a household in India is strictly between 3 and 6, not including the end points 3 and 6?

8. A financial analyst creates the following probability distribution for the performance of an equity income mutual fund.

Performance	Numerical Score	Probability
Very poor	1	0.14
Poor	2	0.43
Neutral	3	0.22
Good	4	0.16
Very good	5	0.05

a. Comment on the optimism or pessimism depicted in the analyst's estimates.

b. Convert the probability distribution to a cumulative probability distribution.

c. What is the probability that this mutual fund will do at least Good?

9. A basketball player is fouled while attempting to make a basket and receives two free throws. The opposing coach believes there is a 55% chance that the player will miss both shots, a 25% chance that he will make one of the shots, and a 20% chance that he will make both shots.

a. Construct the appropriate probability distribution.

b. What is the probability that he makes no more than one of the shots?

c. What is the probability that he makes at least one of the shots?

10. Using new economic data, an analyst believes that there is a 75% chance that the consumer confidence index will fall by more than 10% and only a 5% chance that it will rise by more than 5%. The confidence index is scored as 1 if it falls by more than 10%, 2 if the change is between −10% and 5%, and 3 if it rises by more than 5%.

a. According to the analyst, what is the probability that the confidence score is 2?

b. According to the analyst, what is the probability that the confidence score is not 1?

11. Professor Sanchez has been teaching Principles of Economics for over 25 years. He uses the following scale for grading.

Grade	Numerical Score	Probability
A	4	0.10
B	3	0.30
C	2	0.40
D	1	0.10
F	0	0.10

a. Depict the probability distribution graphically. Comment on whether or not the probability distribution is symmetric.

b. Convert the probability distribution to a cumulative probability distribution.

c. What is the probability of earning at least a B in Professor Sanchez's course?

d. What is the probability of passing Professor Sanchez's course?

12. Professor Khurana expects to be able to use her grant money to fund up to two students for research assistance. While she realizes that there is a 5% chance that she may not be able to fund any student, there is an 80% chance that she will be able to fund two students.

a. What is the probability that Professor Khurana will fund one student?

b. Construct a cumulative probability distribution for the number of students that Professor Khurana will be able to fund.

13. Fifty percent of the customers who go to Auto Center for tires buy four tires and 30% buy two tires. Moreover, 18% buy fewer than two tires, with 5% buying none.

a. What is the probability that a customer buys three tires?

b. Construct a cumulative probability distribution for the number of tires bought.

5.2 EXPECTED VALUE, VARIANCE, AND STANDARD DEVIATION

Calculate and interpret summary measures for a discrete random variable.

The analysis of probability distributions is useful because it allows us to calculate probabilities associated with the different values that the random variable assumes. In addition, it helps us calculate summary measures for a random variable. These summary measures include the mean, the variance, and the standard deviation.

One of the most important probabilistic concepts in statistics is that of the **expected value,** also referred to as the population mean. The expected value of the discrete random variable X, denoted by $E(X)$ or μ, is a weighted average of all possible values of X.

The mean μ of the random variable X provides us with a measure of the central location of the distribution of X, but it does not give us information on how the various values are dispersed from μ. We again use the measures of variance and standard deviation to indicate whether the values of X are clustered about μ or widely scattered from μ. The following definition box gives the formulas for the expected value, the variance, and the standard deviation for a discrete random variable.

SUMMARY MEASURES FOR A DISCRETE RANDOM VARIABLE

Consider a discrete random variable X with values $x_1, x_2, x_3, \ldots$, which occur with probabilities $P(X = x_i)$. The expected value or the mean of X, denoted by $E(X)$ or μ, is calculated as

$$E(X) = \mu = \Sigma x_i P(X = x_i).$$

The variance of X, denoted as $Var(X)$ or σ^2, is calculated as

$$Var(X) = \sigma^2 = \Sigma(x_i - \mu)^2 P(X = x_i).$$

The standard deviation of X, denoted as $SD(X)$ or σ, is calculated as

$$SD(X) = \sigma = \sqrt{\sigma^2}.$$

EXAMPLE 5.3

Brad Williams is the owner of a large car dealership in Chicago. Brad decides to construct an incentive compensation program that equitably and consistently compensates employees on the basis of their performance. He offers an annual bonus of $10,000 for superior performance, $6,000 for good performance, $3,000 for fair performance, and $0 for poor performance. Based on prior records, he expects an employee to perform at superior, good, fair, and poor performance levels with probabilities 0.15, 0.25, 0.40, and 0.20, respectively. Table 5.4 lists the bonus amount, performance type, and the corresponding probabilities.

TABLE 5.4 Probability Distribution for Compensation Program

Bonus (in $1,000s)	Performance Type	Probability
10	Superior	0.15
6	Good	0.25
3	Fair	0.40
0	Poor	0.20

a. Calculate the expected value of the annual bonus amount.

b. Calculate the variance and the standard deviation of the annual bonus amount.

c. What is the total annual amount that Brad can expect to pay in bonuses if he has 25 employees?

SOLUTION:

a. Let the random variable X denote the bonus amount (in $1,000s) for an employee. The first and second columns of Table 5.5 represent the probability distribution of X. The calculations for the expected value are provided in the third column. We weigh each outcome by its respective probability, $x_iP(X = x_i)$, and then sum these weighted values. Thus, as shown at the bottom of the third column, $E(X) = \mu = \Sigma x_iP(X = x_i) = 4.2$, or \$4,200. Note that the expected value is not one of the possible values of X; that is, none of the employees will earn a bonus of \$4,200. We generally interpret expected value as a long-run average.

TABLE 5.5 Calculations for Example 5.3

X_i	$P(X = x_i)$	$x_iP(X = x_i)$	$(x_i - \mu)^2P(X = x_i)$
10	0.15	$10 \times 0.15 = 1.5$	$(10 - 4.2)^2 \times 0.15 = 5.05$
6	0.25	$6 \times 0.25 = 1.5$	$(6 - 4.2)^2 \times 0.25 = 0.81$
3	0.40	$3 \times 0.40 = 1.2$	$(3 - 4.2)^2 \times 0.40 = 0.58$
0	0.20	$0 \times 0.20 = 0$	$(0 - 4.2)^2 \times 0.20 = 3.53$
		Total = 4.2	Total = 9.97

b. The last column of Table 5.5 shows the calculation for the variance. We first calculate each x_i's squared difference from the mean $(x_i - \mu)^2$; weigh each value by the appropriate probability, $(x_i - \mu)^2P(X = x_i)$; and then sum these weighted squared differences. Thus, as shown at the bottom of the last column, $Var(X) = \sigma^2 = \Sigma(x_i - \mu)^2P(X = x_i) = 9.97$, or 9.97 (in (\$1,000s)^2). The standard deviation is the positive square root of the variance, $SD(X) = \sigma = \sqrt{9.97} = 3.158$, or \$3,158.

c. In part a we found that the expected bonus of an employee is \$4,200. Because Brad has 25 employees, he can expect to pay \$4,200 × 25 = \$105,000 in bonuses.

EXERCISES 5.2

Mechanics

14. Calculate the mean, the variance, and the standard deviation of the following discrete probability distribution.

x	5	10	15	20
$P(X = x)$	0.35	0.30	0.20	0.15

15. Calculate the mean, the variance, and the standard deviation of the following discrete probability distribution.

x	−23	−17	−9	−3
$P(X = x)$	0.50	0.25	0.15	0.10

Applications

16. The number of homes that a Realtor sells over a one-month period has the following probability distribution.

Number of Houses Sold	Probability
0	0.30
1	0.50
2	0.15
3	0.05

a. On average, how many houses is the Realtor expected to sell over a one-month period?

b. What is the standard deviation of this probability distribution?

17. A marketing firm is considering making up to three new hires. Given its specific needs, the management feels that there is a 60% chance of hiring at least two candidates. There is only a 5% chance that it will not make any hires and a 10% chance that it will make all three hires.

a. What is the probability that the firm will make at least one hire?

b. Find the expected value and the standard deviation of the number of hires.

18. An analyst has developed the following probability distribution for the rate of return for a common stock.

Scenario	Probability	Rate of Return (in %)
1	0.30	−5
2	0.45	0
3	0.25	10

a. Calculate the expected rate of return.

b. Calculate the variance and the standard deviation of this probability distribution.

19. Organizers of an outdoor summer concert in Toronto are concerned about the weather conditions on the day of the concert. They will make a profit of $25,000 on a clear day and $10,000 on a cloudy day. They will take a loss of $5,000 if it rains. The weather channel has predicted a 60% chance of rain on the day of the concert. Calculate the expected profit from the concert if the likelihood is 10% that it will be sunny and 30% that it will be cloudy.

20. Mark Underwood is a professor of economics at Indiana University. He has been teaching Principles of Economics for over 25 years. Professor Underwood uses the following scale for grading.

Grade	Probability
A	0.10
B	0.30
C	0.40
D	0.10
F	0.10

Calculate the expected numerical grade in Professor Underwood's class using 4.0 for A, 3.0 for B, etc.

21. The manager of a publishing company plans to give a $20,000 bonus to the top 15%, $10,000 to the next 30%, and $5,000 to the next 10% of sales representatives. If the publishing company has a total of 200 sales representatives, what is the expected bonus that the company will pay?

22. An appliance store sells additional warranties on its refrigerators. Twenty percent of the buyers buy the limited warranty for $100 and 5% buy the extended warranty for $200. What is the expected revenue for the store from the warranty if it sells 120 refrigerators?

23. Four years ago, Victor purchased a very reliable automobile. His warranty has just expired, but the manufacturer has just offered him a 5-year, bumper-to-bumper warranty extension. The warranty costs $3,400. Victor constructs the following probability distribution with respect to anticipated costs if he chooses not to purchase the extended warranty.

Cost (in $)	Probability
1,000	0.25
2,000	0.45
5,000	0.20
10,000	0.10

a. Calculate Victor's expected cost.

b. Given your answer in part a, should Victor purchase the extended warranty? Explain.

24. You are considering buying insurance for your new laptop computer, which you have recently bought for $1,500. The insurance premium for three years is $80. Over the three-year period there is an 8% chance that your laptop computer will require work worth $400, a 3% chance that it will require work worth $800, and a 2% chance that it will completely break down with a scrap value of $100. Should you buy the insurance?

25. An investor considers investing $10,000 in the stock market. He believes that the probability is 0.30 that the economy will improve, 0.40 that it will stay the same, and 0.30 that it will deteriorate. Further, if the economy improves, he expects his investment to grow to $15,000, but it can also go down to $8,000 if the economy deteriorates. If the economy stays the same, his investment will stay at $10,000. What is the expected value of his investment?

26. The investment team at a high-tech company is considering an innovative start-up project. According to its estimates, the company can make a profit of $5 million if the project is very successful and $2 million if it is somewhat successful. It also stands to lose $4 million if the project fails. Calculate the expected profit or loss for the company if the probabilities that the project is very successful and somewhat successful are 0.10 and 0.40, respectively.

27. Fifty percent of the customers who go to Auto Center for tires buy four tires and 30% buy two tires. Moreover, 18% buy fewer than two tires, with 5% buying none.

a. Find the expected value of the number of tires a customer buys.

b. If Auto Center makes a $15 profit on every tire it sells, what is its expected profit if it services 120 customers?

28. Rent-to-own (RTO) stores allow consumers immediate access to merchandise in exchange for a series of weekly or monthly payments. The agreement is for a fixed time period. At the same time, the customer has the flexibility to terminate the contract by returning the merchandise. Suppose an RTO store makes a $200 profit on appliances when the customer ends up owning the merchandise by making all payments. It makes a $20 profit when the customer returns the product and a loss of $600 when the customer defaults. Let the return and default probabilities be 0.60 and 0.05, respectively.

a. Construct a probability distribution for the profit per appliance.

b. What is the expected profit for a store that sells 200 rent-to-own contracts?

5.3 THE BINOMIAL DISTRIBUTION

Different types of experiments generate different probability distributions. In the next three sections, we discuss three special cases: the binomial, the Poisson, and the hypergeometric probability distributions. Here we focus on the binomial distribution. Before we can discuss the binomial distribution, we first must ensure that the experiment satisfies the conditions of a **Bernoulli process,** which is a particular type of experiment named after the person who first described it, the Swiss mathematician James Bernoulli (1654–1705).

A BERNOULLI PROCESS

A Bernoulli process consists of a series of n independent and identical trials of an experiment such that on each trial:

- There are only two possible outcomes, conventionally labeled success and failure; and
- The probabilities of success and failure remain the same from trial to trial.

We use p to denote the probability of success, and therefore, $1 - p$ is the probability of failure.

A **binomial random variable** is defined as the number of successes achieved in the n trials of a Bernoulli process. The possible values of a binomial random variable include $0, 1, \ldots, n$. Many experiments fit the conditions of a Bernoulli process. For instance:

- A customer defaults or does not default on a loan.
- A consumer reacts positively or negatively to a social media campaign.
- A drug is effective or ineffective.
- A college graduate applies or does not apply to graduate school.

Based on two parameters, n and p, the **binomial probability distribution,** or simply the **binomial distribution,** allows us to attach probabilities to various outcomes of a Bernoulli process.

THE BINOMIAL DISTRIBUTION

For a binomial random variable X, the probability of x successes in n Bernoulli trials is

$$P(X = x) = \binom{n}{x} p^x (1 - p)^{n-x} = \frac{n!}{x!(n - x)!} p^x (1 - p)^{n-x}$$

where $x = 0, 1, 2, \ldots, n$. By definition, $0! = 1$.

The formula consists of two parts:

- The first part, $\binom{n}{x} = \frac{n!}{x!(n - x)!}$, is referred to as the binomial coefficient, and it tells us how many sequences with x successes and $n - x$ failures are possible in n trials. For instance, suppose we are interested in the number of sequences with 1 success in 3 trials. Letting S = success and F = failure, we find three relevant sequences, denoted by (S, F, F), (F, S, F), and (F, F, S). Alternatively, we can substitute $x = 1$ and $n = 3$ into the formula and calculate $\binom{n}{x} = \frac{n!}{x!(n - x)!} = \frac{3!}{1!(3 - 1)!} = \frac{3 \times 2 \times 1}{(1) \times (2 \times 1)} = 3$. So there are three sequences having exactly 1 success.

- The second part, $p^x(1 - p)^{n-x}$, represents the probability of any particular sequence with x successes and $n - x$ failures. Thus, in order to obtain the overall probability of getting x successes in n trials, we multiply the number of sequences with x successes and $n - x$ failures by the probability of obtaining any one particular sequence.

Moreover, we could use the formulas shown in Section 5.2 to calculate the expected value, the variance, and the standard deviation for any binomial random variable. For the binomial distribution, these formulas simplify to $E(X) = np$, $Var(X) = np(1 - p)$, and $SD(X) = \sqrt{np(1 - p)}$.

SUMMARY MEASURES FOR A BINOMIAL RANDOM VARIABLE

If X is a binomial random variable, then

$$E(X) = \mu = np,$$
$$Var(X) = \sigma^2 = np(1 - p), \text{ and}$$
$$SD(X) = \sigma = \sqrt{np(1 - p)}.$$

EXAMPLE 5.4

A firm has estimated that 30% of its customers react positively to its new web features. Suppose five customers are randomly selected.

a. What is the probability that none of the customers reacts positively to the firm's new web features?

b. Calculate the expected number of customers who react positively to the firm's new web features.

SOLUTION: Note that the given experiment satisfies the conditions for a Bernoulli process with $n = 5$. Here, a customer either reacts positively, with probability $p = 0.30$, or does not react positively, with probability $1 - p = 1 - 0.30 = 0.70$.

a. In order to find the probability that none of the customers reacts positively, we let $x = 0$ and find

$$P(X = 0) = \frac{5!}{0!(5 - 0)!} \times (0.30)^0 \times (0.70)^{5-0} = 0.1681.$$

In other words, from a random sample of five customers, there is a 16.81% chance that none of them reacts positively to the firm's new web features.

b. We calculate the expected number of customers who react positively to the firm's new web features as

$$E(X) = np = 5 \times 0.30 = 1.5 \text{ customers.}$$

Using Excel to Find Binomial Probabilities

It is cumbersome to find binomial probabilities with the formula, especially when n is large and X assumes a wide range of values. In Example 5.5, we will show how to find these probabilities with Excel.

EXAMPLE 5.5

People turn to social media to stay in touch with friends and family members, catch the news, look for employment, and be entertained. According to a recent survey, 68% of all U.S. adults are Facebook users. Consider a sample of 100 randomly selected American adults.

a. What is the probability that exactly 70 American adults are Facebook users?

b. What is the probability that no more than 70 American adults are Facebook users?

c. What is the probability that at least 70 American adults are Facebook users?

SOLUTION: We let X denote the number of American adults who are Facebook users. We also know that $p = 0.68$ and $n = 100$.

We use Excel's **BINOM.DIST** function to calculate binomial probabilities. We enter =BINOM.DIST(x, n, p, TRUE or FALSE), where x is the number of successes, n is the number of trials, and p is the probability of success. For the last input, we enter TRUE if we want to find the cumulative probability $P(X \leq x)$ or FALSE if we want to find the probability $P(X = x)$.

a. In order to find the probability that exactly 70 American adults are Facebook users, $P(X = 70)$, we enter =BINOM.DIST(70, 100, 0.68, FALSE) and Excel returns 0.0791.

b. In order to find the probability that no more than 70 American adults are Facebook users, $P(X \leq 70)$, we enter =BINOM.DIST(70, 100, 0.68, TRUE) and Excel returns 0.7007.

c. In order to find the probability that at least 70 American adults are Facebook users, $P(X \geq 70) = 1 - P(X \leq 69)$, we enter =1-BINOM.DIST(69, 100, 0.68, TRUE) and Excel returns 0.3784.

EXERCISES 5.3

Mechanics

29. Assume that X is a binomial random variable with $n = 6$ and $p = 0.68$. Calculate the following probabilities.
    a. $P(X = 5)$
    b. $P(X = 4)$
    c. $P(X \geq 4)$

30. Assume that X is a binomial random variable with $n = 8$ and $p = 0.32$. Calculate the following probabilities.
    a. $P(3 < X < 5)$
    b. $P(3 < X \leq 5)$
    c. $P(3 \leq X \leq 5)$

31. Let the probability of success on a Bernoulli trial be 0.30. In five Bernoulli trials, what is the probability that there will be (a) four failures and (b) more than the expected number of failures?

32. Let X represent a binomial random variable with $n = 150$ and $p = 0.36$. Find the following probabilities.
    a. $P(X \leq 50)$
    b. $P(X = 40)$

c. $P(X > 60)$
d. $P(X \geq 55)$

33. Let X represent a binomial random variable with $n = 200$ and $p = 0.77$. Find the following probabilities.

    a. $P(X \leq 150)$
    b. $P(X > 160)$
    c. $P(155 \leq X \leq 165)$
    d. $P(X = 160)$

Applications

34. It is reported that only 26% of Americans have confidence in U.S. banks, which is far below the pre-recession level of 41% reported in June 2007.

    a. What is the probability that fewer than half of four Americans have confidence in U.S. banks?

    b. What would have been the corresponding probability in 2007?

35. At a local community college, 40% of students who enter the college as first-year students go on to graduate. Ten first-year students are randomly selected.
    a. What is the probability that none of them graduates from the local community college?
    b. What is the probability that at most nine will graduate from the local community college?
    c. What is the expected number that will graduate?

36. A study finds that approximately 43% of millennials are not investing in stocks, bonds, real estate, and more. This is a problem because people who start investing when they are first starting their careers have more time to generate returns that will help them accomplish their financial goals. Six millennials are randomly selected.
    a. What is the expected number of millennials who are not investing? What is the corresponding standard deviation?
    b. What is the probability that less than two millennials are not investing?
    c. What is the probability that all six millennials are investing?

37. A recent survey suggests that 25 percent of employed adults are unsatisfied with their current job. The remaining employed adults are satisfied with their job.
    a. What is the probability that exactly two in a random sample of five employed adults are satisfied with their job?
    b. What is the probability that two or more in a random sample of five employed adults are satisfied with their job?
    c. What is the probability that more than the expected number of employed adults are satisfied with their job in a random sample of five employed adults?
    d. What is the probability that more than the expected number of employed adults are satisfied with their job in a random sample of 10 employed adults?

38. According to the U.S. Census, roughly half of all marriages in the United States end in divorce. Researchers from leading universities have shown that the emotions aroused by one person's divorce can transfer like a virus, making divorce contagious. A split-up between immediate friends increases a person's own chances of getting divorced from 36% to 63%.
    a. Compute the probability that more than half of four randomly selected marriages will end in divorce.
    b. Redo part a if it is known that the couple's immediate friends have split up.
    c. Redo part a if it is known that none of the couple's immediate friends has split up.

39. Sixty percent of a firm's employees are male. Suppose four of the firm's employees are randomly selected.
    a. What is more likely, finding three male employees or two male employees?
    b. Do you obtain the same answer as in part a if 70% of the firm's employees had been male?

40. The principal of an architecture firm tells her client that there is at least a 50% chance of having an acceptable design by the end of the week. She knows that there is only a 25% chance that any one designer would be able to do so by the end of the week.
    a. Would she be correct in her statement to the client if she asks two of her designers to work on the design, independently?
    b. If not, what if she asks three of her designers to work on the design, independently?

41. Suppose 40% of recent college graduates plan on pursuing a graduate degree. Fifteen recent college graduates are randomly selected.
    a. What is the probability that no more than four of the college graduates plan to pursue a graduate degree?
    b. What is the probability that exactly seven of the college graduates plan to pursue a graduate degree?
    c. What is the probability that at least six but no more than nine of the college graduates plan to pursue a graduate degree?

42. A manager at 24/7 Fitness Center is strategic about contacting open house attendees. With her strategy, she believes that 40% of the attendees she contacts will purchase a club membership. Suppose she contacts 20 open house attendees.
    a. What is the probability that exactly 10 of the attendees will purchase a club membership?
    b. What is the probability that no more than 10 of the attendees will purchase a club membership?
    c. What is the probability that at least 15 of the attendees will purchase a club membership?

43. Fraud detection has become an indispensable tool for banks and credit card companies to combat fraudulent credit card transactions. A fraud detection firm has detected minor fraudulent activities in 1.31% of transactions and serious fraudulent activities in 0.87% of transactions. Assume that fraudulent transactions remain stable.
    a. What is the probability that there are minor fraudulent activities in fewer than 2 out of 100 transactions?
    b. What is the probability that there are serious fraudulent activities in fewer than 2 out of 100 transactions?

44. Apple products have become a household name in America, with 51% of all households owning at least one Apple product.
    a. What is the probability that two in a random sample of four households own an Apple product?
    b. What is the probability that all four in a random sample of four households own an Apple product?
    c. In a random sample of 100 households, find the expected value and the standard deviation for the number of households that own an Apple product.

45. Forty-four percent of consumers with credit cards carry balances from month to month. Four consumers with credit cards are randomly selected.

   a. What is the probability that all four consumers carry a credit card balance?

   b. What is the probability that fewer than two consumers carry a credit card balance?

   c. Calculate the expected value, the variance, and the standard deviation for this distribution.

46. Email spam refers to unsolicited email messages sent in bulk. Recent estimates suggest that spam messages account for 55% of all email traffic. Suppose a service department receives 100 emails daily.

   a. What is the probability that exactly 50 are spam messages?

   b. What is the probability that more than 50 are spam messages?

   c. What is the probability that at least 50 are spam messages?

47. According to the Department of Transportation, 27% of domestic flights are delayed. Suppose five flights are randomly selected at an airport.

   a. What is the probability that all five flights are delayed?

   b. What is the probability that all five are on time?

5.4 THE POISSON DISTRIBUTION

Calculate and interpret probabilities for a Poisson random variable.

Another important discrete probability distribution is the **Poisson distribution,** named after the French mathematician Simeon Poisson (1781–1849). It is particularly useful in problems that deal with finding the number of occurrences of a certain event over time or space, where space refers to area or region. For simplicity, we call these occurrences "successes." Before we can discuss the Poisson distribution, we first must ensure that our experiment satisfies the conditions of a **Poisson process.**

A POISSON PROCESS

An experiment satisfies a Poisson process if

- The number of successes within a specified time or space interval equals any integer between zero and infinity.
- The number of successes counted in nonoverlapping intervals are independent.
- The probability of success in any interval is the same for all intervals of equal size and is proportional to the size of the interval.

For a Poisson process, we define the number of successes achieved in a specified time or space interval as a **Poisson random variable.**

Like the Bernoulli process, many experiments fit the conditions of a Poisson process. For instance:

- The number of customers who use a new banking app in a day.
- The number of spam emails received in a month.
- The number of defects in a 50-yard roll of fabric.
- The number of bacteria in a specified culture.

We use the following formula for calculating probabilities associated with a Poisson random variable.

> ### THE POISSON DISTRIBUTION
>
> For a Poisson random variable X, the probability of x successes over a given interval of time or space is
>
> $$P(X = x) = \frac{e^{-\mu}\mu^x}{x!},$$
>
> for $x = 0, 1, 2, \ldots$, where μ is the mean number of successes and $e \approx 2.718$ is the base of the natural logarithm.

As with the binomial random variable, we have simplified formulas to calculate the variance and the standard deviation of a Poisson random variable. An interesting fact is that the mean of the Poisson random variable is equal to the variance.

> ### SUMMARY MEASURES FOR A POISSON RANDOM VARIABLE
>
> If X is a Poisson random variable, then
>
> $$E(X) = \mu$$
> $$Var(X) = \sigma^2 = \mu, \quad \text{and}$$
> $$SD(X) = \sigma = \sqrt{\mu}.$$

EXAMPLE 5.6

The sales volume of craft beer continues to grow, amounting to 24% of the total beer market in the United States (*USA Today*, April 2, 2019). It has been estimated that 1.5 craft breweries open every day. Assume this number represents an average that remains constant over time.

a. How many craft breweries are expected to open every week?

b. What is the probability that 12 craft breweries will open next week?

SOLUTION: In applications of the Poisson distribution, we first determine the relevant mean using the condition that the probability of success in any interval is the same for all intervals of equal size and is proportional to the size of the interval. We let X denote the number of craft breweries that open every week.

a. Given the estimate of 1.5 openings of craft breweries every day, we compute the weekly expected openings as $E(X) = \mu = 1.5 \times 7 = 10.5$.

b. In order to find the probability that 12 craft breweries will open next week, we calculate $P(X = 12) = \frac{e^{-10.5}10.5^{12}}{12!} = 0.1032$. There is a 10.32% chance that 12 craft breweries will open next week.

Using Excel to Find Poisson Probabilities

As in the case of the binomial distribution, it is cumbersome to find Poisson probabilities with the formula, especially when x and μ values are large. Excel again proves useful for finding Poisson probabilities, as illustrated in Example 5.7.

EXAMPLE 5.7

We can now address questions first posed by Anne Jones in the introductory case of this chapter. Recall that Anne is concerned about staffing needs at the Starbucks that she manages. She has specific questions about the probability distribution of customer arrivals at her store. Anne believes that the typical Starbucks customer averages 18 visits to the store over a 30-day month. She has the following questions:

a. What is the probability that a customer visits the chain five times in a 5-day period?

b. What is the probability that a customer visits the chain no more than two times in a 5-day period?

c. What is the probability that a customer visits the chain at least three times in a 5-day period?

SOLUTION: We let X denote the number of visits over a 5-day period and compute the proportional mean as $\mu = 3$ because $\frac{18}{30} \times 5 = 3$. In other words, on average, a typical Starbucks customer visits the store three times over a 5-day period.

We use Excel's **POISSON.DIST** function to calculate Poisson probabilities. We enter =POISSON.DIST(x, μ, TRUE or FALSE), where x is the number of successes over some interval and μ is the mean over this interval. For the last input, we enter TRUE if we want to find the cumulative probability $P(X \leq x)$ or FALSE if we want to find the probability $P(X = x)$.

a. We need to find the probability that a customer visits the chain five times in a 5-day period; that is, $P(X = 5)$. In Excel, we enter =POISSON.DIST(5, 3, FALSE) and Excel returns 0.1008. There is a 10.08% chance that a customer visits the chain five times in a 5-day period.

b. For the probability that a customer visits the chain no more than two times in a 5-day period, we need to find $P(X \leq 2)$. In Excel, we enter =POISSON.DIST(2, 3, TRUE) and Excel returns 0.4232. There is a 42.32% chance that a customer visits the chain no more than two times in a 5-day period.

c. We write the probability that a customer visits the chain at least three times in a 5-day period as $P(X \geq 3)$. Note that because the probabilities add up to 1, $P(X \geq 3) = 1 - P(X \leq 2)$. In Excel, we enter =1 - POISSON.DIST(2, 3, TRUE) and Excel returns 0.5768. Thus, there is a 57.68% chance that a customer will frequent the chain at least three times in a 5-day period.

SYNOPSIS OF INTRODUCTORY CASE

Anne Jones, the manager of a Starbucks store, is concerned about how the emergence of trendy coffee shops might affect foot traffic at her store. A solid understanding of the likelihood of customer arrivals is necessary before she can make further statistical inference. Historical data allow her to assume that a typical Starbucks customer averages 18 visits to a Starbucks store over a 30-day month. With this information and the knowledge that she can model customer arrivals using the Poisson distribution, she deduces that a typical customer averages three visits in a 5-day period. The likelihood that a typical customer frequents her store five times in a 5-day period is approximately 10%. Moreover, there is approximately a 42% chance that a typical customer goes to Starbucks no more than two times in a 5-day period, while the chances that this

Shutterstock

customer visits the chain at least three times is approximately 58%. These preliminary probabilities will prove vital as Anne plans her future staffing needs.

EXERCISES 5.4

Mechanics

48. Assume that X is a Poisson random variable with $\mu = 1.5$. Calculate the following probabilities.
    a. $P(X = 1)$
    b. $P(X = 2)$
    c. $P(X \geq 2)$

49. Assume that X is a Poisson random variable with $\mu = 4$. Calculate the following probabilities.
    a. $P(X = 4)$
    b. $P(X = 2)$
    c. $P(X \leq 1)$

50. Let the mean success rate of a Poisson process be 8 successes per hour.
    a. Find the expected number of successes in a half-hour period.
    b. Find the probability of at least two successes in a given half-hour period.
    c. Find the expected number of successes in a two-hour period.
    d. Find the probability of 10 successes in a given two-hour period.

51. Assume that X is a Poisson random variable with $\mu = 15$. Calculate the following probabilities.
    a. $P(X \leq 10)$
    b. $P(X = 13)$
    c. $P(X > 15)$
    d. $P(12 \leq X \leq 18)$

52. Assume that X is a Poisson random variable with $\mu = 20$. Calculate the following probabilities.

    a. $P(X < 14)$
    b. $P(X \geq 20)$
    c. $P(X = 25)$
    d. $P(18 \leq X \leq 23)$

Applications

53. On average, there are 12 potholes per mile on a particular stretch of the state highway. Suppose the potholes are distributed evenly on the highway.
    a. Find the probability of finding fewer than two potholes in a quarter-mile stretch of the highway.
    b. Find the probability of finding more than one pothole in a quarter-mile stretch of the highway.

54. A tollbooth operator has observed that cars arrive randomly at an average rate of 360 cars per hour.
    a. Find the probability that two cars arrive during a specified one-minute period.
    b. Find the probability that at least two cars arrive during a specified one-minute period.
    c. Find the probability that 40 cars arrive between 10:00 am and 10:10 am.

55. A textile manufacturing process finds that on average, two flaws occur per every 50 yards of material produced.
    a. What is the probability of exactly two flaws in a 50-yard piece of material?
    b. What is the probability of no more than two flaws in a 50-yard piece of material?
    c. What is the probability of no flaws in a 25-yard piece of material?

56. Motorists arrive at a Gulf gas station at the rate of two per minute during morning hours.
    a. What is the probability that more than two motorists will arrive at the Gulf gas station during a one-minute interval in the morning?
    b. What is the probability that exactly six motorists will arrive at the Gulf gas station during a five-minute interval in the morning?
    c. How many motorists can an employee expect in her three-hour morning shift?

57. Airline travelers should be ready to be more flexible as airlines once again cancel thousands of flights this summer. The Coalition for Airline Passengers Rights, Health, and Safety averages 400 calls a day to help stranded travelers deal with airlines. Suppose the hotline is staffed for 16 hours a day.
    a. Calculate the average number of calls in a one-hour interval, 30-minute interval, and 15-minute interval.
    b. What is the probability of exactly six calls in a 15-minute interval?
    c. What is the probability of no calls in a 15-minute interval?
    d. What is the probability of at least two calls in a 15-minute interval?

58. New Age Solar installs solar panels for residential homes. Because of the company's personalized approach, it averages three home installations daily.
    a. What is the probability that New Age Solar installs solar panels in at most four homes in a day?
    b. What is the probability that New Age Solar installs solar panels in at least three homes in a day?

59. According to a government report, the aging of the U.S. population is translating into many more visits to doctors' offices and hospitals. It is estimated that an average person makes four visits a year to doctors' offices and hospitals.
    a. What are the mean and the standard deviation of an average person's number of monthly visits to doctors' offices and hospitals?
    b. What is the probability that an average person does not make any monthly visits to doctors' offices and hospitals?
    c. What is the probability that an average person makes at least one monthly visit to doctors' offices and hospitals?

60. A local pharmacy administers an average of 84 vaccines per week. The vaccine shots are evenly administered across all days.

   a. Find the probability that the number of vaccine shots administered on a Wednesday is more than 8 but less than 12.

   b. Find the probability that the number of vaccine shots administered on weekdays (Monday through Friday) is more than 60.

61. Last year there were 24,584 age-discrimination claims filed with the Equal Employment Opportunity Commission. Assume there were 260 working days in the fiscal year for which a worker could file a claim.

   a. Calculate the average number of claims filed on a working day.

   b. What is the probability that exactly 100 claims were filed on a working day?

   c. What is the probability that no more than 100 claims were filed on a working day?

62. Studies have shown that bats can consume an average of 10 mosquitoes per minute.

   a. Calculate the average number of mosquitoes that a bat consumes in a 30-second interval.

   b. What is the probability that a bat consumes four mosquitoes in a 30-second interval?

   c. What is the probability that a bat does not consume any mosquitoes in a 30-second interval?

   d. What is the probability that a bat consumes at least one mosquito in a 30-second interval?

63. The police have estimated that there are 12 major accidents per day on a particular 10-mile stretch of a national highway. Suppose the incidence of accidents is evenly distributed on this 10-mile stretch of the highway.

   a. Find the probability that there will be fewer than eight major accidents per day on this 10-mile stretch of the highway.

   b. Find the probability that there will be more than two accidents per day on a one-mile stretch of this highway.

LO 5.5

5.5 THE HYPERGEOMETRIC DISTRIBUTION

Calculate and interpret probabilities for a hypergeometric random variable.

In Section 5.3, we defined a binomial random variable X as the number of successes in the n trials of a Bernoulli process. The trials, according to a Bernoulli process, are independent and the probability of success does not change from trial to trial. The **hypergeometric distribution** is appropriate in applications where we cannot assume that the trials are independent.

Consider a box full of production items, of which 10% are known to be defective. Let success be labeled as the draw of a defective item. The probability of success may not be the same from trial to trial; it will depend on the number of trials and whether the sampling was done with or without replacement. Suppose the box consists of 20 items of which 10%, or 2, are defective. The probability of success in the first draw is 0.10 (= 2/20). However, the probability of success in subsequent draws will depend on the outcome of the first draw. For example, if the first item was defective, the probability of success in the second draw will be 0.0526 (= 1/19), while if the first item was not defective, the probability of success in the second draw will be 0.1053 (= 2/19).

In the preceding example, we assumed sampling without replacement; that is, after an item is drawn, it is not put back in the box for subsequent draws. Therefore, the binomial distribution is not appropriate because the trials are not independent and the probability of success changes from trial to trial. The binomial distribution would be appropriate if we sample with replacement because, in that case, for each draw there will be 20 items, of which 2 are defective, resulting in an unchanging probability of success. It is important to note that the dependence of the trials can be ignored if the population size is very large relative to the sample size. For instance, if the box consists of 10,000, items, of which 10%, or 1,000, are defective, then the probability of success in the second draw will be either 999/9,999 or 1,000/9,999, which are both approximately equal to 0.10.

We use the hypergeometric distribution in place of the binomial distribution when we are sampling without replacement from a population whose size N is not significantly larger than the sample size n. The **hypergeometric random variable** is the number of successes achieved in the n trials of an experiment, where the trials are not assumed to be independent.

THE HYPERGEOMETRIC DISTRIBUTION

For a hypergeometric random variable X, the probability of x successes in a random selection of n items is

$$P(X = x) = \frac{\binom{S}{x}\binom{N-S}{n-x}}{\binom{N}{n}},$$

for $x = 0, 1, 2, \ldots, n$ if $n \leq S$ or $x = 0, 1, 2, \ldots, S$ if $n > S$, where N denotes the number of items in the population of which S are successes.

The formula consists of three parts:

- The first term in the numerator, $\binom{S}{x} = \frac{S!}{x!(S-x)!}$, represents the number of ways x successes can be selected from S successes in the population.
- The second term in the numerator, $\binom{N-S}{n-x} = \frac{(N-S)!}{(n-x)!(N-S-n+x)!}$, represents the number of ways $(n-x)$ failures can be selected from $(N-S)$ failures in the population.
- The denominator, $\binom{N}{n} = \frac{N!}{n!(N-n)!}$, represents the number of ways a sample of size n can be selected from the population of size N.

As with the binomial and Poisson distributions, simplified formulas can be used to calculate the mean, the variance, and the standard deviation for a hypergeometric random variable.

SUMMARY MEASURES FOR A HYPERGEOMETRIC RANDOM VARIABLE

If X is a hypergeometric random variable, then

$$E(X) = \mu = n\left(\frac{S}{N}\right),$$

$$Var(X) = \sigma^2 = n\left(\frac{S}{N}\right)\left(1 - \frac{S}{N}\right)\left(\frac{N-n}{N-1}\right), \text{ and}$$

$$SD(X) = \sigma = \sqrt{n\left(\frac{S}{N}\right)\left(1 - \frac{S}{N}\right)\left(\frac{N-n}{N-1}\right)}.$$

EXAMPLE 5.8

Wooden boxes are commonly used for the packaging and transportation of mangoes. A convenience store in Morganville, New Jersey, regularly buys mangoes from a wholesale dealer. For every shipment, the manager randomly inspects five mangoes from a box containing 20 mangoes for damages due to transportation. Suppose the chosen box contains exactly two damaged mangoes.

a. What is the probability that one out of five mangoes used in the inspection is damaged?

b. Calculate the expected value, the variance, and the standard deviation of the number of damaged mangoes used in the inspection.

SOLUTION: The hypergeometric distribution is appropriate because the probability of finding a damaged mango changes from draw to draw (sampling is without replacement and the population size N is not significantly more than the sample size n). We use the following values to solve the problems: $N = 20$, $n = 5$, $S = 2$.

a. The probability that one out of five mangoes is damaged is $P(X = 1)$. We calculate

$$P(X = 1) = \frac{\binom{2}{1}\binom{20-2}{5-1}}{\binom{20}{5}} = \frac{\left(\frac{2!}{1!1!}\right)\left(\frac{18!}{4!14!}\right)}{\left(\frac{20!}{5!15!}\right)} = \frac{(2)(3,060)}{15,504} = 0.3947.$$

Therefore, the likelihood that exactly one out of five mangoes is damaged is 39.47%.

b. We use the simplified formulas to obtain the mean, the variance, and the standard deviation as

$$E(X) = n\left(\frac{S}{N}\right) = 5\left(\frac{2}{20}\right) = 0.50,$$

$$Var(X) = n\left(\frac{S}{N}\right)\left(1 - \frac{S}{N}\right)\left(\frac{N-n}{N-1}\right) = 5\left(\frac{2}{20}\right)\left(1 - \frac{2}{20}\right)\left(\frac{20-5}{20-1}\right) = 0.3553,$$

$$SD(X) = \sqrt{0.3553} = 0.5960.$$

Using Excel to Find Hypergeometric Probabilities

As in the case of binomial and Poisson distributions, it is cumbersome to find hypergeometric probabilities with the formula. We again use Excel for finding probabilities, as illustrated in Example 5.9.

EXAMPLE 5.9

Employment for management analysts is projected to grow 14% from 2018 to 2028, which is much faster than the average for all occupations (*Bureau of Labor Statistics,* May 2020). Among 25 applicants for a management analyst position, 15 have college degrees in business. Suppose four applicants are randomly chosen for interviews.

a. What is the probability that none of the applicants has a college degree in business?

b. What is the probability that no more than two of the applicants have college degrees in business?

SOLUTION: We let X denote the number of applicants with a college degree in business. We know that $n = 4$, $S = 15$, and $N = 25$.

We use Excel's **HYPGEOM.DIST** function to calculate hypergeometric probabilities. We enter =HYPGEOM.DIST(x, n, S, N, TRUE or FALSE) where x is the number of successes in the sample, n is the sample size, S is the number of successes in the population, and N is the population. For the last input, we enter TRUE if we want to find the cumulative probability $P(X \leq x)$ or FALSE if we want to find the probability $P(X = x)$.

a. In order to find the probability that none of the applicants has a college degree in business, $P(X = 0)$, we enter =HYPGEOM.DIST(0, 4, 15, 25, FALSE) and Excel returns 0.0166.

b. In order to find the probability that no more than two of the applicants have a college degree in business, $P(X \leq 2)$, we enter =HYPGEOM.DIST(2, 4, 15, 25, TRUE) and Excel returns 0.5324.

EXERCISES 5.5

Mechanics

64. Assume that X is a hypergeometric random variable with $N = 25$, $S = 3$, and $n = 4$. Calculate the following probabilities.
    a. $P(X = 0)$
    b. $P(X = 1)$
    c. $P(X \leq 1)$

65. Assume that X is a hypergeometric random variable with $N = 15$, $S = 4$, and $n = 3$. Calculate the following probabilities.
    a. $P(X = 1)$
    b. $P(X = 2)$
    c. $P(X \geq 2)$

66. Compute the probability of zero success in a random sample of three items obtained from a population of 12 items that contains two successes. What are the expected number and the standard deviation of the number of successes from the sample?

67. Assume that X is a hypergeometric random variable with $N = 50$, $S = 20$, and $n = 5$. Calculate the following probabilities.
    a. $P(X = 2)$
    b. $P(X \geq 2)$
    c. $P(X \leq 3)$

68. Compute the probability of at least eight successes in a random sample of 20 items obtained from a population of 100 items that contains 25 successes. What are the expected number and the standard deviation of the number of successes?

Applications

69. Suppose you have an urn of ten marbles, of which five are red and five are green. If you draw two marbles from this urn, what is the probability that both marbles are red? What is the probability that at least one of the marbles is red?

70. A professor of management has heard that eight students in his class of 40 have landed an internship for the summer. Suppose he runs into three of his students in the corridor.
    a. Find the probability that none of these students has landed an internship.
    b. Find the probability that at least one of these students has landed an internship.

71. It is known that 10 out of 15 members of the board of directors of a company are in favor of paying a bonus to its executives. Suppose three members are randomly selected by the media.
    a. What is the probability that all of them are in favor of a bonus?
    b. What is the probability that at least two members are in favor of a bonus?

72. Many programming teams work independently at a large software company. The management has been putting pressure on these teams to finish a project on time. The company currently has 18 large programming projects, of which only 12 are likely to finish on time. Suppose the manager decides to randomly supervise three such projects.
    a. What is the probability that all three projects finish on time?
    b. What is the probability that at least two projects finish on time?

73. David Saha and his fiancée Neha Goel are visiting Hawaii. There are 20 guests registered for orientation. It is announced that 12 randomly selected registered guests will receive a free lesson of Tahitian dance.
    a. What is the probability that both David and Neha get picked for the Tahitian dance lesson?
    b. What is the probability that neither of them gets picked for the Tahitian dance lesson?

74. The National Science Foundation is fielding applications for grants to study climate change. Twenty universities apply for a grant, and only four of them will be awarded. If Syracuse University and Auburn University are among the 20 applicants, what is the probability that these two universities will receive a grant? Assume that the selection is made randomly.

75. A committee of 40 members consists of 24 graduate students and 16 undergraduate students. A subcommittee consisting of 10 randomly selected members will be formed.
    a. What are the expected number of graduate and undergraduate students on the subcommittee?
    b. What is the probability that at least half of the members on the subcommittee will be undergraduate students?

76. Powerball is a jackpot game with a grand prize starting at $20 million that often rolls over into the hundreds of millions.

The winner may choose to receive the jackpot prize paid over 29 years or as a lump-sum payment. For $1 the player selects six numbers for the base game of Powerball. There are two independent stages of the game. Five balls are randomly drawn from 59 consecutively numbered white balls. Moreover, one ball, called the Powerball, is randomly drawn from 39 consecutively numbered red balls. To be a winner, the numbers selected by the player must match the numbers on the randomly drawn white balls as well as the Powerball.

a. What is the probability that the player is able to match the numbers of two out of five randomly drawn white balls?

b. What is the probability that the player is able to match the numbers of all five randomly drawn white balls?

c. What is the probability that the player is able to match the Powerball for a randomly drawn red ball?

d. What is the probability of winning the jackpot? [*Hint: Remember that the two stages of drawing white and red balls are independent.*]

77. Suppose you draw three cards, without replacement, from a deck of well-shuffled cards. Remember that each deck consists of 52 cards, with 13 each of spades, hearts, clubs, and diamonds.

a. What is the probability that you draw all spades?

b. What is the probability that you draw two or fewer spades?

c. What is the probability that you draw all spades or all hearts?

78. A committee of 10 is to be chosen from 50 people, 25 of whom are Republicans and 25 Democrats. The committee is chosen at random.

a. What is the probability that there will be five Republicans and five Democrats?

b. What is the probability that a majority of the committee will be Republicans?

5.6 WRITING WITH DATA

Case Study

ESB Professional/Shutterstock

Senior executives at Skyhigh Construction, Inc., participate in a pick-your-salary plan. They choose salaries in a range between $125,000 and $150,000. By choosing a lower salary, an executive has an opportunity to make a larger bonus. If Skyhigh does not generate an operating profit during the year, then no bonuses are paid. Skyhigh has just hired two new senior executives, Allen Grossman and Felicia Arroyo. Each must decide whether to choose *Option* 1: a base pay of $125,000 with a possibility of a large bonus or *Option* 2: a base pay of $150,000 with a possibility of a bonus, but the bonus would be one-half of the bonus under Option 1.

Grossman, 44 years old, is married with two young children. He bought his home at the height of the market and has a rather large monthly mortgage payment. Arroyo, 32 years old, just completed her MBA at a prestigious Ivy League university. She is single and has no student loans due to a timely inheritance upon entering graduate school. Arroyo just moved to the area, so she has decided to rent an apartment for at least one year. Given their personal profiles, inherent perceptions of risk, and subjective views of the economy, Grossman and Arroyo construct their individual probability distributions with respect to bonus outcomes shown in Table 5.6.

TABLE 5.6 Grossman's and Arroyo's Probability Distributions

Bonus (in $)	Probability	
	Grossman	Arroyo
0	0.35	0.20
50,000	0.45	0.25
100,000	0.10	0.35
150,000	0.10	0.20

Jordan Lake, an independent human resources specialist, is asked to use these probability distributions to help Grossman and Arroyo decide whether to choose Option 1 or Option 2 for their compensation package.

Skyhigh Construction, Inc., has just hired two new senior executives, Allen Grossman and Felicia Arroyo, to oversee planned expansion of operations. As senior executives, they participate in a pick-your-salary plan. Each executive is given two options for compensation:

Option 1: A base pay of $125,000 with a possibility of a large bonus.
Option 2: A base pay of $150,000 with a possibility of a bonus, but the bonus would be one-half of the bonus under *Option 1*.

Grossman and Arroyo understand that if the firm does not generate an operating profit in the fiscal year, then no bonuses are paid. Each executive has constructed a probability distribution given their personal background, underlying risk preferences, and subjective view of the economy.

Given the probability distributions and with the aid of expected values, the following analysis will attempt to choose the best option for each executive. Grossman, a married father with two young children, believes that Table 5.7 best reflects his bonus payment expectations.

TABLE 5.7 Calculating Grossman's Expected Bonus

Bonus (in $), x_i	Probability, $P(x_i)$	Weighted Value, $x_i\,P(x_i)$
0	0.35	$0 \times 0.35 = 0$
50,000	0.45	$50,000 \times 0.45 = 22,500$
100,000	0.10	$100,000 \times 0.10 = 10,000$
150,000	0.10	$150,000 \times 0.10 = 15,000$
		Total = 47,500

Expected bonus, $E(X)$, is calculated as a weighted average of all possible bonus values and is shown at the bottom of the third column of Table 5.7. Grossman's expected bonus is $47,500. Using this value for his bonus, his salary options are

Option1: $125,000 + $47,500 = $172,500
Option2: $150,000 + (1/2 \times $47,500) = $173,750

Grossman should choose *Option2* as his salary plan.

Arroyo is single with few financial constraints. Table 5.8 shows the expected value of her bonus given her probability distribution.

TABLE 5.8 Calculating Arroyo's Expected Bonus title

Bonus(in$), x_i	Probability, $P(x_i)$	Weighted Value, $x_i\,P(x_i)$
0	0.20	$0 \times 0.20 = 0$
50,000	0.25	$50,000 \times 0.25 = 12,500$
100,000	0.35	$100,000 \times 0.35 = 35,000$
150,000	0.20	$150,000 \times 0.20 = 30,000$
		Total = 77,500

Arroyo's expected bonus amounts to $77,500. Thus, her salary options are

Option 1: $125,000 + $77,500 = $202,500
Option 2: $150,000 + (1/2 \times $77,500) = $188,750

Arroyo should choose *Option 1* as her salary plan.

Suggested Case Studies

Report 5.1. Despite a relatively high risk of earthquakes in California, homeowners are not required by state law to carry earthquake insurance. Earthquake insurance covers some of the losses and damage that earthquakes can cause to your home, belongings, and other buildings on your property. A Realtor in California would like to provide guidance to potential homeowners regarding earthquake insurance. She has been told that there is a 1% chance that there will be a major earthquake in the area for which the insurance would pay 15% of the house price for damages. There is also a 0.02% chance of a catastrophic situation for which the insurance would pay 50% of the house price. In a report, use this information to determine how much a homeowner should be willing to pay for earthquake insurance if the house price is $500,000, $750,000, or $1,000,000.

Report 5.2. Call centers are used for receiving or transmitting a large volume of inquiries by telephone. Employees are expected to make an average of 60 calls per day, where they market a product for their firm. It is estimated that the probability of a conversion (purchase) for each call is 4%. The average revenue for the company is $20 for each conversion. In a report, use this information to compute the daily expected revenue for the company for an employee. Also, analyze the probabilities and the resulting revenue for 0, 1, 2, 3, 4, 5, and 6 conversions by an employee.

Report 5.3. Ina Kelly is a manager at Sunnyville Bank in California. The bank has recently developed a new mobile banking app. In addition to features like mobile check deposit, seamless money transfers, and bill pay, the new app also lets customers track accounts from different financial institutions and turns their mobile device into a digital wallet. Ina is exploring staffing needs for customer service employees whose role is to provide customers with information regarding the new app and address their problems and concerns. To decide on staffing needs, she understands the importance of understanding the probability distribution of customer calls. Having too many customer service employees adds to the cost and having too few results in losing angry customers who choose not to wait for service. On a typical weekday, there is an average of 68 customer calls in the morning and 84 customer calls in the afternoon. In a report, use this information to compute the probability of morning and afternoon calls between 0 and 10, 10 and 20, . . . , and 90 and 100. Graph these distributions and summarize the findings.

6 Continuous Probability Distributions

LEARNING OBJECTIVES

After reading this chapter you should be able to:

LO **6.1** Describe a continuous random variable.

LO **6.2** Calculate and interpret probabilities for a random variable that follows the continuous uniform distribution.

LO **6.3** Calculate and interpret probabilities for a random variable that follows the normal distribution.

LO **6.4** Calculate and interpret probabilities for a random variable that follows the exponential distribution.

In Chapter 5, we classified a random variable as either discrete or continuous. A discrete random variable assumes a countable number of distinct values, such as the number of houses that a Realtor sells in a month, the number of defective pieces in a sample of 20 machine parts, and the number of cars lined up at a toll booth. A continuous random variable, on the other hand, is characterized by uncountable values within an interval. Examples of a continuous random variable include the investment return on a mutual fund, the waiting time at a toll booth, and the amount of soda in a cup. In all of these examples, it is impossible to list all possible values of the random variable.

In this chapter, we focus on continuous random variables. Most of this chapter is devoted to the normal distribution, which is the most extensively used continuous probability distribution and is the cornerstone of statistical inference. Other important continuous distributions discussed are the continuous uniform and the exponential distributions.

Vision SRL/Photodisc/Getty Images

INTRODUCTORY CASE

Demand for Salmon

Akiko Hamaguchi is the manager of a small sushi restaurant called Little Ginza in Phoenix, Arizona. As part of her job, Akiko has to purchase salmon every day for the restaurant. For the sake of freshness, it is important that she buys the right amount of salmon daily. Buying too much may result in wastage, and buying too little may disappoint some customers on high-demand days.

Akiko has estimated that the daily consumption of salmon is normally distributed with a mean of 12 pounds and a standard deviation of 3.2 pounds. She has always bought 20 pounds of salmon every day. Often, this amount of salmon has resulted in wastage. As part of cost cutting, Akiko is considering a new strategy. She will buy salmon that is sufficient to meet the daily demand of customers on 90% of the days.

Akiko wants to use this information to

1. Calculate the probability that the demand for salmon at Little Ginza is above 20 pounds.
2. Calculate the probability that the demand for salmon at Little Ginza is below 15 pounds.
3. Determine the amount of salmon that should be bought daily so that the restaurant meets demand on 90% of the days.

A synopsis of this case is provided in Section 6.2.

6.1 CONTINUOUS RANDOM VARIABLES AND THE UNIFORM DISTRIBUTION

Describe a continuous random variable.

As discussed in Chapter 5, a discrete random variable X assumes a countable number of distinct values such as x_1, x_2, x_3, and so on. A continuous random variable, on the other hand, is characterized by uncountable values within an interval. Unlike the case of a discrete random variable, we cannot describe the possible values of a continuous random variable X with a list x_1, x_2, . . . because the value $(x_1 + x_2)/2$, not in the list, might also be possible. Examples of continuous random variables include the return on a mutual fund, the waiting time at a toll booth, or the amount of soda in a cup.

For a discrete random variable, we can compute the probability that it assumes a particular value x, or, written as a probability statement, $P(X = x)$. For instance, for a binomial random variable with a given probability of success p, we can calculate the probability of exactly one success in n trials; that is, $P(X = 1)$.

The probability that a continuous random variable assumes a particular value x is zero; that is, $P(X = x) = 0$. This occurs because we cannot assign a nonzero probability to each of the uncountable values and still have the probabilities sum to one. For a continuous random variable, it is meaningful to calculate the probability within some specified interval. Therefore, for a continuous random variable, $P(a \leq X \leq b) = P(a < X < b) = P(a \leq X < b) = P(a < X \leq b)$ because $P(X = a)$ and $P(X = b)$ are both zero.

As discussed in Chapter 5, every discrete random variable is associated with a probability distribution, also called the probability mass function, that provides the probability that the random variable X assumes a particular value x, or, equivalently, $P(X = x)$. For a continuous random variable, the counterpart to the probability mass function is called the probability density function, denoted by $f(x)$. The graph of $f(x)$ approximates the relative frequency polygon for the population data. The probability that the continuous random variable assumes a value within an interval, say $P(a \leq X \leq b)$, is defined as the area under $f(x)$ between points a and b. Moreover, the entire area under $f(x)$ over all values of x must equal one; this is equivalent to the fact that, for discrete random variables, the probabilities add up to one.

THE PROBABILITY DENSITY FUNCTION

The probability density function $f(x)$ for a continuous random variable X has the following properties:

- $f(x) \geq 0$ for all possible values x of X and
- the area under $f(x)$ over all values x of X equals one.

It is important to emphasize that the value of the probability density function does not directly represent a probability. It is the area under $f(x)$ that corresponds to probability. As in the case for a discrete random variable, we can use the cumulative distribution function, denoted by $F(x)$, to compute probabilities for a continuous random variable. For a value x of the random variable X, $F(x) = P(X \leq x)$ is simply the area under the probability density function up to the value x.

Calculate and interpret probabilities for a random variable that follows the continuous uniform distribution.

The Continuous Uniform Distribution

One of the simplest continuous probability distributions is called the **continuous uniform distribution**, also referred to as the **rectangular distribution**. This distribution is appropriate when the underlying random variable has an equally likely chance of assuming a value within a specified range. Uniformly distributed random variables are often used to approximate the delivery time of an appliance, the scheduled flight time between cities, and the waiting time for a campus bus. Any specified range for each of the above random variables can be assumed to be equally probable.

Suppose you are informed that your new refrigerator will be delivered between 2:00 pm and 3:00 pm. Let the random variable X denote the delivery time of your refrigerator. This variable is bounded below by 2:00 pm and above by 3:00 pm for a total range of 60 minutes. It is reasonable to infer that the probability of delivery between 2:00 pm and 2:30 pm equals 0.50 (= 30/60), as does the probability of delivery between 2:30 pm and 3:00 pm. Similarly, the probability of delivery in any 15-minute interval equals 0.25 (= 15/60), and so on.

Figure 6.1 depicts the probability density function, $f(x) = \frac{1}{b-a}$, for a continuous uniform random variable. The values a and b represent the lower and upper limits, respectively, of the random variable. The continuous uniform distribution is symmetric around its mean μ, computed as $\frac{a+b}{2}$. In the refrigerator delivery example, the mean is $\mu = \frac{2+3}{2} = 2.5$, implying that you expect the delivery at 2:30 pm. The standard deviation σ of a continuous uniform random variable equals $\sqrt{(b-a)^2/12}$.

FIGURE 6.1 Continuous uniform probability density function

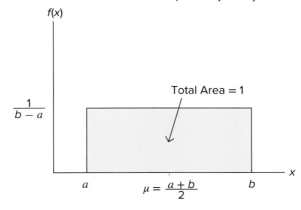

As noted earlier, the height of the probability density function does not directly represent a probability. It is the area under $f(x)$ that corresponds to probability. For the continuous uniform distribution, the probability is essentially the area of a rectangle, which is the base times the height. Therefore, the probability is easily computed by multiplying the length of a specified interval (base) with $f(x) = \frac{1}{b-a}$ (height).

THE CONTINUOUS UNIFORM DISTRIBUTION

A random variable X follows the continuous uniform distribution if its probability density function is

$$f(x) = \begin{cases} \dfrac{1}{b-a} & \text{for } a \leq x \leq b \\ 0 & \text{for } x < a \text{ or } x > b \end{cases}$$

where a and b represent the lower limit and the upper limit, respectively, that the random variable assumes.

The expected value and the standard deviation of X are computed as

$$E(X) = \mu = \frac{a+b}{2} \quad \text{and} \quad SD(X) = \sigma = \sqrt{(b-a)^2/12}.$$

EXAMPLE 6.1

A manager of a local drugstore is projecting next month's sales for a particular cosmetic line. She knows from historical data that sales follow a continuous uniform distribution with a lower limit of $2,500 and an upper limit of $5,000.

a. What are the mean and the standard deviation for the distribution?
b. What is the probability that sales exceed $4,000?
c. What is the probability that sales are between $3,200 and $3,800?

SOLUTION:

a. With a lower limit of $a = 2,500$ and an upper limit of $b = 5,000$, we calculate the mean and the standard deviation for this continuous uniform distribution as

$$\mu = \frac{a+b}{2} = \frac{2,500 + 5,000}{2} = 3,750, \text{ or } \$3,750, \text{ and}$$

$$\sigma = \sqrt{(b-a)^2/12} = \sqrt{(5,000 - 2,500)^2/12} = 721.69, \text{ or } \$721.69.$$

b. When solving for the probability that sales exceed $4,000, we find $P(X > 4,000)$, which is the area between 4,000 and 5,000, as shown in Figure 6.2. The base of the rectangle equals $5,000 - 4,000 = 1,000$ and the height equals $\frac{1}{5,000 - 2,500} = 0.0004$. Thus, $P(X > 4,000) = 1,000 \times 0.0004 = 0.40$.

FIGURE 6.2 Area to the right of 4,000

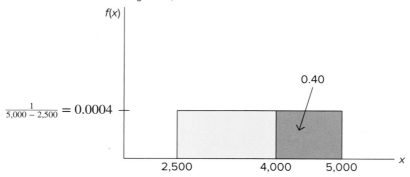

c. When solving for the probability that sales are between $3,200 and $3,800, we find $P(3,200 \le X \le 3,800)$. Using the same methodology as in part b, we multiply the base times the height of the rectangle, as shown in Figure 6.3. Therefore, we obtain the probability as $(3,800 - 3,200) \times 0.0004 = 0.24$.

FIGURE 6.3 Area between 3,200 and 3,800

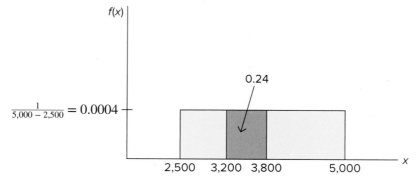

EXERCISES 6.1

Mechanics

1. The cumulative probabilities for a continuous random variable X are $P(X \leq 10) = 0.42$ and $P(X \leq 20) = 0.66$. Calculate the following probabilities.
   a. $P(X > 10)$
   b. $P(X > 20)$
   c. $P(10 < X < 20)$

2. For a continuous random variable X with an upper bound of 4, $P(0 \leq X \leq 2.5) = 0.54$ and $P(2.5 \leq X \leq 4) = 0.16$. Calculate the following probabilities.
   a. $P(X < 0)$
   b. $P(X > 2.5)$
   c. $P(0 \leq X \leq 4)$

3. For a continuous random variable X, $P(20 \leq X \leq 40) = 0.15$ and $P(X > 40) = 0.16$. Calculate the following probabilities.
   a. $P(X < 40)$
   b. $P(X < 20)$
   c. $P(X = 40)$

4. A random variable X follows the continuous uniform distribution with a lower bound of 5 and an upper bound of 35.
   a. What is the height of the density function $f(x)$?
   b. What are the mean and the standard deviation for the distribution?
   c. Calculate $P(X > 10)$.

5. A random variable X follows the continuous uniform distribution with a lower bound of -2 and an upper bound of 4.
   a. What is the height of the density function $f(x)$?
   b. What are the mean and the standard deviation for the distribution?
   c. Calculate $P(X \leq -1)$.

6. A random variable X follows the continuous uniform distribution with a lower limit of 10 and an upper limit of 30.
   a. Calculate the mean and the standard deviation for the distribution.
   b. What is the probability that X is greater than 22?
   c. What is the probability that X is between 15 and 23?

7. A random variable X follows the continuous uniform distribution with a lower limit of 750 and an upper limit of 800.
   a. Calculate the mean and the standard deviation for the distribution.
   b. What is the probability that X is less than 770?

Applications

8. Suppose the price of electricity follows the continuous uniform distribution with a lower bound of 12 cents per kilowatt-hour and an upper bound of 20 cents per kilowatt-hour.
   a. Calculate the average price of electricity.
   b. What is the probability that the price of electricity is less than 15.5 cents per kilowatt-hour?

   c. A local carnival is not able to operate its rides if the price of electricity is more than 14 cents per kilowatt-hour. What is the probability that the carnival will need to close?

9. The arrival time of an elevator in a 12-story dormitory is equally likely at any time during the next 4 minutes.
   a. Calculate the expected arrival time.
   b. What is the probability that an elevator arrives in less than 1½ minutes?
   c. What is the probability that the wait for an elevator is more than 1½ minutes?

10. The Netherlands is one of the world leaders in the production and sale of tulips. Suppose the heights of the tulips in the greenhouse of Rotterdam's Fantastic Flora follow a continuous uniform distribution with a lower bound of 7 inches and an upper bound of 16 inches. You have come to the greenhouse to select a bouquet of tulips, but only tulips with a height greater than 10 inches may be selected. What is the probability that a randomly selected tulip is tall enough to pick?

11. The scheduled arrival time for a daily flight from Boston to New York is 9:25 am. Historical data show that the arrival time follows the continuous uniform distribution with an early arrival time of 9:15 am and a late arrival time of 9:55 am.
   a. Calculate the mean and the standard deviation of the distribution.
   b. What is the probability that a flight arrives late (later than 9:25 am)?

12. You were informed at the nursery that your peach tree will bloom sometime between March 18 and March 30. Assume that the bloom times follow a continuous uniform distribution between these specified dates.
   a. What is the probability that the tree blooms after March 25?
   b. What is the probability that the tree blooms by March 20?

13. You have been informed that the assessor will visit your home sometime between 10:00 am and 12:00 pm. It is reasonable to assume that his visitation time is uniformly distributed over the specified two-hour interval. Suppose you have to run a quick errand at 10:00 am.
   a. If it takes 15 minutes to run the errand, what is the probability that you will be back before the assessor visits?
   b. If it takes 30 minutes to run the errand, what is the probability that you will be back before the assessor visits?

14. A worker at a landscape design center uses a machine to fill bags with potting soil. Assume that the quantity put in each bag follows the continuous uniform distribution with low and high filling weights of 10 pounds and 12 pounds, respectively.
   a. Calculate the expected value and the standard deviation of this distribution.
   b. Find the probability that the weight of a randomly selected bag is no more than 11 pounds.
   c. Find the probability that the weight of a randomly selected bag is at least 10.5 pounds.

Calculate and interpret probabilities for a random variable that follows the normal distribution.

The **normal probability distribution,** or simply the **normal distribution,** is the familiar bell-shaped distribution. It is also referred to as the Gaussian distribution.[1] The normal distribution is the most extensively used probability distribution in statistical work. One reason for this common use is that the normal distribution closely approximates the probability distribution for a wide range of random variables of interest. It is common to use the normal distribution in applications such as:

- Salary of employees in a tech firm
- Scores on the SAT exam
- Cumulative debt of college graduates
- Advertising expenditure of firms
- Rate of return on an investment

Whenever possible, it is instructive to analyze the underlying data to determine if the normal distribution is appropriate for a given application. There are various ways to do this, including inspecting histograms (Chapter 2) and boxplots (Chapter 3) for symmetry and bell shape. In this chapter, we simply assume that the random variable in question is normally distributed and focus on finding probabilities associated with this type of random variable. The computation of these probabilities is easy and direct.

Another important function of the normal distribution is that it serves as the cornerstone of statistical inference. Recall from Chapter 1 that the study of statistics is divided into two branches: descriptive statistics and inferential statistics. Statistical inference is generally based on the assumption of the normal distribution and serves as the major topic in the remainder of this text.

Characteristics of the Normal Distribution

- The normal distribution is bell-shaped and symmetric around its mean; that is, one side of the mean is just the mirror image of the other side. The mean, the median, and the mode are all equal to each other for a normally distributed random variable.
- The normal distribution is described by two parameters—the population mean μ and the population variance σ^2. The population mean describes the central location and the population variance describes the dispersion of the distribution.
- The normal distribution is asymptotic in the sense that the tails get closer and closer to the horizontal axis but never touch it. Thus, theoretically, a normal random variable can assume any value between negative infinity and infinity.

The probability density function for the normal distribution is defined as follows.

> ### THE NORMAL DISTRIBUTION
> A random variable X with mean μ and variance σ^2 follows the normal distribution if its probability density function is
> $$f(x) = \frac{1}{\sigma\sqrt{2\pi}} \exp\left(-\frac{(x-\mu)^2}{2\sigma^2}\right),$$
> where π equals approximately 3.14159 and $\exp(w) = e^w$ is the exponential function, where $e \approx 2.718$ is the base of the natural logarithm.

[1]The discovery of the normal (Gaussian) distribution is often credited to Carl Friedrich Gauss (1777–1855), even though some attribute the credit to De Moivre (1667–1754), who had earlier discovered it in the context of simplifying the binomial distribution calculations.

A graph depicting the normal probability density function is often referred to as the **normal curve** or the **bell curve.** Figure 6.4 represents the normal curve. A normally distributed random variable X is symmetric around its mean of μ, implying that $P(X < \mu) = P(X > \mu) = 0.5$. As is the case with all continuous random variables, we can also write the probabilities as $P(X \le \mu) = P(X \ge \mu) = 0.5$.

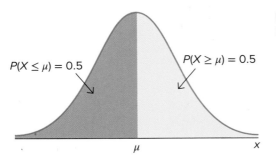

FIGURE 6.4
Normal probability density function

The following example relates the normal curve to the location and the dispersion of the normally distributed random variable.

EXAMPLE 6.2

Suppose we know that the ages of employees in Industries A, B, and C are normally distributed. We are given the following information on the relevant parameters:

Industry A	Industry B	Industry C
$\mu = 42$ years	$\mu = 36$ years	$\mu = 42$ years
$\sigma = 5$ years	$\sigma = 5$ years	$\sigma = 8$ years

Graphically compare the ages of employees in Industry A with Industry B. Repeat the comparison in Industry A with Industry C.

SOLUTION: Because the mean age of employees in Industry A is greater than that in Industry B, the normal curve for Industry A is located to the right of Industry B, as shown in Figure 6.5. Both curves show equal dispersion from the mean, given that the standard deviations are the same.

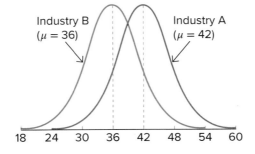

FIGURE 6.5 Normal probability density function for two values of μ along with $\sigma = 5$

Because the mean age of employees in Industry A and Industry C is the same, the normal curves for each industry have the same center, as shown in Figure 6.6.

However, because the standard deviation for Industry A is less than that of Industry C, the normal curve for Industry A is less dispersed. Its peak is higher than that of Industry C, reflecting the fact that an employee's age is likelier to be closer to the mean age in Industry A.

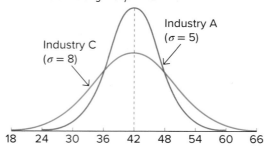

FIGURE 6.6 Normal probability density function for two values of σ along with $\mu = 42$

Figures 6.5 and 6.6 show that we can capture the entire distribution of any normally distributed random variable based on its mean and variance (or standard deviation).

We generally use the cumulative distribution function $F(x)$ to compute probabilities for a normally distributed random variable, where $F(x) = P(X \le x)$ is simply the area under the probability density function $f(x)$ up to the value x. Fortunately, we do not necessarily need the knowledge of integral calculus to compute probabilities for the normal distribution. Traditionally, all introductory business statistics texts have included a normal table that is used to find probabilities. Consistent with the recommendation made by the American Statistical Association, in this text, we do not rely on statistical tables because the problems can easily be solved with Excel. The specifics of how to use Excel are delineated next.

Finding the Probability for a Given Variable Value

In Example 6.3, we will show how to use Excel to solve for probabilities associated with the normal distribution. In particular, we find the probability for a given range of the normally distributed random variable.

EXAMPLE 6.3

Scores on a management aptitude exam are normally distributed with a mean of 72 and a standard deviation of 8.

a. What is the probability that a randomly selected manager will score above 60?

b. What is the probability that a randomly selected manager will score between 68 and 84?

SOLUTION: Let X represent scores with $\mu = 72$ and $\sigma = 8$. It is always advisable to start with a graph.

a. The probability that a manager scores above 60 is $P(X > 60)$. Figure 6.7 shows the probability as the shaded area to the right of 60.

FIGURE 6.7 Finding $P(X > 60)$

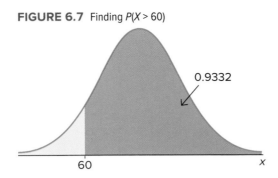

We will now use Excel's **NORM.DIST** to solve for probabilities. We enter `=NORM.DIST(x, μ, σ, TRUE or FALSE)` where x is the value to be evaluated, $μ$ is the mean of the distribution, and $σ$ is the standard deviation of the distribution. If we enter TRUE for the last input, then Excel returns the cumulative probability function $P(X \leq x)$. With continuous probability distributions, we rarely use FALSE; it is a useful input if we are interested in plotting the distribution. In order to find $P(X > 60) = 1 - P(X \leq 60)$, we enter `=1-NORM.DIST(60, 72, 8, TRUE)`, and Excel returns 0.9332.

b. When solving for the probability that a manager scores between 68 and 84, we find $P(68 \leq X \leq 84)$. The shaded area in Figure 6.8 shows this probability. Note that $P(68 \leq X \leq 84) = P(X \leq 84) - P(X \leq 68)$. Using Excel, we enter `=NORM.DIST(84, 72, 8, TRUE) - NORM.DIST(68, 72, 8, TRUE)`, and Excel returns 0.6247.

FIGURE 6.8 Finding $P(68 \leq X \leq 84)$

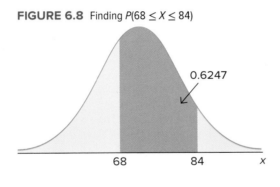

The Standard Normal Distribution

The **standard normal distribution** is a special case of the normal distribution with a mean equal to zero and a standard deviation (or variance) equal to one. Using the letter Z to denote a random variable with the standard normal distribution, we have $μ = E(Z) = 0$ and $σ = SD(Z) = 1$. As usual, we use the lowercase letter z to denote the value that the standard normal variable Z may assume.

The value z is the z-score that we discussed in Chapter 3. It measures the number of standard deviations a given value is away from the mean. For example, a z-score of 2 implies that the given value is 2 standard deviations above the mean. Similarly, a z-score of -1.5 implies that the given value is 1.5 standard deviations below the mean. Recall that converting values into z-scores is called standardizing the data.

Any normally distributed random variable X with mean $μ$ and standard deviation $σ$ can be transformed (standardized) into the standard normal variable Z with mean zero and standard deviation one. We transform X into Z by subtracting from X its mean and dividing by its standard deviation.

> **TRANSFORMATION TO STANDARD NORMAL RANDOM VARIABLE**
>
> Any normally distributed random variable X with mean μ and standard deviation σ can be transformed into the standard normal random variable Z as
>
> $$Z = \frac{X - \mu}{\sigma}.$$
>
> Therefore, any value x has a corresponding value z given by
>
> $$z = \frac{x - \mu}{\sigma}.$$

As illustrated in Figure 6.9, if the x value is at the mean—that is, $x = \mu$—then the corresponding z value is $z = \frac{\mu - \mu}{\sigma} = 0$. Similarly, if the x value is at one standard deviation above the mean—that is, $x = \mu + \sigma$—then the corresponding z value is $z = \frac{\mu + \sigma - \mu}{\sigma} = 1$. Therefore, by construction, $E(Z) = 0$ and $SD(Z) = 1$.

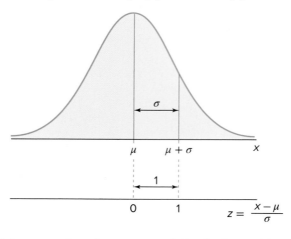

FIGURE 6.9
Transforming X to Z

It is easy to show that any normal distribution problem in terms of X can be converted into a Z problem. Let us revisit Example 6.3, where scores on a management aptitude exam are known to be normally distributed with a mean of 72 and a standard deviation of 8. For part a, the probability that a manager scores above 60 is $P(X > 60)$, where X represents scores.

Figure 6.10 shows the probability as the shaded area to the right of 60. We can transform this problem as $P(X > 60) = P(Z > \frac{60 - 72}{8}) = P(Z > -1.5)$. If a normal distribution table was given, we could use the z-value of -1.5 to find the relevant probability. As mentioned earlier, in this text we rely on Excel to find probabilities. In order to find $P(Z > -1.5) = 1 - P(Z \leq -1.5)$ in Excel, we enter =1-NORM.DIST(-1.5, 0, 1, TRUE). Excel returns 0.9332, which is identical to the probability obtained in Example 6.3.

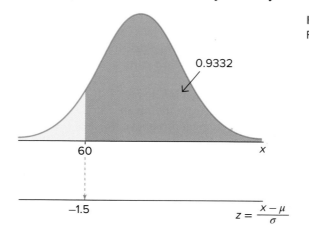

FIGURE 6.10
Finding $P(X > 60)$

Note: We do not use the standard normal distribution to find probabilities in this chapter. Standardized variables, however, are often used in the context of estimation and hypothesis testing discussed in later chapters.

Finding the Variable Value for a Given Probability

So far we have used Excel to compute probabilities for given x values. In Example 6.4, we will show how to compute x values for given probabilities.

EXAMPLE 6.4

Scores on a management aptitude examination are normally distributed with a mean of 72 and a standard deviation of 8.

a. What is the lowest score that will place a manager in the top 10% (90th percentile) of the distribution?

b. What is the highest score that will place a manager in the bottom 25% (25th percentile) of the distribution?

SOLUTION: Let X represent scores on a management aptitude examination with $\mu = 72$ and $\sigma = 8$.

a. The 90th percentile is a numerical value x such that $P(X < x) = 0.90$. Figure 6.11 shows the relevant probability and the desired x value of 82.25.

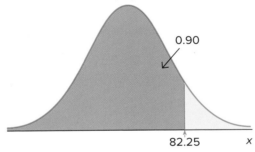

FIGURE 6.11 Finding x given $P(X < x) = 0.90$

We use Excel's **NORM.INV** function to find the desired x value. We enter =NORM.INV(cumulprob, μ, σ), where cumulprob is the cumulative probability associated with the value x, μ is the mean of the distribution, and σ is the standard deviation of the distribution. In order to find the value of x that satisfies $P(X < x) = 0.90$, we enter =NORM.INV(0.90, 72, 8), and Excel returns 82.25.

b. The 25th percentile is a numerical value x such that $P(X < x) = 0.25$. Figure 6.12 shows the relevant probability and the desired x value of 66.60. Using Excel, we enter =NORM.INV(0.25, 72, 8), and Excel returns 66.60.

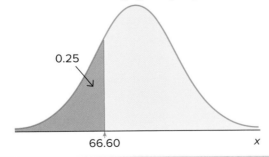

FIGURE 6.12 Finding x given $P(X < x) = 0.25$

EXAMPLE 6.5

We can now answer the questions first posed by Akiko Hamaguchi in the introductory case of this chapter. Recall that Akiko would like to buy the right amount of salmon for daily consumption at Little Ginza. Akiko has estimated that the daily consumption of salmon is normally distributed with a mean of 12 pounds and a standard deviation of 3.2 pounds. She wants to answer the following questions:

a. What is the probability that the demand for salmon at Little Ginza is more than 20 pounds?

b. What is the probability that the demand for salmon at Little Ginza is less than 15 pounds?

c. How much salmon should be bought so that it meets customer demand on 90% of the days?

SOLUTION: Let X denote customer demand for salmon at the restaurant. We solve this problem using Excel, with $\mu = 12$ and $\sigma = 3.2$. Although not shown here, students are advised to start with a graph.

a. In order to find the probability that the demand for salmon is more than 20 pounds, or $P(X > 20) = 1 - P(X \leq 20)$, we enter =1 - NORM.DIST(20, 12, 3.2, TRUE). Excel returns 0.0062.

b. In order to find the probability that the demand for salmon is less than 15 pounds, or $P(X < 15)$, we enter =NORM.DIST(15, 12, 3.2, TRUE). Excel returns 0.8257.

c. In order to compute the required amount of salmon that should be purchased to meet demand on 90% of the days, we solve for x in $P(X \leq x) = 0.90$. We enter =NORM.INV(0.9,12,3.2), and Excel returns 16.10. Therefore, Akiko should buy 16.10 pounds of salmon daily to ensure that customer demand is met on 90% of the days.

A Note on the Normal Approximation of the Binomial Distribution

Recall from Chapter 5 that it is tedious to compute binomial probabilities with the formula when we encounter large values for n. As it turns out, with large values for n, the binomial distribution can be approximated by the normal distribution. It is believed that the normal distribution was discovered in the 18th century as an approximation tool. The popularity of this method, however, has been greatly reduced by the advent of computers. As discussed in Chapter 5, it is easy to compute exact binomial probabilities with Excel. The normal distribution approximation, however, is important when making inferences for the population proportion p, which is the key parameter of the binomial distribution. In later chapters, we will study the details of this approximation and how it is used for making inferences.

SYNOPSIS OF INTRODUCTORY CASE

Akiko Hamaguchi is a manager at a small sushi restaurant called Little Ginza in Phoenix, Arizona. She is aware of the importance of purchasing the right amount of salmon daily. While purchasing too much salmon results in wastage, purchasing too little can disappoint customers who may choose not to frequent the restaurant in the future. In the past, she has always bought 20 pounds of salmon daily.

A careful analysis of her purchasing habits and customer demand reveals that Akiko is buying too much salmon. The probability that the demand for salmon would exceed 20 pounds is very small at 0.0062. Even a purchase of 15 pounds satisfies customer demand on 82.57% of the days. In order to execute her new strategy of meeting daily demand of customers on 90% of the days, Akiko should purchase approximately 16 pounds of salmon daily.

gkrphoto/iStock/Getty Images

EXERCISES 6.2

Mechanics

15. Let X be normally distributed with mean $\mu = 10$ and standard deviation $\sigma = 6$.
    a. Find $P(X \leq 0)$.
    b. Find $P(X > 2)$.
    c. Find $P(4 \leq X \leq 10)$.
    d. Find $P(6 \leq X \leq 14)$.

16. Let X be normally distributed with mean $\mu = 120$ and standard deviation $\sigma = 20$.
    a. Find $P(X \leq 86)$.
    b. Find $P(80 \leq X \leq 100)$.
    c. Find x such that $P(X \leq x) = 0.40$.
    d. Find x such that $P(X > x) = 0.90$.

17. Let X be normally distributed with mean $\mu = 2.5$ and standard deviation $\sigma = 2$.
    a. Find $P(X > 7.6)$.
    b. Find $P(7.4 \leq X \leq 10.6)$.
    c. Find x such that $P(X > x) = 0.025$.
    d. Find x such that $P(x \leq X \leq 2.5) = 0.4943$.

18. Let X be normally distributed with mean $\mu = 2,500$ and standard deviation $\sigma = 800$.
    a. Find x such that $P(X \leq x) = 0.9382$.
    b. Find x such that $P(X > x) = 0.025$.
    c. Find x such that $P(2500 \leq X \leq x) = 0.1217$.
    d. Find x such that $P(X \leq x) = 0.4840$.

Applications

19. The historical returns on a balanced portfolio have had an average return of 8% and a standard deviation of 12%. Assume that returns on this portfolio follow a normal distribution.
    a. What percentage of returns were greater than 20%?
    b. What percentage of returns were below − 16%?

20. Assume that IQ scores follow a normal distribution with a mean of 100 and a standard deviation of 16.
    a. What is the probability that an individual scores between 84 and 116?
    b. What is the probability that an individual scores less than 68?
    c. What is the lowest score that will place an individual in the top 1% of IQ scores?

21. The average rent in a city is $1,500 per month with a standard deviation of $250. Assume rent follows the normal distribution.
    a. What percentage of rents are between $1,250 and $1,750?
    b. What percentage of rents are less than $1,250?
    c. What percentage of rents are greater than $2,000?

22. A professional basketball team averages 80 points per game with a standard deviation of 10 points. Assume points per game follow the normal distribution.
    a. What is the probability that a game's score is between 60 and 100 points?
    b. What is the probability that a game's score is more than 100 points? If there are 82 games in a regular season, in how many games will the team score more than 100 points?

23. In a rural town, the average salary of a high school teacher is $43,000. Let salary be normally distributed with a standard deviation of $18,000.
    a. What percentage of high school teachers make between $40,000 and $50,000?
    b. What percentage of high school teachers make more than $80,000?

24. Americans are increasingly skimping on their sleep. A health expert believes that American adults sleep an average of 6.2 hours on weekdays, with a standard deviation of 1.2 hours. Assume that sleep time on weekdays is normally distributed.
    a. What percentage of American adults sleep more than 8 hours on weekdays?
    b. What percentage of American adults sleep less than 6 hours on weekdays?
    c. What percentage of American adults sleep between 6 and 8 hours on weekdays?

25. The weight of turkeys is normally distributed with a mean of 22 pounds and a standard deviation of 5 pounds.
    a. Find the probability that a randomly selected turkey weighs between 20 and 26 pounds.
    b. Find the probability that a randomly selected turkey weighs less than 12 pounds.

26. Suppose that the miles-per-gallon (mpg) rating of passenger cars is a normally distributed random variable with a mean and a standard deviation of 33.8 mpg and 3.5 mpg, respectively.
    a. What is the probability that a randomly selected passenger car gets at least 40 mpg?
    b. What is the probability that a randomly selected passenger car gets between 30 and 35 mpg?
    c. An automobile manufacturer wants to build a new passenger car with an mpg rating that improves upon 99% of existing cars. What is the minimum mpg that would achieve this goal?

27. According to a company's website, the top 25% of the candidates who take the entrance test will be called for an interview. The reported mean and standard deviation of the test scores are 68 and 8, respectively. If test scores are normally distributed, what is the minimum score required for an interview?

28. A financial advisor informs a client that the expected return on a portfolio is 8% with a standard deviation of 12%. There is a 15% chance that the return would be above 16%. If the advisor is right about her assessment, is it reasonable to assume that the underlying return distribution is normal?

29. A packaging system fills boxes to an average weight of 18 ounces with a standard deviation of 0.2 ounces. It is reasonable to assume that the weights are normally distributed. Calculate the 1st, 2nd, and 3rd quartiles of the box weight.

30. According to the Bureau of Labor Statistics, it takes an average of 22 weeks for someone over 55 to find a new job, compared with 16 weeks for younger workers. Assume that the probability distributions are normal and that the standard deviation is 2 weeks for both distributions.
    a. What is the probability that it takes a worker over the age of 55 more than 19 weeks to find a job?
    b. What is the probability that it takes a younger worker more than 19 weeks to find a job?
    c. What is the probability that it takes a worker over the age of 55 between 23 and 25 weeks to find a job?
    d. What is the probability that it takes a younger worker between 23 and 25 weeks to find a job?

31. Loans that are 60 days or more past due are considered seriously delinquent. It is reported that the rate of seriously delinquent loans has an average of 9.1%. Let the rate of seriously delinquent loans follow a normal distribution with a standard deviation of 0.80%.
    a. What is the probability that the rate of seriously delinquent loans is above 8%?
    b. What is the probability that the rate of seriously delinquent loans is between 9.5% and 10.5%?

32. The time required to assemble an electronic component is normally distributed with a mean and a standard deviation of 16 minutes and 4 minutes, respectively.
    a. Find the probability that a randomly picked assembly takes between 10 and 20 minutes.
    b. It is unusual for the assembly time to be above 24 minutes or below 6 minutes. What proportion of assembly times fall in these unusual categories?

33. Research suggests that Americans make an average of 10 phone calls per day. Let the number of calls be normally distributed with a standard deviation of 3 calls.
    a. What is the probability that an American makes between 4 and 12 calls per day?
    b. What is the probability that an American makes more than 6 calls per day?
    c. What is the probability that an American makes more than 16 calls per day?

34. Scores on a marketing exam are known to be normally distributed with a mean and a standard deviation of 60 and 20, respectively.
    a. Find the probability that a randomly selected student scores between 50 and 80.
    b. Find the probability that a randomly selected student scores between 20 and 40.
    c. The syllabus suggests that the top 15% of the students will get an A in the course. What is the minimum score required to get an A?
    d. What is the passing score if 10% of the students will fail the course?

35. It is reported that the average cumulative debt of recent college graduates is about $22,500. Let the cumulative debt among recent college graduates be normally distributed with a standard deviation of $7,000. If an estimated 1.8 million recent college graduates have debt, approximately how many of them have accumulated debt of more than $30,000?

36. On average, an American professional football game lasts about three hours, even though the ball is actually in play for 11 minutes. Assume that game times are normally distributed with a standard deviation of 0.4 hour.
    a. Find the probability that a game lasts less than 2.5 hours.
    b. Find the probability that a game lasts either less than 2.5 hours or more than 3.5 hours.
    c. Find the maximum value for the game time that will place it in the bottom 1% of the distribution.

37. A construction company in Florida is struggling to sell condominiums. The company believes that it will be able to get an average sale price of $210,000. Let the price of these condominiums in the next quarter be normally distributed with a standard deviation of $15,000.
    a. What is the probability that the condominium will sell at a price (i) below $200,000? (ii) Above $240,000?
    b. The company is also trying to sell an artist's condo. Potential buyers will find the unusual features of this condo either pleasing or objectionable. The manager expects the average sale price of this condo to be the same as others at $210,000, but with a higher standard deviation of $20,000. What is the probability that this condo will sell at a price (i) below $200,000? (ii) Above $240,000?

38. You are considering the risk-return profile of two mutual funds for investment. The relatively risky fund promises an expected return of 8% with a standard deviation of 14%. The relatively less risky fund promises an expected return and standard deviation of 4% and 5%, respectively. Assume that the returns are approximately normally distributed.
    a. Which mutual fund will you pick if your objective is to minimize the probability of earning a negative return?
    b. Which mutual fund will you pick if your objective is to maximize the probability of earning a return above 8%?

39. First introduced in Los Angeles, the concept of Korean-style tacos sold from a catering truck has been gaining popularity nationally. This taco is an interesting mix of corn tortillas with Korean-style beef, garnished with onion, cilantro, and a hash of chili-soy-dressed lettuce. Suppose one such taco truck operates in the Detroit area. The owners have estimated that the daily consumption of beef is normally distributed with a mean of 24 pounds and a standard deviation of 6 pounds. While purchasing too much beef results in wastage, purchasing too little can disappoint customers.
    a. Determine the amount of beef the owners should buy so that it meets demand on 80% of the days.
    b. How much should the owners buy if they want to meet demand on 95% of the days?

40. While Massachusetts is no California when it comes to sun, the solar energy industry is flourishing in this state. The state's capital, Boston, averages 211.7 sunny days per year. Assume that the number of sunny days follows a normal distribution with a standard deviation of 20 days.

    a. What is the probability that Boston has less than 200 sunny days in a given year?
    b. Los Angeles averages 266.5 sunny days per year. What is the probability that Boston has at least as many sunny days as Los Angeles?
    c. Suppose a dismal year in Boston is one where the number of sunny days is in the bottom 10% for that year. At most, how many sunny days must occur annually for it to be a dismal year in Boston?
    d. Last year, Boston experienced unusually warm, dry, and sunny weather. Suppose this occurs only 1% of the time. What is the minimum number of sunny days that would satisfy the criteria for being an unusually warm, dry, and sunny year in Boston?

41. A new car battery is sold with a two-year warranty whereby the owner gets the battery replaced free of cost if it breaks down during the warranty period. Suppose an auto store makes a net profit of $30 on batteries that stay trouble-free during the warranty period; it makes a net loss of $200 on batteries that break down. The life of batteries is known to be normally distributed with a mean and a standard deviation of 40 months and 12 months, respectively.
    a. What is the probability that a battery will break down during the warranty period?
    b. What is the expected profit of the auto store on a battery?
    c. What is the expected monthly profit on batteries if the auto store sells an average of 500 batteries a month?

42. A certain brand of refrigerators has a length of life that is normally distributed with a mean and a standard deviation of 15 years and 2 years, respectively.
    a. What is the probability a refrigerator will last less than 10 years?
    b. What is the probability that a refrigerator will last more than 18 years?
    c. What length of life should the retailer advertise for these refrigerators so that only 3% of the refrigerators fail before the advertised length of life?

43. U.S. consumers are increasingly viewing debit cards as a convenient substitute for cash and checks. The average amount spent annually on a debit card is $7,790. Assume that the average amount spent on a debit card is normally distributed with a standard deviation of $500.
    a. A consumer advocate comments that the majority of consumers spend over $8,000 on a debit card. Find a flaw in this statement.
    b. Compute the 25th percentile of the amount spent on a debit card.
    c. Compute the 75th percentile of the amount spent on a debit card.
    d. What is the interquartile range of this distribution?

44. A study finds that men spend an average of $43.87 on St. Patrick's Day, while women spend an average of $29.54. Assume the standard deviations of spending for men and women are $3 and $11, respectively, and that both distributions are normally distributed.

   a. What is the probability that men spend over $50 on St. Patrick's Day?

   b. What is the probability that women spend over $50 on St. Patrick's Day?

   c. Are men or women more likely to spend over $50 on St. Patrick's Day?

45. Lisa Mendes and Brad Lee work in the sales department of an AT&T Wireless store. Lisa has been signing up an average of 48 new cell phone customers every month with a standard deviation of 22, while Brad signs up an average of 56 new customers with a standard deviation of 17. The store manager offers both Lisa and Brad a $100 incentive bonus if they can sign up more than 100 new customers in a month. Assume a normal distribution to answer the following questions.

   a. What is the probability that Lisa will earn the $100 incentive bonus?

   b. What is the probability that Brad will earn the $100 incentive bonus?

   c. Are you surprised by the results? Explain.

46. The average household income in a community is known to be $80,000. Also, 20% of the households have an income below $60,000 and another 20% have an income above $90,000. Is it reasonable to use the normal distribution to model the household income in this community?

47. Entrance to a prestigious MBA program in India is determined by a national test where only the top 10% of the examinees are admitted to the program. Suppose it is known that the scores on this test are normally distributed with a mean of 420 and a standard deviation of 80. Parul Monga is trying desperately to get into this program. What is the minimum score that she must earn to get admitted?

48. A new water filtration system is sold with a 10-year warranty that includes all parts and repairs. Suppose the life of this water filtration system is normally distributed with a mean and a standard deviation of 16 and 5 years, respectively.

   a. What is the probability that the water filtration system will require a repair during the warranty period?

   b. Suppose the water filtration firm makes a $300 profit for every new system it installs. This profit, however, is reduced to $50 if the system requires repair during the warranty period. Find the expected profit of the firm if it installs 1,000 new water filtration systems.

6.3 THE EXPONENTIAL DISTRIBUTION

Calculate and interpret probabilities for a random variable that follows the exponential distribution.

As discussed earlier, the normal distribution is the most extensively used probability distribution in statistical work. One reason that this occurs is because the normal distribution accurately describes numerous random variables of interest. However, there are applications where other continuous distributions are more appropriate.

A useful nonsymmetric continuous probability distribution is the **exponential distribution.** The exponential distribution is related to the Poisson distribution, even though the Poisson distribution deals with discrete random variables. Recall from Chapter 5 that the Poisson random variable counts the number of occurrences of an event over a given interval of time or space. For instance, the Poisson distribution is used to calculate the likelihood of a specified number of cars arriving at a McDonald's drive-thru over a particular time period or the likelihood of a specified number of defects in a 50-yard roll of fabric. Sometimes we are less interested in the *number* of occurrences over a given interval of time or space, but rather in the time that has elapsed or space encountered *between* such occurrences. For instance, we might be interested in the length of time that elapses between car arrivals at the McDonald's drive-thru or the distance between defects in a 50-yard roll of fabric. We use the exponential distribution for describing these times or distances. The exponential random variable is nonnegative; that is, the underlying variable X is defined for $x \geq 0$.

In order to better understand the connection between the Poisson and the exponential distributions, consider the introductory case of Chapter 5 where Anne was concerned about staffing needs at the Starbucks that she managed. Recall that Anne believed that the typical Starbucks customer averaged 18 visits to the store over 30 days. The Poisson random variable appropriately captures the number of visits, with the expected value (mean), over 30 days, as

$$\mu_{\text{Poisson}} = 18.$$

Because the number of visits follows the Poisson distribution, the time between visits has an exponential distribution. In addition, given the expected number of 18 visits over 30 days, the expected time between visits is derived as

$$\mu_{\text{Exponential}} = \frac{30}{18} = 1.67.$$

It is common to define the exponential probability distribution in terms of its *rate parameter λ* (the Greek letter read as lambda), which is the inverse of its mean. In the above example,

$$\lambda = \frac{1}{\mu} = \frac{1}{1.67} = 0.60.$$

We can think of the mean of the exponential distribution as the average time between arrivals, whereas the rate parameter measures the average number of arrivals per unit of time. Note that the rate parameter is the same as the mean of the Poisson distribution, when defined per unit of time. For a Poisson process, the mean of 18 visits over 30 days is equivalent to a mean of 18/30 = 0.60 per day, which is the same as the rate parameter λ.

The probability density function for the exponential distribution is defined as follows.

THE EXPONENTIAL DISTRIBUTION

A random variable X follows the exponential distribution if its probability density function is

$$f(x) = \lambda e^{-\lambda x} \quad \text{for } x \geq 0,$$

where λ is a rate parameter and $e \approx 2.718$ is the base of the natural logarithm. The mean and the standard deviation of X are equal: $E(X) = SD(X) = \frac{1}{\lambda}$.

For $x \geq 0$, the cumulative distribution function of X is

$$P(X \leq x) = 1 - e^{-\lambda x}.$$

Therefore, $P(X > x) = 1 - P(X \leq x) = e^{-\lambda x}.$

The graphs in Figure 6.13 show the shapes of the exponential probability density function based on various values of the rate parameter λ.

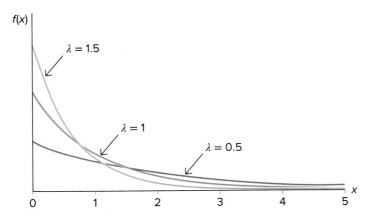

FIGURE 6.13
Exponential probability density function for various values of λ

EXAMPLE 6.6

Let the time between email messages during work hours be exponentially distributed with a mean of 25 minutes.

a. Calculate the rate parameter λ.

b. What is the probability that you do not get an email for more than one hour?

c. What is the probability that you get an email within 10 minutes?

SOLUTION:

a. We compute $\lambda = \frac{1}{\mu} = \frac{1}{25} = 0.04$.

b. The probability that you do not get an email for more than an hour is $P(X > 60)$. We use $P(X > x) = e^{-\lambda x}$ to compute $P(X > 60) = e^{-0.04(60)} = 0.0907$. Figure 6.14 highlights this probability.

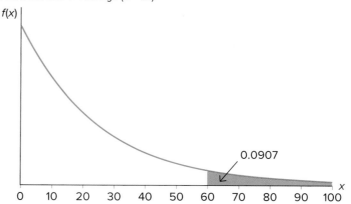

FIGURE 6.14 Finding $P(X > 60)$

We can also use Excel's **EXPON.DIST** function to solve for probabilities associated with the exponential distribution. We enter =EXPON.DIST(x, λ, TRUE or FALSE), where x is the value to be evaluated and λ is the rate parameter. If we enter TRUE for the last input, then Excel returns the cumulative probability function $P(X \le x)$. As mentioned earlier, we use FALSE only if we are interested in plotting the distribution. In order to find $P(X > 60)$ with $\lambda = 1/25$, we enter =1-EXPON.DIST(60, 1/25, TRUE), and Excel returns 0.0907.

c. The probability that you get an email within 10 minutes is $P(X \le 10) = 1 - e^{-0.04(10)} = 1 - 0.6703 = 0.3297$. Figure 6.15 highlights this probability. Using Excel, we enter =EXPON.DIST(10, 1/25, TRUE), and Excel returns 0.3297.

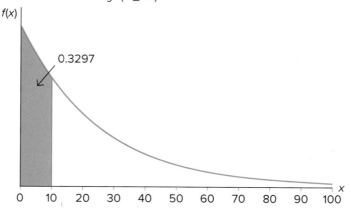

FIGURE 6.15 Finding $P(X \le 10)$

EXERCISES 6.3

Mechanics

49. Assume a Poisson random variable has a mean of 6 successes over a 120-minute period.
   a. Find the mean of the random variable, defined by the time between successes.
   b. What is the rate parameter of the appropriate exponential distribution?
   c. Find the probability that the time to success will be more than 60 minutes.

50. A random variable X is exponentially distributed with a mean of 0.1.
   a. What is the rate parameter λ? What is the standard deviation of X?
   b. Compute $P(X > 0.20)$.
   c. Compute $P(0.10 \le X \le 0.20)$.

51. A random variable X is exponentially distributed with an expected value of 25.
   a. What is the rate parameter λ? What is the standard deviation of X?
   b. Compute $P(20 \le X \le 30)$.
   c. Compute $P(15 \le X \le 35)$.

Applications

52. Studies have shown that bats can consume an average of 10 mosquitoes per minute. Assume that the number of mosquitoes consumed per minute follows a Poisson distribution.
   a. What is the mean time between eating mosquitoes?
   b. Find the probability that the time between eating mosquitoes is more than 15 seconds.
   c. Find the probability that the time between eating mosquitoes is between 15 and 20 seconds.

53. Last year, a study found that there was an average of one complaint every 12 seconds against large corporations. It is reasonable to assume that the time between complaints is exponentially distributed.
   a. What is the mean time between complaints?
   b. What is the probability that the next complaint will take less than the mean time?
   c. What is the probability that the next complaint will take between 5 and 10 seconds?

54. A tollbooth operator has observed that cars arrive randomly at an average rate of 360 cars per hour.
   a. What is the mean time between car arrivals at this tollbooth?
   b. What is the probability that the next car will arrive within 10 seconds?

55. Customers make purchases at a convenience store, on average, every six minutes. It is fair to assume that the time between customer purchases is exponentially distributed. Jack operates the cash register at this store.
   a. What is the rate parameter λ? What is the standard deviation of this distribution?
   b. What is the probability that a customer will show up in less than five minutes?
   c. What is the probability that nobody shows up for over half an hour?

56. A hospital administrator worries about the possible loss of electric power as a result of a power blackout. The hospital, has a standby generator, but it too is subject to failure, having a mean time between failures of 500 hours. It is reasonable to assume that the time between failures is exponentially distributed.
   a. What is the probability that the standby generator fails during the next 24-hour blackout?
   b. Suppose the hospital owns two standby generators that work independently of one another. What is the probability that both generators fail during the next 24-hour blackout?

57. Prior to placing an order, the amount of time (in minutes) that a driver waits in line at a Starbucks drive-thru follows an exponential distribution with a probability density function of $f(x) = 0.2e^{-0.2x}$.
   a. What is the mean waiting time that a driver faces prior to placing an order?
   b. What is the probability that a driver spends more than the average time before placing an order.
   c. What is the probability that a driver spends more than 10 minutes before placing an order.
   d. What is the probability that a driver spends between 4 and 6 minutes before placing an order.

58. On average, the state police catch eight speeders per hour at a certain location on Interstate 90. Assume that the number of speeders per hour follows the Poisson distribution.
   a. What is the probability that the state police wait less than 10 minutes for the next speeder?
   b. What is the probability that the state police wait between 15 and 20 minutes for the next speeder?
   c. What is the probability that the state police wait more than 25 minutes for the next speeder?

59. On a particularly busy section of the Garden State Parkway in New Jersey, police use radar guns to detect speeders. Assume the time that elapses between successive speeders is exponentially distributed with a mean of 15 minutes.
   a. Calculate the rate parameter λ.
   b. What is the probability of a waiting time less than 10 minutes between successive speeders?

c. What is the probability of a waiting time in excess of 25 minutes between successive speeders?

60. In a local law office, jobs to a printer are sent at a rate of 8 jobs per hour. Suppose that the number of jobs sent to a printer follows the Poisson distribution.

    a. What is the expected time between successive jobs?

    b. What is the probability that the next job will be sent within five minutes?

61. The mileage (in 1,000s of miles) that car owners get with a certain kind of radial tire is a random variable having an exponential distribution with a mean of 50.

    a. What is the probability that a tire will last at most 40,000 miles?

    b. What is the probability that a tire will last at least 65,000 miles?

    c. What is the probability that a tire will last between 70,000 and 80,000 miles?

62. Disturbing news regarding Scottish police concerns the number of crashes involving vehicles on operational duties. Statistics showed that Scottish forces' vehicles had been involved in traffic accidents at the rate of 1,000 per year. Suppose the number of crashes involving vehicles on operational duties follows a Poisson distribution.

    a. What is the average number of days between successive crashes?

    b. What is the rate parameter of the appropriate exponential distribution?

    c. What is the probability that the next vehicle will crash within a day?

6.4 WRITING WITH DATA

Case Study

Corbis / Image Source

Professor Lang is a professor of economics at Salem State University. She has been teaching a course in Principles of Economics for over 25 years. Professor Lang has never graded on a curve because she believes that relative grading may unduly penalize (benefit) a good (poor) student in an unusually strong (weak) class. She always uses an absolute scale for making grades, as shown in the two left columns of Table 6.1.

TABLE 6.1 Grading Scales with Absolute Grading versus Relative Grading

Absolute Grading		Relative Grading	
Grade	Score	Grade	Probability
A	92 and above	A	0.10
B	78 up to 92	B	0.35
C	64 up to 78	C	0.40
D	58 up to 64	D	0.10
F	Below 58	F	0.05

A colleague of Professor Lang's has convinced her to move to relative grading because it corrects for unanticipated problems. Professor Lang decides to experiment with grading based on the relative scale as shown in the two right columns of Table 6.1. Using this relative grading scheme, the top 10% of students will get A's, the next 35% B's, and so on. Based on her years of teaching experience, Professor Lang believes that the scores in her course follow a normal distribution with a mean of 78.6 and a standard deviation of 12.4.

Professor Lang wants to use this information to calculate probabilities based on the absolute scale and compare them to the probabilities based on the relative scale. Then, she wants to calculate the range of scores for grades based on the relative scale and compare them to the absolute scale. Finally, she want to determine which grading scale makes it harder to get higher grades.

Many teachers would confess that grading is one of the most difficult tasks of their profession. Two common grading systems used in higher education are relative and absolute. Relative grading systems are norm-referenced or curve-based, in which a grade is based on the student's relative position in the class. Absolute grading systems, on the other hand, are criterion-referenced, in which a grade is related to the student's absolute performance in class. In short, with absolute grading, the student's score is compared to a predetermined scale, whereas with relative grading, the score is compared to the scores of other students in the class.

Let X represent a grade in Professor Lang's class, which is normally distributed with a mean of 78.6 and a standard deviation of 12.4. This information is used to derive the grade probabilities based on the absolute scale. For instance, the probability of receiving an A is derived as $P(X \geq 92) = 0.14$. Other probabilities, derived similarly, are presented in Table 6.2.

TABLE 6.2 Probabilities Based on Absolute Scale and Relative Scale

Grade	Probability Based on Absolute Scale	Probability Based on Relative Scale
A	0.14	0.10
B	0.38	0.35
C	0.36	0.40
D	0.07	0.10
F	0.05	0.05

The second column of Table 6.2 shows that 14% of students are expected to receive A's, 38% B's, and so on. Although these numbers are generally consistent with the relative scale restated in the third column of Table 6.2, it appears that the relative scale makes it harder for students to get higher grades. For instance, 14% get A's with the absolute scale compared to only 10% with the relative scale.

Alternatively, we can compare the two grading methods on the basis of the range of scores for various grades. The second column of Table 6.3 restates the range of scores based on absolute grading. In order to obtain the range of scores based on relative grading, it is once again necessary to apply concepts from the normal distribution. For instance, the minimum score required to earn an A with relative grading is derived by solving for x in $P(X \geq x) = 0.10$. The lowest score that would place a student in the top 10% (90th percentile) of the distribution is found to be 94.49. Ranges for other grades, derived similarly, are presented in the third column of Table 6.3.

TABLE 6.3 Range of Scores with Absolute Grading versus Relative Grading

Grade	Range of Scores Based on Absolute Grading	Range of Scores Based on Relative Grading
A	92 and above	94.49 and above
B	78 up to 92	80.16 up to 94.49
C	64 up to 78	65.75 up to 80.16
D	58 up to 64	58.20 up to 65.75
F	Below 58	Below 58.20

Once again comparing the results in Table 6.3, the use of the relative scale makes it harder for students to get higher grades in Professor Lang's courses. For example, in order to receive an A with relative grading, a student must have a score of at least 94.49 versus a score of at least 92 with absolute grading. Both absolute and relative grading methods have their merits, and teachers often make the decision on the basis of their teaching philosophy. However, if Professor Lang wants to keep the grades consistent with her earlier absolute scale, she should base her relative scale on the probabilities computed in the second column of Table 6.2. For example, the probability of 0.14, instead of 0.10, should be used for calculating an A in the class using the relative scale.

Suggested Case Studies

Report 6.1. Body mass index (BMI) is a reliable indicator of body fat for most children and teens. The Centers for Disease Control and Prevention (CDC) reports BMI-for-age growth charts for children to obtain a percentile ranking. Percentiles are the most commonly used indicator to assess the size and growth patterns of children in the United States. The following table provides weight status categories and the corresponding percentiles and BMI ranges for 10-year-old boys in the United States.

Weight Status Category	Percentile Range	BMI Range
Underweight	Less than 5th	Less than 14.2
Healthy Weight	Between 5th and 85th	Between 14.2 and 19.4
Overweight	Between 85th and 95th	Between 19.4 and 22.2
Obese	More than 95th	More than 22.2

Health officials of a Midwestern town are concerned about the weight of children in their town. They believe that the BMI of their 10-year-old boys is normally distributed with mean 19.2 and standard deviation 2.6. In a report, use this information to compute the proportion of 10-year-old boys in this town that are in the various weight status categories given the BMI ranges. Discuss whether the concern of health officials is justified.

Report 6.2. Two common approaches to mutual fund investing are growth investing and value investing. Growth funds invest in companies whose stock prices are expected to grow at a faster rate, relative to the overall stock market. Value funds, on the other hand, invest in companies whose stock prices are below their true worth.

Dorothy Brennan works as a financial advisor at a large investment firm and has access to the annual return data for Fidelity's Growth Index mutual fund (Growth) and Fidelity's Value Index mutual fund (Value) for years 1984–2019. She calculates the mean and standard deviation for the Growth fund as 15.75% and 23.80%, respectively. The corresponding mean and standard deviation for the Value fund are 12.00% and 17.98%, respectively. She believes that the fund returns are stable and are normally distributed.

In a report, use the sample information to compare and contrast the Growth and Value funds for client objectives such as (a) minimizing the probability of earning a negative return and (b) maximizing the probability of earning a return greater than 10%.

Report 6.3. A variety of packaging solutions exist for products that must be kept within a specific temperature range. A cold chain distribution is a temperature-controlled supply chain. An unbroken cold chain is an uninterrupted series of storage and distribution activities that maintain a given temperature range. Cold chains are particularly useful in the food and pharmaceutical industries. A commonly suggested temperature range for a cold chain distribution in pharmaceutical industries is between 2 and 8 degrees Celsius.

Gopal Vasudeva works in the packaging branch of Merck & Co. He is in charge of analyzing a new package that the company has developed. With repeated trials, Gopal has determined that the mean temperature that this package is able to maintain during its use is 5.6°C with a standard deviation of 1.2°C.

In a report, use the sample information to calculate and interpret the probability that temperature goes (a) below 2°C and (b) above 8°C, using the normal distribution approximation. Calculate and interpret the 10th, 20th, . . . , 90th percentiles of the temperature that the package maintains.

7

Sampling and Sampling Distributions

In the last few chapters, we were given the values of the population parameters, such as the population proportion and the population mean, for the analysis of discrete and continuous random variables. In many instances, we do not have information on the parameters, so we make statistical inferences on the basis of sample statistics. The credibility of any statistical inference depends on the quality of the sample on which it is based.

In this chapter, we first discuss various ways to draw a good sample and also highlight cases in which the sample misrepresents the population. It is important to note that any given statistical problem involves only one population, but many possible samples from which a statistic can be derived. Therefore, while the population parameter is a constant, the sample statistic is a random variable whose value depends on the choice of the random sample.

We then discuss how to evaluate the properties of sample statistics. In particular, we study the probability distributions of the sample mean and the sample proportion based on simple random sampling. Finally, we use these distributions to construct control charts, which are popular statistical tools for monitoring and improving quality.

INTRODUCTORY CASE

Marketing Iced Coffee

Camila Fuentes is the owner of a gourmet coffee shop. She would like to increase her customer base during slow times, which primarily are Mondays through Thursdays between 1:00 pm and 4:00 pm. For one month during this time period, she decides to implement a Happy Hour when customers can enjoy a half-price iced coffee drink. Prior to the promotion, Camila reviews her records and finds that customers spent, on average, $4.18 on iced coffee with a standard deviation of $0.84. In addition, 43% of iced-coffee customers were women and 21% were teenage girls.

After the promotion ends, Camila surveys 50 of her iced-coffee customers and finds that they had spent an average of $4.26. In addition, 23 (46%) of the customers were women and 17 (34%) were teenage girls. Camila wants to determine if the promotion has been effective; that is, would she have gotten such business if she had chosen not to have a Happy Hour?

Camila wants to use the survey information to

1. Calculate the probability that customers spend an average of $4.26 or more on iced coffee.

2. Calculate the probability that 46% or more of iced-coffee customers are women.

3. Calculate the probability that 34% or more of iced-coffee customers are teenage girls.

A synopsis of this case is provided at the end of Section 7.3.

7.1 SAMPLING

A major portion of statistics is concerned with statistical inference, where we examine the problem of estimating population parameters or testing hypotheses about such parameters. Recall that a population consists of all items of interest in the statistical problem. If we had access to data that encompass the entire population, then the values of the parameters would be known and no statistical inference would be needed. Because it is generally not feasible to gather data on an entire population, we use a subset of the population, or a sample, and use this information to make statistical inference. We can think of a census and survey data as representative of population and sample data, respectively. While a census captures almost everyone in the country, a survey captures a small number of people who fit a particular category. We regularly use survey data to analyze government and business activities.

> ### POPULATION VERSUS SAMPLE
> A population consists of all items of interest in a statistical problem, whereas a sample is a subset of the population. We use a sample statistic, or simply statistic, to make inferences about the unknown population parameter.

In later chapters, we explore estimation and hypothesis testing, which are based on sample information. It is important to note that no matter how sophisticated the statistical methods are, the credibility of statistical inference depends on the quality of the sample on which it is based. A primary requisite for a "good" sample is that it be representative of the population we are trying to describe. When the information from a sample is not typical of information in the population in a systematic way, we say that **bias** has occurred.

> ### BIAS
> Bias refers to the tendency of a sample statistic to systematically overestimate or underestimate a population parameter. It is often caused by samples that are not representative of the population.

Sampling Biases

Classic Case of a "Bad" Sample: The *Literary Digest* Debacle of 1936

In theory, drawing conclusions about a population based on a good sample sounds logical; however, in practice, what constitutes a "good" sample? Unfortunately, there are many ways to collect a "bad" sample. One way is to inadvertently pick a sample that represents only a portion of the population. The *Literary Digest*'s attempt to predict the 1936 presidential election is a classic example of an embarrassingly inaccurate poll.

In 1932 and amid the Great Depression, Herbert Hoover was voted out of the White House and Franklin Delano Roosevelt (FDR) was elected the 32nd president of the United States. Although FDR's attempts to end the Great Depression within four years were largely unsuccessful, he retained the general public's faith. In 1936, FDR ran for reelection against Alf Landon, the governor of Kansas and the Republican nominee. The *Literary Digest,* an influential, general-interest weekly magazine, wanted to predict the next U.S. president, as it had done successfully five times before.

After conducting the largest poll in history, the *Literary Digest* predicted a landslide victory for Alf Landon: 57% of the vote to FDR's 43%. Moreover, the *Literary Digest* claimed that its prediction would be within a fraction of 1% of the actual vote. Instead, FDR won in a landslide: 62% of the vote to Landon's 38%. So what went wrong?

The *Literary Digest* sent postcards to 10 million people (one-quarter of the voting population at the time) and received responses from 2.4 million people. The response rate of 24% (= 2.4/10) might seem low to some, but in reality it is a reasonable response rate given this type of polling. What was atypical of the poll is the manner in which the *Literary Digest* obtained the respondents' names. The *Literary Digest* randomly sampled its own subscriber list, club membership rosters, telephone directories, and automobile registration rolls. This sample reflected predominantly middle- and upper-class people; that is, the vast majority of those polled were wealthier people, who were more inclined to vote for the Republican candidate. Back in the 1930s, owning a phone, for instance, was far from universal. Only 11 million residential phones were in service in 1936, and these homes were disproportionately well-to-do and in favor of Landon. The sampling methodology employed by the *Literary Digest* suffered from **selection bias.** Selection bias occurs when portions of the population are underrepresented in the sample. FDR's support came from lower-income classes whose opinion was not reflected in the poll. The sample, unfortunately, misrepresented the general electorate.

SELECTION BIAS

Selection bias refers to a systematic underrepresentation of certain groups from consideration for the sample.

What should the *Literary Digest* have done differently? At a minimum, most would agree that names should have been obtained from voter registration lists rather than telephone directory lists and car registrations.

In addition to selection bias, the *Literary Digest* survey also had a great deal of **nonresponse bias.** This occurs when those responding to a survey or poll differ systematically from the nonrespondents. In the survey, a larger percentage of educated people mailed back the questionnaires. During that time period, the more educated tended to come from affluent families that again favored the Republican candidate.

NONRESPONSE BIAS

Nonresponse bias refers to a systematic difference in preferences between respondents and nonrespondents to a survey or a poll.

The most effective way to deal with nonresponse bias is to reduce nonresponse rates. Paying attention to survey design, wording, and ordering of the questions can increase the response rate. Sometimes, rather than sending out a very large number of surveys, it may be preferable to use a smaller representative sample for which the response rate is likely to be high.

It turns out that someone did accurately predict the 1936 presidential election. From a sample of 50,000 with a response rate of 10% (5,000 respondents), a young pollster named George Gallup predicted that FDR would win 56% of the vote to Landon's 44%. Despite using a far smaller sample with a lower response rate, it was far more representative of the true voting population. Gallup later founded the Gallup Organization, one of the leading polling companies of all time.

Trump's Stunning Victory in 2016

The results of the U.S. presidential election in 2016 came as a surprise to nearly everyone who had been following the national and state election polling, which consistently projected Hillary Clinton as defeating Donald Trump (www.pewresearch.org, November 9, 2016). It appears that problems with selection bias and nonresponse bias persist today. Many pollsters and strategists believe that rural white voters, who were a key demographic for Trump on Election Day, eluded polling altogether. It is also believed that the frustration and anti-institutional feelings that drove the campaign may also have aligned these same voters with an unwillingness to respond to surveys (www.politico.com, March 27, 2017).

Another theory that has gained some traction in explaining the polling missteps in the 2016 election was the presence of **social-desirability bias.** This bias occurs when voters provide incorrect answers to a survey or poll because they think that others will look unfavorably on their ultimate choices.

SOCIAL-DESIRABILITY BIAS

Social-desirability bias refers to a systematic difference between a group's "socially acceptable" responses to a survey or poll and this group's ultimate choice.

Due to Trump's inflammatory comments, many voters did not want to be associated with him by their peers. This was perfectly exemplified by the fact that Trump consistently performed better in online polling. For example, in one aggregation of telephone polls, Clinton led Trump by nine percentage points; however, in a similar aggregation of online polls, Clinton's lead was only four percentage points (*The New York Times,* May 11, 2016). This seems to suggest that one way to battle social-desirability bias is to use online surveys. Despite their flaws, online surveys resemble an anonymous voting booth and remove the human factor of the pollsters.

LO 7.2

Describe various sampling methods.

Sampling Methods

As mentioned earlier, a primary requisite for a "good" sample is that it be representative of the population you are trying to describe. The basic type of sample that can be used to draw statistically sound conclusions about a population is a **simple random sample.**

SIMPLE RANDOM SAMPLE

A simple random sample is a sample of n observations that has the same probability of being selected from the population as any other sample of n observations. Most statistical methods assume a simple random sample.

While a simple random sample is the most commonly used sampling method, in some situations, other sampling methods have an advantage over simple random samples. Two alternative methods for forming a sample are stratified random sampling and cluster sampling.

Political pollsters often employ **stratified random sampling** in an attempt to ensure that each area of the country, each ethnic group, each religious group, and so forth, is appropriately represented in the sample. With stratified random sampling, the population is divided into groups (strata) based on one or more classification criteria. Simple random samples are then drawn from each stratum in sizes proportional to the relative size of each stratum in the population. These samples are then pooled.

STRATIFIED RANDOM SAMPLING

In stratified random sampling, the population is first divided up into mutually exclusive and collectively exhaustive groups, called *strata.* A stratified sample includes randomly selected observations from each stratum. The number of observations per stratum is proportional to the stratum's size in the population. The data for each stratum are eventually pooled.

Stratified random sampling has two advantages. First, it guarantees that the population subdivisions of interest are represented in the sample. Second, the estimates of parameters produced from stratified random sampling have greater precision than estimates obtained from simple random sampling.

Suppose a public opinion survey is to be conducted to determine whether a majority of households favor the opening of a marijuana dispensary in a particular city. Assume that it is known, from previous surveys, that households with school-age children tend to oppose the opening. Seventy percent of the households in this city have school-age children. If the city pursues a proportional stratified sampling plan, then 70% of the sample will consist of households with school-age children and the remaining 30% will consist of households with no school-age children.

Cluster sampling is another method for forming a representative sample. A cluster sample is formed by dividing the population into groups (clusters), such as geographic areas, and then selecting a sample of the groups for the analysis. The technique works best when most of the variation in the population is within the groups and not between the groups. In such instances, a cluster is a miniversion of the population.

CLUSTER SAMPLING

In cluster sampling, the population is first divided up into mutually exclusive and collectively exhaustive groups, called *clusters*. A cluster sample includes observations from randomly selected clusters.

In general, cluster sampling is cheaper as compared to other sampling methods. However, for a given sample size, it provides less precision than either simple random sampling or stratified sampling. Cluster sampling is useful in applications where the population is concentrated in natural clusters such as city blocks, schools, and other geographic areas. It is especially attractive when constructing a complete list of the population members is difficult and/or costly. For example, because it may not be possible to create a full list of customers who go to Walmart, we can form a sample that includes customers only from selected stores.

STRATIFIED VERSUS CLUSTER SAMPLING

In stratified sampling, the sample consists of observations from each group, whereas in cluster sampling, the sample consists of observations from the selected groups. Stratified sampling is preferred when the objective is to increase precision, and cluster sampling is preferred when the objective is to reduce costs.

In practice, it is extremely difficult to obtain a truly random sample that is representative of the underlying population. As researchers, we need to be aware of the population from which the sample was selected and then limit our conclusions to that population. For the remainder of the text, we assume that the sample data are void of "human error." That is, we have sampled from the correct population (no selection bias); we have no nonresponse or social-desirability biases; and we have collected, analyzed, and reported the data properly.

Using Excel to Generate a Simple Random Sample

Example 7.1 illustrates how to use Excel to draw a simple random sample.

EXAMPLE 7.1

There has been an increase in students working their way through college to off-set rising tuition costs. A dean at the Orfalea College of Business (OCOB) wants to analyze the performance of her students who work while they are enrolled. For the analysis, she wants to generate a random sample of 100 students drawn from 2,750 OCOB students.

SOLUTION: Because each student has a unique student identification number, we start by creating an ordered list using 1 and 2,750 as the smallest and largest student identification numbers, respectively. We then generate 100 random integers (numbers) between these values and use them to identify students based on their order on the list.

We use Excel's **RANDBETWEEN** function to generate random integers within some interval. We enter =RANDBETWEEN(lower, upper) where lower and upper refer to the smallest and largest integers in the interval, respectively. In this example, we enter =RANDBETWEEN(1,2750) in cell A1. Suppose Excel returns 983. The student whose order on the list is 983 is then selected for the sample. To generate the remaining 99 numbers, copy and paste the formula from cell A1 to cells A2 through A100.

EXERCISES 7.1

1. AirPods are Apple's most popular accessory product, with 35 million units sold in 2018 alone (*AppleInsider,* March 15, 2019). Suppose you are put in charge of determining the age profile of people who purchased AirPods in the United States. Explain in detail the following sampling strategies that you could use to select a representative sample.
   a. Simple random sampling
   b. Stratified random sampling
   c. Cluster sampling

2. A marketing firm opens a small booth at a local mall over the weekend, where shoppers are asked how much money they spent at the food court. The objective is to determine the average monthly expenditure of shoppers at the food court. Has the marketing firm committed any sampling bias? Discuss.

3. Natalie Min is an undergraduate in the Haas School of Business at Berkeley. She wishes to pursue an MBA from Berkeley and wants to know the profile of other students who are likely to apply to the Berkeley MBA program. In particular, she wants to know the GPA of students with whom she might be competing. She randomly surveys 40 students from her accounting class for the analysis. Discuss in detail whether or not Natalie's analysis is based on a representative sample.

4. Vons, a large supermarket in Grover Beach, California, is considering extending its store hours from 7:00 am to midnight, seven days a week, to 6:00 am to midnight. Discuss the sampling bias in the following sampling strategies:

   a. Mail a prepaid envelope to randomly selected residents in the Grover Beach area, asking for their preference for the store hours.
   b. Ask the customers who frequent the store in the morning if they would prefer an earlier opening time.
   c. Place an ad in the local newspaper, requesting people to submit their preference for store hours on the store's website.

5. In the previous question regarding Vons' store hours, explain how you can obtain a representative sample based on the following sampling strategies:
   a. Simple random sampling.
   b. Stratified random sampling.
   c. Cluster sampling.

6. Research has shown that physical exercise is effective at delaying the onset of deficiencies associated with an increase in brain age (magneticmemorymethod.com, November 12, 2019). For physical exercise, adults are often advised to follow a walking regimen, such as three vigorous 40-minute walks a week. As an assistant manager working for a public health institute based in Florida, you would like to estimate the proportion of adults in Miami who follow such a walking regimen. Discuss the sampling bias in the following strategies where people are asked if they walk regularly:
   a. Randomly selected adult beachgoers in Miami.

b. Randomly selected Miami residents who are requested to disclose the information in prepaid envelopes.

c. Randomly selected Miami residents who are requested to disclose the information on the firm's website.

d. Randomly selected adult patients at all hospitals in Miami.

7. In the previous question regarding walking regimens of the residents of Miami, explain how you can obtain a representative sample based on the following sampling strategies:

a. Simple random sampling.

b. Stratified random sampling.

c. Cluster sampling.

7.2 THE SAMPLING DISTRIBUTION OF THE SAMPLE MEAN

As mentioned earlier, we are generally interested in the characteristics of a population. For instance, a ride-sharing company is interested in the average income (population mean) in a large city. Similarly, a banker is interested in the default probability (population proportion) of mortgage holders. Recall that the population mean describes a numerical variable, and the population proportion describes a categorical variable. Because it is cumbersome, if not impossible, to analyze the entire population, we generally make inferences about the characteristics of the population on the basis of a random sample drawn from the population.

It is important to note that there is only one population, but many possible samples of a given size can be drawn from the population. Therefore, a population parameter is a constant, even though its value may be unknown. On the other hand, a statistic, such as the sample mean or the sample proportion, is a random variable whose value depends on the particular sample that is randomly drawn from the population.

PARAMETER VERSUS STATISTIC

A parameter is a constant, although its value may be unknown. A statistic is a random variable whose value depends on the chosen random sample.

Suppose that the variable of interest is the mean income in a large city. If you decide to make inferences about the population mean income on the basis of a random draw of 38 residents, then the sample mean $\overline{X}$ is the relevant statistic. Note that the value of $\overline{X}$ will change if you choose a different random sample of 38 residents. In other words, $\overline{X}$ is a random variable whose value depends on the chosen random sample. The sample mean is commonly referred to as the **estimator,** or the **point estimator,** of the population mean.

In the income example, the sample mean $\overline{X}$ is the estimator of the mean income in the large city. If the average derived from a specific sample is $54,000, then $\overline{x} = 54,000$ is the **estimate** of the population mean. Similarly, if the variable of interest is the default probability of mortgage holders, then the sample proportion of defaults, denoted by $\overline{P}$, from a random sample of 80 mortgage holders is the estimator of the population proportion. If 10 out of 80 mortgage holders in a given sample default, then $\overline{p} = 10/80 = 0.125$ is the estimate of the population proportion.

> ### ESTIMATOR AND ESTIMATE
> When a statistic is used to estimate a parameter, it is referred to as an estimator. A particular value of the estimator is called an estimate.

In this section, we will focus on the probability distribution of the sample mean $\bar{X}$, which is also referred to as the sampling distribution of $\bar{X}$. Because $\bar{X}$ is a random variable, its sampling distribution is simply the probability distribution derived from all possible samples of a given size from the population. Consider, for example, a mean derived from a sample of n observations. Another mean can similarly be derived from a different sample of n observations. If we repeat this process a very large number of times, then the frequency distribution of the sample means can be thought of as its sampling distribution. In particular, we will discuss the expected value and the standard deviation of the sample mean. We will also study the conditions under which the sampling distribution of the sample mean is normally distributed.

The Expected Value and the Standard Error of the Sample Mean

Let the random variable X represent a certain characteristic of a population under study, with an expected value, $E(X) = \mu$, and a variance, $Var(X) = \sigma^2$. For example, X could represent the income of a resident in a large city or the return on an investment. We can think of μ and σ^2 as the mean and the variance of an individual observation drawn randomly from the population of interest, or simply as the population mean and the population variance. Let the sample mean $\bar{X}$ be based on a random sample of n observations from this population.

If we were to sample repeatedly from a given population, the average value of the sample means will equal the average value of all individual observations in the population, or, simply, the population mean that is, $E(\bar{X}) = E(X) = \mu$. This is an important property of an estimator, called unbiasedness, that holds irrespective of whether the sample mean is based on a small or a large sample. An estimator is **unbiased** if its expected value equals the population parameter.

The variance of $\bar{X}$ is equal to $Var(\bar{X}) = \frac{\sigma^2}{n}$. In other words, if we were to sample repeatedly from a given population, the variance of the sample mean will equal the variance of all individual observations in the population, divided by the sample size, n. Note that $Var(\bar{X})$ is smaller than the variance of X, which is equal to $Var(X) = \sigma^2$. This is an intuitive result, suggesting that the variability between sample means is less than the variability between observations. Because each sample is likely to contain both high and low observations, the highs and lows cancel one another, making the variance of $\bar{X}$ smaller than the variance of X. As usual, the standard deviation of $\bar{X}$ is calculated as the positive square root of the variance. However, in order to distinguish the variability between the sample means from the variability between individual observations, we refer to the standard deviation of $\bar{X}$ as the **standard error** of the sample mean, computed as $se(\bar{X}) = \frac{\sigma}{\sqrt{n}}$.

> ### THE EXPECTED VALUE AND THE STANDARD ERROR OF THE SAMPLE MEAN
>
> - The expected value of the sample mean $\bar{X}$ equals the population mean, or $E(\bar{X}) = \mu$. Because of this equality, the sample mean is an unbiased estimator of the population mean.
> - The standard error of the sample mean $\bar{X}$ is equal to the population standard deviation divided by the square root of the sample size; that is, $se(\bar{X}) = \frac{\sigma}{\sqrt{n}}$.

EXAMPLE 7.2

The chefs at a local pizza chain in Cambria, California, strive to maintain the suggested size of their 16-inch pizzas. Despite their best efforts, they are unable to make every pizza exactly 16 inches in diameter. The manager has determined that the size of the pizzas is normally distributed with a mean of 16 inches and a standard deviation of 0.8 inch.

a. What are the expected value and the standard error of the sample mean derived from a random sample of 2 pizzas?

b. What are the expected value and the standard error of the sample mean derived from a random sample of 4 pizzas?

c. Compare the expected value and the standard error of the sample mean with those of an individual pizza.

SOLUTION: We know that the population mean $\mu = 16$ and the population standard deviation $\sigma = 0.8$. We use $E(\bar{X}) = \mu$ and $se(\bar{X}) = \frac{\sigma}{\sqrt{n}}$ to calculate the following results.

a. With the sample size $n = 2$, $E(\bar{X}) = 16$ and $se(\bar{X}) = \frac{0.8}{\sqrt{2}} = 0.57$.

b. With the sample size $n = 4$, $E(\bar{X}) = 16$ and $se(\bar{X}) = \frac{0.8}{\sqrt{4}} = 0.40$.

c. The expected value of the sample mean for both sample sizes is identical to the expected value of the individual pizza. However, the standard error of the sample mean with $n = 4$ is lower than the one with $n = 2$. For both sample sizes, the standard error of the sample mean is lower than the standard deviation of the individual pizza. This result confirms that averaging reduces variability.

Sampling from a Normal Population

An important feature of the sampling distribution of the sample mean $\bar{X}$ is that, irrespective of the sample size n, $\bar{X}$ is normally distributed if the population X from which the sample is drawn is normally distributed. In other words, if X is normally distributed with expected value μ and standard deviation σ, then $\bar{X}$ is also normally distributed with expected value μ and standard error $\sigma/\sqrt{n}$.

> ### SAMPLING FROM A NORMAL POPULATION
> For any sample size n, the sampling distribution of $\bar{X}$ is normally distributed if the population X from which the sample is drawn is normally distributed.

EXAMPLE 7.3

Use the information in Example 7.2 to answer the following questions:

a. What is the probability that the average size of a randomly selected pizza is less than 15.5 inches?

b. What is the probability that the average size of 2 randomly selected pizzas is less than 15.5 inches?

c. What is the probability that the average size of 4 randomly selected pizzas is less than 15.5 inches?

d. Comment on the computed probabilities.

SOLUTION: Because the population is normally distributed, the sampling distribution of the sample mean is also normally distributed. Figure 7.1 depicts the shapes of the three distributions based on the population mean $\mu = 16$ and the population standard deviation $\sigma = 0.8$.

FIGURE 7.1
Normal distribution of the sample mean

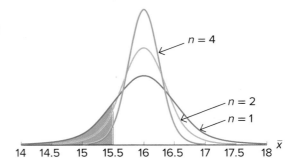

Note that when the sample size $n = 1$, the sample mean $\bar{x}$ is the same as the individual observation x.

a. We use Excel to find $P(X < 15.5)$. Recall that in order to find this probability, we enter `=NORM.DIST(15.5, 16, 0.8, TRUE)`, and Excel returns 0.2660. There is a 26.60% chance that the size of an individual pizza is less than 15.5 inches.

b. Here we need to find $P(\bar{X} < 15.5)$. We make a simple adjustment for the standard error to find this probability in Excel. We enter `=NORM.DIST(15.5, 16, 0.8/SQRT(2), TRUE)` and Excel returns 0.1884. In a random sample of 2 pizzas, there is an 18.84% chance that the average size is less than 15.5 inches.

c. Again we find $P(\bar{X} < 15.5)$, but now $n = 4$. In Excel, we enter `=NORM.DIST(15.5, 16, 0.8/SQRT(4), TRUE)` and Excel returns 0.1056. In a random sample of 4 pizzas, there is a 10.56% chance that the average size is less than 15.5 inches.

d. The probability that the average size is under 15.5 inches, for 4 randomly selected pizzas, is less than half of that for an individual pizza. This is due to the fact that while X and $\bar{X}$ have the same expected value of 16, the variance of $\bar{X}$ is less than that of X.

The Central Limit Theorem for the Sample Mean

LO 7.4

Explain the importance of the central limit theorem.

For making statistical inferences, it is essential that the sampling distribution of $\bar{X}$ is normally distributed. So far we have only considered the case where $\bar{X}$ is normally distributed because the population X from which the sample is drawn is normally distributed. What if the underlying population is not normally distributed? Here we present the **central limit theorem (CLT),** which perhaps is the most remarkable result of probability theory. The CLT states that the sum or the average of a large number of independent observations from the same underlying distribution has an approximate normal distribution. The approximation steadily improves as the number of observations increases. In other words, irrespective of whether or not the population X is normally distributed, the sample mean $\bar{X}$ computed from a random sample of size n will be approximately normally distributed as long as n is sufficiently large.

> ## THE CENTRAL LIMIT THEOREM FOR THE SAMPLE MEAN
>
> For any population X with expected value μ and standard deviation σ, the sampling distribution of $\overline{X}$ will be approximately normally distributed if the sample size n is sufficiently large. As a general guideline, the normal distribution approximation is justified when $n \geq 30$.

Figure 7.1, discussed in Example 7.3, is not representative of the CLT principle because, for a normal population, the sampling distribution of $\overline{X}$ is normally distributed irrespective of the sample size. Figures 7.2 and 7.3, however, illustrate the CLT by using random samples of various sizes drawn from non-normal populations. Figure 7.2 shows the sampling distribution of $\overline{X}$ when generated from repeated draws (computer simulations) from the continuous uniform distribution for three sample sizes: $n = 1$, $n = 5$, and $n = 30$. Figure 7.3 shows the sampling distribution of $\overline{X}$ when generated from repeated draws from the exponential distribution for three sample sizes: $n = 1$, $n = 5$, and $n = 30$. Both of these non-normal distributions were discussed in Chapter 6.

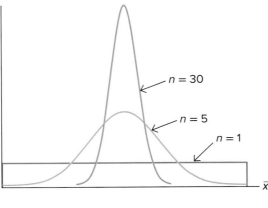

FIGURE 7.2
Sampling distribution of $\overline{X}$ when the population has a continuous uniform distribution

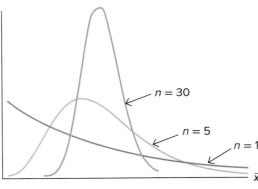

FIGURE 7.3
Sampling distribution of $\overline{X}$ when the population has an exponential distribution

Note that when the sample size $n = 1$, the sample mean is the same as the individual observation (population) with the familiar uniform and exponential shapes. With $n = 5$, the sampling distribution of $\overline{X}$ is already approximately normal when the population has the uniform distribution. With $n = 30$, the shape of the sampling distribution of $\overline{X}$ is approximately normal when the population has the exponential distribution. The CLT can similarly be illustrated with other non-normal distributions of the population. How large a sample is necessary for normal convergence depends on the magnitude of the departure of the population from normality. As mentioned earlier, practitioners often use the normal distribution approximation when $n \geq 30$.

EXAMPLE 7.4

Consider the information presented in the introductory case of this chapter. Recall that Camila wants to determine if the Happy Hour promotion has had a lingering effect on the amount of money customers spend on iced coffee. Before the promotion, customers spent an average of $4.18 on iced coffee with a standard deviation of $0.84. Camila reports that the average amount, based on 50 customers sampled after the campaign, is $4.26. If Camila chose not to pursue the marketing campaign, how likely is it that customers will spend an average of $4.26 or more on iced coffee?

SOLUTION: If Camila did not implement the Happy Hour, then spending on iced coffee would still have mean $\mu = 4.18$ and standard deviation $\sigma = 0.84$. Camila needs to calculate the probability that the sample mean is at least 4.26, or, $P(\bar{X} \geq 4.26)$. The population from which the sample is drawn is not known to be normally distributed. However, from the central limit theorem, we know that $\bar{X}$ is approximately normally distributed because $n \geq 30$. Therefore, as shown in Figure 7.4, $P(\bar{X} \geq 4.26) = 0.2503$. In order to find this probability in Excel, we enter =1-NORM.DIST(4.26, 4.18, 0.84/SQRT(50), TRUE). It is quite plausible (probability = 0.2503) that in a sample of 50 customers, the sample mean is $4.26 or more even if Camila did not implement the Happy Hour.

FIGURE 7.4 Finding $P(\bar{X} \geq 4.26)$

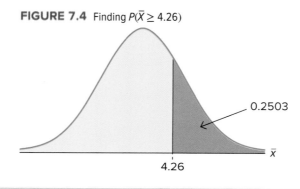

0.2503

4.26

Note: In most applications, the sample size n is very small relative to the population size N. When $n \geq 0.05N$, a finite population correction factor is suggested that reduces the sampling variation of the sample mean $\bar{X}$. We do not discuss this correction in this text.

EXERCISES 7.2

Mechanics

8. A random sample is drawn from a normally distributed population with mean $\mu = 12$ and standard deviation $\sigma = 1.5$.
   a. What are the expected value and the standard error of the sampling distribution of the sample mean with $n = 20$ and $n = 40$.
   b. Can you conclude that the sampling distribution of the sample mean is normally distributed for both sample sizes? Explain.
   c. If the sampling distribution of the sample mean is normally distributed with $n = 20$, then calculate the probability that the sample mean is less than 12.5.
   d. If the sampling distribution of the sample mean is normally distributed with $n = 40$, then calculate the probability that the sample mean is less than 12.5.

9. A random sample is drawn from a population with mean $\mu = 66$ and standard deviation $\sigma = 5.5$.
   a. What are the expected value and the standard error of the sampling distribution of the sample mean with $n = 16$ and $n = 36$.
   b. Can you conclude that the sampling distribution of the sample mean is normally distributed for both sample sizes? Explain.
   c. If the sampling distribution of the sample mean is normally distributed with $n = 16$, then calculate the probability that the sample mean falls between 66 and 68.
   d. If the sampling distribution of the sample mean is normally distributed with $n = 36$, then calculate the probability that the sample mean falls between 66 and 68.

10. A random sample of size $n = 100$ is taken from a population with mean $\mu = 80$ and standard deviation $\sigma = 14$.

a. Calculate the expected value and the standard error for the sampling distribution of the sample mean.

b. What is the probability that the sample mean falls between 77 and 85?

c. What is the probability that the sample mean is greater than 84?

11. A random sample of size $n = 50$ is taken from a population with mean $\mu = -9.5$ and standard deviation $\sigma = 2$.

a. Calculate the expected value and the standard error for the sampling distribution of the sample mean.

b. What is the probability that the sample mean is less than −10?

c. What is the probability that the sample mean falls between −10 and −9?

Applications

12. According to a survey, high school students average 100 text messages daily. Assume that the population standard deviation is 20 text messages. Suppose a random sample of 50 high school students is taken.

a. What is the probability that the sample mean is more than 105?

b. What is the probability that the sample mean is less than 95?

c. What is the probability that the sample mean is between 95 and 105?

13. Beer bottles are filled so that they contain an average of 330 ml of beer in each bottle. Suppose that the amount of beer in a bottle is normally distributed with a standard deviation of 4 ml.

a. What is the probability that a randomly selected bottle will have less than 325 ml of beer?

b. What is the probability that a randomly selected 6-pack of beer will have a mean amount less than 325 ml?

c. What is the probability that a randomly selected 12-pack of beer will have a mean amount less than 325 ml?

d. Comment on the sample size and the corresponding probabilities.

14. Despite its nutritional value, seafood is only a tiny part of the American diet, with the average American eating just 16 pounds of seafood per year. Janice and Nina both work in the seafood industry, and they decide to create their own random samples and document the average seafood diet in their sample. Let the standard deviation of the American seafood diet be 5 pounds.

a. Janice samples 30 Americans and finds an average seafood consumption of 18 pounds. How likely is it to get an average of 18 pounds or more if she had a representative sample?

b. Nina samples 90 Americans and finds an average seafood consumption of 17.5 pounds. How likely is it to get an average of 17.5 pounds or more if she had a representative sample?

c. Which of the two women is likely to have used a more representative sample? Explain.

15. The weight of people in a small town in Missouri is known to be normally distributed with a mean of 180 pounds and a standard deviation of 28 pounds. On a raft that takes people across the river, a sign states, "Maximum capacity 3,200 pounds or 16 persons." What is the probability that a random sample of 16 persons will exceed the weight limit of 3,200 pounds?

16. The weight of turkeys is known to be normally distributed with a mean of 22 pounds and a standard deviation of 5 pounds.

a. What are the expected value and the standard error of the sampling distribution of the sample mean based on a random draw of 16 turkeys. Is the sampling distribution of the sample mean normally distributed? Explain.

b. Find the probability that the mean weight of 16 randomly selected turkeys is more than 25 pounds.

c. Find the probability that the mean weight of 16 randomly selected turkeys is between 18 and 24 pounds.

17. A small hair salon in Denver, Colorado, averages about 30 customers on weekdays with a standard deviation of 6. It is safe to assume that the underlying distribution is normal. In an attempt to increase the number of weekday customers, the manager offers a $2 discount on 5 consecutive weekdays. She reports that her strategy has worked because the sample mean of customers during this 5-weekday period jumps to 35.

a. How unusual would it be to get a sample average of 35 or more customers if the manager had not offered the discount?

b. Do you feel confident that the manager's discount strategy has worked? Explain.

18. One of the best-selling products for a specialty grocery store is a 16-ounce package of almonds. Because it is impossible to pack exactly 16 ounces in each packet, a researcher has determined that the weight of almonds in each packet is normally distributed with a mean and a standard deviation equal to 16.01 ounces and 0.08 ounce, respectively.

a. Discuss the sampling distribution of the sample mean based on any given sample size.

b. Find the probability that a random sample of 20 bags of almonds will average less than 16 ounces.

c. Suppose your cereal recipe calls for no less than 48 ounces of almonds. What is the probability that three packets of almonds will meet your requirement?

19. Forty families gathered for a fund-raising event. Suppose the individual contribution for each family is normally distributed with a mean and a standard deviation of $115 and $35, respectively. The organizers would call this event a success if the total contributions exceed $5,000. What is the probability that this fund-raising event is a success?

20. A doctor is getting sued for malpractice by four of her former patients. It is believed that the amount that each patient will sue her for is normally distributed with a mean of $800,000 and a standard deviation of $250,000.

a. What is the probability that a given patient sues the doctor for more than $1,000,000?

b. If the four patients sue the doctor independently, what is the probability that the total amount that they sue her for is over $4,000,000?

21. Suppose that the miles-per-gallon (mpg) rating of passenger cars is normally distributed with a mean and a standard deviation of 33.8 mpg and 3.5 mpg, respectively.

a. What is the probability that a randomly selected passenger car gets more than 35 mpg?

b. What is the probability that the average mpg of four randomly selected passenger cars is more than 35 mpg?

c. If four passenger cars are randomly selected, what is the probability that all of the passenger cars get more than 35 mpg?

22. Suppose that IQ scores are normally distributed with a mean of 100 and a standard deviation of 16.

a. What is the probability that a randomly selected person will have an IQ score of less than 90?

b. What is the probability that the average IQ score of four randomly selected people is less than 90?

c. If four people are randomly selected, what is the probability that all of them have an IQ score of less than 90?

7.3 THE SAMPLING DISTRIBUTION OF THE SAMPLE PROPORTION

Describe the sampling distribution of the sample proportion.

Our discussion thus far has focused on the population mean, but many business, socioeconomic, and political matters are concerned with the population proportion. For instance, a banker is interested in the default probability of mortgage holders; a superintendent may note the proportion of students suffering from the flu when determining whether to keep school open; an incumbent seeking reelection cares about the proportion of constituents who will ultimately cast a vote for her. In all of these examples, the parameter of interest is the population proportion p. As in the case of the population mean, we almost always make inferences about the population proportion on the basis of sample data. Here, the relevant statistic (estimator) is the sample proportion, $\bar{P}$; a particular value (estimate) is denoted by $\bar{p}$. Because $\bar{P}$ is a random variable, we need to discuss its sampling distribution.

The Expected Value and the Standard Error of the Sample Proportion

We first introduced the population proportion p in Chapter 5, when we discussed the binomial distribution. It turns out that the sampling distribution of $\bar{P}$ is closely related to the binomial distribution. Recall that the binomial distribution describes the number of successes X in n trials of a Bernoulli process where p is the probability of success; thus, $\bar{P} = \frac{X}{n}$ is the number of successes X divided by the sample size n. We can derive the expected value and the variance of the sampling distribution of $\bar{P}$ as $E(\bar{P}) = p$ and $Var(\bar{P}) = \frac{p(1-p)}{n}$, respectively. Note that because $E(\bar{P}) = p$, it implies that $\bar{P}$ is an unbiased estimator of p.

Analogous to our discussion in the last section, we refer to the standard deviation of the sample proportion as the standard error of the sample proportion; that is, $se(\bar{P}) = \sqrt{\frac{p(1-p)}{n}}$.

THE EXPECTED VALUE AND THE STANDARD ERROR OF THE SAMPLE PROPORTION

- The expected value of the sample proportion $\bar{P}$ is equal to the population proportion, or $E(\bar{P}) = p$. Because of this equality, the sample proportion is an unbiased estimator of the population proportion.
- The standard error of the sample proportion $\bar{P}$ is equal to $se(\bar{P}) = \sqrt{\frac{p(1-p)}{n}}$.

EXAMPLE 7.5

A study found that 55% of British firms experienced a cyberattack in the past year (*BBC*, April 23, 2019).

a. What are the expected value and the standard error of the sample proportion derived from a random sample of 100 firms?

b. What are the expected value and the standard error of the sample proportion derived from a random sample of 200 firms?

c. Comment on the value of the standard error as the sample size gets larger.

SOLUTION: Given that $p = 0.55$, we can derive the expected value and the standard error of $\bar{P}$ as follows.

a. With $n = 100$, $E(\bar{P}) = 0.55$ and $se(\bar{P}) = \sqrt{\frac{0.55(1 - 0.55)}{100}} = 0.0497$.

b. With $n = 200$, $E(\bar{P}) = 0.55$ and $se(\bar{P}) = \sqrt{\frac{0.55(1 - 0.55)}{200}} = 0.0352$.

c. As in the case of the sample mean, while the expected value of the sample proportion is unaffected by the sample size, the standard error of the sample proportion is reduced as the sample size increases.

The Central Limit Theorem for the Sample Proportion

In this text, we make statistical inferences about the population proportion only when the sampling distribution of $\bar{P}$ is approximately normally distributed. From the discussion of the central limit theorem (CLT) in Section 7.2, we can conclude that $\bar{P}$ is approximately normally distributed when the sample size is sufficiently large.

> **THE CENTRAL LIMIT THEOREM FOR THE SAMPLE PROPORTION**
>
> For any population proportion p, the sampling distribution of $\bar{P}$ is approximately normally distributed if the sample size n is sufficiently large. As a general guideline, the normal distribution approximation is justified when $np \geq 5$ and $n(1 - p) \geq 5$.

According to the CLT, the sampling distribution of $\bar{P}$ approaches the normal distribution as the sample size increases. However, as the population proportion deviates from $p = 0.50$, we need a larger sample size for the approximation. We illustrate these results by generating the sampling distribution of $\bar{P}$ from repeated draws from a population with various values of the population proportion and sample sizes. Figure 7.5 shows the sampling distribution of $\bar{P}$ based on the population proportion $p = 0.10$ for sample sizes of $n = 20$ and $n = 100$. Figure 7.6 shows the sampling distribution of $\bar{P}$ based on the population proportion $p = 0.30$ for sample sizes of $n = 20$ and $n = 100$.

FIGURE 7.5
Sampling distribution of $\bar{P}$ when the population proportion is $p = 0.10$

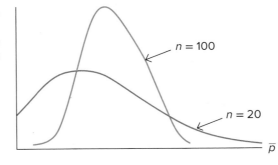

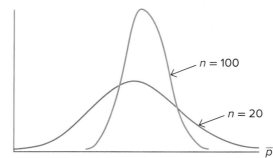

FIGURE 7.6
Sampling distribution
of $\overline{P}$ when the population
proportion is $p = 0.30$

$n = 100$

$n = 20$

$\overline{p}$

When $p = 0.10$, the sampling distribution of $\overline{P}$ does not resemble the bell shape of the normal distribution with $n = 20$ because the approximation condition $np \geq 5$ and $n(1 - p) \geq 5$ is not satisfied. However, the distribution is approximately normal with $n = 100$. When $p = 0.30$, the shape of the sampling distribution of $\overline{P}$ is approximately normal because the approximation condition is satisfied with both sample sizes. In empirical work, it is common to work with large survey data, and, as a result, the normal distribution approximation is justified.

EXAMPLE 7.6

Consider the information presented in the introductory case of this chapter. Recall that Camila wants to determine if the Happy Hour promotion has had a lingering effect on the proportion of customers who are women and teenage girls. Prior to the Happy Hour promotion, 43% of the customers were women and 21% were teenage girls. Based on a random sample of 50 customers after the Happy Hour promotion, these proportions increase to 46% for women and 34% for teenage girls. Camila has the following questions.

a. If Camila chose not to pursue the Happy Hour promotion, how likely is it that 46% or more of iced-coffee customers are women?

b. If Camila chose not to pursue the Happy Hour promotion, how likely is it that 34% or more of iced-coffee customers are teenage girls?

SOLUTION: If Camila had not pursued the Happy Hour promotion, then the proportion of customers would still be $p = 0.43$ for women and $p = 0.21$ for teenage girls. With $n = 50$, the normal approximation for the sample proportion is justified for both population proportions.

a. As shown in Figure 7.7, we find that $P(\overline{P} \geq 0.46) = 0.3341$.

FIGURE 7.7 Finding $P(\overline{P} \geq 0.46)$

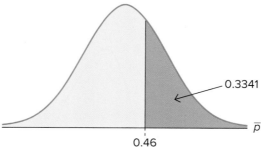

0.3341

$\overline{p}$

0.46

In order to find this probability in Excel, we enter =1-NORM.DIST(0.46, 0.43, SQRT(0.43*(1-0.43)/50), TRUE). With a chance of 33.41%, it is quite plausible that the proportion of women who purchase iced coffee is at least 0.46 even if Camila did not pursue the Happy Hour promotion.

b. As shown in Figure 7.8, we find $P(\overline{P} \geq 0.34) = 0.0120$.

FIGURE 7.8 Finding $P(\overline{P} \geq 0.34)$

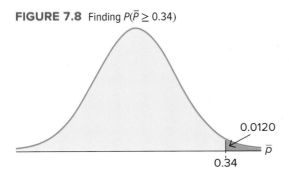

0.0120

$\overline{P}$

0.34

In order to find this probability in Excel, we enter =1-NORM.DIST(0.34, 0.21, SQRT(0.21*(1-0.21)/50), TRUE). With only a 1.20% chance, it is unlikely that the proportion of teenage girls who purchase iced coffee is at least 0.34 if Camila did not pursue the Happy Hour promotion.

SYNOPSIS OF INTRODUCTORY CASE

Camila Fuentes, the owner of a gourmet coffee shop, would like to increase her customer base during slow times, which primarily are Mondays through Thursdays between 1:00 pm and 4:00 pm. For one month during this time period, she implements a Happy Hour when customers can enjoy a half-price iced coffee drink. After the Happy Hour promotion ends, Camila surveys 50 of her customers. She reports an increase in spending in the sample, as well as an increase in the proportion of customers who are women and teenage girls. Camila wants to determine if the increase is due to chance or due to the Happy Hour promotion. Based on an analysis with probabilities, Camila finds that higher spending in a sample of 50 customers is plausible even if she had not pursued the Happy Hour promotion. Using a similar analysis with proportions, she infers that while the Happy Hour promotion may not have necessarily increased the proportion of women customers,

M. Unal Ozmen/Shutterstock

it seems to have attracted more teenage girls. The findings are consistent with current market research, which has shown that teenage girls have substantial income of their own to spend and often purchase items that some may perceive as indulgences.

Note: In most applications, the sample size n is very small relative to the population size N. When $n \geq 0.05N$, a finite population correction factor is suggested that reduces the sampling variation of the sample proportion $\overline{P}$. We do not discuss this correction in this text.

EXERCISES 7.3

Mechanics

23. Consider a population proportion $p = 0.68$.
    a. Calculate the expected value and the standard error of $\bar{P}$ with $n = 20$. Is it appropriate to use the normal distribution approximation for $\bar{P}$? Explain.
    b. Calculate the expected value and the standard error of $\bar{P}$ with $n = 50$. Is it appropriate to use the normal distribution approximation for $\bar{P}$? Explain.

24. Consider a population proportion $p = 0.12$.
    a. What are the expected value and the standard error for the sampling distribution of the sample proportion with $n = 20$ and $n = 50$?
    b. Can you conclude that the sampling distribution of the sample proportion is approximately normally distributed for both sample sizes? Explain.
    c. If the sampling distribution of the sample proportion is approximately normally distributed with $n = 20$, then calculate the probability that the sample proportion is between 0.10 and 0.12.
    d. If the sampling distribution of the sample proportion is approximately normally distributed with $n = 50$, then calculate the probability that the sample proportion is between 0.10 and 0.12.

25. A random sample of size $n = 200$ is taken from a population with a population proportion $p = 0.75$.
    a. Calculate the expected value and the standard error for the sampling distribution of the sample proportion.
    b. What is the probability that the sample proportion is between 0.70 and 0.80?
    c. What is the probability that the sample proportion is less than 0.70?

Applications

26. According to research, 26% of Americans are always online.
    a. What is the probability that fewer than 60 of 200 Americans are always online?
    b. What is the probability that more than 150 of 200 Americans are *not* always online?

27. A survey found that 82% of college graduates believe their degree was a good investment. Suppose a random sample of 100 college graduates is taken.

a. What are the expected value and the standard error for the sampling distribution of the sample proportion?
b. What is the probability that the sample proportion is less than 0.80?
c. What is the probability that the sample proportion is within ± 0.02 of the population proportion?

28. A pharmaceutical company knows that five percent of all users of a certain drug experience a serious side effect. A researcher examines a sample of 200 users of the drug.
    a. What is the probability of finding between 8 and 12 cases with side effects?
    b. What is the probability of finding more than 16 cases with side effects?

29. A car manufacturer is concerned about poor customer satisfaction at one of its dealerships. The management decides to evaluate the satisfaction surveys of its next 40 customers. The dealership will be fined if the number of customers who report favorably is between 22 and 26. The dealership will be dissolved if fewer than 22 customers report favorably. It is known that 70% of the dealership's customers report favorably on satisfaction surveys.
    a. What is the probability that the dealership will be fined?
    b. What is the probability that the dealership will be dissolved?

30. At an exhibit in the Museum of Science, people are asked to choose between 50 or 100 random draws from a machine. The machine is known to have 60 green balls and 40 red balls. After each draw, the color of the ball is noted and the ball is put back for the next draw. You win a prize if more than 70% of the draws result in a green ball. Would you choose 50 or 100 draws for the game? Explain.

31. Twenty-three percent of the employees at a large biotech firm are working from home.
    a. In a sample of 50 employees, what is the probability that more than 20% of them are working from home?
    b. In a sample of 200 employees, what is the probability that more than 20% of them are working from home?
    c. Comment on the reason for the difference between the computed probabilities in parts a and b.

7.4 STATISTICAL QUALITY CONTROL

Construct and interpret control charts for numerical and categorical variables.

Now more than ever, a successful firm must focus on the quality of the products and services it offers. Global competition, technological advances, and consumer expectations are all factors contributing to the quest for quality. In order to ensure the production of high-quality goods and services, a successful firm implements some form of quality control. In this section, we give a brief overview of the field of **statistical quality control.**

> ### STATISTICAL QUALITY CONTROL
> Statistical quality control involves statistical techniques used to develop and maintain a firm's ability to produce high-quality goods and services.

In general, two approaches are used for statistical quality control. A firm uses **acceptance sampling** if it produces a product (or offers a service) and at the completion of the production process, the firm then inspects a portion of the products. If a particular product does not conform to certain specifications, then it is either discarded or repaired. There are several problems with this approach to quality control. First, it is costly to discard or repair a product. Second, the detection of all defective products is not guaranteed. Defective products may be delivered to customers, thus damaging the firm's reputation.

A preferred approach to quality control is the **detection approach.** A firm using the detection approach inspects the production process and determines at which point the production process does not conform to specifications. The goal is to determine whether the production process should be continued or adjusted before a large number of defects are produced. In this section, we focus on the detection approach to quality control.

> ### ACCEPTANCE SAMPLING VERSUS THE DETECTION APPROACH
> Two approaches are generally used for statistical quality control.
> - Acceptance sampling is a technique in which a portion of the completed products is inspected.
> - The detection approach is a technique that determines at which point the production process does not conform to specification.

In general, no two products or services are identical. In any production process, variation in the quality of the end product is inevitable. Two types of variation occur. **Chance variation** is caused by a number of randomly occurring events that are part of the production process. This type of variation is not generally considered to be under the control of the individual worker or machine. For example, suppose a machine fills one-gallon jugs of milk. It is unlikely that the filling weight of each jug is exactly 128 ounces. Very slight differences in the production process lead to minor differences in the weights of one jug to the next. Chance variation is expected and is not a source of alarm in the production process so long as its magnitude is tolerable and the end product meets acceptable specifications.

The other source of variation is referred to as **assignable variation.** This type of variation in the production process is caused by specific events or factors that can usually be identified and eliminated. Suppose in the milk example that the machine is "drifting" out of alignment. This causes the machine to overfill each jug—a costly expense for the firm. Similarly, it is bad for the firm in terms of its reputation if the machine begins to underfill each jug. The firm wants to identify and correct these types of variations in the production process.

> ### CHANCE VARIATION VERSUS ASSIGNABLE VARIATION
> Two types of variation occur in any production process.
> - Chance variation is expected and is not grounds for alarm. It is caused by a number of randomly occurring events that are part of the production process.
> - Assignable variation is caused by specific events or factors that can usually be identified and eliminated.

A Control Chart

Walter A. Shewhart, a researcher at Bell Telephone Laboratories during the 1920s, is often credited as being the first to apply statistics to improve the quality of output. He developed the **control chart**—a tool used to monitor the behavior of a production process.

We can construct a number of different control charts where each differs by either the variable of interest and/or the type of data that are available. For a numerical variable, examples of control charts include

- The $\bar{x}$ chart, which monitors the *central tendency* of a production process, and
- The R chart and the s chart, which monitor the *variability* of a production process.

For a categorical variable, examples of control charts include

- The p chart, which monitors the *proportion* of defectives (or some other characteristic) in a production process, and
- The c chart, which monitors the *count* of defects per item, such as the number of blemishes on a sampled piece of furniture.

In general, all of these control charts (and others that we have not mentioned) have the following characteristics:

1. A control chart plots the sample estimates, such as $\bar{x}$ or $\bar{p}$. So as more and more samples are taken, the resulting control chart provides one type of safeguard when assessing if the production process is operating within predetermined guidelines.

2. All sample estimates are plotted with reference to a **centerline.** The centerline represents the variable's expected value when the production process is in control.

3. In addition to the centerline, all control charts include an **upper control limit (UCL)** and a **lower control limit (LCL).** These limits indicate excessive deviation above or below the expected value of the variable of interest. A control chart is valid only if the sampling distribution of the relevant estimator is (approximately) normally distributed. Under this assumption, the control limits are generally set at three standard deviations from the centerline. The area under the normal curve that corresponds to ± 3 standard deviations from the expected value is 0.9973. Thus, there is only a $1 - 0.9973 = 0.0027$ chance that the sample estimates will fall outside the limit boundaries. In general, we define the upper and lower control limits as follows:

$$\text{UCL: Expected Value} + (3 \times \text{Standard Error})$$

$$\text{LCL: Expected Value} - (3 \times \text{Standard Error})$$

If the sample estimates fall randomly within the upper and lower control limits, then the production process is deemed in control. Any sample estimate that falls above the upper control limit or below the lower control limit is considered evidence that the production process is out of control and should be adjusted. In addition, any type of patterns within the control limits may suggest possible problems with the process. One indication of a process that is potentially heading out of control is unusually long runs above or below the centerline. Another possible problem is any evidence of a trend within the control limits.

A CONTROL CHART

The most commonly used statistical tool in quality control is a control chart, which is a plot of the sample estimates of the production process over time. If the sample estimates fall within the upper and lower control limits, then the production process is in control. If the sample estimates reveal an undesirable trend, then adjustment of the production process is likely necessary.

The $\bar{x}$ Chart

In the next example, we focus on a numerical variable and illustrate the $\bar{x}$ chart.

EXAMPLE 7.7

A firm that produces one-gallon jugs of milk wants to ensure that the machine is operating properly. Every two hours, the company samples 25 jugs and calculates the following sample mean filling weights (in ounces):

$\bar{x}_1 = 128.7$	$\bar{x}_2 = 128.4$	$\bar{x}_3 = 128.0$	$\bar{x}_4 = 127.8$	$\bar{x}_5 = 127.5$	$\bar{x}_6 = 126.9$

Assume that when the machine is operating properly, $\mu = 128$ and $\sigma = 2$, and that filling weights follow the normal distribution. Can the firm conclude that the machine is operating properly? Should the firm have any concerns with respect to this machine?

SOLUTION: Here the firm is interested in monitoring the population mean. To answer these questions, we construct an $\bar{x}$ chart. As mentioned earlier, this chart relies on the normal distribution for the sampling distribution of the estimator $\bar{X}$. Recall that if we are sampling from a normal population, then $\bar{X}$ is normally distributed even for small sample sizes. In this example, we are told that filling weights follow the normal distribution, a common assumption in the literature on quality control.

For the $\bar{x}$ chart, the centerline is the mean when the process is in control. Here, we are given that $\mu = 128$. We then calculate the UCL as three standard deviations above the mean and the LCL as three standard deviations below the mean:

$$\text{UCL: } \mu + 3\frac{\sigma}{\sqrt{n}} = 128 + 3\frac{2}{\sqrt{25}} = 129.2$$

$$\text{LCL: } \mu - 3\frac{\sigma}{\sqrt{n}} = 128 - 3\frac{2}{\sqrt{25}} = 126.8$$

Figure 7.9 shows the centerline and the control limits as well as the sample means.

FIGURE 7.9 Mean chart for milk production process

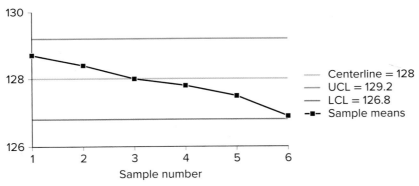

All of the sample means fall within the UCL and the LCL, which indicates, at least initially, that the production process is in control. However, the sample means should be randomly spread between these limits; there should be no pattern. In this example, there is clearly a downward trend in the sample means. It appears as though the machine is beginning to underfill the one-gallon jugs. So even though none of the sample means lies beyond the control limits, the production process is likely veering out of control and the firm would be wise to inspect the machine sooner rather than later.

The p Chart

A firm may be interested in the stability of the proportion of its goods or services possessing a certain attribute or characteristic. For example, most firms strive to produce high-quality goods (or services) and thus hope to keep the proportion of defects at a minimum. When a production process is to be assessed based on sample proportions—here, the proportion of defects—then a p chart proves quite useful. Because the primary purpose of the p chart is to track the proportion of defects in a production process, it is also referred to as a fraction defective chart or a percent defective chart. Consider the next example.

EXAMPLE 7.8

A production process has a 5% defective rate. A quality inspector takes 6 samples of $n = 500$. The following sample proportions are obtained:

$\bar{p}_1 = 0.065$	$\bar{p}_2 = 0.075$	$\bar{p}_3 = 0.082$	$\bar{p}_4 = 0.086$	$\bar{p}_5 = 0.090$	$\bar{p}_6 = 0.092$

a. Construct a p chart. Plot the sample proportions on the p chart.

b. Is the production process in control? Explain.

SOLUTION:

a. The p chart relies on the central limit theorem for the normal approximation for the sampling distribution of the estimator $\bar{P}$. Recall that so long as np and $n(1 - p)$ are greater than or equal to five, then the sampling distribution of $\bar{P}$ is approximately normally distributed. This condition is satisfied in this example. Given that the expected proportion of defects is equal to 0.05, we set the centerline at $p = 0.05$. We then calculate the UCL and the LCL as follows.

$$\text{UCL: } p + 3\sqrt{\frac{p(1-p)}{n}} = 0.05 + 3\sqrt{\frac{0.05(1 - 0.05)}{500}} = 0.079$$

$$\text{LCL: } p - 3\sqrt{\frac{p(1-p)}{n}} = 0.05 - 3\sqrt{\frac{0.05(1 - 0.05)}{500}} = 0.021$$

We note that if the UCL is a value greater than one, then we reset the UCL to one in the control chart. Similarly, if the LCL is a negative value, we reset the LCL to zero in the control chart.

Plotting the values for the centerline, the UCL, the LCL, as well as the sample proportions, yields Figure 7.10.

FIGURE 7.10 Proportion of defects

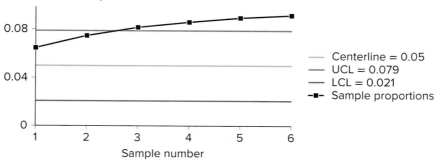

b. Four of the most recent sample proportions fall above the UCL. This provides evidence that the process is out of control and needs adjustment.

Using Excel to Create a Control Chart

Even though Excel does not have a built-in function to create a control chart, it is still relatively easy to construct one. If we are not given values for the centerline, the UCL, the LCL, and the sample means, then we first must provide these values in an Excel spreadsheet. We illustrate the construction of an $\bar{x}$ chart using Excel in Example 7.9.

EXAMPLE 7.9

JK Paints manufactures various kinds of paints in 4-liter cans. The cans are filled on an assembly line with an automatic valve regulating the amount of paint. To ensure that the correct amount of paint goes into each can, the quality control manager draws a random sample of four cans each hour and measures their amounts of paint. Because past experience has produced a standard deviation of $\sigma = 0.25$, the quality control manager has been able to calculate the LCL and the UCL as 3.625 ($= 4 - 3 \times 0.25/\sqrt{4}$) and 4.375 ($= 4 + 3 \times 0.25/\sqrt{4}$), respectively. Table 7.1 shows a portion of the results from the last 25 hours. The table also includes the sample mean of the four randomly selected cans, the LCL, the centerline, and the UCL. Use Excel to create an $\bar{x}$ chart to determine whether the cans are being filled properly.

TABLE 7.1 Data for Example 7.9

Sample	Obs. 1	Obs. 2	Obs. 3	Obs. 4	$\bar{x}$	LCL	Centerline	UCL
1	4.175	3.574	3.795	4.211	3.939	3.625	4	4.375
2	4.254	4.012	4.119	3.866	4.063	3.625	4	4.375
⋮	⋮	⋮	⋮	⋮	⋮	⋮	⋮	⋮
25	4.104	4.107	4.236	3.505	3.988	3.625	4	4.375

SOLUTION: As mentioned earlier, if only the first five columns of Table 7.1 were provided, we would have had to first populate the rest of the table by finding values for $\bar{x}$, LCL, Centerline, and UCL to make the $\bar{x}$ chart in Excel.

a. Open the data file *Paint*.

b. Simultaneously select cells F1:I26. From the menu, select **Insert,** and in the Charts group, expand the selection by clicking on the arrow at the bottom right. Select the **All Charts** tab and then select **Line**. Then select the option at the top left.

c. Formatting (regarding axis titles, colors, etc.) can be done by selecting **Format > Add Chart Element** from the menu.

Figure 7.11 shows the control chart that Excel produces. All sample means fall within the UCL and the LCL, and they also fall randomly above and below the centerline. This indicates that the cans are being filled properly.

FIGURE 7.11 Using Excel to create a control chart

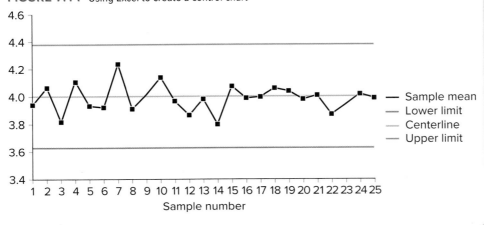

EXERCISES 7.4

Mechanics

32. Consider a normally distributed population with mean $\mu = 80$ and standard deviation $\sigma = 14$.
    a. Construct the centerline and the upper and lower control limits for the $\bar{x}$ chart if samples of size 5 are used.
    b. Repeat the analysis with samples of size 10.
    c. Discuss the effect of the sample size on the control limits.

33. Random samples of size $n = 250$ are taken from a population with $p = 0.04$.
    a. Construct the centerline and the upper and lower control limits for the p chart.
    b. Repeat the analysis with $n = 150$.
    c. Discuss the effect of the sample size on the control limits.

34. Random samples of size $n = 25$ are taken from a normally distributed population with mean $\mu = 20$ and standard deviation $\sigma = 10$.
    a. Construct the centerline and the upper and lower control limits for the $\bar{x}$ chart.
    b. Suppose six samples of size 25 produced the following sample means: 18, 16, 19, 24, 28, and 30. Plot these values on the $\bar{x}$ chart.
    c. Are any points outside the control limits? Does it appear that the process is under control? Explain.

35. Random samples of size $n = 36$ are taken from a population with mean $\mu = 150$ and standard deviation $\sigma = 42$.
    a. Construct the centerline and the upper and lower control limits for the $\bar{x}$ chart.
    b. Suppose five samples of size 36 produced the following sample means: 133, 142, 150, 165, and 169. Plot these values on the $\bar{x}$ chart.
    c. Are any points outside the control limits? Does it appear that the process is under control? Explain.

36. Random samples of size $n = 500$ are taken from a population with $p = 0.34$.
    a. Construct the centerline and the upper and lower control limits for the p chart.
    b. Suppose six samples of size 500 produced the following sample proportions: 0.28, 0.30, 0.33, 0.34, 0.37, and 0.39. Plot these values on the p chart.
    c. Are any points outside the control limits? Does it appear that the process is under control? Explain.

37. Random samples of size $n = 400$ are taken from a population with $p = 0.10$.
    a. Construct the centerline and the upper and lower control limits for the p chart.
    b. Suppose six samples of size 400 produced the following sample proportions: 0.06, 0.11, 0.09, 0.08, 0.14, and 0.16. Plot these values on the p chart.
    c. Is the production process under control? Explain.

Applications

38. **FILE** *MLB* Major League Baseball Rule 1.09 states that "the baseball shall weigh not less than 5 or more than 5¼ ounces" (www.mlb.com). Use these values as the lower and the upper control limits, respectively. Assume the centerline equals 5.125 ounces. Periodic samples of 50 baseballs produce the sample means that are reported in the accompanying data file.
    a. Construct an $\bar{x}$ chart. Plot the sample means on the $\bar{x}$ chart.
    b. Are any points outside the control limits? Does it appear that the process is under control? Explain.

39. **FILE** *Boxes.* A production process is designed to fill boxes with an average of 14 ounces of cereal. The population of filling weights is normally distributed with a standard deviation of 2 ounces. Inspectors take periodic samples of 10 boxes. The sample means are reported in the accompanying data file.
    a. Construct an $\bar{x}$ chart. Plot the sample means on the $\bar{x}$ chart.
    b. Can the firm conclude that the production process is operating properly? Explain.

40. **FILE** *Cricket.* Fast bowling, also known as pace bowling, is an important component of the bowling attack in the sport of cricket. The objective is to bowl at a high speed and make the ball turn in the air and off the ground so that it becomes difficult for the batsman to hit it cleanly. Kalwant Singh is a budding Indian cricketer in a special bowling camp. It is fair to assume that Kalwant's bowling speed is normally distributed with a mean and a standard deviation of 94 miles per hour and 2.8 miles per hour, respectively. While his coach is happy with Kalwant's average bowling speed, he feels that Kalwant lacks consistency. The coach records Kalwant's bowling speed on the next four overs, where each over consists of six balls. The accompanying data file shows the results.
    a. Construct the centerline and the upper and lower control limits for the $\bar{x}$ chart. Plot the average speed of Kalwant's four overs on the $\bar{x}$ chart.
    b. Is there any pattern in Kalwant's bowling that justifies his coach's concerns that he is not consistent in bowling? Explain.

41. A manufacturing process produces steel rods in batches of 1,000. The firm believes that the percent of defective items generated by this process is 5%.
    a. Construct the centerline and the upper and lower control limits for the p chart.
    b. An engineer inspects the next batch of 1,000 steel rods and finds that 6.2% are defective. Is the manufacturing process under control? Explain.

42. **FILE** *Chips.* A firm produces computer chips. From past experience, the firm knows that 4% of the chips are defective. The firm collects a sample of the first 500 chips manufactured

at 1:00 pm for the past two weeks. The sample proportions are reported in the accompanying data file.

a. Construct a p chart. Plot the sample proportions on the p chart.

b. Can the firm conclude that the process is operating properly?

43. **FILE** *Sodium.* The producer of a particular brand of soup claims that its sodium content is 50% less than that of its competitor. The food label states that the sodium content measures 410 milligrams per serving. Assume the population of sodium content is normally distributed with a standard deviation of 25 milligrams. Inspectors take periodic samples of 25 cans and measure the sodium content. The sample means are reported in the accompanying data file.

a. Construct an $\bar{x}$ chart for sodium content. Plot the sample means on the $\bar{x}$ chart.

b. Can the inspectors conclude that the producer is advertising the sodium content accurately? Explain.

44. The admissions office at a local university usually admits 750 students and knows from previous experience that 25% of these students choose not to enroll at the university.

a. Construct the centerline and the upper and lower control limits for the p chart.

b. Assume that this year the university admits 750 students and 240 choose not to enroll at the university. Should the university be concerned? Explain.

45. **FILE** *Production.* Suppose that 10% of produced items are known to be nonconforming. The firm analyzes a batch of production items for 6 weeks. The accompanying data file reports the sample proportion of nonconforming items for each week.

a. Suppose the weekly batches consisted of 50 items. Construct the p chart for the proportion of nonconforming items and determine if the machine needs adjustment in any of the weeks.

b. Suppose the weekly batches consisted of 100 items. Construct the p chart for the proportion of nonconforming items and determine if the machine needs adjustment in any of the weeks.

46. **FILE** *Complaints.* Following customer complaints about the quality of service, a large U.S. corporation stopped routing customers to a certain technical support call center. The accompanying data file reports the number of complaints per month for 80 randomly selected customers over the last six months.

a. Construct the centerline and the upper and lower control limits for the p chart if the corporation allows a 15% complaint rate.

b. Can you justify the corporation's decision to direct customers away from this call center?

7.5 WRITING WITH DATA

Case Study

Barbara Dwyer, the manager at Lux Hotel, makes every effort to ensure that customers attempting to make phone reservations wait an average of only 60 seconds to speak with a reservations specialist. She knows that this is likely to be the customer's first impression of the hotel, and she wants the initial interaction to be a positive one. Because the hotel accepts phone reservations 24 hours a day, Barbara wonders if the quality of service is consistently maintained throughout the day. She takes six samples of $n = 4$ calls during each of four shifts over one 24-hour period and records the wait time of each call. A portion of the data, in seconds, is presented in Table 7.2.

Barbara assumes that wait times are normally distributed with a mean and standard deviation of 60 seconds and 30 seconds, respectively. She wants to use the sample information to construct a control chart for wait times. Using the control chart, she then wants to determine if the quality of service is consistently maintained throughout the day.

Gabriel Georgescu/Shutterstock

TABLE 7.2 Wait times for phone reservations

Shift	Sample	Wait Time (in seconds)				Sample Mean, $\bar{x}$
Shift 1: 12 am–6 am	1	67	48	52	71	60
	2	57	68	60	66	63
	3	37	41	60	41	45
	4	83	59	49	66	64
	5	82	63	64	83	73
	6	87	53	66	69	69
⋮	⋮	⋮	⋮	⋮	⋮	⋮
Shift 4: 6 pm–12 am	19	6	11	8	9	9
	20	10	8	10	9	9
	21	11	7	14	7	10
	22	8	9	9	12	10
	23	9	12	9	14	11
	24	5	8	15	11	10

Sample Report— Customer Wait Time

When potential customers phone Lux Hotel, it is imperative for the reservations specialists to set a tone that relays the high standard of service that the customers will receive if they choose to stay at the Lux. For this reason, management at the Lux strives to minimize the time that elapses before a potential customer speaks with a reservations specialist; however, management also recognizes the need to use its resources wisely. If too many reservations specialists are on duty, then resources are wasted due to idle time. Yet, if too few reservations specialists are on duty, then the result might be unhappy customers, or worse.

In order to ensure customer satisfaction as well as an efficient use of resources, a study is conducted to determine whether a typical customer waits an average of 60 seconds to speak with a reservations specialist. Before data are collected, a control chart is constructed. The upper control limit (UCL) and the lower control limit (LCL) are set three standard deviations from the desired average of 60 seconds. Figure 7.12 shows the control chart where the centerline is at 60 seconds and the UCL and the LCL are at 105 seconds and 15 seconds, respectively. The reservation process is deemed under control if the sample means fall randomly within the control limits; otherwise, the process is out of control and adjustments should be made.

FIGURE 7.12 The control chart for wait times

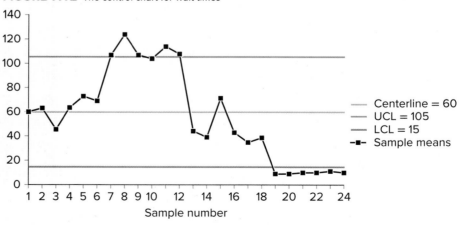

During each of four shifts, six samples of $n = 4$ calls are randomly selected over one 24-hour period and the average wait time of each sample is recorded. All six sample means from the first shift (12 am–6 am, sample numbers 1 through 6) fall within the control limits, indicating that the reservation process is in control. However, five sample means from the second shift (6 am–12 pm, sample numbers 7 through 12) lie above the UCL. Customers calling during the second shift are waiting too long before they speak with a specialist. In terms of quality standards, this is unacceptable from the hotel's perspective. All six sample means from the third shift (12 pm–6 pm, sample numbers 13 through 18) fall within the control limits, yet all sample means for the fourth shift (6 pm–12 am, sample numbers 19 through 24) fall below the LCL. Customers are waiting for very short periods of time to speak with a reservations specialist, but reservations specialists may have too much idle time. Perhaps one solution is to shift some reservations specialists from the fourth shift to the second shift.

Suggested Case Studies

Report 7.1 According to the Bureau of Economic Analysis, the savings rate of American households, defined as a percentage of the disposable personal income, was 7.90% in 2019. The reported savings rate is not uniform across the country. A public policy institute conducts two of its own surveys to compute the savings rate in the Midwest. In the first survey, a sample of 160 households is taken and the average savings rate is found to be 8.18%. Another sample of 40 households finds an average savings rate of 8.30%. Assume that the population standard deviation is 1.4%.

In a report, use this information to compute the probability of obtaining a sample mean that is at least as high as the one computed in each of the two surveys. Then use these probabilities to decide which of the two samples is likely to be more representative of the United States as a whole.

Report 7.2 In 2019, the Bureau of Labor Statistics reported that the jobless rate for college graduates under age 25 was 4%. For high school graduates under age 25 who did not enroll in college, the jobless rate was 9.1%. Cindy Chan works in the sales department of a trendy apparel company and has recently been relocated to a small town in Iowa. She finds that there are a total of 220 college graduates and 140 high school graduates under age 25 who live in this town. Cindy wants to gauge the demand for her products by the number of youths in this town who are employed.

In a report, use this information to compute the expected number of college and high school graduates who are employed. Then, report the probabilities that at least 200 college graduates and at least 100 high school graduates under age 25 are employed.

Report 7.3 **FILE** *Hockey_Puck* Hockey pucks used by the National Hockey League (NHL) and other professional leagues weigh an average of 163 grams (5.75 ounces). A quality inspector monitors the manufacturing process for hockey pucks. She takes eight samples of $n = 10$. It is believed that puck weights are normally distributed, and when the production process is in control, $\mu = 163$ and $\sigma = 7.5$.

In a report, use this information to construct a control chart for the weight of hockey pucks. Then, using the control chart, determine whether the manufacturing process is in control.

8 Interval Estimation

LEARNING OBJECTIVES

After reading this chapter you should be able to:

LO 8.1 Calculate a confidence interval for the population mean when the population standard deviation is known.

LO 8.2 Calculate a confidence interval for the population mean when the population standard deviation is not known.

LO 8.3 Calculate a confidence interval for the population proportion.

LO 8.4 Select a sample size to estimate the population mean and the population proportion.

So far, we have made a distinction between a population parameter, such as the population mean, and a corresponding sample statistic, such as the sample mean. A sample statistic is used to make statistical inferences regarding the unknown value of the population parameter. In general, two basic methodologies emerge from the inferential branch of statistics: estimation and hypothesis testing. In this chapter, we focus on estimation, which is approximating the value of an unknown population parameter. In the next chapter, we will discuss hypothesis testing.

We learned in Chapter 7 that one way to estimate an unknown population parameter is to use a point estimator. A point estimator produces a single value as an estimate for the parameter. A confidence interval, on the other hand, produces a range of values as an estimate for the parameter. In this chapter, we develop and interpret confidence intervals for the population mean and the population proportion. Because obtaining a sample is one of the first steps in making statistical inferences, we also learn how an appropriate sample size is determined in order to achieve a certain level of precision in the estimates.

1000 Words/Shutterstock

INTRODUCTORY CASE

Efficiency of Hybrid SUVs

A car manufacturer advertises that its hybrid sports utility vehicle (SUV) obtains an average of 50 miles per gallon (mpg) and, based on its fuel emissions, is one of the few SUVs that earns an A+ rating from the Environmental Protection Agency. Jared Beane, an analyst at Pinnacle Research, records the mpg for a sample of 25 of these SUVs after the SUVs were driven equal distances under identical conditions. Table 8.1 shows a portion of the data.

TABLE 8.1 MPG for a Sample of 25 Hybrid SUVs

SUV	MPG
1	49
2	69
⋮	⋮
25	50

FILE
MPG

Jared would like to make statistical inferences regarding key population parameters. In particular, he wants to use the sample information to

1. Estimate the mean mpg of all hybrid SUVs with 90% confidence.
2. Estimate the proportion of all hybrid SUVs that obtain over 50 mpg with 90% confidence.
3. Determine the sample size that will enable him to achieve a specified level of precision in his mean and proportion estimates.

A synopsis of this case is provided at the end of Section 8.4.

8.1 CONFIDENCE INTERVAL FOR THE POPULATION MEAN WHEN σ IS KNOWN

Recall that a population consists of all items of interest in a statistical problem, whereas a sample is a subset of the population. Given sample data, we use the sample statistics to make inferences about the unknown population parameters, such as the population mean and the population proportion. Two basic methodologies emerge from the inferential branch of statistics: estimation and hypothesis testing. Although the sample statistics are based on a portion of the population, they contain useful information to estimate the population parameters and to conduct tests regarding the population parameters. In this chapter, we focus on estimation.

As discussed in Chapter 7, when a statistic is used to estimate a parameter, it is referred to as a point estimator, or simply an estimator. A particular value of the estimator is called a point estimate or an estimate. Recall that the sample mean $\overline{X}$ is the estimator of the population mean μ, and the sample proportion $\overline{P}$ is the estimator of the population proportion p.

Let us consider the introductory case where Jared Beane records the mpg for a sample of 25 hybrid SUVs. We use the sample information in the **MPG** data file to compute the mean mpg of the SUVs as $\bar{x} = 48.40$mpg. Similarly, because Jared is also interested in the proportion of these SUVs that get an mpg greater than 50, and seven of the SUVs in the sample satisfied this criterion, we compute the relevant sample proportion as $\bar{p} = 7/25 = 0.28$. Therefore, our estimate for the mean mpg of all hybrid SUVs is 48.40 mpg, and our estimate for the proportion of all hybrid SUVs with mpg greater than 50 is 0.28.

It is important to note that the above estimates are based on a sample of 25 SUVs and, therefore, are likely to vary between samples. For instance, the values will change if another sample of 25 SUVs is used. What Jared really wishes to estimate are the mean and the proportion (parameters) of all hybrid SUVs (population), not just those comprising the sample. We now examine how we can extract useful information from a single sample to make inferences about these population parameters.

So far we have only discussed point estimators. Often it is more informative to provide a range of values—an interval—rather than a single point estimate for the unknown population parameter. This range of values is called a **confidence interval,** also referred to as an **interval estimate,** for the population parameter.

> ### CONFIDENCE INTERVAL
> A confidence interval, or interval estimate, provides a range of values that, with a certain level of confidence, contains the population parameter of interest.

In order to construct a confidence interval for the population mean μ or the population proportion p, it is essential that the sampling distributions of $\overline{X}$ and $\overline{P}$ follow, or approximately follow, a normal distribution. Other methods that do not require the normality condition are not discussed in this text. Recall from Chapter 7 that $\overline{X}$ follows a normal distribution when the underlying population is normally distributed; this result holds irrespective of the sample size n. If the underlying population is not normally distributed, then by the central limit theorem, the sampling distribution of $\overline{X}$ will be approximately normally distributed if the sample size is sufficiently large—that is, when $n \geq 30$. Similarly, the sampling distribution of $\overline{P}$ is approximately normally distributed if the sample size is sufficiently large—that is, when $np \geq 5$ and $n(1 - p) \geq 5$.

A confidence interval is generally associated with a **margin of error** that accounts for the standard error of the estimator and the desired confidence level of the interval. As we have just stressed, the sampling distributions of the estimators for the population mean and the population proportion must be approximately normally distributed. The symmetry implied by the normal distribution allows us to construct a confidence interval by adding and subtracting the same margin of error to the point estimate.

GENERAL FORMAT OF THE CONFIDENCE INTERVAL FOR μ AND p

The confidence interval for the population mean and the population proportion is constructed as

Point Estimate $\pm$ Margin of Error.

An analogy to a simple weather example is instructive. If you feel that the outside temperature is about 50 degrees, then perhaps you can, with a certain level of confidence, suggest that the actual temperature is between 40 and 60 degrees. In this example, 50 degrees is analogous to the point estimate of the actual temperature, and 10 degrees is the margin of error that is added to and subtracted from this point estimate.

We know from the introductory case study that the point estimate for the population mean mpg of all hybrid SUVs is 48.40 mpg; that is, $\bar{x} = 48.40$. We can construct a confidence interval by using the point estimate as a base to which we add and subtract the margin of error.

Constructing a Confidence Interval for μ When σ Is Known

In Chapter 6 we showed that any normally distributed random variable can be transformed into its corresponding standard normal random variable Z with mean 0 and standard deviation 1. Recall too that Excel's **NORM.INV** function finds a particular z value for a given cumulative probability; so we can use this function to find the z value that satisfies $P(Z > z) = 0.025$. We enter =NORM.INV(0.975, 0, 1), and Excel returns 1.96. In other words, $P(Z > 1.96) = 0.025$. Using the symmetry of the z distribution, we can state that $P(Z < -1.96) = 0.025$. Finally, given that the area under the z distribution is equal to 1, we can state that $P(-1.96 \leq Z \leq 1.96) = 0.95$. Figure 8.1 graphically depicts these probability statements.

FIGURE 8.1 Graphical depiction of $P(Z < -1.96) = 0.025$ and $P(Z > 1.96) = 0.025$

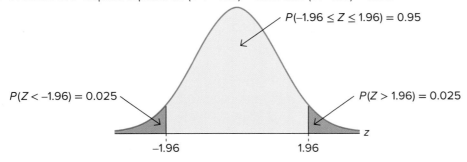

Let us now construct the 95% confidence interval for μ when the sampling distribution of $\bar{X}$ is normally distributed. The formula for transforming, or standardizing, the random variable $\bar{X}$ into the random variable Z is $Z = (\bar{X} - \mu)/(\sigma/\sqrt{n})$. Using this formula, we can write the following probability statement

$$P(-1.96 \leq Z \leq 1.96) = P\left(-1.96 \leq \frac{\bar{X} - \mu}{\sigma/\sqrt{n}} \leq 1.96\right) = 0.95.$$

We isolate $\bar{X}$ within the probability statement to obtain

$$P(\mu - 1.96\sigma/\sqrt{n} \leq \bar{X} \leq \mu + 1.96\sigma/\sqrt{n}) = 0.95.$$

This equation implies that there is a 0.95 probability that the sample mean $\bar{X}$ will fall between $\mu - 1.96\sigma/\sqrt{n}$ and $\mu + 1.96\sigma/\sqrt{n}$, that is, within the interval $\mu \pm 1.96\sigma/\sqrt{n}$. If samples of size n are drawn repeatedly from a given population, 95% of the computed sample means, $\bar{x}$'s, will fall within the interval and the remaining 5% will fall outside the interval.

We do not know the population mean μ and, therefore, cannot determine if a particular $\bar{x}$ falls within the interval or not. However, we do know that $\bar{x}$ will fall within the interval $\mu \pm 1.96\sigma/\sqrt{n}$ if, and only if, μ falls within the interval $\bar{x} \pm 1.96\sigma/\sqrt{n}$. This will happen 95% of the time given how the interval is constructed. Therefore, we call the interval $\bar{x} \pm 1.96\sigma/\sqrt{n}$ the 95% confidence interval for the population mean, where $1.96\sigma/\sqrt{n}$ is its margin of error.

EXAMPLE 8.1

A sample of 25 cereal boxes of Granola Crunch, a generic brand of cereal, yields a mean weight of 1.02 pounds of cereal per box. Construct the 95% confidence interval for the mean weight of all cereal boxes. Assume that the weight is normally distributed with a population standard deviation of 0.03 pound.

SOLUTION: Note that the normality condition of $\bar{X}$ is satisfied because the underlying population is normally distributed. The 95% confidence interval for the population mean is computed as

$$\bar{x} \pm 1.96\frac{\sigma}{\sqrt{n}} = 1.02 \pm 1.96\frac{0.03}{\sqrt{25}} = 1.02 \pm 0.012.$$

With 95% confidence, we can report that the mean weight of all cereal boxes falls between 1.008 and 1.032 pounds.

While it is common to report the 95% confidence interval, in theory we can construct an interval of any level of confidence ranging from 0 to 100%. Let's now extend the analysis to include intervals for any confidence level. Let the Greek letter α (alpha) denote the allowed probability of error; in Chapter 9 this is referred to as the significance level. This is the probability that the estimation procedure will generate an interval that does not contain μ. The **confidence coefficient** $(1 - \alpha)$ is interpreted as the probability that the estimation procedure will generate an interval that contains μ. Thus, the probability of error α is related to the confidence coefficient and the confidence level as follows:

- Confidence coefficient $= 1 - \alpha$, and
- Confidence level $= (1 - \alpha)100\%$.

For example, the confidence coefficient of 0.95 implies that the probability of error α equals $1 - 0.95 = 0.05$ and the confidence level equals $(1 - 0.05)100\% = 95\%$. Similarly, for the 90% confidence interval, the confidence coefficient equals 0.90 and $\alpha = 1 - 0.90 = 0.10$. The following statement generalizes the construction of a confidence interval for μ when σ is known.

CONFIDENCE INTERVAL FOR μ WHEN σ IS KNOWN

A $(1 - \alpha)100\%$ confidence interval for the population mean μ when the population standard deviation σ is known is computed as

$$\bar{x} \pm z_{\alpha/2}\frac{\sigma}{\sqrt{n}} \quad \text{or} \quad \left[\bar{x} - z_{\alpha/2}\frac{\sigma}{\sqrt{n}}, \bar{x} + z_{\alpha/2}\frac{\sigma}{\sqrt{n}}\right],$$

where $z_{\alpha/2}$ is the z value associated with the probability of $\alpha/2$ in the upper tail of the standard normal distribution. This formula is valid only if $\bar{X}$ (approximately) follows a normal distribution.

When constructing a confidence interval for μ when σ is known, we use the notation $z_{\alpha/2}$ to denote the z value associated with the probability of $\alpha/2$ in the upper tail of the standard normal probability distribution. In other words, if Z is the standard normal random variable and α is any probability, then $z_{\alpha/2}$ represents the z value such that the area under the standard normal distribution to the right of $z_{\alpha/2}$ is $\alpha/2$, that is, $P(Z \geq z_{\alpha/2}) = \alpha/2$. Figure 8.2 depicts the notation $z_{\alpha/2}$.

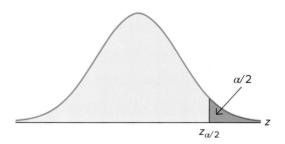

FIGURE 8.2 Graphical depiction of the notation $z_{\alpha/2}$

As discussed earlier, for the 95% confidence interval, $\alpha = 0.05$ and $\alpha/2 = 0.025$. Therefore, $z_{\alpha/2} = z_{0.025} = 1.96$. Similarly, for 90% and 99% confidence intervals, we find the associated $z_{\alpha/2}$ values as follows:

- For the 90% confidence interval, $\alpha = 0.10$ and $\alpha/2 = 0.05$. In Excel, we enter =NORM.INV(0.95, 0, 1), and find that $z_{\alpha/2} = z_{0.05} = 1.645$.

- For the 99% confidence interval, $\alpha = 0.01$ and $\alpha/2 = 0.005$. In Excel, we enter =NORM.INV(0.995, 0, 1), and find that $z_{\alpha/2} = z_{0.005} = 2.576$.

Confidence intervals are often misinterpreted; we need to exercise care in characterizing them. For instance, the above 95% confidence interval does *not* imply that the probability that μ falls in the confidence interval is 0.95. Remember that μ is a constant, although its value is not known. It either falls in the interval (probability equals one) or does not fall in the interval (probability equals zero). The randomness comes from $\overline{X}$, not μ, because many possible sample means can be derived from a population. Therefore, it is incorrect to say that the probability that μ falls in the $\overline{x} \pm 1.96\sigma/\sqrt{n}$ interval is 0.95. The 95% confidence interval simply implies that if numerous samples of size n are drawn from a given population, then 95% of the intervals formed by the procedure (formula) will contain μ. Keep in mind that we only use a single sample to derive the estimates. Because there are many possible samples, we will be right 95% of the time, thus giving us 95% confidence.

> **INTERPRETING THE 95% CONFIDENCE INTERVAL**
>
> Technically, the 95% confidence interval for the population mean μ implies that for 95% of the samples, the procedure (formula) produces an interval that contains μ. Informally, we can report with 95% confidence that μ lies in the given interval. It is not correct to say that there is a 95% chance that μ lies in the given interval.

The Width of a Confidence Interval

The margin of error used in the computation of the confidence interval for the population mean, when the population standard deviation is known, is $z_{\alpha/2}\frac{\sigma}{\sqrt{n}}$. Because we are basically adding and subtracting this quantity from $\overline{x}$, the width of the confidence interval is two times the margin of error. In Example 8.1, the margin of error for the 95% confidence interval is 0.012 and the width of the interval is $1.032 - 1.008 = 0.024$; or equivalently, the width of the interval is $2(0.012) = 0.024$. Now let's examine how the width of a confidence interval is influenced by various factors.

> I. For a given confidence level $(1 - \alpha)100\%$ and sample size n, the larger the population standard deviation σ, the wider the confidence interval.

EXAMPLE 8.2

Let the population standard deviation in Example 8.1 be 0.05 pound instead of 0.03 pound. Compute the 95% confidence interval using the same sample mean of 1.02 pounds and the same sample size of 25.

SOLUTION: We use the same formula as before, but we use 0.05 for σ instead of 0.03:

$$1.02 \pm 1.96 \frac{0.05}{\sqrt{25}} = 1.02 \pm 0.020.$$

The width has increased from 0.024 to 2(0.020) = 0.040.

II. For a given confidence level $(1 - \alpha)100\%$ and population standard deviation σ, the smaller the sample size n, the wider the confidence interval.

EXAMPLE 8.3

Instead of 25 observations, let the sample in Example 8.1 be based on 16 observations. Compute the 95% confidence interval using the same sample mean of 1.02 pounds and the same population standard deviation of 0.03 pound.

SOLUTION: Again, we use the same formula as before, but this time we use 16 for n instead of 25:

$$1.02 \pm 1.96 \frac{0.03}{\sqrt{16}} = 1.02 \pm 0.015.$$

The width has increased from 0.024 to 2(0.015) = 0.030.

III. For a given sample size n and population standard deviation σ, the greater the confidence level $(1 - \alpha)100\%$, the wider the confidence interval.

EXAMPLE 8.4

Instead of a 95% confidence interval, compute the 99% confidence interval for Example 8.1, using the same sample mean of 1.02 pounds, the same population standard deviation of 0.03 pound, and the same sample size of 25.

SOLUTION: Again, we use the same formula as before, but this time we use the value 2.576 for $z_{\alpha/2}$ instead of 1.96:

$$1.02 \pm 2.576 \frac{0.03}{\sqrt{25}} = 1.02 \pm 0.015.$$

The width has increased from 0.024 to 2(0.015) = 0.030.

The precision is directly linked with the width of the confidence interval—the wider the interval, the lower its precision. Continuing with the weather analogy, a temperature estimate of 40 to 80 degrees is imprecise because the interval is too wide to be of value. We lose precision when the sample does not reveal a great deal about the population, resulting in a wide confidence interval. Relative to Example 8.1, Examples 8.2 and 8.3 show that the estimate will be less precise if the variability of the underlying population is high (σ is high) or a small segment of the population is sampled (n is small). Example 8.4 relates the width with the confidence level. For given sample information, the only way we can gain confidence is by making the interval wider. If you are 95% confident that the outside temperature is between 40 and 60 degrees, then you can increase your confidence level to 99% only by using a wider range, say between 35 and 65 degrees. This result also helps us understand the difference between precision (width of the interval) and the confidence level. There is a trade-off between the amount of confidence we have in an interval and its width.

EXAMPLE 8.5

IQ tests are designed to yield scores that are approximately normally distributed. A reporter is interested in estimating the average IQ of employees in a large high-tech firm in California. She gathers the IQ scores from 22 employees of this firm and records the sample mean IQ as 106. She assumes that the population standard deviation is 15.

a. Compute 90% and 99% confidence intervals for the average IQ in this firm.

b. Use these results to infer if the mean IQ in this firm is significantly different from the national average of 100.

SOLUTION:

a. For the 90% confidence interval, $z_{\alpha/2} = z_{0.05} = 1.645$. Similarly, for the 99% confidence interval, $z_{\alpha/2} = z_{0.005} = 2.576$.

The 90% confidence interval is $106 \pm 1.645 \frac{15}{\sqrt{22}} = 106 \pm 5.26$ or [100.74, 111.26].

The 99% confidence interval is $106 \pm 2.576 \frac{15}{\sqrt{22}} = 106 \pm 8.24$ or [97.76, 114.24].

Note that the 99% interval is wider than the 90% interval.

b. With 90% confidence, the reporter can infer that the average IQ of this firm's employees differs from the national average because the value 100 falls outside the 90% confidence interval, [100.74, 111.26]. However, she cannot infer the same result with 99% confidence because the wider range of the interval, [97.76, 114.24], includes the value 100.

Using Excel to Construct a Confidence Interval for μ When σ Is Known

We can use functions in Excel to construct confidence intervals. These functions are particularly useful with large data sets. Consider the following example.

EXAMPLE 8.6

Table 8.2 lists a portion of the weights (in grams) for a sample of 80 hockey pucks. Construct the 90% confidence interval for the population mean weight assuming that the population standard deviation is 7.5 grams.

TABLE 8.2 Hockey Puck
Weights, $n = 80$

Weight
162.2
159.8
⋮
171.3

SOLUTION: We compute $\bar{x} \pm z_{\alpha/2} \frac{\sigma}{\sqrt{n}}$, or, equivalently, we find the lower and upper limits of the confidence interval: $\left[\bar{x} - z_{\alpha/2} \frac{\sigma}{\sqrt{n}}, \bar{x} + z_{\alpha/2} \frac{\sigma}{\sqrt{n}}\right]$. We are given $\sigma = 7.5$ and $n = 80$.

Using Excel

a. Open the *Hockey_Pucks* data file. Note that the values for weights are in cells A2 through A81.

b. Recall that Excel's **NORM.INV** function finds a particular z value for a given cumulative probability. For the 90% confidence interval, $\alpha = 0.10$ and $z_{\alpha/2} = z_{0.05}$. To find the z value such that the area under the z curve to the right of $z_{0.05}$ is 0.05 (and the area to the left of $z_{0.05}$ is 0.95), we use =NORM.INV(0.95, 0, 1). In order to find the lower limit of the confidence interval, we enter =AVERAGE(A2:A81)−NORM.INV(0.95, 0, 1) * 7.5/SQRT(80), and Excel returns 165.33. For the upper limit of the confidence interval, we enter =AVERAGE(A2:A81) + NORM.INV(0.95, 0, 1) * 7.5/SQRT(80), and Excel returns 168.09. With 90% confidence, we conclude that the mean weight of all hockey pucks falls between 165.33 and 168.09 grams.

EXERCISES 8.1

Mechanics

1. Find $z_{\alpha/2}$ for each of the following confidence levels used in estimating the population mean.
   a. 90%
   b. 98%
   c. 88%

2. Find $z_{\alpha/2}$ for each of the following confidence levels used in estimating the population mean.
   a. 89%
   b. 92%
   c. 96%

3. A simple random sample of 25 observations is derived from a normally distributed population with a population standard deviation of 8.2.
   a. Is the condition that $\bar{X}$ is normally distributed satisfied? Explain.
   b. Compute the margin of error with 80% confidence.
   c. Compute the margin of error with 90% confidence.
   d. Which of the two margins of error will lead to a wider interval?

4. Consider a population with a population standard deviation of 26.8. In order to compute an interval estimate for the population mean, a sample of 64 observations is drawn.
   a. Is the condition that $\bar{X}$ is normally distributed satisfied? Explain.
   b. Compute the margin of error at the 95% confidence level.
   c. Compute the margin of error at the 95% confidence level based on a larger sample of 225 observations.
   d. Which of the two margins of error will lead to a wider confidence interval?

5. Discuss the factors that influence the margin of error for the confidence interval for the population mean. What can a practitioner do to reduce the margin of error?

Applications

6. A researcher finds that the average life expectancy for Bostonians is 78.1 years. He uses a sample of 50 Bostonians and assumes that the population standard deviation is 4.5 years.
   a. What is the point estimate for the population mean?

b. At 90% confidence, what is the margin of error?

c. Construct the 90% confidence interval for the population average life expectancy of Bostonians.

7. In order to estimate the mean 30-year fixed mortgage rate for a home loan in the United States, a random sample of 28 recent loans is taken. The average calculated from this sample is 5.25%. It can be assumed that 30-year fixed mortgage rates are normally distributed with a population standard deviation of 0.50%. Compute 90% and 99% confidence intervals for the population mean 30-year fixed mortgage rate.

8. A researcher in a small Midwestern town wants to estimate the mean weekday sleep time of its adult residents. He takes a random sample of 80 adult residents and records their weekday mean sleep time as 6.4 hours. Assume that the population standard deviation is fairly stable at 1.8 hours.

a. Calculate the 95% confidence interval for the population mean weekday sleep time of all adult residents of this Midwestern town.

b. Can we conclude with 95% confidence that the mean sleep time of all adult residents in this Midwestern town is not 7 hours?

9. A family is relocating from St. Louis, Missouri, to California. Due to an increasing inventory of houses in St. Louis, it is taking longer than before to sell a house. The family is concerned and wants to know when it is optimal to put their house on the market. A Realtor informs them that the last 26 houses that sold in their neighborhood took an average time of 218 days to sell. The Realtor also tells them that based on her prior experience, the population standard deviation is 72 days.

a. What assumption regarding the population is necessary for making an interval estimate for the population mean?

b. Construct the 90% confidence interval for the mean sale time for all homes in the neighborhood.

10. Based on a sample of 100 U.S. consumers, a researcher finds that the average amount spent annually on a debit card is $7,790. Assume that the population standard deviation is $500.

a. At 99% confidence, what is the margin of error?

b. Construct the 99% confidence interval for the population mean amount spent annually on a debit card.

11. Suppose the 95% confidence interval for the mean salary of college graduates in a town in Mississippi is given by [$36,080, $43,920]. The population standard deviation used for the analysis is known to be $12,000.

a. What is the point estimate of the mean salary for all college graduates in this town?

b. Determine the sample size used for the analysis.

12. A manager is interested in estimating the mean time (in minutes) required to complete a job. His assistant uses a sample of 100 observations to report the confidence interval as [14.355, 17.645]. The population standard deviation is known to be equal to 10 minutes.

a. Find the sample mean time used to compute the confidence interval.

b. Determine the confidence level used for the analysis.

13. **FILE** *PA_Debt.* A study reports that recent college graduates from Connecticut face the highest average debt of $38,510 (forbes.com, September 18, 2019). A researcher from Pennsylvania wants to determine how recent undergraduates from that state fare. The accompanying file contains data on debt from 40 recent undergraduates. Assume that the population standard deviation is $5,000.

a. Construct the 95% confidence interval for the mean debt of all undergraduates from Pennsylvania.

b. Use the 95% confidence interval to determine if the debt of Pennsylvania undergraduates differs from that of Connecticut undergraduates.

14. **FILE** *Hourly_Wage.* An economist wants to estimate the mean hourly wage (in $) of all workers. The accompanying file contains data on 50 hourly wage earners. Assume that the population standard deviation is $6. Construct and interpret 90% and 99% confidence intervals for the mean hourly wage of all workers.

15. **FILE** *Highway_Speeds.* A safety officer is concerned about speeds on a certain section of the New Jersey Turnpike. The accompanying file contains the speeds of 40 cars on a Saturday afternoon. Assume that the population standard deviation is 5 mph. Construct the 95% confidence interval for the mean speed of all cars on that section of the turnpike. Are the safety officer's concerns valid if the speed limit is 55 mph? Explain.

8.2 CONFIDENCE INTERVAL FOR THE POPULATION MEAN WHEN σ IS UNKNOWN

LO 8.2

So far we have considered confidence intervals for the population mean when the population standard deviation σ is known. In reality, σ is rarely known. Recall from Chapter 3 that the population variance and the population standard deviation are calculated as $\sigma^2 = \frac{\Sigma(x_i - \mu)^2}{N}$ and $\sigma = \sqrt{\sigma^2}$, respectively. It is highly unlikely that σ is known when μ is not.

Calculate a confidence interval for the population mean when the population standard deviation is not known.

However, there are instances when the population standard deviation is considered fairly stable and, therefore, can be determined from prior experience. In these cases, the population standard deviation is treated as known.

Recall that the margin of error in a confidence interval depends on the standard error of the estimator and the desired confidence level. With σ unknown, the standard error of $\overline{X}$, given by $\sigma/\sqrt{n}$, can be conveniently estimated by $s/\sqrt{n}$, where s denotes the sample standard deviation; that is, $se(\overline{X}) = s/\sqrt{n}$.

The t Distribution

As discussed earlier, in order to derive a confidence interval for μ, it is essential that $\overline{X}$ be normally distributed. A normally distributed $\overline{X}$ is standardized as $Z = \frac{\overline{X} - \mu}{\sigma/\sqrt{n}}$ where Z follows the z distribution. Another standardized statistic, which uses s in place of σ, is computed as $T = \frac{\overline{X} - \mu}{s/\sqrt{n}}$. The random variable T follows the **Student's t distribution,** more commonly known as the t **distribution.**[1]

> ### THE t DISTRIBUTION
> If a random sample of size n is taken from a normal population with a finite variance, then the statistic $T = \frac{\overline{X} - \mu}{s/\sqrt{n}}$ follows the t distribution with $(n - 1)$ degrees of freedom, df.

The t distribution is actually a family of distributions that are similar to the z distribution in that they are all bell-shaped and symmetric around zero. However, all t distributions have slightly broader tails than the z distribution. Each t distribution is identified by the **degrees of freedom,** or, simply, df. The degrees of freedom determine the extent of the broadness of the tails of the distribution; the fewer the degrees of freedom, the broader the tails. Because the t distribution is defined by the degrees of freedom, it is common to refer to it as the t_{df} distribution.

Summary of the t_{df} Distribution

- Like the z distribution, the t_{df} distribution is bell-shaped and symmetric around 0 with asymptotic tails (the tails get closer and closer to the horizontal axis but never touch it).
- The t_{df} distribution has slightly broader tails than the z distribution.
- The t_{df} distribution consists of a family of distributions where the actual shape of each one depends on the degrees of freedom df. As df increases, the t_{df} distribution becomes similar to the z distribution; it is identical to the z distribution when df approaches infinity.

From Figure 8.3 we note that the tails of the t_2 and t_5 distributions are broader than the tails of the t_{50} distribution. For instance, for t_2 and t_5, the area exceeding a value of 3, or $P(T_{df} > 3)$, is greater than that for t_{50}. In addition, the t_{50} distribution resembles the z distribution.

---

[1]William S. Gossett (1876–1937) published his research concerning the t distribution under the pen name "Student" because his employer, the Guinness Brewery, did not allow employees to publish their research results.

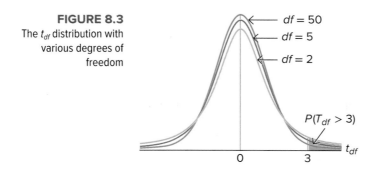

FIGURE 8.3

The t_{df} distribution with various degrees of freedom

Finding t_{df} Values

Similar to $z_{\alpha/2}$, we use the notation $t_{\alpha/2,df}$ to represent a value such that $P(T_{df} \geq t_{\alpha/2,df}) = \alpha/2$. Figure 8.4 illustrates the notation.

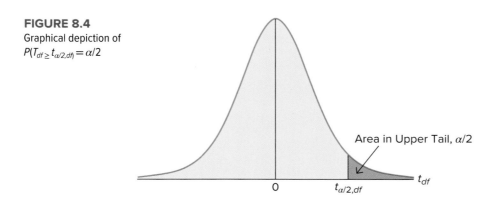

FIGURE 8.4

Graphical depiction of $P(T_{df} \geq t_{\alpha/2,df}) = \alpha/2$

We use Excel's **T.INV** function to find a particular $t_{\alpha/2,df}$ value. We enter =T.INV(cumulprob, df) where *cumulprob* is the cumulative probability associated with the $t_{\alpha/2,df}$ value and *df* is the respective degrees of freedom. For instance, suppose we want to find the value $t_{\alpha/2,df}$ with $\alpha/2 = 0.05$ and $df = 10$; that is, $t_{0.05,10}$. Because we want 0.05 in the right tail of the t_{10} distribution, the cumulative probability is $1 - 0.05 = 0.95$. We enter =T.INV(0.95, 10) and find that $t_{0.05,10} = 1.812$. The value 1.812 indicates that $P(T_{10} \geq 1.812) = 0.05$. Due to the symmetry of the t_{df} distribution, we can infer that $P(T_{10} \leq -1.812) = 0.05$; or we can arrive at the same conclusion in Excel by entering =T.INV(0.05, 10). Figure 8.5 shows these results graphically.

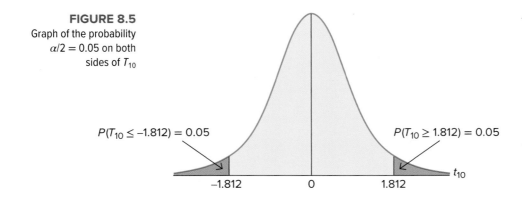

FIGURE 8.5

Graph of the probability $\alpha/2 = 0.05$ on both sides of T_{10}

EXAMPLE 8.7

Find $t_{\alpha/2,df}$ for $\alpha = 0.05$ using 2, 5, and 50 degrees of freedom.

SOLUTION: With $\alpha = 0.05$, we calculate $\alpha/2 = 0.025$.

- Using Excel with $df = 2$, we enter =T.INV(0.975, 2) and find that $t_{0.025,2} = 4.303$.
- Using Excel with $df = 5$, we enter =T.INV(0.975, 5) and find that $t_{0.025,5} = 2.571$.
- Using Excel with $df = 50$, we enter =T.INV(0.975, 50) and find that $t_{0.025,50} = 2.009$.

Note that the $t_{\alpha/2,df}$ values change with the degrees of freedom. Moreover, as df increases, the t_{df} distribution begins to resemble the z distribution. In fact, with $df = \infty$, $t_{0.025,\infty} = 1.96$, which is identical to the corresponding z value; recall that $P(Z \geq 1.96) = 0.025$.

Constructing a Confidence Interval for μ When σ Is Unknown

We can never stress enough the importance of the requirement that $\overline{X}$ follows the normal distribution in estimating the population mean. Recall that $\overline{X}$ follows the normal distribution when the underlying population is normally distributed or when the sample size is sufficiently large ($n \geq 30$). We still construct the confidence interval for μ as point estimate $\pm$ margin of error. However, when the population standard deviation is unknown, we now use the t_{df} distribution to calculate the margin of error.

> **CONFIDENCE INTERVAL FOR μ WHEN σ IS NOT KNOWN**
>
> A $(1 - \alpha)100\%$ confidence interval for the population mean μ when the population standard deviation σ is not known is computed as
>
> $$\bar{x} \pm t_{\alpha/2,df}\frac{s}{\sqrt{n}} \quad \text{or} \quad \left[\bar{x} - t_{\alpha/2,df}\frac{s}{\sqrt{n}}, \bar{x} + t_{\alpha/2,df}\frac{s}{\sqrt{n}}\right],$$
>
> where $t_{\alpha/2,df}$ is the t_{df} value associated with the probability of $\alpha/2$ in the upper tail of the t_{df} distribution and $df = n - 1$. This formula is valid only if $\overline{X}$ (approximately) follows a normal distribution.

EXAMPLE 8.8

In the introductory case of this chapter, Jared Beane wants to estimate the mean mpg for all hybrid SUVs. The accompanying data file lists the mpg for a sample of 25 cars. Use this information to construct the 90% confidence interval for the population mean. Assume that mpg follows a normal distribution.

SOLUTION: The condition that $\overline{X}$ follows a normal distribution is satisfied because we assumed that mpg is normally distributed. Thus, we construct the confidence interval as $\bar{x} \pm t_{\alpha/2,df}\frac{s}{\sqrt{n}}$. This is a classic example where a statistician has access only to sample data. Because the population standard deviation is not known, the sample standard deviation has to be computed from the sample. From the sample data, we find that $\bar{x} = 48.40$ and $s = 10.70$. For the 90% confidence interval,

$\alpha = 0.10$, $\alpha/2 = 0.05$, and, given $n = 25$, $df = 25 - 1 = 24$. Using Excel, we enter =T.INV(0.95, 24) and find that $t_{0.05,24} = 1.711$.

The 90% confidence interval for μ is computed as

$$\bar{x} \pm t_{\alpha/2,df}\frac{s}{\sqrt{n}} = 48.40 \pm 1.711\frac{10.70}{\sqrt{25}} = 44.80 \pm 3.66 \text{ or } [44.74, 52.06].$$

Thus, Jared concludes with 90% confidence that the average mpg of all hybrid SUVs is between 44.74 mpg and 52.06 mpg. Note that the manufacturer's claim that the hybrid SUVs will average 50 mpg cannot be rejected by the sample data because the value 50 falls within the 90% confidence interval.

Using Excel to Construct a Confidence Interval for μ When σ Is Unknown

Again we find that functions in Excel are quite useful when constructing confidence intervals. Consider the following example.

EXAMPLE 8.9

Amazon Prime is a $139-per-year service that gives the company's customers free two-day shipping and discounted rates on overnight delivery. Prime customers also get other perks, such as free e-books. Table 8.3 shows a portion of the annual expenditures (in $) for 100 Prime customers. Use Excel to construct the 95% confidence interval for the average annual expenditures of all Prime customers. Summarize the results.

TABLE 8.3 Annual Prime Expenditures (in $)

Customer	Expenditures
1	1272
2	1089
⋮	⋮
100	1389

FILE

Prime

SOLUTION: We compute $\bar{x} \pm t_{\alpha/2,df}\frac{s}{\sqrt{n}}$, or, equivalently, we find the lower and upper limits of the confidence interval: $\left[\bar{x} - t_{\alpha/2,df}\frac{s}{\sqrt{n}}, \bar{x} + t_{\alpha/2,df}\frac{s}{\sqrt{n}}\right]$.

I. Using Excel's Formula Option

a. Open the *Prime* data file. Note that the observations for the Expenditures variable are in cells B2 through B101.

b. For the 95% confidence interval with $n = 100$, we find $t_{0.025,99}$ using =T.INV(0.975,99). Thus, in order to obtain the lower limit, we enter =AVERAGE(B2:B101) - T.INV(0.975,99)*STDEV.S(B2:101)/SQRT(100). Excel returns 1240.24. For the upper limit, we enter =AVERAGE(B2:B101) + T.INV(0.975,99)*STDEV.S(B2:101)/SQRT(100). Excel returns 1373.64.

II. Excel's Data Analysis Toolpak Option:
Another way to obtain the confidence interval is to use Excel's Data Analysis Toolpak option.

a. Open the *Prime* data file.

b. From the menu, choose **Data > Data Analysis > Descriptive Statistics > OK.**

c. See Figure 8.6. In the *Descriptive Statistics* dialog box, click on the box next to *Input Range,* then select the observations for the Expenditures variable as well as its heading. Check the box in front of *Labels in First Row, Summary Statistics,* and *Confidence Interval for Mean.* By default, Excel uses a 95%

confidence level, but you can easily enter another level. Select *Output Range* and enter cell E1. Click **OK.**

FIGURE 8.6 Excel's *Descriptive Statistics* dialog box

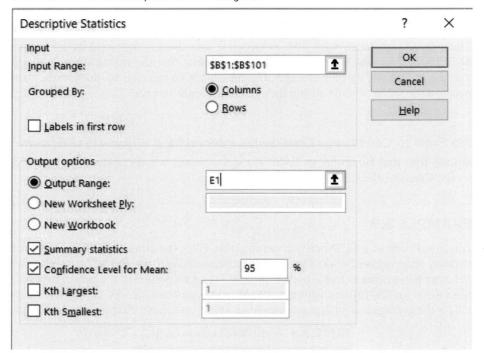

Source: Microsoft Office 2019

d. Table 8.4 presents the Excel output. As noted in Chapter 3, Excel provides numerous summary measures; however, for the confidence interval, all we need is the mean and the margin of error, which is labeled Confidence Level(95.0%). We have put these values in boldface.

TABLE 8.4 Excel's Output Using the Data Analysis Toolpak Option

Mean	**1306.94**
Standard Error	33.61354591
Median	1287.5
Mode	1272
Standard Deviation	336.1354591
Sample Variance	112987.0469
Kurtosis	−0.180207661
Skewness	−0.172329114
Range	1649
Minimum	467
Maximum	2116
Sum	130694
Count	100
Confidence Level(95.0%)	**66.6965676**

Summary:

The 95% confidence interval for the average annual expenditures is $1306.94 ± $66.70. Or, equivalently, with 95% confidence, we conclude that the average annual expenditures fall between $1,240.24 and $1,373.64.

EXERCISES 8.2

Mechanics

16. Find $t_{\alpha/2,df}$ given the following information.
    a. $\alpha = 0.05$ and $df = 12$
    b. $\alpha = 0.20$ and $df = 12$
    c. $\alpha = 0.05$ and $df = 25$
    d. $\alpha = 0.20$ and $df = 25$

17. We use the t distribution to construct a confidence interval for the population mean when the underlying population standard deviation is not known. Under the assumption that the population is normally distributed, find $t_{\alpha/2,df}$ for the following scenarios.
    a. A 90% confidence level and a sample of 28 observations.
    b. A 95% confidence level and a sample of 28 observations.
    c. A 90% confidence level and a sample of 15 observations.
    d. A 95% confidence level and a sample of 15 observations.

18. A random sample of 24 observations is used to estimate the population mean. The sample mean and the sample standard deviation are calculated as 104.6 and 28.8, respectively. Assume that the population is normally distributed.
    a. Construct the 90% confidence interval for the population mean.
    b. Construct the 99% confidence interval for the population mean.
    c. Use your answers to discuss the impact of the confidence level on the width of the interval.

19. Consider a normal population with an unknown population standard deviation. A random sample results in $\bar{x} = 48.68$ and $s^2 = 33.64$.
    a. Compute the 95% confidence interval for μ if $\bar{x}$ and s^2 were obtained from a sample of 16 observations.
    b. Compute the 95% confidence interval for μ if $\bar{x}$ and s^2 were obtained from a sample of 25 observations.
    c. Use your answers to discuss the impact of the sample size on the width of the interval.

20. Let the following sample of 8 observations be drawn from a normal population with unknown mean and standard deviation: 22, 18, 14, 25, 17, 28, 15, 21.
    a. Calculate the sample mean and the sample standard deviation.
    b. Construct the 80% confidence interval for the population mean.
    c. Construct the 90% confidence interval for the population mean.
    d. What happens to the margin of error as the confidence level increases from 80% to 90%?

Applications

21. **FILE** *Salon.* The accompanying data file reports the number of customers who visit a hair salon for seven randomly selected weekdays. It can be assumed that weekday customer visits follow a normal distribution.
    a. Construct the 90% confidence interval for the average number of customers who visit the salon on weekdays.
    b. Construct the 99% confidence interval for the average number of customers who visit the salon on weekdays.
    c. What happens to the width of the interval as the confidence level increases?

22. A popular weight loss program claims that with its recommended healthy diet regimen, customers lose significant weight within a month. In order to estimate the mean weight loss of all customers, a nutritionist takes a sample of 18 customers and records their weight loss one month after joining the program. He computes the sample mean and the standard deviation of weight loss as 12.5 pounds and 9.2 pounds, respectively. He believes that weight loss is likely to be normally distributed.
    a. Calculate the margin of error with 95% confidence.
    b. Calculate the 95% confidence interval for the population mean.

23. **FILE** *Customers.* The accompanying data file reports the number of customers who were served at a restaurant on six randomly selected weekdays. Assume that the number of customers served on weekdays follows a normal distribution. Construct the 90% confidence interval for the average number of customers served on weekdays.

24. According to a survey, high school students average 100 text messages daily. Assume that the survey was based on a random sample of 36 high school students. The sample standard deviation is computed as 10 text messages daily.
    a. Calculate the margin of error with 99% confidence.
    b. What is the 99% confidence interval for the population mean texts that all high school students send daily?

25. The Chartered Financial Analyst (CFA) designation is fast becoming a requirement for serious investment professionals. Although it requires a successful completion of three levels of grueling exams, it also entails promising careers with lucrative salaries. A student of finance is curious about the average salary of a CFA charterholder. He takes a random sample of 36 recent charterholders and computes a mean salary of $158,000 with a standard deviation of $36,000. Use this sample information to determine the 95% confidence interval for the average salary of a CFA charterholder.

26. **FILE** *Sudoku.* The sudoku puzzle has become very popular all over the world. It is based on a 9×9 grid and the challenge is to fill in the grid so that every row, every column, and every 3×3 box contains the digits 1 through 9. A researcher is interested in estimating the average time taken by a college student to solve the puzzle. The accompanying data file records the solving time (in minutes) for eight college students.

a. Construct the 99% confidence interval for the average time taken by a college student to solve a sudoku puzzle.

b. What assumption is necessary to make this inference?

27. **FILE** *Compensation.* Executive compensation has risen dramatically compared to the rising levels of an average worker's wage over the years. Sarah is an MBA student who decides to use her statistical skills to estimate the mean CEO compensation for all large companies in the United States. She takes a random sample of six CEO compensations (in $ millions) and obtains the values shown in the accompanying data file.

a. Help Sarah use the information to construct the 90% confidence interval for the mean CEO compensation for all large companies in the United States.

b. What assumption is necessary for deriving the interval estimate?

c. How can the margin of error reported in part a be reduced?

28. **FILE** *Unemployment.* The accompanying data file reports the unemployment rate (in %) for seven major economies around the world.

a. Calculate the margin of error used in the 95% confidence level for the population mean unemployment rate. Explain the assumption made for the analysis.

b. How can we reduce the margin of error for the 95% confidence interval?

c. What is the 95% confidence interval for the mean unemployment rate?

29. **FILE** *Footwear.* A price-earnings ratio, or P/E ratio, is calculated as a firm's share price compared to the income or profit earned by the firm per share. Generally, a high P/E ratio suggests that investors are expecting higher earnings growth in the future compared to companies with a lower P/E ratio. The accompanying data file reports the P/E ratio for five firms in the footwear industry. Let these ratios represent a random sample drawn from a normally distributed population. Construct the 90% confidence interval for the mean P/E ratio for the entire footwear industry.

30. **FILE** *Returns.* The accompanying data file shows the annual returns (in percent) for Firm A and Firm B over the last five years.

a. Derive the 99% confidence interval for the mean return for Firm A and the 99% confidence interval for the mean return for Firm B.

b. What did you have to assume to make the above inferences?

c. Which confidence interval is wider? Explain.

31. **FILE** *Stock_Price.* The accompanying data file shows the monthly closing stock price (in $) for a firm over the past six months.

a. Calculate the sample mean and the sample standard deviation.

b. Calculate the 90% confidence interval for the mean stock price of the firm assuming that the stock price is normally distributed.

c. What happens to the margin of error if a higher confidence level is used for the interval estimate?

32. Suppose the 90% confidence interval for the mean SAT scores of applicants at a business college is given by [1690, 1810]. This confidence interval uses the sample mean and the sample standard deviation based on 25 observations. What are the sample mean and the sample standard deviation used when computing the interval?

33. A teacher wants to estimate the mean time (in minutes) that students take to go from one classroom to the next. His research assistant uses the sample time of 36 students to report the confidence interval as [8.20, 9.80].

a. Find the sample mean time used to compute the confidence interval.

b. Determine the confidence level if the sample standard deviation used for the interval is 2.365.

34. In order to attract more Millenials, a new clothing store offers free gourmet coffee and pastry to its customers. The average daily revenue over the past five-week period has been $1,080 with a standard deviation of $260. Use this sample information to construct the 95% confidence interval for the average daily revenue. The store manager believes that the coffee and pastry strategy would lead to an average daily revenue of $1,200. Use the 95% interval to determine if the manager is wrong.

35. **FILE** *Debt_Payments.* The accompanying data file lists average monthly debt payments (Debt in $) for 26 metropolitan areas. Construct the 90% and the 95% confidence intervals for the population mean. Compare the widths of the intervals.

36. **FILE** *Economics.* An associate dean of a university wishes to compare the means on the standardized final exams in microeconomics and macroeconomics. He has access to a random sample of 40 scores from each of these two courses. The accompanying data file shows the results.

a. Construct the 95% confidence intervals for the mean score in microeconomics and the mean score in macroeconomics.

b. Explain why the widths of the two intervals are different.

37. **FILE** *Math_Scores.* Recent research shows that while the average math scores for boys and girls may be the same, there is more variability in math ability for boys than girls, resulting in some boys with soaring math skills. The accompanying data file shows the math scores for a sample of boys and girls.

a. Construct the 95% confidence intervals for the mean score of boys and the mean score of girls. Explain your assumptions.

b. Explain why the widths of the two intervals are different.

38. **FILE** *SLO.* The accompanying data file reports the sale price (in $1,000s) for six single-family homes in San Luis Obispo County in California.

a. Construct the 95% confidence interval for the mean sale price in San Luis Obispo County.

b. What assumption have you made when constructing this confidence interval?

8.3 CONFIDENCE INTERVAL FOR THE POPULATION PROPORTION

LO 8.3

Calculate a confidence interval for the population proportion.

Recall that while the population mean μ describes a numerical variable, the population proportion p is the essential descriptive measure for a categorical variable. The parameter p represents the proportion of successes in the population, where success is defined by a particular outcome. Examples of population proportions include the proportion of female students at a university, the proportion of defective items in a manufacturing process, and the default probability on a mortgage loan.

As in the case of the population mean, we estimate the population proportion on the basis of its sample counterpart. In particular, we use the sample proportion $\bar{P}$ as the point estimator of the population proportion p. Also, although the sampling distribution of $\bar{P}$ is based on the binomial distribution, we can approximate it by a normal distribution for large samples, according to the central limit theorem. This approximation is valid when the sample size n is such that $np \geq 5$ and $n(1 - p) \geq 5$.

Using the normal approximation for $\bar{P}$ with $E(\bar{P}) = p$ and $se(\bar{P}) = \sqrt{p(1 - p)/n}$, and analogous to the derivation of the confidence interval for the population mean, a $(1 - \alpha)100\%$ confidence interval for the population proportion is

$$\bar{p} \pm z_{\alpha/2}\sqrt{\frac{p(1 - p)}{n}} \quad \text{or} \quad \left[\bar{p} - z_{\alpha/2}\sqrt{\frac{p(1 - p)}{n}}, \bar{p} + z_{\alpha/2}\sqrt{\frac{p(1 - p)}{n}}\right].$$

This confidence interval is theoretically sound; however, it cannot be implemented because it uses p in the derivation, which is unknown. Because we always use large samples for the normal distribution approximation, we can also conveniently replace p with its estimate $\bar{p}$ in the construction of the interval. Therefore, for $\sqrt{\frac{p(1 - p)}{n}}$, we substitute $\sqrt{\frac{\bar{p}(1 - \bar{p})}{n}}$. This substitution yields a feasible confidence interval for the population proportion.

CONFIDENCE INTERVAL FOR p

A $(1 - \alpha)100\%$ confidence interval for the population proportion p is computed as

$$\bar{p} \pm z_{\alpha/2}\sqrt{\frac{\bar{p}(1 - \bar{p})}{n}} \quad \text{or} \quad \left[\bar{p} - z_{\alpha/2}\sqrt{\frac{\bar{p}(1 - \bar{p})}{n}}, \bar{p} + z_{\alpha/2}\sqrt{\frac{\bar{p}(1 - \bar{p})}{n}}\right],$$

where $z_{\alpha/2}$ is the z value associated with the probability of $\alpha/2$ in the upper tail of the standard normal distribution. This formula is valid only if $\bar{P}$ (approximately) follows a normal distribution.

The normality condition is evaluated at the sample proportion $\bar{p}$. In other words, for constructing a confidence interval for the population proportion p, we require that $n\bar{p} \geq 5$ and $n(1 - \bar{p}) \geq 5$.

EXAMPLE 8.10

In the introductory case of this chapter, Jared Beane wants to estimate the proportion of all hybrid SUVs that obtain over 50 mpg. The **MPG** data file lists the mpg for a sample of 25 cars. Use the information to construct the 90% and the 99% confidence intervals for the population proportion.

SOLUTION: In the **MPG** data file, we find that 7 cars obtain over 50 mpg; thus, the point estimate of the population proportion is $\bar{p} = 7/25 = 0.28$. Note that the normality condition is satisfied because $np \geq 5$ and $n(1 - p) \geq 5$, where p is evaluated at $\bar{p} = 0.28$. For the 90% confidence level, $\alpha/2 = 0.10/2 = 0.05$. Using Excel we enter =NORM.INV(0.95, 0, 1) and find that $z_{0.05} = 1.645$. Substituting the appropriate values into $\bar{p} \pm z_{\alpha/2} \sqrt{\frac{\bar{p}(1-\bar{p})}{n}}$ yields

$$0.28 \pm 1.645 \sqrt{\frac{0.28(1 - 0.28)}{25}} = 0.28 \pm 0.148.$$

With 90% confidence, Jared reports that the percentage of hybrid SUVs that obtain over 50 mpg is between 13.2% and 42.8%.

For the 99% confidence level, $\alpha/2 = 0.01/2 = 0.005$. Using Excel we enter =NORM.INV(0.995, 0, 1) and find that $z_{0.005} = 2.576$. We calculate

$$0.28 \pm 2.576 \sqrt{\frac{0.28(1 - 0.28)}{25}} = 0.28 \pm 0.231.$$

At a higher confidence level of 99%, the interval for the percentage of hybrid SUVs that obtain over 50 mpg is 4.9% to 51.1%. Given the current sample size of 25 cars, Jared can gain confidence (from 90% to 99%) at the expense of precision, as the corresponding margin of error increases from 0.148 to 0.231.

EXERCISES 8.3

Mechanics

39. A random sample of 80 observations results in 50 successes.
    a. Construct the 95% confidence interval for the population proportion of successes.
    b. Construct the 95% confidence interval for the population proportion of failures.

40. Assume $\bar{p} = 0.6$ in a sample of size $n = 50$.
    a. Construct the 95% confidence interval for the population proportion.
    b. What happens to the margin of error if the sample proportion is based on $n = 200$ instead of $n = 50$?

41. A sample of 80 results in 30 successes.
    a. Calculate the point estimate for the population proportion of successes.
    b. Construct the 90% and the 99% confidence intervals for the population proportion.

c. Can we conclude at 90% confidence that the population proportion differs from 0.5?
d. Can we conclude at 99% confidence that the population proportion differs from 0.5?

42. A random sample of 100 observations results in 40 successes.
    a. What is the point estimate for the population proportion of successes?
    b. Construct the 90% and the 99% confidence intervals for the population proportion.
    c. Can we conclude at 90% confidence that the population proportion differs from 0.5?
    d. Can we conclude at 99% confidence that the population proportion differs from 0.5?

43. In a sample of 30 observations, the number of successes equals 18.

a. Construct the 88% confidence interval for the population proportion of successes.

b. Construct the 98% confidence interval for the population proportion of successes.

c. What happens to the margin of error as you move from the 88% confidence interval to the 98% confidence interval?

Applications

44. In a sample of 400 patients, a pharmaceutical company finds that 20 of the patients experienced a serious side effect from a particular drug. Use the sample information to construct the 95% confidence interval for the population proportion of all patients who experience a serious side effect from the drug.

45. A survey of 1,026 people asked: "What would you do with an unexpected tax refund?" Forty-seven percent responded that they would pay off debts.

a. For the 95% confidence interval, what is the margin of error for the proportion of people who would pay off debts with an unexpected tax refund?

b. Construct the 95% confidence interval for the population proportion of people who would pay off debts with an unexpected tax refund.

46. A sample of 5,324 Americans were asked about what matters most to them in a place to live. Thirty-seven percent of the respondents felt that good job opportunities matter most.

a. Construct the 90% confidence interval for the proportion of Americans who feel that good job opportunities matter most in a place to live.

b. Construct the 99% confidence interval for the proportion of Americans who feel that good job opportunities matter most in a place to live.

c. Which of the above two intervals has a higher margin of error? Explain why.

47. An economist reports that 560 out of a sample of 1,200 middle-income American households actively participate in the stock market.

a. Construct the 90% confidence interval for the proportion of middle-income Americans who actively participate in the stock market.

b. Can we conclude that the percentage of middle-income Americans who actively participate in the stock market is not 50%?

48. According to a survey, 44% of adults admit to keeping money secrets from a partner (cnbc.com, February 20, 2020). Suppose this survey was based on 1,000 respondents.

a. Compute the 90% confidence interval for the proportion of all adults who keep money secrets from a partner.

b. What is the resulting margin of error?

c. Compute the margin of error associated with the 99% confidence level.

49. In a recent poll of 760 homeowners in the United States, one in five homeowners reports having a home equity loan that is currently being paid off. Using a confidence coefficient of 0.90, derive the interval estimate for the proportion of all homeowners in the United States that hold a home equity loan.

50. **FILE** *Field_Choice.* A survey asks 30 college-bound students in Portland, Oregon, about the field they wish to pursue in college. Choices for the Field variable include Science, Business, and Other. The survey also asks whether the student is male or female (Sex = Male or Female). The responses can be found in the accompanying data file. [Note that for the Sex variable, there are no non-binary observations in this data set.]

a. Compare the 95% confidence intervals for the proportion of students who would like to pursue science with the proportion who would like to pursue business.

b. Construct and interpret the 90% confidence interval for the proportion of female students who are college bound.

51. An accounting professor is notorious for being stingy in giving out good letter grades. In a large section of 140 students in the fall semester, she gave out only 5% A's, 23% B's, 42% C's, and 30% D's and F's. Assuming that this was a representative class, compute the 95% confidence interval for the probability of getting at least a B from this professor.

52. A study found that 55% of British firms experienced a cyber-attack in the past year (bbc.com, April 23, 2019). Suppose that the study was based on 600 British firms.

a. For the 95% confidence interval, what is the margin of error for the proportion of British firms that experienced a cyber-attack in the past year?

b. Construct the 95% confidence interval for the population proportion of British firms that experienced a cyber-attack in the past year.

c. At 95% confidence, what can be done to reduce the margin of error?

53. A survey asked 5,324 individuals: What's most important to you when choosing where to live? The responses are shown by the following frequency distribution.

Response	Frequency
Good jobs	1,969
Affordable homes	799
Top schools	586
Low crime	1,225
Things to do	745

a. Calculate the margin of error used in the 95% confidence level for the population proportion of those who believe that low crime is most important.

b. Calculate the margin of error used in the 95% confidence level for the population proportion of those who believe that good jobs or affordable homes are most important.

c. Explain why the margins of error in parts a and b are different.

54. One in five 18-year-old Americans has not graduated from high school. A mayor of a Northeastern city comments that its residents do not have the same graduation rate as the rest of the country. An analyst from the Department of Education decides to test the mayor's claim. In particular, she draws a random sample of 80 18-year-olds in the city and finds that 20 of them have not graduated from high school.

a. Compute the point estimate for the proportion of 18-year-olds who have not graduated from high school in this city.

b. Use this point estimate to derive the 95% confidence interval for the population proportion.

c. Can the mayor's comment be justified at 95% confidence?

8.4 SELECTING THE REQUIRED SAMPLE SIZE

Select a sample size to estimate the population mean and the population proportion.

So far we have discussed how a confidence interval provides useful information on an unknown population parameter. We compute the confidence interval by adding and subtracting the margin of error to/from the point estimate. If the margin of error is very large, the confidence interval becomes too wide to be of much value. For instance, little useful information can be gained from a confidence interval that suggests that the average annual starting salary of a business graduate is between $16,000 and $64,000. Similarly, an interval estimate that 10% to 60% of business students pursue an MBA is not very informative.

Statisticians like precision in their interval estimates, which is implied by a low margin of error. If we are able to increase the size of the sample, the larger n reduces the margin of error for the interval estimates. Although a larger sample size improves precision, it also entails the added cost in terms of time and money. Before getting into data collection, it is important that we first decide on the sample size that is adequate for what we wish to accomplish. In this section, we examine the required sample size, for a desired margin of error, in the confidence intervals for the population mean μ and the population proportion p. In order to be conservative, we always round up noninteger values for the required sample size.

Selecting n to Estimate μ

Consider a confidence interval for μ with a known population standard deviation σ. In addition, let E denote the desired margin of error. In other words, you do not want the sample mean to deviate from the population mean by more than E for a given level of confidence. Because $E = z_{\alpha/2} \frac{\sigma}{\sqrt{n}}$, we rearrange this equation to derive the formula for the required sample size as $n = \left(\frac{z_{\alpha/2}\sigma}{E}\right)^2$. The sample size can be computed if we specify the population standard deviation σ, the value of $z_{\alpha/2}$ based on the confidence level $(1 - \alpha)100\%$, and the desired margin of error E.

This formula is based on a knowledge of σ. However, in most cases σ is not known and, therefore, has to be estimated. Note that the sample standard deviation s cannot be used as an estimate for σ because s can be computed only after a sample of size n has been selected. In such cases, we replace σ with its reasonable estimate $\hat{\sigma}$.

> THE REQUIRED SAMPLE SIZE WHEN ESTIMATING THE POPULATION MEAN
>
> For a desired margin of error E, the minimum sample size n required to estimate a $(1 - \alpha)100\%$ confidence interval for the population mean μ is
>
> $$n = \left(\frac{z_{\alpha/2}\hat{\sigma}}{E}\right)^2,$$
>
> where $\hat{\sigma}$ is a reasonable estimate of σ in the planning stage.

If σ is known, we replace $\hat{\sigma}$ with σ. Sometimes we use the sample standard deviation from a preselected sample as $\hat{\sigma}$ in the planning stage. Another choice for $\hat{\sigma}$ is to use an estimate of the population standard deviation from prior studies. Finally, if the minimum and maximum values of the population are available, a rough approximation for the population standard deviation is given by $\hat{\sigma} = \text{range}/4$.

EXAMPLE 8.11

Let us revisit Example 8.8, where Jared Beane wants to construct the 90% confidence interval for the mean mpg of all hybrid SUVs. Suppose Jared would like to constrain the margin of error to within 2 mpg. Jared knows that the minimum and maximum values in the population are 30 mpg and 72 mpg, respectively. How large a sample does Jared need in order to compute the 90% confidence interval for the population mean?

SOLUTION: For the 90% confidence level, $\alpha/2 = 0.10/2 = 0.05$. Using Excel, Jared enters =NORM.INV(0.95, 0, 1) and finds that $z_{0.05} = 1.645$. He estimates the population standard deviation as $\hat{\sigma} = \text{range}/4 = (72 - 30)/4 = 10.50$. Given $E = 2$, the required sample size is

$$n = \left(\frac{z_{\alpha/2}\hat{\sigma}}{E}\right)^2 = \left(\frac{1.645 \times 10.50}{2}\right)^2 = 74.58,$$

which is rounded up to 75. Therefore, Jared needs a random sample of at least 75 hybrid SUVs to constrain the margin of error to within 2 mpg.

Selecting n to Estimate p

The margin of error E for the confidence interval for the population proportion p is $E = z_{\alpha/2}\sqrt{\frac{\bar{p}(1-\bar{p})}{n}}$, where $\bar{p}$ represents the sample proportion. By rearranging, we derive the formula for the required sample size as $n = \left(\frac{z_{\alpha/2}}{E}\right)^2 \bar{p}(1-\bar{p})$. Analogous to the case of the population mean, this formula is not feasible because it uses $\bar{p}$, which cannot be computed unless a sample of size n has already been selected. We replace $\bar{p}$ with a reasonable estimate $\hat{p}$ of the population proportion p.

THE REQUIRED SAMPLE SIZE WHEN ESTIMATING THE POPULATION PROPORTION

For a desired margin of error E, the minimum sample size n required to estimate a $(1 - \alpha)100\%$ confidence interval for the population proportion p is

$$n = \left(\frac{z_{\alpha/2}}{E}\right)^2 \hat{p}(1 - \hat{p}),$$

where $\hat{p}$ is a reasonable estimate of p in the planning stage.

Sometimes we use the sample proportion from a preselected sample as $\hat{p}$ in the planning stage. Another choice for $\hat{p}$ is to use an estimate of the population proportion from prior studies. If no other reasonable estimate of the population proportion is available, we can use $\hat{p} = 0.5$ as a conservative estimate to derive the optimal sample size; note that the required sample is the largest when $\hat{p} = 0.5$.

EXAMPLE 8.12

Let us revisit Example 8.10, where Jared Beane wants to construct the 90% confidence interval for the proportion of all hybrid SUVs that obtain over 50 mpg. Jared does not want the margin of error to be more than 0.10. How large a sample does Jared need for his analysis of the population proportion?

SOLUTION: For the 90% confidence level, $\alpha/2 = 0.10/2 = 0.05$. Using Excel, Jared enters =NORM.INV(0.95, 0, 1) and finds that $z_{0.05} = 1.645$. Because no estimate for the population proportion is readily available, Jared uses a conservative estimate of $\hat{p} = 0.50$. Given $E = 0.10$, the required sample size is

$$n = \left(\frac{z_{\alpha/2}}{E}\right)^2 \hat{p}(1 - \hat{p}) = \left(\frac{1.645}{0.10}\right)^2 0.50(1 - 0.50) = 67.65,$$

which is rounded up to 68. Therefore, Jared needs to find another random sample of at least 68 hybrid SUVs to constrain the margin of error to within 0.10.

SYNOPSIS OF INTRODUCTORY CASE

Jared Beane, an analyst at a research firm, prepares to write a report on the new hybrid SUVs that boasts an average of 50 mpg. Based on a sample of 25 cars, Jared reports, with 90% confidence, that the average mpg of all hybrid SUVs is between 44.74 mpg and 52.06 mpg. Jared also constructs the 90% confidence interval for the proportion of cars that obtain more than 50 mpg and reports the interval between 0.132 and 0.428. Jared wishes to increase the precision of his confidence intervals by reducing the margin of error. If his desired margin of error is 2 mpg for the population mean, he must use a sample of at least 75 hybrid SUVs for the analysis. Jared also wants to reduce the margin of error to 0.10 for the proportion of hybrid SUVs that obtain more than 50 mpg. Using a conservative estimate, he calculates that a sample of at least 68 hybrid SUVs is needed to achieve this goal. Thus, in order to gain precision in the interval estimate for both the mean and the proportion with 90% confidence, Jared's sample must contain at least 75 hybrid SUVs.

Travelerpix/Shutterstock

EXERCISES 8.4

Mechanics

55. The minimum and maximum observations in a population are 20 and 80, respectively. What is the minimum sample size n required to estimate μ with 80% confidence if the desired margin of error is $E = 2.6$? What happens to n if you decide to estimate μ with 95% confidence?

56. Find the required sample size for estimating the population mean in order to be 95% confident that the sample mean is within 10 units of the population mean. Assume that the population standard deviation is 40.

57. You need to compute the 99% confidence interval for the population mean. How large a sample should you draw to ensure that the sample mean does not deviate from the population mean by more than 1.2? (Use 6.0 as an estimate of the population standard deviation from prior studies).

58. What is the minimum sample size n required to estimate μ with 90% confidence if the desired margin of error is $E = 1.2$? The population standard deviation is estimated as $\hat{\sigma} = 3.5$. What happens to n if the desired margin of error decreases to $E = 0.7$?

59. In the planning stage, a sample proportion is estimated as $\hat{p} = 40/50 = 0.80$. Use this information to compute the minimum sample size n required to estimate p with 99% confidence if the desired margin of error $E = 0.12$. What happens to n if you decide to estimate p with 90% confidence?

60. What is the minimum sample size n required to estimate p with 95% confidence if the desired margin of error $E = 0.08$? The population proportion is estimated as $\hat{p} = 0.36$ from prior studies. What happens to n if the desired margin of error increases to $E = 0.12$?

61. You wish to compute the 95% confidence interval for the population proportion. How large a sample should you draw to ensure that the sample proportion does not deviate from the population proportion by more than 0.06? No prior estimate for the population proportion is available.

Applications

62. Mortgage lenders often use FICO scores to check the credit worthiness of consumers applying for real estate loans. In general, FICO scores range from 300 to 850 with higher scores representing a better credit profile. A lender in a Midwestern town would like to estimate the mean credit score of its residents. What is the required number of sample FICO scores needed if the lender does not want the margin of error to exceed 20, with 95% confidence?

63. An analyst from an energy research institute in California wishes to estimate the 99% confidence interval for the average price of unleaded gasoline in the state. In particular, she does not want the sample mean to deviate from the population mean by more than $0.06. What is the minimum number of gas stations that she should include in her sample if she uses the standard deviation estimate of $0.32, as reported in the popular press?

64. An analyst would like to construct 95% confidence intervals for the mean stock returns in two industries. Industry A is a high-risk industry with a known population standard deviation of 20.6%, whereas Industry B is a low-risk industry with a known population standard deviation of 12.8%.
    a. What is the minimum sample size required by the analyst if he wants to restrict the margin of error to 4% for Industry A?
    b. What is the minimum sample size required by the analyst if he wants to restrict the margin of error to 4% for Industry B?
    c. Why do the results differ if they use the same margin of error?

65. The manager of a pizza chain in Albuquerque, New Mexico, wants to determine the average size of their advertised 16-inch pizzas. She takes a random sample of 25 pizzas and records their mean and standard deviation as 16.10 inches and 1.8 inches, respectively. She subsequently computes the 95% confidence interval of the mean size of all pizzas as [15.36, 16.84]. However, she finds this interval to be too broad to implement quality control and decides to reestimate the mean based on a bigger sample. Using the standard deviation estimate of 1.8 from her earlier analysis, how large a sample must she take if she wants the margin of error to be under 0.5 inch?

66. The manager of a newly opened Target store wants to estimate the average expenditure of his customers. From a preselected sample, the standard deviation was determined to be $18. The manager would like to construct the 95% confidence interval for the mean customer expenditure.
    a. Find the appropriate sample size necessary to achieve a margin of error of $5.
    b. Find the appropriate sample size necessary to achieve a margin of error of $3.

67. An economist would like to estimate the 95% confidence interval for the average real estate taxes collected by a small town in California. In a prior analysis, the standard deviation of real estate taxes was reported as $1,580. What is the minimum sample size required by the economist if he wants to restrict the margin of error to $500?

68. A newscaster wishes to estimate the proportion of registered voters who support the incumbent candidate in the mayoral election. In an earlier poll of 240 registered voters, 110 had supported the incumbent candidate. Find the sample size required to construct the 90% confidence interval if the newscaster does not want the margin of error to exceed 0.02.

69. A survey reported that approximately 70% of people in the 50 to 64 age bracket have tried some type of alternative therapy (for instance, acupuncture or the use of nutrition supplements). Assume this survey was based on a sample of 400 people.
    a. Identify the relevant parameter of interest for this categorical variable and compute its point estimate as well as the margin of error with 90% confidence.
    b. You decide to redo the analysis with the margin of error reduced to 2%. How large a sample do you need to draw? State your assumptions in computing the required sample size.

70. A report finds that two in five subprime mortgages are likely to default in the United States. A research economist is interested in estimating default rates in the state of Illinois with 95% confidence. How large a sample is needed to restrict the margin of error to within 0.06, using the reported national default rate?

71. A business student is interested in estimating the 99% confidence interval for the proportion of students who bring laptops to campus. He wants a precise estimate and is willing to draw a large sample that will keep the sample proportion within five percentage points of the population proportion. What is the minimum sample size required by this student, given that no prior estimate of the population proportion is available?

72. A machine that is programmed to package 1.20 pounds of cereal is being tested for its accuracy. In a sample of 36 cereal boxes, the sample mean filling weight is calculated as 1.22 pounds. The population standard deviation is known to be 0.06 pound.
    a. Identify the relevant parameter of interest for this numerical variable and compute its point estimate as well as the margin of error with 95% confidence.
    b. Can we conclude that the packaging machine is operating improperly?

    c. How large a sample must we take if we want the margin of error to be at most 0.01 pound with 95% confidence?

73. Scores on the math portion of the SAT are believed to be normally distributed and range from 200 to 800. A researcher from the admissions department at the University of New Hampshire is interested in estimating the mean math SAT scores of the incoming class with 90% confidence. How large a sample should she take to ensure that the margin of error is below 15?

8.5 WRITING WITH DATA

Andrew Resek/McGraw Hill

Todd A. Merport/Shutterstock

Callie Fitzpatrick, a research analyst with an investment firm, has been asked to write a report summarizing the weekly stock performance of Home Depot and Lowe's. Her manager is trying to decide whether or not to include one of these stocks in a client's portfolio, and the average stock performance is one of the factors influencing this decision. Callie decides to use descriptive measures to summarize stock returns in her report, as well as provide confidence intervals for the average return for Home Depot and Lowe's. She collects weekly returns for each firm from January through December of 2019. A portion of the return data is shown in Table 8.5.

TABLE 8.5 Weekly Returns (in percent) for Home Depot and Lowe's

FILE
Weekly_Returns

Date	Home Depot	Lowe's
1/7/2019	3.33	3.65
1/14/2019	0.09	−2.38
⋮	⋮	⋮
12/30/2019	−1.21	−0.15

Sample Report— Weekly Stock Performance: Home Depot vs. Lowe's

Home Depot and Lowe's are the two largest home-improvement retailers in the United States. An analysis of their recent stock performance proves useful in understanding each firm's financial stability, especially when determining whether to hold either stock in a client's portfolio.

Weekly stock return data for each firm were gathered from January through December of 2019. Table 8.6 summarizes some important descriptive statistics.

TABLE 8.6 Descriptive Statistics for Weekly Returns of Home Depot and Lowe's ($n = 52$)

	Home Depot (in %)	Lowe's (in %)
Mean	0.52	0.58
Median	0.55	0.88
Minimum	−8.12	−12.52
Maximum	6.79	13.28
Standard deviation	2.78	3.77
Margin of error with 95% confidence	0.77	1.05

As compared to Home Depot, Lowe's posted both a higher average return (0.58% > 0.52%) and a higher median return (0.88% > 0.55%) over this time period. However, the standard deviation for Lowe's weekly return was higher than Home Depot's (3.77% > 2.78%), implying that an investment in Lowe's stock was riskier than an investment in Home Depot's stock.

Table 8.6 also shows the margins of error for 95% confidence intervals for the mean returns. With 95% confidence, the mean return for Home Depot fell in the range [−0.25%, 1.29%], while that for Lowe's fell in the range [−0.47%, 1.63%]. Given that these two intervals overlap, one cannot conclude that Lowe's delivered the higher reward over this period—a conclusion one may have arrived at had only the point estimates been evaluated. It is not possible to recommend one stock over the other for inclusion in a client's portfolio based solely on the mean return performance. Other factors, such as the correlation between the stock and the existing portfolio, must be analyzed before this decision can be made.

Suggested Case Studies

REPORT 8.1 FILE **Wages.** The accompanying data file shows the hourly wages (in $) of 30 workers with a bachelor's degree or higher, 30 workers with only a high school diploma, and 30 workers who did not finish high school. In a report, use summary measures to compare the hourly wages for the three education levels. In addition, construct and interpret confidence intervals for the mean hourly wage at each education level.

REPORT 8.2 FILE **Fidelity Returns.** The accompanying data file shows the annual returns for two mutual funds offered by the investment giant Fidelity. The *Fidelity Select Automotive Fund* invests primarily in companies engaged in the manufacturing, marketing, or sales of automobiles, trucks, specialty vehicles, parts, tires, and related services. The *Fidelity Select Gold Fund* invests primarily in companies engaged in exploration, mining, processing, or dealing in gold and, to a lesser degree, in other precious metals and minerals. In a report, use summary measures to compare the returns of the mutual funds. In addition, assess reward by constructing and interpreting confidence intervals for the mean return. State any assumptions that you make for the interval estimates.

REPORT 8.3 Go to https://www.realclearpolitics.com/ and find the most current approval rating for the U.S. president using the RCP average. Construct a confidence interval for the approval rating assuming that the sample size is 600. Next find the approval rating when the president first assumed office. Construct another confidence interval for the approval rating using a sample size of 600. Comment on the similarities and differences between the intervals. Repeat this process with another elected official.

9 Hypothesis Testing

In Chapter 8, we used confidence intervals to estimate an unknown population parameter of interest. We now focus on the second major area of statistical inference: hypothesis testing. We use a hypothesis test to challenge the status quo, or some belief about an underlying population parameter, based on sample data.

In this chapter, we develop hypothesis tests for the population mean and the population proportion. For instance, we may wish to test whether the average age of MBA students in the United States is less than 30 years or whether the percentage of defective items in a production process differs from 5%. In either case, because we do not have access to the entire population, we have to perform statistical inference on the basis of limited sample information. If the sample information is not consistent with the status quo, we use the hypothesis testing framework to determine if the inconsistency is real (that is, we contradict the status quo) or due to chance (that is, we do not contradict the status quo).

fizkes/Shutterstock

INTRODUCTORY CASE

Undergraduate Study Habits

Are today's college students studying hard or hardly studying? A study asserts that, over the past six decades, the number of hours that the average college student studies each week has been steadily dropping (*The Wall Street Journal,* April 10, 2019). In 1961, students invested 24 hours per week in their academic pursuits, whereas today's students study an average of 14 hours per week.

Aaliyah Knight is an assistant dean of students at a large university in California. She wonders if the study trend is reflective of the students at her university. She randomly selects 35 students and asks their average study time per week (in hours). A portion of the responses is shown in Table 9.1.

TABLE 9.1 Number of Hours Spent Studying

FILE
Study_Hours

Student	Hours
1	25
2	19
⋮	⋮
35	16

Aaliyah wants to use the sample information to

1. Determine if the mean study time of students at her university is below the 1961 national average of 24 hours per week.

2. Determine if the mean study time of students at her university differs from today's national average of 14 hours per week.

A synopsis of this case is provided at the end of Section 9.3.

Every day people make decisions based on their beliefs about the true state of the world. They hold certain things to be true and others to be false, and then act accordingly. For example, an engineer believes that a certain steel cable has a breaking strength of 5,000 pounds or more, and then permits its use at a construction site; a manufacturer believes that a certain process yields capsules that contain precisely 100 milligrams of a drug, and then ships the capsules to a pharmacy; a manager believes that an incoming shipment contains 2 percentage, or fewer, defects, and then accepts the shipment.

In these cases, and many more, the formation of these beliefs may have started as mere conjecture, an informed guess, or a proposition tentatively advanced as true. When people formulate a belief in this way, we refer to it as a hypothesis. Sooner or later, however, every hypothesis eventually confronts evidence that either substantiates or refutes it. Determining the validity of an assumption of this nature is called hypothesis testing.

We use the hypothesis testing framework to resolve conflicts between two competing hypotheses on a particular population parameter of interest. We refer to one hypothesis as the **null hypothesis,** denoted H_0, and the other as the **alternative hypothesis,** denoted H_A. We think of the null hypothesis as corresponding to a presumed default state of nature or status quo. The alternative hypothesis, on the other hand, contradicts the default state or status quo.

> ### NULL HYPOTHESIS VERSUS ALTERNATIVE HYPOTHESIS
> When constructing a hypothesis test, we define a null hypothesis, denoted H_0, and an alternative hypothesis, denoted H_A. We conduct a hypothesis test to determine whether or not sample evidence contradicts H_0.

The hypothesis testing procedure enables us to make one of two decisions. If sample evidence is inconsistent with the null hypothesis, we reject the null hypothesis. Conversely, if sample evidence is not inconsistent with the null hypothesis, then we do not reject the null hypothesis. It is not correct to conclude that "we accept the null hypothesis" because while the sample information may not be inconsistent with the null hypothesis, it does not necessarily prove that the null hypothesis is true.

> On the basis of sample information, we either "reject the null hypothesis" or "do not reject the null hypothesis."

Consider an example from the medical field where the null is defined as "an individual is free of a particular disease." Suppose a medical procedure does not detect this disease. On the basis of this limited information, we can only conclude that we are unable to detect the disease (do not reject the null hypothesis). It does not necessarily prove that the person does not have the disease (accept the null hypothesis).

LO 9.1

Define the null hypothesis and the alternative hypothesis.

Defining the Null and the Alternative Hypotheses

A very crucial step in a hypothesis test concerns the formulation of the two competing hypotheses because the conclusion of the test depends on how the hypotheses are stated. As a general guideline, whatever we wish to establish is placed in the alternative hypothesis, whereas the null hypothesis includes the status quo. If we are unable to reject the null hypothesis, then we maintain the status quo, or "business as usual." However, if we reject the null hypothesis, this establishes that the evidence supports the alternative hypothesis, which may require that we take some kind of action. For instance, if we reject the null hypothesis that an individual is free of a particular disease, then we conclude that the person is sick and, therefore, treatment should be prescribed.

In most applications, we require some form of the equality sign in the null hypothesis. (The justification for the equality sign will be provided later.) In general, the null hypothesis typically includes one of the following three signs: $=$, $\leq$, or $\geq$. Given that the alternative hypothesis states the opposite of the null hypothesis, the alternative hypothesis is then specified with the corresponding opposite sign: $\neq$, $>$, or $<$.

> As a general guideline, we use the alternative hypothesis as a vehicle to establish something new—that is, contest the status quo. In most applications, the null hypothesis regarding a particular population parameter of interest is specified with one of the following signs: $=$, $\leq$, or $\geq$; the alternative hypothesis is then specified with the corresponding opposite sign: $\neq$, $>$, or $<$.

A hypothesis test can be **one-tailed** or **two-tailed.** A two-tailed test is defined when the alternative hypothesis includes the $\neq$ sign. For example, $H_0: \mu = \mu_0$ versus $H_A: \mu \neq \mu_0$ and $H_0: p = p_0$ versus $H_A: p \neq p_0$ are examples of two-tailed tests, where μ_0 and p_0 represent hypothesized values of the population mean and the population proportion, respectively. If the null hypothesis is rejected, it suggests that the true parameter does not equal the hypothesized value.

A one-tailed test, on the other hand, involves a null hypothesis that can only be rejected on one side of the hypothesized value. For example, consider $H_0: \mu \leq \mu_0$ versus $H_A: \mu > \mu_0$. Here, we reject the null hypothesis when there is substantial evidence that the population mean is greater than μ_0. It is also referred to as a **right-tailed test** because rejection of the null hypothesis occurs on the right side of the hypothesized mean. Another example is a **left-tailed test,** $H_0: \mu \geq \mu_0$ versus $H_A: \mu < \mu_0$, where the rejection of the null hypothesis occurs on the left side of the hypothesized mean. One-tailed tests for the population proportion are defined similarly.

> ONE-TAILED VERSUS TWO-TAILED HYPOTHESIS TESTS
>
> Hypothesis tests can be one-tailed or two-tailed. In a one-tailed test, we can reject the null hypothesis only on one side of the hypothesized value of the population parameter. In a two-tailed test, we can reject the null hypothesis on either side of the hypothesized value of the population parameter.

In general, we follow three steps when formulating the competing hypotheses:

1. Identify the relevant population parameter of interest.
2. Determine whether it is a one- or two-tailed test.
3. Include some form of the equality sign in the null hypothesis and use the alternative hypothesis to establish a claim.

The following examples highlight one- and two-tailed tests for the population mean and the population proportion. In each example, we want to state the appropriate competing hypotheses.

EXAMPLE 9.1

A trade group predicts that back-to-school spending will average $606.40 per family this year. A different economic model is needed if the prediction is wrong. Specify the null and the alternative hypotheses to determine if a different economic model is needed.

SOLUTION: Given that we are examining average back-to-school spending, the parameter of interest is the population mean μ. Because we want to be able to determine if the population mean differs from $606.40 ($\mu \neq 606.40$), we formulate the null and the alternative hypotheses for a two-tailed test as

$$H_0: \mu = 606.40$$
$$H_A: \mu \neq 606.40$$

The trade group is advised to use a different economic model if the null hypothesis is rejected.

EXAMPLE 9.2

An advertisement for a popular weight-loss clinic suggests that participants in its new diet program experience an average weight loss of more than 10 pounds. A consumer activist wants to determine if the advertisement's claim is valid. Specify the null and the alternative hypotheses to validate the advertisement's claim.

SOLUTION: The advertisement's claim concerns average weight loss; thus, the parameter of interest is again the population mean μ. This is an example of a one-tailed test because we want to determine if the mean weight loss is more than 10 pounds ($\mu > 10$). We specify the competing hypotheses as

$$H_0: \mu \leq 10 \text{ pounds}$$
$$H_A: \mu > 10 \text{ pounds}$$

The underlying claim that the mean weight loss is more than 10 pounds is valid if our decision is to reject the null hypothesis. Conversely, if we do not reject the null hypothesis, we cannot support the claim.

EXAMPLE 9.3

A television research analyst wishes to test a claim that more than 50% of households will tune in for a TV episode. Specify the null and the alternative hypotheses to test the claim.

SOLUTION: This is an example of a one-tailed test regarding the population proportion p. Given that the analyst wants to determine whether $p > 0.50$, this claim is placed in the alternative hypothesis, whereas the null hypothesis is just its opposite.

$$H_0: p \leq 0.50$$
$$H_A: p > 0.50$$

The claim that more than 50% of households will tune in for a TV episode is valid only if the null hypothesis is rejected.

EXAMPLE 9.4

It is generally believed that at least 60% of the residents in a small town in Texas are happy with their lives. A sociologist wonders whether recent economic woes have adversely affected the happiness level in this town. Specify the null and the alternative hypotheses to determine if the sociologist's concern is valid.

SOLUTION: This is also a one-tailed test regarding the population proportion p. While the population proportion has been at least 0.60 ($p \geq 0.60$), the sociologist wants to establish that the current population proportion is below 0.60 ($p < 0.60$). Therefore, the hypotheses are formulated as

$$H_0: p \geq 0.60$$
$$H_A: p < 0.60$$

In this case, the sociologist's concern is valid if the null hypothesis is rejected. Nothing new is established if the null hypothesis is not rejected.

Type I and Type II Errors

LO 9.2

Distinguish between
Type I and Type II errors.

Because the decision of a hypothesis test is based on limited sample information, we are bound to make errors. Ideally, we would like to be able to reject the null hypothesis when the null hypothesis is false and not reject the null hypothesis when the null hypothesis is true. However, we may end up rejecting or not rejecting the null hypothesis erroneously. In other words, sometimes we reject the null hypothesis when we should not, or not reject the null hypothesis when we should.

We consider two types of errors in the context of hypothesis testing: a **Type I error** and a **Type II error.** A Type I error is committed when we reject the null hypothesis when the null hypothesis is true. On the other hand, a Type II error is made when we do not reject the null hypothesis when the null hypothesis is false.

Table 9.2 summarizes the circumstances surrounding Type I and Type II errors. Two correct decisions are possible: not rejecting the null hypothesis when the null hypothesis is true and rejecting the null hypothesis when the null hypothesis is false. Conversely, two incorrect decisions (errors) are also possible: rejecting the null hypothesis when the null hypothesis is true (Type I error) and not rejecting the null hypothesis when the null hypothesis is false (Type II error).

TABLE 9.2 Type I and Type II Errors

Decision	Null hypothesis is true	Null hypothesis is false
Reject the null hypothesis	Type I error	Correct decision
Do not reject the null hypothesis	Correct decision	Type II error

EXAMPLE 9.5

An online retailer is deciding whether or not to build a brick-and-mortar store in a new marketplace. A market analysis determines that the venture will be profitable if average pedestrian traffic exceeds 500 people per day. The competing hypotheses are specified as follows.

$$H_0: \mu \leq 500 \text{ (Do not build brick-and-mortar store.)}$$
$$H_A: \mu > 500 \text{ (Build brick-and-mortar store.)}$$

Discuss the consequences of a Type I error and a Type II error.

SOLUTION: A Type I error occurs when the retailer rejects H_0, but H_0 is true; that is, the retailer builds the brick-and-mortar store, but average pedestrian traffic does not exceed 500 people per day and the venture will not be profitable. A Type II error occurs when the retailer does not reject H_0, but H_0 is false; that is, the retailer does not build the brick-and-mortar store, but average pedestrian traffic exceeds 500 people per day and the venture would have been profitable. Arguably, the consequences of a Type I error in this example are more serious than those of a Type II error.

It is not always easy to determine which of the two errors has more serious consequences. For given evidence, there is a trade-off between these errors; by reducing the likelihood of a Type I error, we implicitly increase the likelihood of a Type II error, and vice versa. The only way we can reduce both errors is by collecting more evidence. Let us denote the probability of a Type I error by α, the probability of a Type II error by β, and the strength of the evidence by the sample size n. The only way we can lower both α and β is by increasing n. For a given n, however, we can reduce α only at the expense of a higher β and reduce β only at the expense of a higher α.

The optimal choice of α and β depends on the relative cost of these two types of errors, and determining these costs is not always easy. Typically, the decision regarding the optimal level of Type I and Type II errors is made by the management of a firm where the job of a data analyst is to conduct the hypothesis test for a chosen value of α.

EXERCISES 9.1

1. Explain why the following hypotheses are not constructed correctly.
   a. $H_0: \mu \leq 10; H_A: \mu \geq 10$
   b. $H_0: \mu \neq 500; H_A: \mu = 500$
   c. $H_0: p \leq 0.40; H_A: p > 0.42$
   d. $H_0: \bar{X} \leq 128; H_A: \bar{X} > 128$

2. Which of the following statements are valid null and alternative hypotheses? If they are invalid hypotheses, explain why.
   a. $H_0: \bar{X} \leq 210; H_A: \bar{X} > 210$
   b. $H_0: \mu = 120; H_A: \mu \neq 120$
   c. $H_0: p \leq 0.24; H_A: p > 0.24$
   d. $H_0: \mu < 252; H_A: \mu > 252$

3. Explain why the following statements are not correct.
   a. "With my methodological approach, I can reduce the Type I error with the given sample information without changing the Type II error."
   b. "I have already decided how much of the Type I error I am going to allow. A bigger sample will not change either the Type I or Type II error."
   c. "I can reduce the Type II error by making it difficult to reject the null hypothesis."
   d. "By making it easy to reject the null hypothesis, I am reducing the Type I error."

4. Which of the following statements are correct? Explain if incorrect.
   a. "I accept the null hypothesis because sample evidence is not inconsistent with the null hypothesis."
   b. "Because sample evidence cannot be supported by the null hypothesis, I reject the null hypothesis."
   c. "I can establish a given claim if sample evidence is consistent with the null hypothesis."
   d. "I cannot establish a given claim if the null hypothesis is not rejected."

5. Construct the null and the alternative hypotheses for the following tests:
   a. Test if the mean weight of cereal in a cereal box differs from 18 ounces.
   b. Test if the stock price increases on more than 60% of the trading days.
   c. Test if Americans get an average of less than seven hours of sleep.

6. Define the consequences of Type I and Type II errors for each of the tests considered in the preceding question.

7. Construct the null and the alternative hypotheses for the following claims:
   a. "I am going to get the majority of the votes to win this election."

b. "I suspect that your 10-inch pizzas are, on average, less than 10 inches in size."

c. "I will have to fine the company because its tablets do not contain an average of 250 mg of ibuprofen as advertised."

8. Discuss the consequences of Type I and Type II errors for each of the claims considered in the preceding question.

9. A polygraph (lie detector) is an instrument used to determine if an individual is telling the truth. These tests are considered to be 95% reliable. In other words, if an individual lies, there is a 0.95 probability that the test will detect a lie. Let there also be a 0.005 probability that the test erroneously detects a lie even when the individual is actually telling the truth. Consider the null hypothesis, "the individual is telling the truth," to answer the following questions.

a. What is the probability of a Type I error?

b. What is the probability of a Type II error?

c. What are the consequences of Type I and Type II errors?

d. What is wrong with the statement, "I can prove that the individual is telling the truth on the basis of the polygraph result"?

10. The manager of a large manufacturing firm is considering switching to new and expensive software that promises to reduce its assembly costs. Before purchasing the software, the manager wants to conduct a hypothesis test to determine if the new software does reduce its assembly costs.

a. Would the manager of the manufacturing firm be more concerned about a Type I error or a Type II error? Explain.

b. Would the software company be more concerned about a Type I error or a Type II error? Explain.

11. The screening process for detecting a rare disease is not perfect. Researchers have developed a blood test that is considered fairly reliable. It gives a positive reaction in 98% of the people who have that disease. However, it erroneously gives a positive reaction in 3% of the people who do not have the disease. Consider the null hypothesis "the individual does not have the disease" to answer the following questions.

a. What is the probability of a Type I error?

b. What is the probability of a Type II error?

c. What are the consequences of Type I and Type II errors?

d. What is wrong with the nurse's analysis, "The blood test result has proved that the individual is free of disease"?

12. A consumer group has accused a restaurant of using higher fat content than what is reported on its menu. The group has been asked to conduct a hypothesis test to substantiate its claims.

a. Is the manager of the restaurant more concerned about a Type I error or a Type II error? Explain.

b. Is the consumer group more concerned about a Type I error or a Type II error? Explain.

13. A pharmaceutical company has developed a new drug for depression. There is a concern, however, that the drug also raises the blood pressure of its users. A researcher wants to conduct a test to validate this claim. Would the manager of the pharmaceutical company be more concerned about a Type I error or a Type II error? Explain.

14. A company has developed a new diet that it claims will lower one's weight by more than 10 pounds. Health officials decide to conduct a test to validate this claim.

a. Would the manager of the company be more concerned about a Type I error or a Type II error? Explain.

b. Would the consumers be more concerned about a Type I error or a Type II error? Explain.

9.2 HYPOTHESIS TEST FOR THE POPULATION MEAN WHEN σ IS KNOWN

In order to introduce the basic methodology for hypothesis testing, we first conduct a hypothesis test regarding the population mean μ under the assumption that the population standard deviation σ is known. While it is true that σ is rarely known, there are instances when σ is considered fairly stable and, therefore, can be determined from prior experience. In such cases, σ is treated as known. Fortunately, this assumption has no bearing on the overall procedure of conducting a hypothesis test, a procedure we use throughout the remainder of the text.

A hypothesis test regarding the population mean μ is based on the sampling distribution of the sample mean $\overline{X}$. In particular, it uses the fact that $E(\overline{X}) = \mu$ and $se(\overline{X}) = \sigma/\sqrt{n}$. Also, in order to implement the test, it is essential that $\overline{X}$ is normally distributed. Recall that $\overline{X}$ is normally distributed when the underlying population is normally distributed. If the underlying population is not normally distributed, then, by the central limit theorem,

$\overline{X}$ is approximately normally distributed if the sample size is sufficiently large—that is, $n \geq 30$.

The basic principle of hypothesis testing is to first assume that the null hypothesis is true and then determine if sample evidence contradicts this assumption. This principle is analogous to the scenario in the court of law where the null hypothesis is defined as "the individual is innocent" and the decision rule is best described by "innocent until proven guilty."

There are two approaches to implementing a hypothesis test—the p-value approach and the critical value approach. Both approaches always lead to the same conclusion. The critical value approach is attractive when calculations are done by hand and statistical tables are used for the analysis. Most statistics and business analytics professionals favor the p-value approach because virtually every statistical software package reports p-values. In this text, we focus on the p-value approach; we outline the critical value approach in the appendix to this chapter. In addition, we show how a confidence interval can be used for conducting a two-tailed test.

LO 9.3

Conduct a hypothesis test for the population mean when σ is known.

The p-Value Approach

When implementing the p-value approach, we use a four-step procedure. This procedure is valid for implementing one- and two-tailed tests regarding the population mean, the population proportion, or any other population parameter of interest.

Suppose a sociologist wants to establish that the mean retirement age is greater than 67 ($\mu > 67$). It is assumed that the retirement age is normally distributed with a known population standard deviation of 9 years ($\sigma = 9$). We can investigate the sociologist's belief by specifying the competing hypotheses as

$$H_0: \mu \leq 67$$
$$H_A: \mu > 67$$

Let a random sample of 25 retirees produce an average retirement age of 71—that is, $\overline{x} = 71$. This sample evidence casts doubt on the validity of the null hypothesis because the sample mean is greater than the hypothesized value, $\mu_0 = 67$. However, the discrepancy between $\overline{x}$ and μ_0 does not necessarily imply that the null hypothesis is false. Perhaps the discrepancy can be explained by pure chance. It is common to evaluate this discrepancy in terms of the appropriate **test statistic.** The following definition box shows the formula for the test statistic when testing the population mean μ when the population standard deviation σ is known.

THE TEST STATISTIC FOR μ WHEN σ IS KNOWN

The value of the test statistic for the hypothesis test of the population mean μ when the population standard deviation σ is known is computed as

$$z = \frac{\overline{x} - \mu_0}{\sigma/\sqrt{n}},$$

where z is the standardized value of $\overline{x}$ and μ_0 is the hypothesized value of the population mean. This formula is valid only if $\overline{X}$ (approximately) follows a normal distribution.

Thus, the value of the test statistic z is the standardized value of $\overline{x}$ and it is evaluated at $\mu = \mu_0$, which explains why we need some form of the equality sign in the null hypothesis.

Recall that if the random variable $\overline{X}$ is normally distributed with mean μ and standard error $\sigma/\sqrt{n}$, then we can transform it to the standard normal random variable Z with mean 0 and standard deviation 1. For the retirement example, given that the population is normally distributed with $\sigma = 9$, we compute the value of the test statistic as $z = \frac{\overline{x} - \mu_0}{\sigma/\sqrt{n}} = \frac{71 - 67}{9/\sqrt{25}} = 2.2222$. Note that comparing $\overline{x} = 71$ with 67 is identical to comparing $z = 2.2222$ with 0, where 67 and 0 are the means of $\overline{X}$ and Z, respectively.

We now find the **p-value,** which is the likelihood of obtaining a sample mean that is at least as extreme as the one derived from the given sample, under the assumption that the null hypothesis is true as an equality—that is, $\mu_0 = 67$. Because in this example $\overline{x} = 71$, we define the extreme value as a sample mean of 71 or higher and find the p-value as $P(\overline{X} \geq 71) = P(Z \geq 2.2222) = 0.0131$. Recall that in order to find this probability in Excel, we enter =1-NORM.DIST(2.2222,0,1,TRUE).

We should note that in this example, we could skip the intermediate step of computing the test statistic z and find the p-value directly from the sample data; that is, with $\overline{x} = 71$, $\mu_0 = 67$, $\sigma = 9$, and $n = 25$, we find $P(\overline{X} \geq 71)$ in Excel by entering =1-NORM.DIST(71, 67, 9/√25, TRUE), and Excel returns 0.0131. As we will see with many hypothesis tests going forward, it will be necessary to first implement the intermediate step of computing the test statistic. Figure 9.1 shows the computed p-value for the retirement example.

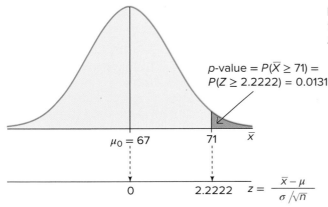

FIGURE 9.1 The p-value for a right-tailed test with $z = 2.2222$

p-value = $P(\overline{X} \geq 71)$ = $P(Z \geq 2.2222)$ = 0.0131

Note that when the null hypothesis is true, there is only a 1.31% chance that the sample mean will be 71 or more. This seems like a very small chance, but is it small enough to allow us to reject the null hypothesis in favor of the alternative hypothesis? Let's see how we define "small enough."

Remember that a Type I error occurs when we reject the null hypothesis when it is true. We define the *allowed* probability of making a Type I error as α and refer to $\alpha \times 100\%$ as the **significance level.** We generally choose a value for α *before* implementing a hypothesis test; that is, we set the rules of the game before playing. Care must be exercised in choosing α because important decisions are often based on the results of a hypothesis test, which in turn depend on α. Most hypothesis tests are conducted using a significance level of 1%, 5%, or 10%, using $\alpha = 0.01$, 0.05, or 0.10, respectively. For example, $\alpha = 0.05$ means that we allow a 5% chance of rejecting a true null hypothesis.

The p-value is referred to as the *observed* probability of making a Type I error. In the retirement example, given the p-value of 0.0131, if we decide to reject the null hypothesis, then there is a 1.31% chance that our decision will be erroneous. So, how do we decide whether or not to reject the null hypothesis, or equivalently, is this p-value "small enough"? We decide to reject the null hypothesis when the observed probability of a Type

I error (the p-value) is less than the allowed probability of a Type I error (α). Or more formally, the decision rule in a hypothesis test is:

- Reject the null hypothesis if the p-value $< \alpha$, or
- Do not reject the null hypothesis if the p-value $\geq \alpha$.

Suppose we had chosen $\alpha = 0.05$ to conduct the hypothesis test in the retirement example. At this significance level, we reject the null hypothesis because $0.0131 < 0.05$. This means that the sample data support the sociologist's claim that the average retirement age is greater than 67 years old. Individuals may be working past the normal retirement age of 67 because of lack of savings and/or because this generation is expected to outlive any previous generation and needs jobs to pay the bills. We should note that if α had been set at 0.01, then the findings would have been different. At this smaller significance level, the evidence does not allow us to reject the null hypothesis ($0.0131 > 0.01$). At the 1% significance level, we cannot conclude that the mean retirement age is greater than 67.

In the retirement example of a right-tailed test, we calculated the p-value as $P(Z \geq z)$. Analogously, for a left-tailed test, the p-value is given by $P(Z \leq z)$. For a two-tailed test, the extreme values exist on both sides of the distribution of the test statistic. Given the symmetry of the z distribution, the p-value for a two-tailed test is twice that of the p-value for a one-tailed test. It is calculated as $2 \times P(Z \geq z)$ if $z > 0$ or as $2 \times P(Z \leq z)$ if $z < 0$.

CALCULATING THE p-VALUE AND THE DECISION RULE

Under the assumption that $\mu = \mu_0$, the p-value is the likelihood of observing a sample mean that is at least as extreme as the one derived from the given sample. The p-value is also referred to as the observed probability of a Type I error. Its calculation depends on the specification of the alternative hypothesis.

Alternative Hypothesis	p-value
$H_A: \mu > \mu_0$	Right-tail probability: $P(Z \geq z)$
$H_A: \mu < \mu_0$	Left-tail probability: $P(Z \leq z)$
$H_A: \mu \neq \mu_0$	Two-tail probability: $2 \times P(Z \geq z)$ if $z > 0$ or $2 \times P(Z \leq z)$ if $z < 0$

The decision rule is:

- Reject H_0 if the p-value $< \alpha$, or
- Do not reject H_0 if p-value $\geq \alpha$,

where α is the allowed probability of a Type I error. The significance level of a hypothesis test is defined as $\alpha \times 100\%$.

Figure 9.2 shows the three different scenarios of determining the p-value depending on the specification of the competing hypotheses. Figure 9.2a shows the p-value for a left-tailed test. Because the appropriate test statistic follows the standard normal distribution, we compute the p-value as $P(Z \leq z)$. When calculating the p-value for a right-tailed test (see Figure 9.2b), we find the area to the right of the value of the test statistic z or, equivalently, $P(Z \geq z)$. Figure 9.2c shows the p-value for a two-tailed test, calculated as $2 \times P(Z \leq z)$ when $z < 0$ or as $2 \times P(Z \geq z)$ when $z > 0$.

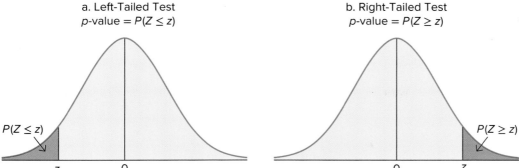

a. Left-Tailed Test
p-value $= P(Z \le z)$

b. Right-Tailed Test
p-value $= P(Z \ge z)$

$P(Z \le z)$

$P(Z \ge z)$

FIGURE 9.2 The p-values for one- and two-tailed tests

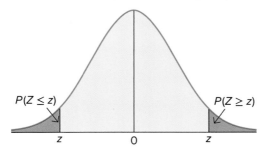

c. Two-Tailed Test
If $z < 0$, then p-value $= 2 \times P(Z \le z)$
If $z > 0$, then p-value $= 2 \times P(Z \ge z)$

$P(Z \le z)$

$P(Z \ge z)$

It is important to note that we *cannot* reject H_0 for a right-tailed test if $\bar{x} \le \mu_0$ or, equivalently, $z \le 0$. Consider, for example, a right-tailed test with the hypotheses specified as $H_0: \mu \le 67$ versus $H_A: \mu > 67$. Here, if $\bar{x} = 65$, there is no need for formal testing because we have no discrepancy between the sample mean and the hypothesized value of the population mean. Similarly, we *cannot* reject H_0 for a left-tailed test if $\bar{x} \ge \mu_0$ or, equivalently, $z \ge 0$. We will now summarize the four-step procedure using the p-value approach.

THE FOUR-STEP PROCEDURE USING THE p-VALUE APPROACH

Step 1. Specify the null and the alternative hypotheses. We identify the relevant population parameter of interest, determine whether it is a one- or a two-tailed test, and, most importantly, include some form of the equality sign in the null hypothesis and place whatever we wish to establish in the alternative hypothesis.

Step 2. Specify the significance level. Before implementing a hypothesis test, we first specify α, which is the *allowed* probability of making a Type I error. The significance level is calculated as $\alpha \times 100\%$.

Step 3. Calculate the value of the test statistic and the p-value. When the population standard deviation σ is known, the value of the test statistic is $z = \frac{\bar{x} - \mu}{\sigma/\sqrt{n}}$, where μ_0 is the hypothesized value of the population mean. For a right-tailed test, the p-value is $(Z \ge z)$, and for a left-tailed test, the p-value is $P(Z \le z)$. For a two-tailed test, the p-value is $2 \times P(Z \ge z)$ if $z > 0$, or $2 \times P(Z \le z)$ if $z < 0$.

Step 4. State the conclusion and interpret results. The decision rule is to reject the null hypothesis when the p-value $< \alpha$ and not reject the null hypothesis when the p-value $\ge \alpha$. We interpret the results in the context of the application.

EXAMPLE 9.6

A research analyst disputes a trade group's prediction that back-to-school spending will average $606.40 per family this year. She believes that average back-to-school spending will differ from this amount. She decides to conduct a test on the basis of a random sample of 30 households with school-age children. She calculates the sample mean as $622.85. She also believes that back-to-school spending is normally distributed with a population standard deviation of $65. She wants to conduct the test at the 5% significance level.

a. Specify the competing hypotheses in order to test the research analyst's claim.

b. What is the allowed probability of a Type I error?

c. Calculate the value of the test statistic and the p-value.

d. At the 5% significance level, does average back-to-school spending differ from $606.40?

SOLUTION:

a. Because we want to determine if the average is different from the predicted value of $606.40, we specify the hypotheses as

$$H_0: \mu = 606.40$$
$$H_A: \mu \neq 606.40$$

b. The allowed probability of a Type I error is equivalent to the significance level of the test, which in this example is given as $\alpha = 0.05$.

c. Note that $\overline{X}$ is normally distributed because it is computed from a random sample drawn from a normal population. Because σ is known, the value of the test statistic z is calculated as

$$z = \frac{\overline{x} - \mu_0}{\sigma/\sqrt{n}} = \frac{622.85 - 606.40}{65/\sqrt{30}} = 1.3862.$$

For a two-tailed test with a positive value for the test statistic, we find the p-value as $2 \times P(Z \geq 1.3862) = 0.1657$. In order to find the p-value in Excel, we enter =2*(1-NORM.DIST(1.3862,0,1,TRUE)).

d. The decision rule is to reject the null hypothesis if the p-value is less than α. Because $0.1657 > 0.05$, we do not reject H_0. Therefore, at the 5% significance level, we cannot conclude that average back-to-school spending differs from $606.40 per family this year. The sample data do not support the research analyst's claim.

Confidence Intervals and Two-Tailed Hypothesis Tests

A confidence interval for the population parameter is sometimes used as an alternative method for conducting a two-tailed hypothesis test. Informally, we had used this procedure when discussing confidence intervals in Chapter 8. Given that we conduct the hypothesis test at the $\alpha \times 100\%$ significance level, we can use the sample data to determine a corresponding $(1 - \alpha)100\%$ confidence interval for the population mean μ. If the confidence interval does not contain the hypothesized value of the population mean μ_0, then we reject the null hypothesis. If the confidence interval contains μ_0, then we do not reject the null hypothesis.

> **IMPLEMENTING A TWO-TAILED TEST USING A CONFIDENCE INTERVAL**
>
> The general specification for the $(1 - \alpha)100\%$ confidence interval for the population mean μ when the population standard deviation σ is known is computed as
>
> $$\bar{x} \pm z_{\alpha/2}\frac{\sigma}{\sqrt{n}} \quad \text{or} \quad \left[\bar{x} - z_{\alpha/2}\frac{\sigma}{\sqrt{n}}, \bar{x} + z_{\alpha/2}\frac{\sigma}{\sqrt{n}}\right].$$
>
> Given a hypothesized value of the population mean μ_0, the decision rule is:
> - Reject H_0 if μ_0 does not fall within the confidence interval, or
> - Do not reject H_0 if μ_0 falls within the confidence interval.

EXAMPLE 9.7

Use the confidence interval approach to conduct the hypothesis test described in Example 9.6.

SOLUTION: We are testing H_0: $\mu = 606.40$ versus H_A: $\mu \neq 606.40$ at the 5% significance level. We use $n = 30$, $\bar{x} = 622.85$, and $\sigma = 65$, along with $\alpha = 0.05$, to determine the 95% confidence interval for μ. Recall that in order to find $z_{\alpha/2} = z_{0.025}$ in Excel, we enter =NORM.INV(0.975, 0,1), and Excel returns 1.96. We then calculate

$$\bar{x} \pm z_{\alpha/2}\frac{\sigma}{\sqrt{n}} = 622.85 \pm 1.96\frac{65}{\sqrt{30}} = 622.85 \pm 23.26,$$

resulting in the interval [599.59, 646.11]. Because the hypothesized value of the population mean $\mu_0 = 606.40$ falls within the 95% confidence interval, we do not reject H_0. Thus, we arrive at the same conclusion as with the p-value approach; that is, the sample data do not support the research analyst's claim that average back-to-school spending differs from \$606.40 per family this year.

As shown in Example 9.7, we use the confidence interval as an alternative method for conducting a two-tailed test. It is possible to adjust the confidence interval to accommodate a one-tailed test, but we do not discuss this adjustment in this text.

One Last Remark

An important component of any well-executed statistical analysis is to clearly communicate the results. Thus, it is not sufficient to end the analysis with a conclusion that you reject the null hypothesis or you do not reject the null hypothesis. You must interpret the results, clearly reporting whether or not the claim regarding the population parameter of interest can be justified on the basis of the sample information.

EXERCISES 9.2

Mechanics

15. Consider the following hypotheses:

$$H_0: \mu \leq 12.6$$
$$H_A: \mu > 12.6$$

A sample of 25 observations yields a sample mean of 13.4. Assume that the sample is drawn from a normal population with a population standard deviation of 3.2.

a. Calculate the p-value. What is the conclusion to the hypothesis test if $\alpha = 0.10$?

b. Calculate the p-value if the above sample mean was based on a sample of 100 observations. What is the conclusion to the hypothesis test if $\alpha = 0.10$?

16. Consider the following hypotheses:

$$H_0: \mu = 100$$
$$H_A: \mu \neq 100$$

A sample of 16 observations yields a sample mean of 95. Assume that the sample is drawn from a normal population with a population standard deviation of 10.

a. Calculate the value of the test statistic.

b. Find the p-value.

c. At the 10% significance level, what is the conclusion to the hypothesis test?

17. Consider the following hypotheses:

$$H_0: \mu \geq 150$$
$$H_A: \mu < 150$$

A sample of 80 observations results in a sample mean of 144. The population standard deviation is known to be 28.

a. Calculate the value of the test statistic and the p-value.

b. Does the sample evidence enable us to reject the null hypothesis at $\alpha = 0.01$?

c. Does the sample evidence enable us to reject the null hypothesis at $\alpha = 0.05$?

18. A researcher wants to determine if the population mean is greater than 45. A random sample of 36 observations yields a sample mean of 47. Assume that the population standard deviation is 8.

a. Specify the competing hypotheses to test the researcher's claim.

b. Calculate the value of the test statistic.

c. Find the p-value.

d. At the 5% significance level, what is the conclusion to the hypothesis test?

19. Consider the following hypotheses:

$$H_0: \mu = 1,800$$
$$H_A: \mu \neq 1,800$$

The population is normally distributed with a population standard deviation of 440. Compute the value of the test statistic and the resulting p-value for each of the following sample results. For each sample, determine if you can reject the null hypothesis at the 10% significance level.

a. $\bar{x} = 1,850; n = 110$

b. $\bar{x} = 1,850; n = 280$

c. $\bar{x} = 1,650; n = 32$

d. $\bar{x} = 1,700; n = 32$

20. Consider the following hypothesis test:

$$H_0: \mu \leq -5$$
$$H_A: \mu > -5$$

A random sample of 50 observations yields a sample mean of -3. The population standard deviation is 10. Calculate the p-value. What is the conclusion to the hypothesis test if $\alpha = 0.05$?

21. Consider the following hypothesis test:

$$H_0: \mu \leq 75$$
$$H_A: \mu > 75$$

A random sample of 100 observations yields a sample mean of 80. The population standard deviation is 30. Calculate the p-value. What is the conclusion to the hypothesis test if $\alpha = 0.10$?

22. Consider the following hypothesis test:

$$H_0: \mu = -100$$
$$H_A: \mu \neq -100$$

A random sample of 36 observations yields a sample mean of -125. The population standard deviation is 42. Conduct the test at $\alpha = 0.01$.

23. Consider the following hypotheses:

$$H_0: \mu = 120$$
$$H_A: \mu \neq 120$$

The population is normally distributed with a population standard deviation of 46.

a. If $\bar{x} = 132$ and $n = 50$, what is the conclusion to the hypothesis test at the 5% significance level?

b. If $\bar{x} = 108$ and $n = 50$, what is the conclusion to the hypothesis test at the 10% significance level?

Applications

24. It is advertised that the average braking distance for a small car traveling at 65 miles per hour equals 120 feet. A transportation researcher wants to determine if the statement made in the advertisement is false. She randomly test drives 36 small cars at 65 miles per hour and records the braking distance. The sample average braking distance is computed as 114 feet. Assume that the population standard deviation is 22 feet.

a. State the null and the alternative hypotheses for the test.

b. Calculate the value of the test statistic and the p-value.

c. Use $\alpha = 0.01$ to determine if the average breaking distance differs from 120 feet.

25. Customers at Costco spend an average of $130 per trip. One of Costco's rivals would like to determine whether its customers spend more per trip. A survey of the receipts of 25 customers found that the sample mean was $135.25. Assume that the population standard deviation is $10.50 and that spending follows a normal distribution.

a. Specify the null and alternative hypotheses to test whether average spending at the rival's store is more than $130.

b. Calculate the value of the test statistic and the p-value.

c. At the 5% significance level, what is the conclusion to the hypothesis test?

26. A sales manager of a used car dealership for sports utility vehicle (SUVs) believes that it takes more than 90 days, on average, to sell an SUV. In order to test his claim, he samples 40 recently sold SUVs and finds that it took an average of 95 days to sell an SUV. He believes that the population standard deviation is fairly stable at 20 days.

a. State the null and the alternative hypotheses for the hypothesis test.

b. What is the *p*-value?

c. Is the sales manager's claim justified at $\alpha = 0.01$?

27. A researcher wants to determine if Americans are sleeping less than the recommended 7 hours of sleep on weekdays. He takes a random sample of 150 Americans and computes the average sleep time of 6.7 hours on weekdays. Assume that the population is normally distributed with a known standard deviation of 2.1 hours. Test the researcher's claim at $\alpha = 0.01$.

28. A local bottler in Hawaii wishes to ensure that an average of 16 ounces of passion fruit juice is used to fill each bottle. In order to analyze the accuracy of the bottling process, she takes a random sample of 48 bottles. The mean weight of the passion fruit juice in the sample is 15.80 ounces. Assume that the population standard deviation is 0.8 ounce.

a. State the null and the alternative hypotheses to test if the bottling process is inaccurate.

b. What are the value of the test statistic and the *p*-value?

c. At $\alpha = 0.05$, what is the conclusion to the hypothesis test? Make a recommendation to the bottler.

29. **FILE** *MV_Houses.* The accompanying data file shows the selling price (in $1,000s) for 36 recent house sales in Mission Viejo, California. A Realtor believes that the average price of a house is more than $500,000. Assume the population standard deviation is $100 (in $1,000s).

a. State the null and the alternative hypotheses for the test.

b. What are the value of the test statistic and the *p*-value?

c. At $\alpha = 0.05$, what is the conclusion to the hypothesis test? Is the Realtor's claim supported by the data?

30. **FILE** *Home.* The accompanying data file shows the weekly stock price (Price in $) for a home improvement store. Assume that stock prices are normally distributed with a population standard deviation of $3.

a. State the null and the alternative hypotheses in order to test whether or not the average weekly stock price differs from $30.

b. Find the value of the test statistic and the *p*-value.

c. At $\alpha = 0.05$, can you conclude that the average weekly stock price does not equal $30?

31. **FILE** *Hourly_Wage.* The accompanying data file shows hourly wages (Wage in $) for 50 employees. An economist wants to test if the average hourly wage is less than $22. Assume that the population standard deviation is $6.

a. State the null and the alternative hypotheses for the test.

b. Find the value of the test statistic and the *p*-value.

c. At $\alpha = 0.05$, what is the conclusion to the hypothesis test? Is the average hourly wage less than $22?

32. **FILE** *Undergrad_Debt.* The accompanying data file lists the student debt for 40 recent undergraduates. A researcher believes that average student debt is more than $25,000. Assume that the population standard deviation is $5,000.

a. Specify the competing hypotheses to test the researcher's belief.

b. Find the value of the test statistic and the *p*-value.

c. Do the data support the researcher's claim, at $\alpha = 0.10$?

33. **FILE** *Stock_Return.* The accompanying data file shows the annual return for a stock over the past 25 years (Return in %). An investor wants to test whether the average return on the stock is greater than 12%. Assume returns are normally distributed with a population standard deviation of 30%.

a. State the null and the alternative hypotheses for the test.

b. Calculate the value of the test statistic and the *p*-value.

c. At $\alpha = 0.05$, what is the conclusion to the hypothesis test? Is the average stock return greater than 12%?

34. **FILE** *MI_Life.* The average life expectancy for residents of Hawaii is 81.48 years (travelandleisure.com, July 16, 2018). A sociologist collects data on the age at death for 50 recently deceased Michigan residents as shown in the accompanying data file. Assume that the population standard deviation is 5 years.

a. The sociologist believes that the average life expectancy for Michigan residents is less than the average life expectancy for Hawaii residents. Specify the competing hypotheses to test this belief.

b. Calculate the value of the test statistic and the *p*-value.

c. At the 1% significance level, do the data support the sociologist's belief?

9.3 HYPOTHESIS TEST FOR THE POPULATION MEAN WHEN σ IS UNKNOWN

LO 9.4

So far we have considered hypothesis tests for the population mean μ under the assumption that the population standard deviation σ is known. In most business applications, σ is not known and we replace σ with the sample standard deviation s to estimate the standard error of $\overline{X}$ and the resulting t_{df} test statistic. The following definition box shows the formula for the test statistic when testing the population mean μ when the population standard deviation σ is unknown.

Conduct a hypothesis test for the population mean when σ is unknown.

> ### THE TEST STATISTIC FOR μ WHEN σ IS UNKNOWN
>
> The value of the test statistic for the hypothesis test of the population mean μ when the population standard deviation σ is unknown is computed as
>
> $$t_{df} = \frac{\bar{x} - \mu_0}{s/\sqrt{n}},$$
>
> where t_{df} is the standardized value of $\bar{x}$, μ_0 is the hypothesized value of the population mean, and the degrees of freedom $df = n - 1$. This formula is valid only if $\bar{X}$ (approximately) follows a normal distribution.

In the next two examples, we conduct hypothesis tests for the population mean μ when the population standard deviation σ is unknown.

FILE

Study_Hours

EXAMPLE 9.8

In the introductory case to this chapter, the assistant dean of students at a large university in California wonders if students at her university study less than the 1961 national average of 24 hours per week. She randomly selects 35 students and asks their average study time per week (in hours). From their responses, she calculates a sample mean of 16.3714 hours and a sample standard deviation of 7.2155 hours.

a. Specify the competing hypotheses to test the assistant dean's concern.

b. Calculate the value of the test statistic.

c. Find the p-value.

d. At the 5% significance level, what is the conclusion to the hypothesis test?

SOLUTION:

a. This is an example of a one-tailed test where we would like to determine if the mean hours studied is less than 24; that is, $\mu < 24$. We formulate the competing hypotheses as

$$H_0: \mu \geq 24 \text{ hours}$$
$$H_A: \mu < 24 \text{ hours}$$

b. Recall that for any statistical inference regarding the population mean, it is essential that the sample mean $\bar{X}$ is normally distributed. This condition is satisfied because the sample size is greater than 30, specifically, $n = 35$. The degrees of freedom, $df = n - 1 = 34$. Given $\bar{x} = 16.3714$ and $s = 7.2155$, we compute the value of the test statistic as

$$t_{34} = \frac{\bar{x} - \mu_0}{s/\sqrt{n}} = \frac{16.3714 - 24}{7.2155/\sqrt{35}} = -6.255.$$

c. Even though Excel offers a number of functions that generate p-values, we use the **T.DIST** function. If we enter =T.DIST(t_{df}, df, TRUE), where t_{df} is the value of the test statistic and df is the relevant degrees of freedom, then Excel returns the cumulative probability $P(T_{df} \leq t_{df})$, which is the p-value for a left-tailed test. If we enter =1 - T.DIST(t_{df}, df, TRUE), then Excel returns $P(T_{df} \geq t_{df})$, which is the p-value for a right-tailed test. As with the z-test, the p-value for a two-tailed test is $2 \times P(T_{df} \leq t_{df})$ if $t_{df} < 0$ or $2 \times P(T_{df} \geq t_{df})$ if $t_{df} > 0$. (We rarely use FALSE instead of TRUE as an input in the **T.DIST** function; this input is useful if we are interested in plotting the distribution.)

In order to find the *p*-value for this left-tailed test, or equivalently $P(T_{df} \le -6.255)$, we enter =T.DIST(-6.255, 34, TRUE). Excel returns 2.01306E-07, which when rounded to four decimal places is equal to 0.0000.

d. We reject the null hypothesis because the *p*-value of 0.0000 is less than $\alpha = 0.05$. At the 5% significance level, we conclude that the average study time at the university is less than the 1961 average of 24 hours per week.

In Example 9.8, we were given summary statistics to conduct the hypothesis test. In Example 9.9, we use raw data to conduct the hypothesis test.

EXAMPLE 9.9

As mentioned in the introductory case to this chapter, research finds that today's undergraduates study an average of 14 hours per week. Using the ***Study_Hours*** data file, the assistant dean would also like to test if the mean study time of students at her university differs from today's national average of 14 hours per week. At the 5% significance level, what is the conclusion to this hypothesis test?

FILE

Study_Hours

SOLUTION: Because the assistant dean would like to test if the mean study time of students at her university differs from 14 hours per week, we formulate the competing hypotheses for the test as

$$H_0: \mu = 14 \text{ hours}$$
$$H_A: \mu \ne 14 \text{ hours}$$

a. Open the ***Study_Hours*** data file. Note that the values for hours studied are in cells B2 through B36.

b. We use Excel's **AVERAGE** and **STDEV.S** functions to help in the calculation of the value of the test statistic $t_{df} = \frac{\bar{x} - \mu}{s/\sqrt{n}}$. We enter =(AVERAGE(B2:B36) - 14)/ (STDEV.S(B2:B36)/SQRT(35)). Excel returns 1.9444, so $t_{34} = 1.9444$.

c. In order to find the *p*-value for the two-tailed test where $t_{34} = 1.9444$, we enter =2*(1-T.DIST(1.9444, 34, TRUE)). Excel returns 0.0602.

d. Because the *p*-value of 0.0602 is not less than $\alpha = 0.05$, we do not reject the null hypothesis. At the 5% significance level, we cannot conclude that the mean study time of students at the university is different from today's national average of 14 hours per week.

SYNOPSIS OF INTRODUCTORY CASE

A report claims that undergraduates are studying far less today as compared to six decades ago (*The Wall Street Journal,* April 10, 2019). The report finds that in 1961, students invested 24 hours per week in their academic pursuits, whereas today's students study an average of 14 hours per week. In an attempt to determine whether or not this national trend is present at a large university in California, 35 students are randomly selected and asked their average study time per week (in hours). The sample produces a mean of 16.37 hours with a standard deviation of 7.22 hours. Two hypothesis tests are conducted. The first test examines whether the mean study time of students at this university is below the 1961 national average of 24 hours per week. At the 5% significance level, the sample data

Asia Images Group/Getty Images

suggest that the mean is less than 24 hours per week. The second test investigates whether the mean study time of students at this university differs from today's national average of 14 hours per week. At the 5% significance level, the results do not suggest that the mean study time differs from 14 hours per week. Thus, the sample results support the overall findings of the report: Undergraduates study, on average, 14 hours per week, far below the 1961 average of 24 hours per week. The present analysis, however, does not explain why that might be the case. For instance, it cannot be determined whether students are devoting less time to their studies, or if, with the advent of the computer, they can access information in less time.

EXERCISES 9.3

Mechanics

35. Consider the following hypotheses:

$$H_0: \mu \leq 210$$
$$H_A: \mu > 210$$

Find the p-value for this hypothesis test based on the following sample information.

a. $\bar{x} = 216; s = 26; n = 40$
b. $\bar{x} = 216; s = 26; n = 80$
c. $\bar{x} = 216; s = 16; n = 40$
d. $\bar{x} = 214; s = 16; n = 40$

36. Which of the sample information in the preceding question enables us to reject the null hypothesis at $\alpha = 0.01$ and at $\alpha = 0.10$?

37. Consider the following hypotheses:

$$H_0: \mu = 12$$
$$H_A: \mu \neq 12$$

Find the p-value for this hypothesis test based on the following sample information.

a. $\bar{x} = 11; s = 3.2; n = 36$
b. $\bar{x} = 13; s = 3.2; n = 36$
c. $\bar{x} = 11; s = 2.8; n = 36$
d. $\bar{x} = 11; s = 2.8; n = 49$

38. Which of the sample information in the preceding question enables us to reject the null hypothesis at $\alpha = 0.01$ and at $\alpha = 0.10$?

39. Consider the following hypotheses:

$$H_0: \mu = 50$$
$$H_A: \mu \neq 50$$

A sample of 16 observations yields a sample mean of 46. Assume that the sample is drawn from a normal population with a sample standard deviation of 10.

a. Calculate the value of the test statistic.
b. At the 5% significance level, does the population mean differ from 50? Explain.

40. In order to test if the population mean differs from 16, you draw a random sample of 32 observations and compute the sample mean and the sample standard deviation as 15.2 and 0.6, respectively. Conduct the hypothesis test at the 1% level of significance.

41. In order to conduct a hypothesis test for the population mean, a random sample of 24 observations is drawn from a normally distributed population. The resulting sample mean and sample standard deviation are calculated as 4.8 and 0.8, respectively. Conduct the following tests at $\alpha = 0.05$.

a. $H_0: \mu \leq 4.5$ against $H_A: \mu > 4.5$
b. $H_0: \mu = 4.5$ against $H_A: \mu \neq 4.5$

42. Consider the following hypotheses:

$$H_0: \mu \geq -10$$
$$H_A: \mu < -10$$

A sample of 25 observations yields a sample mean of -12. Assume that the sample is drawn from a normal population with a sample standard deviation of 4.

a. Calculate the value of the test statistic.
b. At the 5% significance level, is the population mean less than -10? Explain.

43. Consider the following hypotheses:

$$H_0: \mu = 8$$
$$H_A: \mu \neq 8$$

The population is normally distributed. A sample produces the following observations:

6	9	8	7	7	11	10

Conduct the hypothesis test at the 5% level of significance.

44. Consider the following hypotheses:

$$H_0: \mu \geq 100$$
$$H_A: \mu < 100$$

The population is normally distributed. A sample produces the following observations:

95	99	85	80	98	97

Conduct the hypothesis test at the 1% level of significance.

Applications

45. A machine that is programmed to package 1.20 pounds of cereal in each cereal box is being tested for its accuracy. In a sample of 36 cereal boxes, the mean and the standard deviation are calculated as 1.22 pounds and 0.06 pound, respectively.
    a. Set up the null and the alternative hypotheses to determine if the machine is working improperly—that is, it is either underfilling or overfilling the cereal boxes.
    b. Calculate the value of the test statistic and the p-value.
    c. At the 5% level of significance, can you conclude that the machine is working improperly? Explain.

46. The manager of a small convenience store does not want her customers standing in line for too long prior to a purchase. In particular, she is willing to hire an employee for another cash register if the average wait time of the customers is more than five minutes. She randomly observes the wait time (in minutes) for 20 customers and calculates a mean and standard deviation of 6.5 and 2.2, respectively.
    a. Set up the null and the alternative hypotheses to determine if the manager needs to hire another employee.
    b. Calculate the value of the test statistic and the p-value. What assumption regarding the population is necessary to implement this step?
    c. Decide whether the manager needs to hire another employee at $\alpha = 0.10$.

47. **FILE** *Prime.* Amazon Prime is a $139-per-year service that gives the company's customers free two-day shipping and discounted rates on overnight delivery. Prime customers also get other perks, such as free e-books. An analyst believes that Prime customers spend more than $1,200 per year on this service. The accompanying data file shows the annual expenditures (Expenditures in $) of 100 Prime customers.
    a. Specify the null and alternative hypotheses to test the analyst's claim.
    b. Calculate the value of the test statistic and the p-value.
    c. At the 5% significance level, what is the conclusion to the hypothesis test? Is the analyst's claim supported by the sample data?

48. A local brewery wishes to ensure that an average of 12 ounces of beer is used to fill each bottle. In order to analyze the accuracy of the bottling process, the bottler takes a random sample of 48 bottles. The sample mean weight and the sample standard deviation of the bottles are 11.80 ounces and 0.8 ounce, respectively.
    a. State the null and the alternative hypotheses to test if the accuracy of the bottling process is compromised.
    b. Do you need to make any assumption regarding the population before implementing the hypothesis test?
    c. Calculate the value of the test statistic and the p-value.
    d. At $\alpha = 0.05$, what is the conclusion to the hypothesis test? Make a recommendation to the bottler.

49. Based on the average predictions of 45 economists, the U.S. gross domestic product (GDP) will expand by 2.8% this year. Suppose the sample standard deviation of their predictions was 1%. At the 5% significance level, test if the mean forecast GDP of all economists is less than 3%.

50. This past year, home prices in the Midwest increased by an average of 6.6%. A Realtor collects data on 36 recent home sales in the West. He finds an average increase in home prices of 7.5% with a standard deviation of 2%. Can he conclude that the average increase in home prices in the West is greater than the increase in the Midwest? Use a 5% significance level for the analysis.

51. A car manufacturer is trying to develop a new sports car. Engineers are hoping that the average amount of time that the car takes to go from 0 to 60 miles per hour is below 6 seconds. The manufacturer tested 12 of the cars and clocked their performance times. Three of the cars clocked in at 5.8 seconds, 5 cars at 5.9 seconds, 3 cars at 6.0 seconds, and 1 car at 6.1 seconds. At the 5% level of significance, test if the new sports car is meeting its goal to go from 0 to 60 miles per hour in less than 6 seconds. Assume a normal distribution for the analysis.

52. **FILE** *APR.* A mortgage analyst collects data from seven financial institutions on the mortgage rate for a 30-year fixed loan. The data file accompanying this exercise show the results (APR in %).
    a. State the null and the alternative hypothesis in order to test whether the mean mortgage rate for the population exceeds 4.2%.
    b. What assumption regarding the population is necessary in order to implement part a?
    c. Calculate the value of the test statistic and the p-value.
    d. At a 10% significance level, what is the conclusion to the hypothesis test? Does the mean mortgage rate for the population exceed 4.2%?

53. **FILE** *PE_Ratio.* A price-earnings ratio or P/E ratio is calculated as a firm's share price compared to the income or profit earned by the firm per share. Generally, a high P/E ratio suggests that investors are expecting higher earnings growth in the future compared to firms with a lower P/E ratio. The data file accompanying this exercise show P/E ratios for 30 firms.
    a. State the null and the alternative hypotheses in order to test whether the P/E ratio of all firms differs from 15.
    b. Calculate the value of the test statistic and the p-value.
    c. At $\alpha = 0.05$, does the P/E ratio of all firms differ from 15? Explain.

54. **FILE** *MPG.* The accompanying data files shows the miles per gallon (MPG) for 25 hybrid SUVs.
    a. State the null and the alternative hypotheses in order to test whether the average MPG differs from 50.
    b. Calculate the value of the test statistic and the p-value.
    c. At $\alpha = 0.05$, can you conclude that the average MPG differs from 50?

55. **FILE** *Debt_Payments.* The accompanying data file shows the average debt payments (Debt, in $) for 26 metropolitan areas.

   a. State the null and the alternative hypotheses in order to test whether average monthly debt payments are greater than $900.

   b. What assumption regarding the population is necessary in order to implement part a?

   c. Calculate the value of the test statistic and the p-value.

   d. At $\alpha = 0.05$, are average monthly debt payments greater than $900? Explain.

56. **FILE** *Highway_Speeds.* A police officer is concerned about speeds on a certain section of Interstate 95. The accompanying data file shows the speeds (Speed in mph) for 40 cars on a Saturday afternoon.

   a. The speed limit on this portion of Interstate 95 is 65 mph. Specify the competing hypotheses in order to determine if the average speed is greater than the speed limit.

   b. Calculate the value of the test statistic and the p-value.

   c. At $\alpha = 0.01$, are the officer's concerns warranted? Explain.

57. **FILE** *Lottery.* An article found that Massachusetts residents spent an average of $860.70 on the lottery, more than three times the U.S. average. A researcher at a Boston think tank believes that Massachusetts residents spend less than this amount. He surveys 100 Massachusetts residents and asks them about their annual expenditures on the lottery. The accompanying data file shows the responses (Expenditure in $).

   a. Specify the competing hypotheses to test the researcher's claim.

   b. Calculate the value of the test statistic and the p-value.

   c. At the 10% significance level, do the data support the researcher's claim? Explain.

58. An advertisement for a popular weight loss clinic suggests that participants in its new diet program lose, on average, more than 10 pounds. A consumer activist decides to test the authenticity of the claim. She follows the progress of 18 participants who recently joined the weight reduction program. She calculates the mean weight loss of these participants as 10.8 pounds with a standard deviation of 2.4 pounds.

   a. Set up the competing hypotheses to test the advertisement's claim.

   b. Calculate the value of the test statistic and the p-value.

   c. At the 5% significance level, what does the consumer activist conclude?

59. A promising start-up wants to compete in the cell phone market. It understands that the lead product has a battery life of approximately 12 hours. The start-up claims that while its new cell phone is more expensive, its battery life is more than twice as long as that of the leading product. In order to test the claim, a researcher samples 45 units of the new cell phone and finds that the sample battery life averages 24.5 hours with a sample standard deviation of 1.8 hours.

   a. Set up the competing hypotheses to test the start-up's claim.

   b. Calculate the value of the test statistic and the p-value.

   c. Test the start-up's claim at $\alpha = 0.05$.

60. A city council is deciding whether or not to spend additional money to reduce the amount of traffic. The council decides that it will increase the transportation budget if the amount of waiting time for drivers exceeds 20 minutes. A sample of 32 main roads results in a mean waiting time of 22.08 minutes with a standard deviation of 5.42 minutes. Conduct a hypothesis test at the 1% level of significance to determine whether or not the city should increase its transportation budget.

61. **FILE** *Rental.* A real estate analyst examines the rental market in a college town. The accompanying data file shows the data that she has gathered on the monthly rent and the square footage for 40 rentals.

   a. The analyst believes that the average monthly rent is less than $1,400. At the 5% significance level, is her belief supported by the data?

   b. The analyst believes that the average square footage is more than 1,200 square feet. At the 5% significance level, is her belief supported by the data?

62. **FILE** *Convenience_Stores.* An entrepreneur examines monthly sales (Sales in $1,000s) for 40 convenience stores in Rhode Island.

   a. State the null and the alternative hypotheses in order to test whether average sales differ from $130,000.

   b. Calculate the value of the test statistic and the p-value.

   c. At $\alpha = 0.05$, what is your conclusion to the hypothesis test? Do average sales differ from $130,000?

63. **FILE** *DJIA_Volume.* A portfolio analyst wonders if the average trading volume on the Dow Jones Industrial Average (DJIA) has decreased since the beginning of the year. The accompanying data files shows the trading volume (Volume in millions) for the past 30 days.

   a. The average trading volume in the beginning of the year was about 4,000 shares (in millions). Specify the competing hypotheses to test the analyst's claim.

   b. Calculate the value of the test statistic and the p-value.

   c. At the 5% significance level, does it appear that the trading volume has decreased since the beginning of the year?

9.4 HYPOTHESIS TEST FOR THE POPULATION PROPORTION

LO 9.5

Conduct a hypothesis test for the population proportion.

Recall that the population mean μ describes a numerical variable whereas the population proportion p is the essential descriptive measure for a categorical variable. The parameter p represents the proportion of observations with a particular attribute, labeled as success. As in the case for the population mean, we estimate the population proportion on the basis of its sample counterpart. In particular, we use the sample proportion $\bar{p} = x/n$ as an estimate of p where x denotes the number of successes in n observations.

Recall from Chapter 7 that the mean and the standard error of the estimator $\bar{P} = X/n$ are given by $E(\bar{P}) = p$ and $se(\bar{P}) = \sqrt{p(1-p)/n}$, respectively. The following definition box shows the formula for the test statistic when testing the population proportion p.

THE TEST STATISTIC FOR p

The value of the test statistic for the hypothesis test of the population proportion p is computed as

$$z = \frac{\bar{p} - p_0}{\sqrt{p_0(1-p_0)/n}},$$

where z is the standardized value of $\bar{p}$ and p_0 is the hypothesized value of the population proportion. This formula is valid only if $\bar{P}$ (approximately) follows a normal distribution.

The normal distribution approximation is justified in large samples; in particular, when $np \geq 5$ and $n(1-p) \geq 5$. Because p is not known, we evaluate this requirement under the hypothesized value of the population proportion p_0.

The following examples elaborate on the four-step procedure for a hypothesis test for the population proportion.

EXAMPLE 9.10

A popular weekly magazine asserts that fewer than 40% of households in the United States have changed their lifestyles because of environmental concerns. A recent survey of 180 households finds that 67 households have made lifestyle changes due to environmental concerns.

a. Specify the competing hypotheses to test the magazine's claim.

b. Calculate the value of the test statistic and the p-value.

c. At the 5% level of significance, what is the conclusion to the hypothesis test?

SOLUTION:

a. We wish to establish that the population proportion is less than 0.40—that is, $p < 0.40$. Thus, we construct the competing hypotheses as

$$H_0: p \geq 0.40$$
$$H_A: p < 0.40$$

b. When evaluated at $p_0 = 0.40$ with $n = 180$, the normality requirement that $np \geq 5$ and $n(1-p) \geq 5$ is satisfied. We use the sample proportion, $\bar{p} = 67/180 = 0.3722$, to compute the value of the test statistic as

$$z = \frac{\bar{p} - p_0}{\sqrt{P_0(1-p_0)/n}} = \frac{0.3722 - 0.40}{\sqrt{0.40(1-0.40)/180}} = -0.7613.$$

Because this is a left-tailed test for the population proportion, we find the p-value as $P(Z \le z) = P(Z \le -0.7613) = 0.2232$. In order to find the p-value in Excel, we enter =NORM.DIST(-0.7613,0,1,TRUE).

c. The p-value of 0.2232 is greater than the chosen $\alpha = 0.05$. Therefore, we do not reject the null hypothesis. This means that the magazine's claim that fewer than 40% of households in the United States have changed their lifestyles because of environmental concerns is not justified by the sample data at the 5% significance level. Such a conclusion may be welcomed by firms that have invested in alternative energy.

EXAMPLE 9.11

Driven by growing public support, the legalization of marijuana in America has been moving at a breakneck speed. Approximately 67% of adults say the use of marijuana should be made legal (www.pewresearch.org, November 14, 2019). A health practitioner in Ohio collects data from 200 adults and finds that 122 of them favor marijuana legalization.

a. The health practitioner believes that the proportion of adults who favor marijuana legalization in Ohio is not representative of the national proportion. Specify the competing hypotheses to test his claim.

b. Calculate the value of the test statistic and the p-value.

c. At the 10% significance level, do the sample data support the health practitioner's belief?

SOLUTION:

a. The parameter of interest is again the population proportion p. The health practitioner wants to test if the population proportion of those who favor marijuana legalization in Ohio differs from the national proportion of 0.67. We construct the competing hypotheses as

$$H_0: p = 0.67$$
$$H_A: p \ne 0.67$$

b. When evaluated at $p_0 = 0.67$ with $n = 200$, the normality requirement that $np \ge 5$ and $n(1 - p) \ge 5$ is easily satisfied. We use the sample proportion $\bar{p} = 122/200 = 0.61$ to compute the value of the test statistic as

$$z = \frac{\bar{p} - p_0}{\sqrt{p_0(1 - p_0)/n}} = \frac{0.61 - 0.67}{\sqrt{0.67(1 - 0.67)/200}} = -1.8046$$

Given a two-tailed test and $z < 0$, we compute the p-value as $2 \times P(Z \le z) = 2 \times P(Z \le -1.8046) = 0.0711$. In order to find the p-value in Excel, we enter =2*NORM.DIST(-1.8046,0,1,TRUE).

c. Because the p-value of 0.0711 is less than $\alpha = 0.10$, we reject the null hypothesis. Therefore, at the 10% significance level, the proportion of adults who favor marijuana legalization in Ohio differs from the national proportion of 0.67.

EXERCISES 9.4

Mechanics

64. Consider the following hypotheses:

$$H_0: p \geq 0.38$$
$$H_A: p < 0.38$$

Calculate the p-value based on the following sample information.

a. $x = 22; n = 74$
b. $x = 110; n = 300$
c. $\bar{p} = 0.34; n = 50$
d. $\bar{p} = 0.34; n = 400$

65. Which sample information in the preceding question enables us to reject the null hypothesis at $\alpha = 0.01$ and at $\alpha = 0.10$?

66. Consider the following hypotheses

$$H_0: p = 0.32$$
$$H_A: p \neq 0.32$$

Calculate the p-value based on the following sample information

a. $x = 20; n = 66$
b. $x = 100; n = 264$
c. $\bar{p} = 0.40; n = 40$
d. $\bar{p} = 0.38; n = 180$

67. Which sample information in the preceding question enables us to reject the null hypothesis at $\alpha = 0.05$ and at $\alpha = 0.10$?

68. In order to test if the population proportion differs from 0.40, you draw a random sample of 100 observations and obtain a sample proportion of 0.48.

a. Specify the competing hypotheses.
b. Is the normality condition satisfied? Explain.
c. Calculate the value of the test statistic and the p-value.
d. At the 5% significance level, does the population proportion differ from 0.40? Explain.

69. In order to conduct a hypothesis test for the population proportion, you sample 320 observations that result in 128 successes. Conduct the following tests at $\alpha = 0.05$.

a. $H_0: p \geq 0.45; H_A: p < 0.45$
b. $H_0: p = 0.45; H_A: p \neq 0.45$

70. In order to test if the population proportion is greater than 0.65, you draw a random sample of 200 observations and obtain a sample proportion of 0.72.

a. Specify the competing hypotheses.
b. Is the normality condition satisfied? Explain.
c. Calculate the value of the test statistic and the p-value.
d. At the 5% significance level, is the population proportion greater than 0.65? Explain.

71. You would like to determine if the population probability of success differs from 0.70. You find 62 successes in 80 binomial trials. Implement the test at the 1% level of significance.

72. You would like to determine if more than 50% of the observations in a population are below 10. At $\alpha = 0.05$, conduct the test on the basis of the following 20 sample observations:

8	12	5	9	14	11	9	3	7	8
12	6	8	9	2	6	11	4	13	10

Applications

73. A study finds that 82% of employees will likely quit because of lack of progression at the job (msn.com, January 14, 2020). A human resources manager would like to determine whether the percentage has decreased due to uncertainty in the job market. The manager conducts an anonymous survey and finds that 150 out of 200 employees will likely quit because of lack of progression at the job.

a. State the null and the alternative hypotheses to test the manager's claim.
b. What is the value of the test statistic? What is the p-value?
c. At $\alpha = 0.05$, is the manager's claim supported by the data? Explain.

74. An economist is concerned that more than 20% of American households have raided their retirement accounts to endure financial hardships such as unemployment and medical emergencies. He randomly surveys 190 households with retirement accounts and finds that 50 are borrowing against them.

a. Set up the null and the alternative hypotheses to test the economist's concern.
b. Calculate the value of the test statistic and the p-value.
c. Determine if the economist's concern is justifiable at $\alpha = 0.05$.

75. The margarita is one of the most common tequila-based cocktails, made with tequila mixed with triple sec and lime or lemon juice, often served with salt on the glass rim. A common ratio for a margarita is 2:1:1, which includes 50% tequila, 25% triple sec, and 25% fresh lime or lemon juice. A manager at a local bar is concerned that the bartender uses incorrect proportions in more than 50% of margaritas. He secretly observes the bartender and finds that he used the correct proportions in only 10 out of 30 margaritas. Test if the manager's suspicion is justified at $\alpha = 0.05$.

76. Many financial institutions are unwittingly training their online customers to take risks with their passwords and other sensitive account information, leaving them more vulnerable to fraud. Researchers at the University of Michigan found design flaws in 78% of the 214 financial institution websites they studied. Is the sample evidence sufficient to conclude that more than three out of four of these websites are prone to fraud? Use a 5% significance level for the test.

77. A report suggests that older workers are the happiest employees. It documents that 70% of older workers in Europe feel fulfilled, compared with just 50% of younger workers. A demographer believes that an identical pattern does not exist in Asia. A survey of 120 older workers in Asia finds that 75 feel fulfilled. A similar survey finds that 58% of 210 younger workers feel fulfilled.

    a. At the 5% level of significance, test if older workers in Asia feel less fulfilled than their European counterparts.

    b. At the 5% level of significance, test if younger workers in Asia feel more fulfilled than their European counterparts.

78. A politician claims that he is supported by a clear majority of voters. In a recent survey, 24 out of 40 randomly selected voters indicated that they would vote for the politician. Is the politician's claim justified at the 5% level of significance?

79. A movie production company is releasing a movie with the hopes of many viewers returning to see the movie in the theater for a second time. Their target is to have 30 million viewers, and they want more than 30% of the viewers to want to see the movie again. They show the movie to a test audience of 200 people, and after the movie they asked them if they would see the movie in theaters again. Of the test audience, 68 people said they would see the movie again.

    a. At the 5% level of significance, test if more than 30% of the viewers will return to see the movie again.

    b. Repeat the analysis at the 10% level of significance.

    c. Interpret your results.

80. With increasing out-of-pocket healthcare costs, it is claimed that more than 60% of older adults are likely to make serious adjustments to their lifestyle. Test this claim at the 1% level of significance if in a survey of 140 older adults, 90 reported that they have made serious adjustments to their lifestyle.

81. **FILE** *Silicon_Valley.* An analyst is exploring workforce diversity at a large high-tech firm in Silicon Valley. The accompanying data file shows sex and ethnicity information for 50 employees at the firm.

    a. At the 5% level of significance, determine if the proportion of women at the firm is different from 0.30.

    b. At the 5% level of significance, determine if the proportion of white employees is more than 0.50.

82. According to a poll, 33% of those surveyed said America was headed in the right direction. Suppose this poll was based on a sample of 1,000 people. Does the sample evidence suggest that the proportion of Americans who feel that America is headed in the right direction is below 35%? Use a 5% level of significance for the analysis. What if the sample size was 2,000?

83. A retailer is looking to evaluate its customer service. Management has determined that if the retailer wants to stay competitive, then it will have to have at least a 90% satisfaction rate among its customers. Management will take corrective actions if the satisfaction rate falls below 90%. A survey of 1,200 customers showed that 1,068 were satisfied with their customer service.

    a. State the hypotheses to test if the retailer needs to improve its services.

    b. What is the value of the test statistic?

    c. Find the *p*-value.

    d. Interpret the results at $\alpha = 0.05$.

84. One-fifth of Britons are not using the Internet (bbc.com, September 9, 2019). A researcher believes that the proportion of Americans who do not use the Internet is less than Britain's proportion. She surveys 200 Americans and finds that 30 of them do not use the Internet. Test the researcher's claim at the 5% significance level.

85. A television network is deciding whether or not to give its newest television show a spot during prime viewing time at night. For this to happen, it will have to move one of its most viewed shows to another slot. The network conducts a survey asking its viewers which show they would rather watch. The network will keep its current lineup of shows unless the majority of the customers want to watch the new show. The network receives 827 responses, of which 428 indicate that they would like to see the new show in the lineup.

    a. Set up the hypotheses to test if the television network should give its newest television show a spot during prime viewing time at night.

    b. Calculate the value of the test statistic and the *p*-value.

    c. At $\alpha = 0.01$, what should the television network do?

86. A survey finds that 17% of Americans cannot part with their landlines. A researcher in the rural South collects data from 200 households and finds that 45 of them still have landlines.

    a. The researcher believes that the proportion of households with landlines in the rural South is not representative of the national proportion. Specify the competing hypotheses to test his claim.

    b. Calculate the value of the test statistic and the *p*-value.

    c. At the 5% significance level, do the sample data support the researcher's belief?

87. **FILE** *Study_Hard.* A report suggests that business majors spend the least amount of time on course work than do all other college students. A provost of a university conducts a survey of 50 business and 50 nonbusiness students. Students are asked if they study hard, defined as spending at least 20 hours per week on course work. The accompanying data file shows the responses where Yes indicates that the student studies hard and No indicates otherwise.

    a. At the 5% level of significance, determine if the percentage of business majors who study hard is less than 20%.

    b. At the 5% level of significance, determine if the percentage of nonbusiness majors who study hard is more than 20%.

88. According to a survey, half of U.S. households have no emergency savings (*The Wall Street Journal,* April 16, 2020). An analyst in the Midwest collects data on 200 households and finds that 84 of them have no emergency savings.

    a. The analyst believes that the proportion of Midwestern households with no emergency savings is not representative of the national proportion. Specify the competing hypotheses to test the analyst's claim.

    b. Calculate the value of the test statistic and the *p*-value.

    c. At the 1% significance level, do the sample data support the analyst's claim?

9.5 WRITING WITH DATA

Case Study

According to a 2018 paper released by the Economic Policy Institute, a non-profit, nonpartisan think tank in Washington, D.C., income inequality continues to grow in the United States. Over the years, the rich have become richer while working-class wages have stagnated. A local politician has been vocal regarding his concern about the the financial well-being of low-income households. In various speeches, he has stated that the mean salary of low-income households in his county has fallen below the 2017 mean of approximately $50,000. He has also stated that the population of low-income households making less than $30,000 has risen above the 2017 level of 20%. Both of his statements are based on income data for 36 low-income households in the county. A portion of the data is shown in Table 9.3.

Rido/Shutterstock

TABLE 9.3 Household Income (in $1,000s)

FILE

Income

Household	Income
1	23
2	63
⋮	⋮
36	47

Andy Huang is a newspaper reporter who is interested in verifying the concerns of the local politician. He uses the sample information to determine if the mean income of low-income households has fallen below the 2017 level of $50,000, and if the percentage of low-income households making less than $30,000 has risen above 20%.

Sample Report— Income Inequality in the United States

One of the hotly debated topics in the United States is that of growing income inequality. This trend, which has picked up post Great Recession, is a reversal of what was seen during and after the Great Depression, where the gap between rich and poor narrowed. Market forces such as increased trade and technological advances have made highly skilled and well-educated workers more productive, thus increasing their pay. Institutional forces, such as deregulation, the decline of unions, and the stagnation of the minimum wage, have contributed to income inequality.

A sample of 36 low-income households resulted in a mean household income of $47,278 with a standard deviation of $19,524. The sample mean is below the 2017 level of $50,000. In addition, eight of the households, or approximately 22%, make less than $30,000. Based on these results, a politician concludes that current market conditions continue to negatively impact the welfare of low-income households. However, it is essential to provide statistically significant evidence to substantiate these claims. Toward this end, formal tests of hypotheses regarding the population mean and the population proportion are conducted. The results of the tests are summarized in Table 9.4.

TABLE 9.4 Test Statistic Values and *p*-Values for Hypothesis Tests

Hypotheses	Test Statistic Value	*p*-value
$H_0: \mu \geq 50$ $H_A: \mu < 50$	$t_{35} = \dfrac{47.278 - 50}{19.524/\sqrt{36}} = -0.837$	0.204
$H_0: p \leq 0.20$ $H_A: p > 0.20$	$z = \dfrac{0.222 - 0.20}{\sqrt{\dfrac{(0.20)(0.80)}{36}}} = 0.333$	0.369

Given the *p*-value of 0.204, the null hypothesis regarding the population mean, specified in Table 9.4, cannot be rejected at any reasonable level of significance. Similarly, given the *p*-value of 0.369, the null hypothesis regarding the population proportion cannot be rejected. Therefore, sample evidence does not support the claims that the mean income of low-income households has fallen below $50,000 or that the proportion of low-income households making less than $30,000 has risen above 20%. Perhaps the politician's remarks were based on a cursory look at the sample statistics and not on a thorough statistical analysis.

Suggested Case Studies

Report 9.1 `FILE` *Wellbeing.* The Gallup-Healthways Well-Being Index provides an assessment measure of health and well-being of U.S. residents. The overall composite score is calculated on a scale from 0 to 100, where 100 represents fully realized well-being. In 2017, the overall well-being of American residents was reported as 61.5—a decline from 62.1 in 2016. The accompanying data file shows the overall well-being score for a random sample of 35 residents from South Dakota—the state with the highest level of well-being. In a report, conduct hypothesis tests to (i) determine whether the well-being score of South Dakotans is more than the national average of 61.5 and (ii) determine if fewer than 40% of South Dakotans report a score below 50. Use a reasonable significance level for the tests. Given your findings, comment on the well-being of South Dakotans at the chosen significance level.

Report 9.2 `FILE` *SPAM.* Peter Derby works as a cybersecurity analyst at a private equity firm. He has been asked to implement a spam detection system on the company's email server. He has access to a sample of 100 spam and legitimate emails with two variables: spam (1 if spam, 0 otherwise) and the number of hyperlinks in the message. Before implementing a spam detection system, he wants to better understand the company's emails. In a report, conduct hypothesis tests at a reasonable significance level to (i) determine whether more than 50% of the company's email are spam and (ii) determine whether the average number of hyperlinks is more than 5.

Report 9.3 `FILE` *Salary_MIS.* At the bachelor's degree level, recent graduates with a concentration in management information systems (MIS) continue to land high-paying, entry-level positions. This is due, in large part, to the concentration's linkage to the exploding field of data analytics. At a University of California campus, data were collected on the starting salary of business graduates (Salary in $1,000s) along with whether they have an MIS concentration (MIS = 1 if yes, 0 otherwise) and whether they have a statistics minor (Statistics = 1 if yes, 0 otherwise). In a report, use the sample information to compare the average salary of business students without an MIS concentration or a statistics minor with those who have (i) an MIS concentration but not a statistics minor, (ii) a statistics minor but not an MIS concentration, and (iii) an MIS concentration and a statistics minor. Then, conduct hypothesis tests to determine whether the average salary in the (i), (ii), and (iii) categories are greater than $70,000. Use a reasonable significance level for the tests.

APPENDIX 9.1 The Critical Value Approach

We always use sample evidence and the chosen significance level α to conduct hypothesis tests. The p-value approach makes the comparison in terms of probabilities. Recall that we find the value of the test statistic and use it to compute the p-value. We then compare the p-value with α in order to arrive at a decision to the hypothesis test. The critical value approach, on the other hand, makes the comparison directly in terms of the value of the test statistic.

As mentioned earlier, the critical value approach is attractive when calculations are done by hand and statistical tables are used for the analysis. Most statistics and business analytics professionals favor the p-value approach because virtually every statistical software package reports p-values. Both approaches, however, always lead to the same conclusion.

The critical value approach specifies a region of values, also called the **rejection region,** such that if the value of the test statistic falls into this region, then we reject the null hypothesis. **The critical value** is a point that separates the rejection region from the nonrejection region. Once again, we need to make distinctions between the three types of competing hypotheses. For the illustration, we assume that the test statistic follows the z distribution.

- For a left-tailed test, the critical value is $-z_\alpha$, where $P(Z \le -z_\alpha) = \alpha$. The resulting rejection region includes values less than $-z_\alpha$.
- For a right-tailed test, the critical value is z_α, where $P(Z \ge z_\alpha) = \alpha$. The resulting rejection region includes values greater than z_α.
- For a two-tailed test, there are two critical values; they are $-z_{\alpha/2}$ and $z_{\alpha/2}$, where $P(Z \ge z_{\alpha/2}) = \alpha/2$. The resulting rejection regions include values less than $-z_{\alpha/2}$ and values greater than $z_{\alpha/2}$.

For a given α, Figure A9.1 shows the three different scenarios of determining the critical value(s) depending on the specification of the competing hypotheses.

FIGURE A9.1 Critical values for one- and two-tailed tests

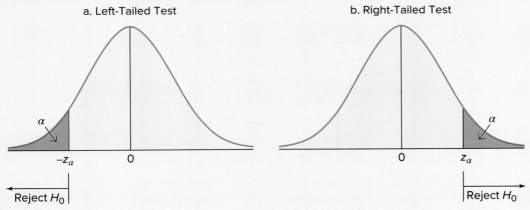

a. Left-Tailed Test

b. Right-Tailed Test

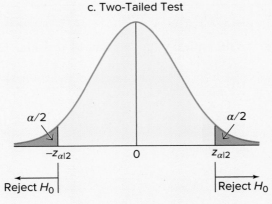

c. Two-Tailed Test

With α known, we can easily find the corresponding critical value(s) using Excel. Suppose we have a right-tailed test with $\alpha = 0.05$. The critical value is $z_{0.05}$. Recall that in order to find this critical value in Excel, we enter =NORM.INV(0.95, 0, 1), and Excel returns 1.645. Thus, the decision rule is to reject H_0 if the value of the test statistic z is greater than 1.645. Figure A9.2 shows this critical value as well as the corresponding rejection region.

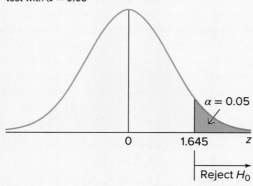

FIGURE A9.2 The critical value for a right-tailed test with $\alpha = 0.05$

We now summarize the general procedure for implementing the critical value approach.

THE FOUR-STEP PROCEDURE USING THE CRITICAL VALUE APPROACH

Step 1. Specify the null and the alternative hypotheses. This step is the same as in the *p*-value approach.

Step 2. Specify the significance level and find the critical value(s). If the test statistic follows the z distribution, then, for a given α, we find the critical value(s) as

- z_α where $P(Z \geq z_\alpha) = \alpha$ for a right-tailed test,
- $-z_\alpha$ where $P(Z \leq -z_\alpha) = \alpha$ for a left-tailed test, or
- $-z_{\alpha/2}$ and $z_{\alpha/2}$ where $P(Z \geq z_{\alpha/2}) = \alpha/2$ for a two-tailed test.

Z and z_α are replaced with T_{df} and $t_{\alpha, df}$ if the test statistic follows the t_{df} distribution with degrees of freedom $df = n - 1$.

Step 3. Calculate the value of the test statistic.

Step 4. State the conclusion and interpret the results. The decision rule is to reject the null hypothesis if the test statistic falls in the rejection region. We interpret the results in the context of the application.

Example A9.1 illustrates the critical value approach by revisiting Example 9.6.

EXAMPLE A9.1

A research analyst disputes a trade group's prediction that back-to-school spending will average $606.40 per family this year. She believes that average back-to-school spending will differ from this amount. She decides to conduct a test on the basis of a random sample of 30 households with school-age children. She calculates the sample mean as $622.85. She also believes that back-to-school spending is normally distributed with a population standard deviation of $65. She wants to conduct the test at the 5% significance level.

SOLUTION: We are testing $H_0: \mu = 606.40$ versus $H_A: \mu \neq 606.40$ at the 5% significance level. We have a two-tailed test with $\alpha = 0.05$; thus, the critical values are $-z_{0.025}$ and $z_{0.025}$. In Excel, we enter =NORM.INV(0.975, 0, 1), and Excel returns 1.96. Thus, the decision rule is to reject H_0 if the value of the test statistic z is less than -1.96 or greater than 1.96.

   With $n = 30$, $\bar{x} = 622.85$, and $\sigma = 65$, we find the value of the test statistic as $z = \frac{622.85 - 606.40}{65/\sqrt{30}} = 1.3862$. Because $-1.96 < 1.3862 < 1.96$—that is, the test statistic does not fall in either rejection region—we do not reject H_0. We cannot conclude that average back-to-school spending differs from $606.40.

Note: We would like to stress that we always arrive at the same conclusion whether we use the p-value approach or the critical value approach. If z falls in the rejection region, then the p-value must be less than α. Similarly, if z does not fall in the rejection region, then the p-value must be greater than α.

10 Comparisons Involving Means

LEARNING OBJECTIVES

After reading this chapter you should be able to:

LO **10.1** Make inferences about the difference between two population means based on independent sampling.

LO **10.2** Make inferences about the mean difference based on matched-pairs sampling.

LO **10.3** Conduct and evaluate a one-way ANOVA test.

In the preceding two chapters, we used estimation and hypothesis testing to analyze a single parameter, such as the population mean and the population proportion. In this chapter, we extend our discussion from the analysis of a single population to the comparison of two or more population means.

We first analyze differences between two population means. For instance, an economist may be interested in analyzing the salary difference between two major cities. Similarly, a marketing researcher might want to compare the operating lives of two popular brands of batteries. In these examples, we use independent sampling for the analysis. We will also consider the mean difference of two populations based on matched-pairs sampling. An example would be a consumer group activist wanting to analyze the mean weight of participants before and after they enroll in a new diet program.

Finally, we use analysis of variance (ANOVA) to test for differences between three or more population means. For instance, we may want to determine whether mean monthly sales differ depending on the store layout. ANOVA tests are based on a new distribution called the F distribution.

INTRODUCTORY CASE

Effectiveness of Mandatory Caloric Postings

In today's busy world, Americans eat and drink about one-third of their calories from foods prepared away from home. In general, these foods provide more calories, sodium, and saturated fat than meals consumed at home. The U.S. Food and Drug Administration believes that caloric labeling on menus can help the public make informed and healthful decisions about meals and snacks. Molly Saetang, a nutritionist in San Mateo, California, would like to study the effects of the caloric postings on consumer choices. She obtains transaction data for 40 customers at a popular cafe and records their drink and food calories prior to the caloric postings and after the caloric postings. Table 10.1 shows a portion of the data.

TABLE 10.1 Caloric Intake Before and After Caloric Postings

FILE
Calories

Customer	Before_Drink	After_Drink	Before_Food	After_Food
1	141	142	395	378
2	137	140	404	392
⋮	⋮	⋮	⋮	⋮
40	147	141	406	400

Molly wants to use the sample information to

1. Determine whether the average calories of purchased drinks declined after caloric postings.
2. Determine whether the average calories of purchased food declined after caloric postings.
3. Assess the implications of caloric postings for cafes.

A synopsis of this case is provided at the end of Section 10.2.

10.1 INFERENCE CONCERNING THE DIFFERENCE BETWEEN TWO POPULATION MEANS

Make inferences about the difference between two population means based on independent sampling.

In this section, we consider statistical inference about the difference between two population means based on **independent random samples.** Independent random samples are samples that are completely unrelated to one another. Consider the example where we are interested in the difference in salaries between residents of Chicago and Seattle. For one sample, we collect data from Chicago residents, while for the other sample we collect data from Seattle residents. The two samples are considered to be independent because the selection of one is in no way influenced by the selection of the other. Similarly, in a comparison of battery lives between Brand A and Brand B, one sample comes from the Brand A population, while the other sample comes from the Brand B population. Again, both samples can be considered to be drawn independently.

> ### INDEPENDENT RANDOM SAMPLES
> Two (or more) random samples are considered independent if the process that generates one sample is completely separate from the process that generates the other sample. The samples are clearly delineated.

Confidence Interval for $\mu_1 - \mu_2$

As discussed in earlier chapters, we use sample statistics to estimate the population parameter of interest. For example, the sample mean $\overline{X}$ is the point estimator for the population mean μ. In a similar vein, the difference between the two sample means $\overline{X}_1 - \overline{X}_2$ is a point estimator for the difference between two population means $\mu_1 - \mu_2$, where μ_1 is the mean of the first population and μ_2 is the mean of the second population. The estimate is found by taking the difference of the sample means $\bar{x}_1$ and $\bar{x}_2$ computed from two independent random samples with n_1 and n_2 observations, respectively.

Let's first discuss the sampling distribution of $\overline{X}_1 - \overline{X}_2$. As in the case of a single population mean, this estimator is unbiased; that is, $E(\overline{X}_1 - \overline{X}_2) = \mu_1 - \mu_2$. Moreover, recall that the statistical inference regarding the population mean μ is based on the condition that the sample mean $\overline{X}$ is normally distributed. Similarly, for statistical inference regarding $\mu_1 - \mu_2$, it is imperative that the sampling distribution of $\overline{X}_1 - \overline{X}_2$ is normally distributed. Therefore, if we assume that the two sample means are derived from two independent and normally distributed populations, then $\overline{X}_1 - \overline{X}_2$ is also normally distributed. If the underlying populations cannot be assumed to be normally distributed, then by the central limit theorem, the sampling distribution of $\overline{X}_1 - \overline{X}_2$ is approximately normally distributed only if both sample sizes are sufficiently large—that is, $n_1 \geq 30$ and $n_2 \geq 30$.

As in the case of a single population mean, we consider two scenarios. If we know the variances of the two populations σ_1^2 and σ_2^2 (or the population standard deviations σ_1 and σ_2), then we use the z distribution for the statistical inference. A more common case is to use the t_{df} distribution, where the sample variances s_1^2 and s_2^2 are used in place of the unknown population variances. When σ_1^2 and σ_2^2 are not known, we will examine two cases: (i) the population variances can be assumed equal ($\sigma_1^2 = \sigma_2^2$) or (ii) the population variances cannot be assumed equal ($\sigma_1^2 \neq \sigma_2^2$).

The confidence interval for the difference in means is based on the same procedure outlined in Chapter 8. In particular, the formula for the confidence interval will follow the standard format given by Point Estimate ± Margin of Error.

We use sample data to calculate the point estimate for $\mu_1 - \mu_2$ as the difference between the two sample means $\bar{x}_1 - \bar{x}_2$. The margin of error equals $z_{\alpha/2}$ or $t_{\alpha/2,df}$ (which one depends on whether or not the population variances are known) multiplied by the standard error $se(\overline{X}_1 - \overline{X}_2)$. The following definition box shows the formula for constructing a confidence interval for $\mu_1 - \mu_2$ under three scenarios.

> ### CONFIDENCE INTERVAL FOR $\mu_1 - \mu_2$
>
> A $(1 - \alpha)100\%$ confidence interval for the difference between two population means $\mu_1 - \mu_2$ is given by
>
> 1. $(\bar{x}_1 - \bar{x}_2) \pm z_{\alpha/2}\sqrt{\frac{\sigma_1^2}{n_1} + \frac{\sigma_2^2}{n_2}}$, if the population variances, σ_1^2 and σ_2^2, are known.
>
> 2. $(\bar{x}_1 - \bar{x}_2) \pm t_{\alpha/2,df}\sqrt{s_p^2\left(\frac{1}{n_1} + \frac{1}{n_2}\right)}$, if σ_1^2 and σ_2^2 are unknown but assumed equal. A pooled estimate of the common variance is $s_p^2 = \frac{(n_1 - 1)s_1^2 + (n_2 - 1)s_2^2}{n_1 + n_2 - 2}$, where s_1^2 and s_2^2 are the corresponding sample variances and the degrees of freedom $df = n_1 + n_2 - 2$.
>
> 3. $(\bar{x}_1 - \bar{x}_2) \pm t_{\alpha/2,df}\sqrt{\frac{s_1^2}{n_1} + \frac{s_2^2}{n_2}}$, if σ_1^2 and σ_2^2 are unknown and cannot be assumed equal. The degrees of freedom $df = \frac{(s_1^2/n_1 + s_2^2/n_2)^2}{(s_1^2/n_1)^2/(n_1 - 1)+(s_2^2/n_2)^2/(n_2 - 1)}$. Because the resultant value for df is rarely an integer, we generally round the value down. Software packages use various rounding rules when reporting the resultant value for df.
>
> These formulas are valid only if $\bar{X}_1 - \bar{X}_2$ (approximately) follows a normal distribution.

Note that in the case when we construct a confidence interval for $\mu_1 - \mu_2$ where σ_1^2 and σ_2^2 are unknown but assumed equal, we calculate a pooled estimate of the common variance s_p^2. In other words, because the two populations are assumed to have the same population variance, the two sample variances s_1^2 and s_2^2 are simply two separate estimates of this population variance. We estimate the population variance by a weighted average of s_1^2 and s_2^2, where the weights applied are their respective degrees of freedom relative to the total number of degrees of freedom. In the case when σ_1^2 and σ_2^2 are unknown and cannot be assumed equal, we cannot calculate a pooled estimate of the population variance.

EXAMPLE 10.1

A consumer advocate analyzes the nicotine content in two brands of cigarettes. A sample of 20 cigarettes of Brand A resulted in an average nicotine content of 1.68 milligrams with a standard deviation of 0.22 milligram; 25 cigarettes of Brand B yielded an average nicotine content of 1.95 milligrams with a standard deviation of 0.24 milligram.

Brand A	Brand B
$\bar{x}_1 = 1.68$	$\bar{x}_2 = 1.95$
$s_1 = 0.22$	$s_2 = 0.24$
$n_1 = 20$	$n_2 = 25$

Construct the 95% confidence interval for the difference between the two population means. Nicotine content is assumed to be normally distributed. In addition, the population variances are unknown but assumed equal.

SOLUTION: We wish to construct a confidence interval for $\mu_1 - \mu_2$ where μ_1 is the mean nicotine level for Brand A and μ_2 is the mean nicotine level for Brand B. Because the population variances are unknown but assumed equal, we use the formula

$$(\bar{x}_1 - \bar{x}_2) \pm t_{\alpha/2,df}\sqrt{s_p^2\left(\frac{1}{n_1} + \frac{1}{n_2}\right)}.$$

We calculate the point estimate $\bar{x}_1 - \bar{x}_2 = 1.68 - 1.95 = -0.27$. In order to find $t_{\alpha/2,df}$ for the 95% confidence interval, we determine that $\alpha/2 = 0.05/2 = 0.025$ and $df = n_1 + n_2 - 2 = 20 + 25 - 2 = 43$. Using Excel with $df = 43$, we enter =T.INV(0.975, 43) and find that $t_{0.025,43} = 2.017$.

We then calculate the pooled estimate of the population variance as

$$s_p^2 = \frac{(n_1 - 1)s_1^2 + (n_2 - 1)s_2^2}{n_1 + n_2 - 2} = \frac{(20 - 1)(0.22)^2 + (25 - 1)(0.24)^2}{20 + 25 - 2} = 0.0535.$$

Inserting the appropriate values into the formula, we have

$$-0.27 \pm 2.017 \sqrt{0.0535 \left(\frac{1}{20} + \frac{1}{25} \right)} = -0.27 \pm 0.14.$$

In other words, the 95% confidence interval for the difference between the two means ranges from -0.41 to -0.13. Shortly, we will use this interval to conduct a two-tailed hypothesis test.

Hypothesis Test for $\mu_1 - \mu_2$

As always, when specifying the competing hypotheses, it is important to (1) identify the relevant population parameter, (2) determine whether a one- or a two-tailed test is appropriate, and (3) include some form of the equality sign in the null hypothesis and use the alternative hypothesis to establish a claim. In order to conduct a hypothesis test concerning the parameter $\mu_1 - \mu_2$, the competing hypotheses will take one of the following general forms:

Two-Tailed Test	Right-Tailed Test	Left-Tailed Test
$H_0: \mu_1 - \mu_2 = d_0$	$H_0: \mu_1 - \mu_2 \leq d_0$	$H_0: \mu_1 - \mu_2 \geq d_0$
$H_A: \mu_1 - \mu_2 \neq d_0$	$H_A: \mu_1 - \mu_2 > d_0$	$H_A: \mu_1 - \mu_2 < d_0$

In most applications, the hypothesized difference d_0 between two population means μ_1 and μ_2 is zero. In this scenario, a two-tailed test determines whether the two means differ from one another, a right-tailed test determines whether μ_1 is greater than μ_2, and a left-tailed test determines whether μ_1 is less than μ_2.

We can also construct hypotheses where the hypothesized difference d_0 is a value other than zero. For example, if we wish to determine if the mean return of an emerging market fund (Population 1) is more than two percentage points higher than that of a developed market fund (Population 2), the resulting hypotheses are $H_0: \mu_1 - \mu_2 \leq 2$ versus $H_A: \mu_1 - \mu_2 > 2$.

EXAMPLE 10.2

Revisit Example 10.1.

a. Specify the competing hypotheses in order to determine whether the average nicotine levels differ between Brand A and Brand B.

b. Using the 95% confidence interval, what is the conclusion to the test?

SOLUTION:

a. We want to determine if the average nicotine levels differ between the two brands, or $\mu_1 \neq \mu_2$, so we formulate a two-tailed hypothesis test as

$$H_0: \mu_1 - \mu_2 = 0$$
$$H_A: \mu_1 - \mu_2 \neq 0$$

b. In Example 10.1, we calculated the 95% confidence interval for the difference between the two means as -0.27 ± 0.14 or, equivalently, the confidence interval ranges from -0.41 to -0.13. This interval does not contain zero, the value hypothesized under the null hypothesis. This information allows us to reject H_0; the sample data support the conclusion that average nicotine levels between the two brands differ at the 5% significance level.

While it is true that we can use confidence intervals to conduct two-tailed hypothesis tests, the four-step procedure outlined in Chapter 9 can be implemented to conduct one- or two-tailed hypothesis tests. The only real change in the process is the specification of the test statistic. We derive the value of the test statistic, z or t_{df}, by dividing $(\bar{x}_1 - \bar{x}_2) - d_0$ by the standard error of the estimator $se(\bar{X}_1 - \bar{X}_2)$. The following definition box shows the formula for the test statistic when testing $\mu_1 - \mu_2$ under three scenarios.

THE TEST STATISTIC FOR TESTING $\mu_1 - \mu_2$

The value of the test statistic for a hypothesis test concerning the difference between two population means, $\mu_1 - \mu_2$, is computed using one of the following three formulas:

1. If σ_1^2 and σ_2^2 are known, then the value of the test statistic is computed as

$$z = \frac{(\bar{x}_1 - \bar{x}_2) - d_0}{\sqrt{\frac{\sigma_1^2}{n_1} + \frac{\sigma_2^2}{n_2}}}.$$

2. If σ_1^2 and σ_2^2 are unknown but assumed equal, then the value of the test statistic is computed as $t_{df} = \dfrac{(\bar{x}_1 - \bar{x}_2) - d_0}{\sqrt{s_p^2\left(\frac{1}{n_1} + \frac{1}{n_2}\right)}}$, where $s_p^2 = \dfrac{(n_1 - 1)s_1^2 + (n_2 - 1)s_2^2}{n_1 + n_2 - 2}$ and

$df = n_1 + n_2 - 2$.

3. If σ_1^2 and σ_2^2 are unknown and cannot be assumed equal, then the value of the test statistic is computed as $t_{df} = \dfrac{(\bar{x}_1 - \bar{x}_2) - d_0}{\sqrt{\frac{s_1^2}{n_1} + \frac{s_2^2}{n_2}}}$, where

$df = \dfrac{(s_1^2/n_1 + s_2^2/n_2)^2}{(s_1^2/n_1)^2/(n_1 - 1) + (s_2^2/n_2)^2/(n_2 - 1)}$. For df, we generally round the value down; software packages use various rounding rules when reporting the resultant value for df.

These formulas are valid only if $\bar{X}_1 - \bar{X}_2$ (approximately) follows a normal distribution.

EXAMPLE 10.3

An economist claims that average weekly food expenditure for households in City 1 is more than the average weekly food expenditure for households in City 2. She surveys 35 households in City 1 and obtains an average weekly food expenditure of $164. A sample of 30 households in City 2 yields an average weekly food expenditure of $159. Prior studies suggest that the population standard deviation for City 1 is $12.50 and the population standard deviation for City 2 is $9.25. Table 10.2 summarizes the results.

a. Specify the competing hypotheses to test the economist's claim.

b. Calculate the value of the test statistic and the p-value.

c. At the 5% significance level, is the economist's claim supported by the data?

TABLE 10.2 Descriptive Statistics for City 1 and City 2

City 1	City 2
$\bar{x}_1 = 164$	$\bar{x}_2 = 159$
$\sigma_1 = 12.50$	$\sigma_2 = 9.25$
$n_1 = 35$	$n_2 = 30$

SOLUTION:

a. The relevant parameter of interest is $\mu_1 - \mu_2$, where μ_1 is the mean weekly food expenditure for City 1 and μ_2 is the mean weekly food expenditure for City 2. The economist wishes to determine if the mean weekly food expenditure in City 1 is more than that of City 2; that is, $\mu_1 > \mu_2$. This is an example of a right-tailed test where the appropriate hypotheses are

$$H_0: \mu_1 - \mu_2 \le 0$$
$$H_A: \mu_1 - \mu_2 > 0$$

b. Because the population standard deviations are known, we compute the value of the test statistic as

$$z = \frac{(\bar{x}_1 - \bar{x}_2) - d_0}{\sqrt{\dfrac{\sigma_1^2}{n_1} + \dfrac{\sigma_2^2}{n_2}}} = \frac{(164 - 159) - 0}{\sqrt{\dfrac{(12.50)^2}{35} + \dfrac{(9.25)^2}{30}}} = \frac{5}{2.70} = 1.8485.$$

In Excel, in order to find the p-value for this right-tailed test, or equivalently $P(Z > 1.8485)$, we enter =1-NORM.DIST(1.8485, 0, 1, TRUE). Excel returns 0.0323.

c. We reject the null hypothesis because the p-value = 0.0323 is less than the chosen $\alpha = 0.05$. Therefore, at the 5% significance level, the economist concludes that average weekly food expenditure in City 1 is more than that of City 2.

Using Excel for Testing Hypotheses about $\mu_1 - \mu_2$

Excel's Analysis Toolpak provides several options that simplify the steps when conducting a hypothesis test about $\mu_1 - \mu_2$. Consider the following example.

EXAMPLE 10.4

Table 10.3 shows a portion of the annual returns (in %) for 10 firms in the gold industry and 10 firms in the oil industry. Can we conclude at the 5% significance level that the average returns in the two industries differ? Here we assume that the sample data are drawn independently from normally distributed populations. The variance is a common measure of risk when analyzing financial returns and we cannot assume that the risk from investing in the gold industry is the same as the risk from investing in the oil industry.

TABLE 10.3 Annual Returns (in percent)

FILE
Gold_Oil

Gold	Oil
6	−3
15	15
⋮	⋮
16	15

SOLUTION: We let μ_1 denote the mean return for the gold industry and μ_2 denote the mean return for the oil industry. Because we wish to test whether the mean returns differ, we set up the null and alternative hypotheses as

$$H_0: \mu_1 - \mu_2 = 0$$
$$H_A: \mu_1 - \mu_2 \neq 0$$

Given that we are testing the difference between two means when the population variances are unknown and not equal, we need to calculate $t_{df} = \dfrac{(\bar{x}_1 - \bar{x}_2) - d_0}{\sqrt{\frac{s_1^2}{n_1} + \frac{s_2^2}{n_2}}}$. Recall that the calculation for the degrees of freedom for the corresponding test statistic is rather involved. Fortunately, Excel provides the degrees of freedom, the value of the test statistic, and the p-value.

Using Excel

a. Open the *Gold_Oil* data file.

b. Choose **Data > Data Analysis > t-Test: Two-Sample Assuming Unequal Variances > OK.** (Note: Excel provides two other options when we want to test the difference between two population means from independent samples and we have access to the raw data. If the population variances are known, we use the option **z-Test: Two-Sample for Means.** If the population variances are unknown but assumed equal, we use the option **t-Test: Two-Sample Assuming Equal Variances.**)

c. See Figure 10.1. In the dialog box, choose *Variable 1 Range* and select cells A1:A11. Then, choose *Variable 2 Range* and select cells B1:B11. Enter a *Hypothesized Mean Difference* of 0 because $d_0 = 0$ and check the *Labels* box. Click **OK.**

FIGURE 10.1 Excel's dialog box for *t*-test with unequal variances

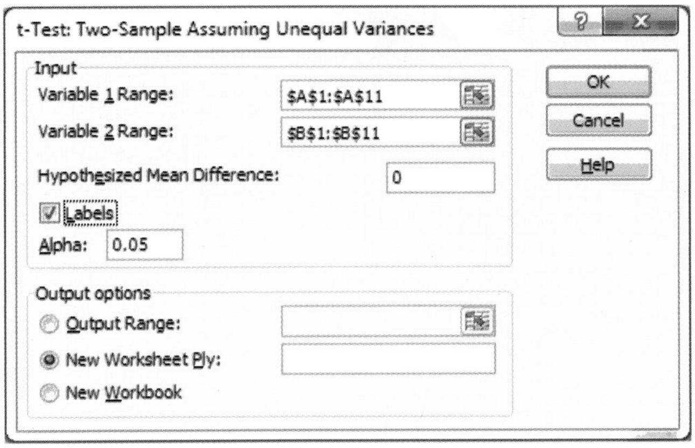

Source: Microsoft Office 2019

Table 10.4 shows the Excel output.

TABLE 10.4 Excel's Output for t-Test concerning $\mu_1 - \mu_2$

	Gold	Oil
Mean	16	17.3
Variance	70.6667	114.2333
Observations	10	10
Hypothesized Mean Difference	0	
Df	17	
t Stat	**−0.3023**	
P(T ≤ t) one-tail	0.3830	
t Critical one-tail	1.7396	
P(T ≤ t) two-tail	**0.7661**	
t Critical two-tail	2.1098	

SUMMARY: The value of the test statistic and the p-value for this two-tailed test are −0.3023 and 0.7661, respectively (see these values in boldface in Table 10.4). At the 5% significance level, we cannot reject H_0 because the p-value is greater than 0.05. While average returns in the oil industry seem to slightly outperform average returns in the gold industry ($\bar{x}_2 = 17.3 > 16.0 = \bar{x}_1$), the difference is not statistically significant.

EXERCISES 10.1

Mechanics

1. Consider the following data drawn independently from normally distributed populations:

$$\bar{x}_1 = 25.7 \quad \bar{x}_2 = 30.6$$
$$\sigma_1^2 = 98.2 \quad \sigma_2^2 = 87.4$$
$$n_1 = 20 \quad n_2 = 25$$

a. Construct the 95% confidence interval for the difference between the population means.

b. Specify the competing hypotheses in order to determine whether or not the population means differ.

c. Using the confidence interval from part a, can you reject the null hypothesis? Explain.

2. Consider the following data drawn independently from normally distributed populations:

$$\bar{x}_1 = -10.5 \quad \bar{x}_2 = -16.8$$
$$s_1^2 = 7.9 \quad s_2^2 = 9.3$$
$$n_1 = 15 \quad n_2 = 20$$

a. Construct the 95% confidence interval for the difference between the population means. Assume that the population variances are equal.

b. Specify the competing hypotheses in order to determine whether or not the population means differ.

c. Using the confidence interval from part a, can you reject the null hypothesis? Explain.

3. Consider the following competing hypotheses and accompanying sample data drawn independently from normally distributed populations.

$$H_0: \mu_1 - \mu_2 = 0$$
$$H_A: \mu_1 - \mu_2 \neq 0$$

$$\bar{x}_1 = 57 \quad \bar{x}_2 = 63$$
$$\sigma_1 = 11.5 \quad \sigma_2 = 15.2$$
$$n_1 = 20 \quad n_2 = 20$$

Test whether the population means differ at the 5% significance level.

4. Consider the following competing hypotheses and accompanying sample data. The two populations are known to be normally distributed.

$$H_0: \mu_1 - \mu_2 \leq 0$$
$$H_A: \mu_1 - \mu_2 > 0$$

$$\bar{x}_1 = 20.2 \quad \bar{x}_2 = 17.5$$
$$s_1 = 2.5 \quad s_2 = 4.4$$
$$n_1 = 10 \quad n_2 = 12$$

a. Implement the hypothesis test at the 5% significance level under the assumption that the population variances are equal.

b. Repeat the analysis at the 10% significance level.

5. Consider the following competing hypotheses and accompanying sample data drawn independently from normally distributed populations.

$$H_0: \mu_1 - \mu_2 \geq 0$$

$$H_A: \mu_1 - \mu_2 < 0$$

$\bar{x}_1 = 249$	$\bar{x}_2 = 262$
$s_1 = 35$	$s_2 = 23$
$n_1 = 10$	$n_2 = 10$

a. Implement the hypothesis test at the 5% significance level under the assumption that the population variances are equal.

b. Implement the hypothesis test at the 5% significance level under the assumption that the population variances are not equal.

6. Consider the following competing hypotheses and accompanying sample data.

$$H_0: \mu_1 - \mu_2 = 5$$

$$H_A: \mu_1 - \mu_2 \neq 5$$

$\bar{x}_1 = 57$	$\bar{x}_2 = 43$
$s_1 = 21.5$	$s_2 = 15.2$
$n_1 = 22$	$n_2 = 18$

Assume that the populations are normally distributed with equal variances.

a. Calculate the value of the test statistic and the p-value.

b. At the 5% significance level, can you conclude that the difference between the two means differs from 5?

7. **FILE** *Exercise_10.7.* The accompanying file contains sample data drawn independently from normally distributed populations with equal population variances.

a. Construct the relevant hypotheses to test if the mean of the second population is greater than the mean of the first population.

b. Implement the hypothesis test at the 1% significance level.

c. Implement the hypothesis test at the 10% significance level.

8. **FILE** *Exercise_10.8.* The accompanying file contains sample data drawn independently from normally distributed populations with unequal population variances.

a. Construct the relevant hypotheses to test if the means of the two populations differ.

b. What are the value of the test statistic and the p-value?

c. At the 10% significance level, do the two population means differ?

Applications

9. You find that the average life expectancy of female Bostonians is 81.1 years and the average life expectancy of male Bostonians is 74.8 years. You use a random sample of 32 females and 32 males and assume a population standard deviation of 8.2 years for females and 8.6 years for males.

a. Set up the hypotheses to test whether the average life expectancy of female Bostonians is higher than that of male Bostonians.

b. Calculate the value of the test statistic and the p-value.

c. At the 10% significance level, can you conclude that female Bostonians live longer than male Bostonians?

10. A report finds that graduates with a bachelor's degree who transferred from a community college earn less than those who start at a four-year school; this occurrence is referred to as the "community college penalty." Lucille Cardozo wonders if a similar pattern applies to her university. In a sample of 100 graduates who transferred from a community college, she finds that their average salary was $52,000. In a sample of 100 graduates who did not transfer from a community college, she finds that their average salary was $54,700. Lucille believes that the population standard deviation is $4,400 for graduates who transferred from a community college and $1,500 for graduates who did not transfer from a community college.

a. Set up the hypotheses to test if the report's conclusion also applies to Lucille's university.

b. Calculate the value of the test statistic and the p-value.

c. At the 5% significance level, can we conclude that there is a "community college penalty" at Lucille's university?

11. The Chartered Financial Analyst (CFA) designation is fast becoming a requirement for serious investment professionals. It is an attractive alternative to getting an MBA for students wanting a career in investment. A student of finance is curious to know if a CFA designation is a more lucrative option than an MBA. He collects data on 38 recent CFAs with a mean salary of $138,000 and a standard deviation of $34,000. A sample of 80 MBAs results in a mean salary of $130,000 with a standard deviation of $46,000.

a. Specify the hypotheses to test whether a CFA designation is more lucrative than an MBA.

b. Calculate the value of the test statistic and the p-value. Do not assume that the population variances are equal.

c. At the 5% significance level, is a CFA designation more lucrative than an MBA?

12. An entrepreneur owns some land that he wishes to develop. He identifies two development options: build condominiums or build apartment buildings. Accordingly, he reviews public records and finds that the average profitability was $244,200 for condominiums and $235,800 for apartment buildings. For the analysis, he uses a random sample of 30 for each venture and assumes a historical (population) standard deviation of $22,500 for condominiums and $20,000 for apartment buildings.

a. Set up the hypotheses to test whether the mean profitability differs between condominiums and apartment buildings.

b. Calculate the value of the test statistic and the p-value.

c. At the 5% significance level, what is the conclusion to the test? What if the significance level is 10%?

13. David Anderson has been working as a lecturer at Michigan State University for the last three years. He teaches two large sections of introductory accounting every semester. While he uses the same lecture notes in both sections, his students in the first section outperform those in the second section. He believes that students in the first section not only tend to get higher scores, they also tend to have lower variability in scores. David decides to carry out a formal test to validate his hunch regarding the difference in average scores. In a random sample of 18 students in the first section, he computes a mean and a standard deviation of 77.4 and 10.8, respectively. In the second section, a random sample of 14 students results in a mean of 74.1 and a standard deviation of 12.2.

    a. Construct the null and the alternative hypotheses to test David's hunch.

    b. Compute the value of the test statistic. What assumption regarding the populations is necessary to implement this step?

    c. Implement the test at $\alpha = 0.01$ and interpret your results.

14. A design engineer at Sperling Manufacturing, a supplier of high-quality ball bearings, claims a new machining process can result in a higher daily output rate. Accordingly, the production group is conducting an experiment to determine if this claim can be substantiated. The mean and the standard deviation of bearings in a sample of 8 days' output using the new process equal 2,613.63 and 90.78, respectively. A similar sample of 10 days' output using the old process yields a mean and a standard deviation of 2,485.10 and 148.22, respectively.

    a. Set up the hypotheses to test whether the mean output rate of the new process exceeds that of the old process. Assume normally distributed populations and equal population variances for each process.

    b. Compute the value of the test statistic and the p-value.

    c. At the 5% significance level, what is the conclusion to the hypothesis test?

    d. At the 1% significance level, what is the conclusion to the hypothesis test?

15. A promising start-up wants to compete in the cell phone market. The start-up believes that the battery life of its cell phone is more than two hours longer than that of the leading product. A recent sample of 120 units of the leading product provides a mean battery life of 5 hours and 40 minutes with a standard deviation of 30 minutes. A similar analysis of 100 units of the start-up's product results in a mean battery life of 8 hours and 5 minutes and a standard deviation of 55 minutes. It is not reasonable to assume that the population variances of the two products are equal.

    a. Set up the hypotheses to test if the start-up's product has a battery life that is more than two hours longer than that of the leading product.

    b. Implement the hypothesis test at the 5% significance level.

16. A sales manager of a used car dealership believes that it takes an average of 30 days longer to sell a sports-utility vehicle (SUV) as compared to a small car. In the last two months, she sold 18 SUVs that took an average of 95 days to sell with a standard deviation of 32 days. She also sold 38 small cars with an average of 48 days to sell and a standard deviation of 24 days.

    a. Construct the null and the alternative hypotheses to contradict the manager's claim.

    b. Compute the value of the test statistic and the p-value. Assume that the populations are normally distributed and that the variability of selling time for the SUVs and the small cars is the same.

    c. Implement the test at $\alpha = 0.10$ and interpret your results.

17. **FILE** *Longevity.* A consumer advocate researches the length of life between two brands of refrigerators, Brand A and Brand B. He collects data (measured in years) on the longevity of 40 refrigerators for Brand A and repeats the sampling for Brand B. The accompanying data file shows the results.

    a. Specify the competing hypotheses to test whether the average length of life differs between the two brands.

    b. Calculate the value of the test statistic and the p-value. Assume that $\sigma_A^2 = 4.4$ and $\sigma_B^2 = 5.2$.

    c. At the 5% significance level, what is the conclusion to the hypothesis test?

18. **FILE** *Searches.* The "See Me" marketing agency wants to determine if time of day for a television advertisement influences website searches for a product. They have extracted the number of website searches occurring during a one-hour period after an advertisement was aired for a random sample of 30 day and 30 evening advertisements. The accompanying data file shows the results.

    a. Set up the hypotheses to test whether the mean number of website searches differs between the day and evening advertisements.

    b. Calculate the value of the test statistic and the p-value. Assume that the population variances are equal.

    c. At the 5% significance level, what is the conclusion to the hypothesis test?

19. **FILE** *Diets.* According to a report, overweight people on low-carbohydrate diets lost more weight and got greater cardiovascular benefits than people on a conventional low-fat diet (healthline.com, March 24, 2020). A nutritionist wishes to verify these results and documents the weight loss (in pounds) of 30 dieters on the low carbohydrate diet and 30 dieters on the low-fat diet. The accompanying data file shows the results.

    a. Set up the hypotheses to test the claim that the mean weight loss for those on the low carbohydrate diet is greater than the mean weight loss for those on a conventional low-fat diet.

    b. Calculate the value of the test statistic and the p-value. Assume that the population variances are equal.

    c. At the 5% significance level, can the nutritionist conclude that people on the low carbohydrate diet lost more weight than people on a conventional low-fat diet?

20. **FILE** *Tractor_Times.* The production department at Green-side Corporation, a manufacturer of lawn equipment, has devised a new manual assembly method for its lawn tractors. Now it wishes to determine if it is reasonable to conclude that the mean assembly time of the new method is less than that of the old method. Accordingly, they have randomly sampled assembly times (in minutes) from 40 tractors using the old method and 32 tractors using the new method. The accompanying data file shows the results.

   a. Set up the hypotheses to test the claim that the mean assembly time using the new method is less than that using the old method.

   b. Calculate the value of the test statistic and the *p*-value. Assume that the population variances are not equal.

   c. At the 5% significance level, what is the conclusion to the hypothesis test? What if the significance level is 10%?

21. **FILE** *Nicknames.* Baseball has always been a favorite pastime in America and is rife with statistics and theories. One study found that major league players who have nicknames live an average of 2½ years longer than those without them. You do not believe in this result and decide to collect data on the lifespan of 30 baseball players along with a nickname variable that equals 1 if the player had a nickname and 0 otherwise. The accompanying data file shows the results.

   a. Create two subsamples consisting of players with and without nicknames. Calculate the average longevity for each subsample.

   b. Specify the hypotheses to contradict the claim made by the researchers.

   c. Calculate the value of the test statistic and the *p*-value. Assume that the population variances are equal.

   d. What is the conclusion of the hypothesis test using a 5% level of significance?

22. **FILE** *Salaries.* A report suggests that graduating from college during bad economic times can impact the graduate's earning power for a long time. The admissions director at a regional state university wants to determine if the starting salary of his college graduates has declined from 2018 to 2020. She expects the variance of the salaries to be different between these two years. The accompanying data file shows the results. At the 5% significance level, determine if the mean starting salary has decreased from 2018 to 2020.

23. **FILE** *Spending.* The accompanying data file shows the amount spent (in $) over the weekend by 40 men and 60 women at a local mall. At the 1% significance level, determine if the mean amount spent by men is more than that by women. Assume that the population variances are equal.

10.2 INFERENCE CONCERNING THE MEAN DIFFERENCE

Make inferences about the mean difference based on matched-pairs sampling.

One of the crucial assumptions in Section 10.1 concerning differences between two population means is that the samples are drawn independently. As mentioned in that section, two samples are independent if the selection of one is not influenced by the selection of the other. When we want to conduct tests on two population means based on samples that we believe are not independent, we need to employ a different methodology.

A common case of dependent sampling, commonly referred to as **matched-pairs sampling,** is when the samples are paired or matched in some way. Such samples are useful in evaluating strategies because the comparison is made between "apples" and "apples." For instance, an effective way to assess the benefits of a new medical treatment is by evaluating the same patients before and after the treatment. If, however, one group of people is given the treatment and another group is not, then it is not clear if the observed differences are due to the treatment or due to other important differences between the groups.

For matched-pairs sampling, the parameter of interest is referred to as the mean difference μ_D where $D = X_1 - X_2$. The statistical inference regarding μ_D is based on the estimator $\overline{D}$, representing the sample mean difference. It requires that $\overline{D}$ is normally distributed; this requirement is satisfied if $X_1 - X_2$ is normally distributed or if the sample size is large ($n \geq 30$).

Recognizing a Matched-Pairs Experiment

It is important to be able to determine whether a particular experiment uses independent or matched-pairs sampling. In general, two types of matched-pairs sampling occur:

1. The first type of matched-pairs sample is characterized by a measurement, an intervention of some type, and then another measurement. We generally refer to these experiments as "before" and "after" studies. For example, an operation manager of a production facility wants to determine whether a new workstation layout improves productivity at her plant. She first measures output of employees before the layout change. Then she measures output of the same employees after the change. Another classic before-and-after example concerns weight loss of clients at a diet center. In these examples, the same individual gets sampled before and after the experiment.

2. The second type of matched-pairs sample is characterized by a pairing of observations, where it is not the same individual who gets sampled twice. Suppose an agronomist wishes to switch to an organic fertilizer but is unsure what the effects might be on his crop yield. It is important to the agronomist that the yields be similar. He matches 20 adjacent plots of land using the nonorganic fertilizer on one half of the plot and the organic fertilizer on the other. Similarly, two portfolio returns over a specific time period also represent a matched-pairs sample because they are both influenced by the state of the economy.

In order to recognize a matched-pairs experiment, we watch for a natural pairing between one observation in the first sample and one observation in the second sample. If a natural pairing exists, then the experiment involves matched samples.

Confidence Interval for μ_D

When constructing a confidence interval for the mean difference μ_D, we follow the same standard format given by Point Estimate $\pm$ Margin of Error. The following definition box shows the formula for constructing a confidence interval for μ_D.

CONFIDENCE INTERVAL FOR μ_D

A $(1 - \alpha)100\%$ confidence interval for the mean difference μ_D is given by

$$\bar{d} \pm t_{\alpha/2,df} s_d/\sqrt{n}$$

where $\bar{d}$ and s_d are the mean and the standard deviation, respectively, of the n sample differences, and $df = n - 1$. This formula is valid only if $\bar{D}$ (approximately) follows a normal distribution.

Productivity

EXAMPLE 10.5

A manager is interested in improving productivity at a plant by changing the layout of the workstation. For each of 10 workers, she measures the time it takes to complete a task before the change and again after the change. A portion of the data is shown in Table 10.5. Construct the 95% confidence interval for the mean difference in productivity, defined as Before minus After. Assume that the sample differences are normally distributed.

TABLE 10.5 Data and Calculations for Example 10.5

Employee	Before	After	d
1	118	116	2
2	140	121	19
⋮	⋮	⋮	⋮
10	149	145	4

SOLUTION: For the 95% confidence interval for the mean difference, we use $\bar{d} \pm t_{\alpha/2,df}s_d/\sqrt{n}$. In order to determine $\bar{d}$ and s_d, we first calculate the difference d for each employee. For instance, Employee 1 completes the task in 118 minutes before the layout change and 116 minutes after the layout change, for a difference $d = 118 - 116 = 2$. The differences for a portion of the other employees is shown in the last column of Table 10.5.

Using the **AVERAGE** function in Excel we find that the sample mean difference $\bar{d}$ is equal to 9.6. Using the **STDEV.S** function in Excel we find that the sample standard deviation of the difference s_d is equal to 16.352.

With $df = n - 1 = 10 - 1 = 9$ and $\alpha = 0.05$, we enter =T.INV(0.975, 9) in Excel and find that $t_{\alpha/2,df} = t_{0.025,9} = 2.262$. Plugging the relevant values into the formula, we calculate

$$9.6 \pm 2.262(16.352/\sqrt{10}) = 9.6 \pm 11.70$$

That is, the 95% confidence interval for the mean difference ranges from –2.10 to 21.30. This represents a fairly wide interval, caused by the high standard deviation s_d of the 10 sample differences.

Hypothesis Test for μ_D

In order to conduct a hypothesis test concerning the parameter μ_D, the competing hypotheses will take one of the following general forms:

Two-Tailed Test	Right-Tailed Test	Left-Tailed Test
$H_0: \mu_D = d_0$	$H_0: \mu_D \le d_0$	$H_0: \mu_D \ge d_0$
$H_A: \mu_D \ne d_0$	$H_A: \mu_D > d_0$	$H_A: \mu_D < d_0$

In practice, the competing hypotheses tend to be based on $d_0 = 0$. For example, when testing if the mean difference differs from zero, we use a two-tailed test with the competing hypotheses defined as $H_0: \mu_D = 0$ versus $H_A: \mu_D \ne 0$. If, on the other hand, we wish to determine whether or not the mean difference differs by some amount, say by 5 units, we set $d_0 = 5$ and define the competing hypotheses as $H_0: \mu_D = 5$ versus $H_A: \mu_D \ne 5$. One-tailed tests are defined similarly.

EXAMPLE 10.6

Using the information from Example 10.5, can the manager conclude at the 5% significance level that there has been a change in productivity since the adoption of the new workstation?

SOLUTION: In order to determine whether or not there has been a change in the mean difference, we formulate the null and the alternative hypotheses as

$$H_0: \mu_D = 0$$

$$H_A: \mu_D \ne 0$$

In Example 10.5, we found that the 95% confidence interval for the mean difference ranges from -2.10 to 21.30. The interval includes the hypothesized value d_0 of zero. Therefore, at the 5% significance level, the sample data suggest that the mean difference does not differ from zero. In other words, the manager cannot conclude that there has been a change in productivity due to the different layout in the workstation.

We now examine the four-step procedure to conduct one- or two-tailed hypothesis tests concerning the mean difference. We again find the value of the t_{df} statistic by dividing the difference between the sample mean difference and the hypothesized mean difference by the standard error of the estimator $se(\overline{D})$. The following definition box shows the formula for the test statistic when testing μ_D.

THE TEST STATISTIC FOR TESTING μ_D

The value of the test statistic for a hypothesis test concerning the population mean difference μ_D is computed as

$$t_{df} = \frac{\bar{d} - d_0}{s_d/\sqrt{n}},$$

where $df = n - 1$; $\bar{d}$ and s_d are the mean and the standard deviation, respectively, of the n sample differences; and d_0 is the hypothesized mean difference. This formula is valid only if $\overline{D}$ (approximately) follows a normal distribution.

We should note that a hypothesis test for μ_D is equivalent to finding the differences between the paired items and then using the one-sample t-test discussed in Chapter 9.

Using Excel's Analysis Toolpak for Testing Hypotheses about μ_D

Excel's Analysis Toolpak provides an option that simplifies the steps when conducting a hypothesis test about μ_D. Consider the following example.

EXAMPLE 10.7

Calories

Recall from the introductory case that chain restaurants are required to post caloric information on their menus. A nutritionist wants to examine whether average drink and/or average food calories declined at a popular cafe after the caloric postings. The nutritionist obtains transaction data for 40 customers and records each customer's drink and food calories prior to the caloric postings and then after the caloric postings. Can she conclude at the 5% significance level that the ordinance reduced average drink and/or average food calories?

SOLUTION: First note that this is a matched-pairs experiment; specifically, it conforms to a "before" and "after" study. Here, we provide explicit instructions to conduct the hypothesis test for average drink calories. You would follow similar steps to conduct the hypothesis test for average food calories. At the end of this example, we summarize the results for both hypothesis tests.

We want to determine whether average drink calories prior to the caloric postings are greater than average drink calories after the caloric postings. Thus, we want to test if the mean difference μ_D is greater than zero, where $D = X_1 - X_2$, X_1 denotes drink calories before the caloric postings, and X_2 denotes drink calories after the caloric postings for a randomly selected customer. We specify the competing hypotheses as

$$H_0: \mu_D \leq 0$$

$$H_A: \mu_D > 0$$

a. Open the ***Calories*** data file.

b. Choose **Data > Data Analysis >** *t*-**Test: Paired Two Sample for Means > OK.**

c. See Figure 10.2. In the dialog box, choose *Variable 1 Range* and select observations B1:B41 (the Before_Drink variable). Choose *Variable 2 Range* and select observations C1:C41 (the After_Drink variable). Enter a *Hypothesized Mean Difference* of 0 because $d_0 = 0$ and check the *Labels* box. Click **OK.**

FIGURE 10.2 Excel's dialog box for *t*-test with paired sample

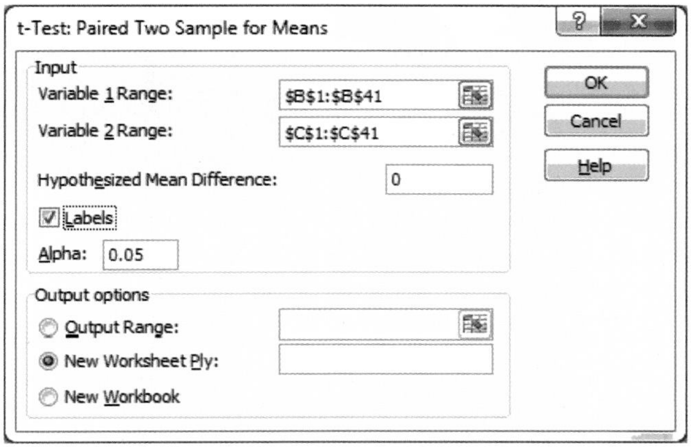

Source: Microsoft Office 2019

Table 10.6 shows the Excel output.

TABLE 10.6 Excel's Analysis Toolpak Output for *t*-Test with paired sample

	Before_Drink	After_Drink
Mean	142.95	140.85
Variance	34.25385	32.3359
Observations	40	40
Pearson Correlation	0.00131	
Hypothesized Mean Difference	0	
Df	39	
t Stat	**1.628659**	
P(T ≤ t) one-tail	**0.055719**	
t Critical one-tail	1.684875	
P(T ≤ t) two-tail	0.111438	
t Critical two-tail	2.022691	

Note: Although Excel calculates the *p*-value correctly, the expression it uses to denote the *p*-value is not always correct. In this example with a positive value for the test statistic, the expression should be "$P(T \geq t)$ one-tail" rather than "$P(T \leq t)$ one-tail."

When you conduct the hypothesis test for average food calories, you repeat these steps and simply substitute cells D1:D41 for cells B1:B41, and substitute cells E1:E41 for cells C1:C41. Verify that your obtain a test statistic of 6.7795 and *p*-value of 2.15E-08.

SUMMARY: When testing whether the posting of caloric information decreases average drink calories (a one-tailed test), we obtain a test statistic and *p*-value of 1.629 and 0.056, respectively. These values are in boldface in Table 10.6. At the 5% significance level, we cannot conclude that the posting of caloric information decreases average drink calories. However, when we conduct a similar test concerning average food calories, we are able to conclude that average food calories have declined after the caloric postings at the 5% significance level.

SYNOPSIS OF INTRODUCTORY CASE

In an effort to make it easier for consumers to select healthier options, many restaurants and cafes have started to post caloric information on their menus. A nutritionist studies the effects of the caloric postings at a popular cafe in San Mateo, California. She obtains transaction data for 40 customers and records each customer's drink and food calories prior to the caloric postings and then after the caloric postings. Two hypothesis tests are conducted. The first test examines whether average drink calories are less since the caloric postings. After conducting a test on the mean difference at the 5% significance level, the nutritionist infers that the caloric postings did not prompt customers to reduce their consumption of drink calories. The second test investigates whether average food calories are less since the caloric postings. At the 5% significance level, the sample data suggest that customers have reduced their consumption of food calories since the caloric postings. These results are consistent with research that has shown mixed results on whether mandatory caloric postings are prompting customers to select healthier foods.

Chris Hondros/Getty Images

EXERCISES 10.2

Mechanics

24. A sample of 20 paired observations generates the following data: $\bar{d} = 1.3$ and $s_d = 1.612$. Assume that the differences are normally distributed.
    a. Construct the 90% confidence interval for the mean difference μ_D.
    b. Using the confidence interval, test whether the mean difference differs from zero. Explain.

25. **FILE** *Exercise_10.25.* The accompanying data file contains information on matched sample observations whose differences are normally distributed.
    a. Construct the 95% confidence interval for the mean difference μ_D.
    b. Specify the competing hypotheses in order to test whether the mean difference differs from zero.
    c. Using the confidence interval from part a, are you able to reject H_0? Explain.

26. Consider the following competing hypotheses and accompanying results from a matched-pairs sample:
    $$H_0: \mu_D \geq 0; H_A: \mu_D < 0$$
    $$\bar{d} = -2.8, s_d = 5.7, n = 12$$
    a. Calculate the value of the test statistic and the p-value, assuming that the sample difference is normally distributed.
    b. At the 5% significance level, what is the conclusion to the hypothesis test?

27. Consider the following competing hypotheses and accompanying results from a matched-pairs sample:
    $$H_0: \mu_D \leq 2; H_A: \mu_D > 2$$
    $$\bar{d} = 5.6, s_d = 6.2, n = 10$$
    a. Calculate the value of the test statistic and the p-value, assuming that the sample difference is normally distributed.
    b. Use the 1% significance level to make a conclusion.

28. A sample of 35 paired observations generates the following results: $\bar{d} = 1.2$ and $s_d = 3.8$.
    a. Specify the appropriate hypotheses to test if the mean difference is greater than zero.
    b. Calculate the value of the test statistic and the p-value.
    c. At the 5% significance level, can you conclude that the mean difference is greater than zero? Explain.

29. **FILE** *Exercise_10.29.* The accompanying data file shows matched-pairs observations for a before-and-after experiment. Assume that the sample differences are normally distributed.
    a. Construct the competing hypotheses to determine if the experiment increases the magnitude of the observations.
    b. Implement the test at the 5% significance level.
    c. Do the results change if we implement the test at the 1% significance level?

Applications

30. **FILE** *Industrial.* A manager of an industrial plant asserts that workers on average do not complete a job using Method A in the same amount of time as they would using Method B. Seven workers are randomly selected. Each worker's completion time (in minutes) is recorded by the use of Method A and Method B. The accompanying data file shows the results.
    a. Specify the null and alternative hypotheses to test the manager's assertion.
    b. Assuming that the completion time difference is normally distributed, calculate the value of the test statistic.
    c. Find the p-value.
    d. At the 10% significance level, is the manager's assertion supported by the data?

31. **FILE** *Diet_Center.* A diet center claims that it has the most effective weight loss program in the region. Its advertisements say, "Participants in our program lose more than 5 pounds within a month." Six clients of this program are weighed on the first day (Before) of the diet and then one month later (After). The accompanying data file shows the results.
    a. Specify the null and alternative hypotheses that test the diet center's claim.
    b. Assuming that weight loss is normally distributed, calculate the value of the test statistic.
    c. Find the p-value.
    d. At the 5% significance level, do the data support the diet center's claim?

32. **FILE** *Appraisers.* A bank employs two appraisers. When approving borrowers for mortgages, it is imperative that the appraisers value the same types of properties consistently. To make sure that this is the case, the bank examines six appraisals (in $1,000s) that the appraisers had valued recently. The accompanying data file shows the results.
    a. Specify the competing hypotheses that determine whether there is any difference between the values estimated by Appraiser 1 and Appraiser 2.
    b. Assuming that the value difference is normally distributed, calculate the value of the test statistic.
    c. Find the p-value.
    d. At the 5% significance level, is there sufficient evidence to conclude that the appraisers are inconsistent in their estimates? Explain.

33. **FILE** *Defects.* The quality department at ElectroTech is examining which of two microscope brands (Brand A or Brand B) to purchase. Using each microscope, an inspector examines six circuit boards and records the number of defects (e.g., solder voids, misaligned components, etc.). The accompanying data file shows the results.
    a. Specify the null and alternative hypotheses to test if the mean difference in defects between the microscopes differs from zero.

    b. Assuming that the difference in defects is normally distributed, calculate the value of the test statistic and the p-value.
    c. At the 5% significance level, is there a difference between the microscope brands?

34. **FILE** *Speed.* A computer technology firm wishes to check whether the speed of a new processor exceeds that of an existing processor when used in one of its popular laptop computer models. Accordingly, it measures the time required (in seconds) to complete seven common tasks on two otherwise-identical computers, one with the new processor and one with the existing processor. The accompanying data file shows the results.
    a. Specify the null and alternative hypotheses to test whether the time required for the new processor is less than that for the existing processor.
    b. Assuming that the difference in time is normally distributed, calculate the value of the test statistic and the p-value.
    c. At the 5% significance level, is the new processor faster than the old processor?

35. **FILE** *SAT_Scores.* A report criticizes SAT-test-preparation providers for promising big score gains without any hard data to back up such claims. Suppose eight college-bound students take a mock SAT, complete a three-month test-prep course, and then take the real SAT. The accompanying data file shows the results.
    a. Specify the competing hypotheses that determine whether completion of the test-prep course increases a student's score on the real SAT.
    b. Calculate the value of the test statistic and the p-value. Assume that the SAT scores difference is normally distributed.
    c. At the 5% significance level, do the sample data support the test-prep providers' claims?

36. **FILE** *Premiums.* The marketing department at Insure-Me, a large insurance company, wants to advertise that customers can save, on average, more than $100 on their annual automotive insurance policies (relative to their closest competitor) by switching their policies to Insure-Me. However, to avoid potential litigation for false advertising, they select a random sample of 50 policyholders and compare their premiums to those of their closest competitor. The accompanying data file shows the results.
    a. Specify the competing hypotheses to determine whether the mean difference between the competitor's premium and *Insure-Me's* premium is over $100.
    b. Calculate the value of the test statistic and the p-value.
    c. What is the conclusion at the 5% significance level? What is the conclusion at the 10% significance level?

37. **FILE** *Returns.* The accompanying data file shows the annual returns for Stock A and Stock B over the past nine years.

   a. Set up the hypotheses to test the claim that the mean difference between the returns differs from zero. (*Hint:* This is a matched-pairs comparison.)

   b. Calculate the value of the test statistic and the *p*-value.

   c. At the 5% significance level, does the mean difference between the returns differ from zero?

38. **FILE** *Labor_Costs.* The labor quotation department at Excabar, a large manufacturing company, wants to verify the accuracy of their labor bidding process (estimated cost per unit versus actual cost per unit). They have randomly chosen 35 product quotations that subsequently were successful (meaning the company won the contract for the product). The accompanying data file shows the results.

   a. Specify the competing hypotheses to determine whether there is a difference between the estimated cost and the actual cost.

   b. Calculate the value of the test statistic and the *p*-value.

   c. At the 1% significance level, what is the conclusion?

39. **FILE** *Smoking.* For 50 women, the accompanying data file shows a woman's weight before she quit smoking and six months after she quit smoking.

   a. Construct and interpret the 95% confidence interval for the mean gain in weight.

   b. Use the confidence interval to determine if the mean gain in weight differs from 5 pounds.

40. **FILE** *Shift.* When faced with a power hitter, many baseball teams utilize a defensive shift. A shift usually involves putting three infielders on one side of second base against pull hitters. Many believe that a power hitter's batting average is lower when they face a shift defense as compared to when they face a standard defense. The accompanying data file shows the batting averages of 10 power hitters when they faced a shift defense versus when they faced a standard defense.

   a. Specify the competing hypotheses to determine whether the use of the defensive shift lowers a power hitter's batting average.

   b. Calculate the value of the test statistic and the *p*-value. Assume that the batting average difference is normally distributed.

   c. At the 5% significance level, is the defensive shift effective in lowering a power hitter's batting average?

41. **FILE** *Fertilizer.* A farmer is concerned that a change in fertilizer to an organic variant might change his crop yield. He subdivides six lots and uses the old fertilizer on one half of each lot and the new fertilizer on the other half. The accompanying data file shows the crop yields with the old and new fertilizers.

   a. Specify the competing hypotheses that determine whether there is any difference between the average crop yields from the use of the different fertilizers.

   b. Assuming that differences in crop yields are normally distributed, calculate the value of the test statistic.

   c. Find the *p*-value.

   d. At the 5% significance level, is there sufficient evidence to conclude that the crop yields are different? Should the farmer be concerned?

42. **FILE** *Pregnancy.* The accompanying data file shows the weight of 40 women before and after pregnancy.

   a. At the 5% level of significance, determine if the mean weight gain of women due to pregnancy is more than 30 pounds.

   b. At the 5% level of significance, determine if the mean weight gain of women due to pregnancy is more than 35 pounds.

43. **FILE** *Safety_Program.* An engineer wants to determine the effectiveness of a safety program. The accompanying data file shows the annual loss of hours due to accidents in 12 plants before and after the program was put into operation.

   a. Specify the competing hypotheses that determine whether the safety program was effective.

   b. Calculate the value of the test statistic and the *p*-value. Assume that the hours difference is normally distributed.

   c. At the 5% significance level, is there sufficient evidence to conclude that the safety program was effective? Explain.

LO 10.3

10.3 INFERENCE CONCERNING DIFFERENCES AMONG MANY MEANS

Conduct and evaluate a one-way ANOVA test.

We use an **analysis of variance (ANOVA) test** to determine if differences exist between the means of three or more populations under independent sampling. The ANOVA test can be thought of as a generalization of the two-sample *t* test with equal but unknown variances discussed in Section 10.1. A **one-way ANOVA test** compares population means based on one categorical variable or factor. In general, it is used for testing c population means under the following assumptions:

1. The populations are normally distributed.
2. The population standard deviations are unknown but assumed equal.
3. The samples are selected independently.

We will discuss a one-way ANOVA test through an example. Sean Cox is vice president of sales and marketing for a large grocery chain. He wants to know if mean sales differ depending on the store layout. Sean implements three different store layouts at 10 different stores for one month and measures total sales for each store at the end of the month. Table 10.7 shows a portion of the results as well as the relevant summary statistics.

TABLE 10.7 Monthly Sales (in $ millions)

Layout 1	Layout 2	Layout 3
1.3	2.0	2.3
1.8	2.2	2.3
⋮	⋮	⋮
2.0	1.8	2.2
$\bar{x}_1 = 1.92$ $s_1^2 = 0.0973$	$\bar{x}_2 = 2.08$ $s_2^2 = 0.1062$	$\bar{x}_3 = 2.42$ $s_3^2 = 0.0373$

Because we want to determine whether some differences exist in the mean monthly sales of a grocery store depending on one of three possible store layouts, we formulate the following competing hypotheses:

$$H_0: \mu_1 = \mu_2 = \mu_3$$
$$H_A: \text{Not all population means are equal.}$$

Note that H_A does not require that all means must differ from one another. In principle, the sample data may support the rejection of H_0 in favor of H_A even if only two means differ.

When conducting the equality of means test, you might be tempted to set up a series of hypothesis tests, comparing μ_1 and μ_2, μ_1 and μ_3, and μ_2 and μ_3, and then use the two-sample t test with equal variances discussed in Section 10.1. However, such an approach is not only cumbersome, but also flawed. In this example, where we evaluate the equality of three means, we would have to compare three combinations of two means at a time. Also, by conducting numerous pairwise comparisons, we inflate the risk of a Type I error α; that is, we increase the risk of incorrectly rejecting the null hypothesis. In other words, if we conduct all three pairwise tests at the 5% level of significance, the resulting significance level for the overall test will be greater than 5%.

Fortunately, the ANOVA technique avoids this problem by providing one test that simultaneously evaluates the equality of several means. In the store layout example, if the three population means are equal, we would expect the resulting sample means, $\bar{x}_1$, $\bar{x}_2$, and $\bar{x}_3$, to be relatively close to one another. Figure 10.3a illustrates the distribution of the sample means if H_0 is true. Here, the relatively small variability in the sample means can be explained by chance. What if the population means differ? Figure 10.3b shows the distributions of the sample means if the sample data support H_A. In this scenario, the sample means are relatively far apart because each sample mean is calculated from a population with a different mean. The resulting variability in the sample means cannot be explained by chance alone.

FIGURE 10.3
The logic of ANOVA

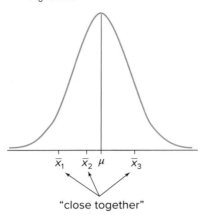

a. Distribution of sample means if H_0 is true

"close together"

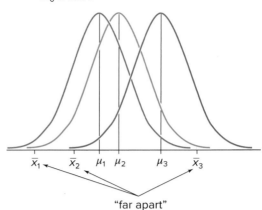

b. Distributions of sample means if H_0 is false

"far apart"

The term *treatments* is often used to identify the c populations being examined. The practice of referring to different populations as different treatments is due to the fact that many ANOVA applications were originally developed in connection with agricultural experiments where different fertilizers were regarded as different treatments applied to soil.

In order to determine if significant differences exist between some of the population means, we develop two independent estimates of the common population variance σ^2. One estimate of σ^2 can be attributed to the variability *between* the sample means. It is referred to as **between-treatments variance.** The other estimate of σ^2 can be attributed to the variability of the observations *within* each sample; that is, the variability due to chance. It is referred to as **within-treatments variance.**

If the two independent estimates of σ^2 are relatively close together, then it is likely that the variability of the sample means can be explained by chance and the null hypothesis of equal population means is not rejected. However, if the between-treatments variance is significantly greater than the within-treatments variance, then the null hypothesis of equal population means is rejected. This is equivalent to concluding that the ratio of between-treatments variance to within-treatments variance is significantly greater than one. We will come back to this ratio shortly.

Between-Treatments Estimate of σ^2: *MSTR*

The between-treatments variance is based on a weighted sum of the squared difference between each sample mean, denoted as $\bar{x}_i$, and the overall sample mean, referred to as the **grand mean** and denoted as $\bar{\bar{x}}$. We compute the grand mean by summing all observations of the variable and dividing by the total number of observations, denoted as n_T.

Each squared difference of a sample mean from the grand mean $(\bar{x}_i - \bar{\bar{x}})^2$ is multiplied by the respective sample size, n_i, for each treatment. After summing the weighted squared differences, we arrive at a value called the **sum of squares due to treatments** or *SSTR*. When we divide *SSTR* by its degrees of freedom $c - 1$, we arrive at the **mean square for treatments,** or, equivalently, the between-treatments estimate of σ^2, which we denote by *MSTR*.

CALCULATIONS FOR *MSTR*

- The grand mean: $\bar{\bar{x}} = \dfrac{\sum\limits_{i=1}^{c}\sum\limits_{j=1}^{n_i} x_{ij}}{n_T}$,

- The sum of squares due to treatments: $SSTR = \sum\limits_{i=1}^{c} n_i (\bar{x}_i - \bar{\bar{x}})^2$, and

---

- The between-treatments estimate of σ^2: $MSTR = \dfrac{SSTR}{c-1}$,

where c is the number of populations (treatments); $\bar{x}_i$ and n_i are the sample mean and the sample size respectively, of the ith sample; and n_T is the total sample size.

Referring back to the store layout example, we first find the sample mean $\bar{x}_i$ and the sample size n_i for each layout. Table 10.7 shows that the sample means for Layout 1, Layout 2, and Layout 3 are $\bar{x}_1 = 1.92$, $\bar{x}_2 = 2.08$, and $\bar{x}_3 = 2.42$, respectively. There are 10 observations in each of the three samples, so $n_1 = n_2 = n_3 = 10$, which implies that the total sample size n_T is equal to 30. The calculations for $\bar{\bar{x}}$, $SSTR$, and $MSTR$ for the store layout example are as follows:

$$\bar{\bar{x}} = \frac{\sum\limits_{i=1}^{c}\sum\limits_{j=1}^{n_i} x_{ij}}{n_T} = \frac{1.3 + 1.8 + \cdots + 2.2}{30} = 2.14$$

$$SSTR = \sum_{i=1}^{c} n_i(\bar{x}_i - \bar{\bar{x}})^2 = 10(1.92 - 2.14)^2 + 10(2.08 - 2.14)^2 + 10(2.42 - 2.14)^2 = 1.304.$$

$$MSTR = \frac{SSTR}{c-1} = \frac{1.304}{3-1} = 0.652$$

Within-Treatments Estimate of σ^2: MSE

We just calculated a value of $MSTR$ equal to 0.652. Is this value of $MSTR$ large enough to indicate that the population means differ? To answer this question, we compare $MSTR$ to the variability that we expect due to chance. In other words, we compare this between-treatments variance to the within-treatments variance. In order to calculate the within-treatments variance, we first calculate the **error sum of squares,** denoted as SSE. SSE provides a measure of the degree of variability that exists even if all population means are the same. We calculate SSE as a weighted sum of the sample variances of each treatment. When we divide SSE by its degrees of freedom $n_T - c$, we arrive at the **mean square error** or, equivalently, the within-treatments estimate of σ^2, which we denote by MSE.

CALCULATIONS FOR *MSE*

- The error sum of squares: $SSE = \sum\limits_{i=1}^{c} (n_i - 1)s_i^2$, and
- The within-treatments estimate of σ^2: $MSE = \dfrac{SSE}{n_T - c}$,

where c is the number of populations (treatments); s_i^2 and n_i are the sample variance and the sample size, respectively, of the ith sample; and n_T is the total sample size.

Table 10.7 shows that the sample variances for Layout 1, Layout 2, and Layout 3 are $s_1^2 = 0.0973$, $s_2^2 = 0.1062$, and $s_3^2 = 0.0373$, respectively. The values of SSE and MSE for the store layout example are calculated as follows:

$$SSE = \sum_{i=1}^{c} (n_i - 1)s_i^2 = (10 - 1)0.0973 + (10 - 1)0.1062 + (10 - 1)0.0373 = 2.168$$

$$MSE = \frac{SSE}{n_T - c} = \frac{2.168}{30 - 3} = 0.0803$$

The F Distribution

As mentioned earlier, if the ratio of the between-treatments variance to the within-treatments variance is significantly greater than one, then this finding provides evidence for rejecting the null hypothesis of equal population means. Thus, this ratio is the test statistic for a one-way ANOVA test, and it follows a new distribution, called **the F distribution.**[1] We define the test statistic in the following definition box. We then summarize the F distribution.

THE TEST STATISTIC FOR A ONE-WAY ANOVA TEST

The value of the test statistic for testing whether some differences exist between the population means is computed as

$$F_{(df_1, df_2)} = \frac{MSTR}{MSE},$$

where $df_1 = c - 1$, $df_2 = n_T - c$, c is the number of populations (treatments), and n_T is the total sample size; $MSTR$ is the between-treatments variance and MSE is the within-treatments variance.

The values for $MSTR$ and MSE are based on independent samples drawn from c normally distributed populations with a common variance. ANOVA tests are always implemented as right-tailed tests.

Like the t_{df} distribution, the F distribution is characterized by a family of distributions; however, each distribution depends on two degrees of freedom: the numerator degrees of freedom df_1 and the denominator degrees of freedom df_2. It is common to refer to it as the $F_{(df_1, df_2)}$ distribution.

Figure 10.4 shows the $F_{(df_1, df_2)}$ distribution with various degrees of freedom. Note that each $F_{(df_1, df_2)}$ distribution is positively skewed; however, as df_1 and df_2 grow larger, the $F_{(df_1, df_2)}$ distribution becomes less skewed and approaches the normal distribution. For instance, $F_{(20,20)}$ is relatively less skewed as compared to $F_{(2,8)}$ or $F_{(6,8)}$.

FIGURE 10.4 The $F_{(df_1, df_2)}$ distribution with various degrees of freedom

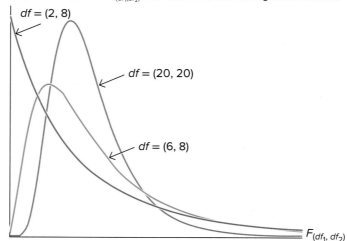

[1]The F distribution is named in honor of Sir Ronald Fisher, who discovered the distribution in 1922.

We are now in a position to conduct a four-step hypothesis test at the 5% significance level for the store layout example.

Step 1. Specify the null and the alternative hypotheses. For completeness, we repeat the competing hypotheses to determine whether mean sales differ between the three store layouts:

$$H_0: \mu_1 = \mu_2 = \mu_3$$
$$H_A: \text{Not all population means are equal.}$$

Step 2. Specify the significance level. We conduct the hypothesis test at the 5% significance level, so $\alpha = 0.05$.

Step 3. Calculate the value of the test statistic and the *p*-value. Given $MSTR = 0.652$, $MSE = 0.0803$, $df_1 = c - 1 = 3 - 1 = 2$ and $df_2 = n_T - c = 30 - 3 = 27$, we compute the value of the test statistic as

$$F_{(df_1, df_2)} = F_{(2,27)} = \frac{MSTR}{MSE} = \frac{0.652}{0.0803} = 8.1199.$$

Because the ANOVA test is always implemented as a right-tailed test, we find the *p*-value as $P(F_{2,27} \geq 8.1199)$.

We could use Excel's **F.DIST** function, which, like the **NORM.DIST** and **T.DIST** functions, returns a cumulative probability. In order to find the *p*-value for the ANOVA test, we would need to subtract the cumulative probability from one. Instead, we use Excel's **F.DIST.RT** function because it directly returns the probability in the right tail of the F distribution. This function requires three inputs: the value of the test statistic, df_1, and df_2. For the store layout example, we enter =F.DIST.RT(8.1199, 2, 27), and Excel returns 0.002. Figure 10.5 graphically depicts the test statistic and the *p*-value for the store layout example.

FIGURE 10.5 Graphical depiction of the test statistic and the *p*-value for the store layout example

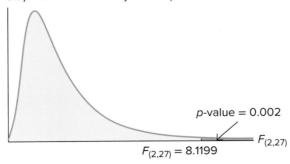

p-value $= 0.002$

$F_{(2,27)}$

$F_{(2,27)} = 8.1199$

Step 4. State the conclusion and interpret the results. Because the *p*-value is less than 0.05, we reject H_0. Therefore, at the 5% significance level, we conclude that the mean monthly sales differ between the three store layouts.

It is important to note that if we reject the null hypothesis, we can only conclude that not all population means are equal. The one-way ANOVA test does not allow us to infer which individual means differ. Therefore, even though the sample mean is the highest for Layout 3, we cannot conclude that Layout 3 produces the highest sales. Further analysis of the difference between paired population means is beyond the scope of this text.

Using Excel to Construct a One-Way ANOVA Table

Most software packages summarize the ANOVA calculations in a table. The general format of the ANOVA table is presented in Table 10.8.

TABLE 10.8 General Format of a One-Way ANOVA Table

Source of Variation	SS	df	MS	F	p-value
Between Groups	SSTR	$c - 1$	MSTR	$F_{(df_1, df_2)} = \dfrac{MSTR}{MSE}$	$P\left(F_{(df_1, df_2)} \geq \dfrac{MSTR}{MSE}\right)$
Within Groups	SSE	$n_T - c$	MSE		
Total	SST	$n_T - 1$			

We should also note that total sum of squares *SST* is equal to the sum of the squared differences of each observation from the grand mean. This is equivalent to summing *SSTR* and *SSE*; that is, $SST = SSTR + SSE$.

Consider the next example, which uses Excel to construct a one-way ANOVA table for the store layout example.

FILE

Store_Layout

EXAMPLE 10.8

Use Excel to obtain the ANOVA table for the store layout example.

SOLUTION:

a. Open the ***Store_Layout*** data file.

b. From the menu, choose **Data > Data Analysis > ANOVA: Single Factor.**

c. See Figure 10.6. In the dialog box, choose *Input Range* and select cells A1:C11. Check the box in front of *Labels in First Row*. Click **OK.**

FIGURE 10.6
Excel's *ANOVA: Single Factor* dialog box

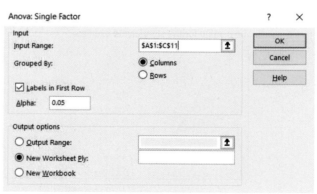

Source: Microsoft Office 2019

Table 10.9 shows Excel's results for the store layout example. The top portion of the table provides summary statistics for the three different layouts. The bottom portion of the table shows the ANOVA table. You should verify that all values in the ANOVA table match our manual calculations. We have put the value of the test statistic, $F_{(2,27)} = 8.1199$ and the p-value in boldface. As found earlier, we can conclude at the 5% significance level that mean monthly sales are not the same for the three store layouts. (Excel also provides a statistic called F-crit (not shown) which would be useful if we were using the critical-value approach to conduct a hypothesis test.)

TABLE 10.9 ANOVA Table for Store Layout Example

SUMMARY					
Groups	**Count**	**Sum**	**Average**	**Variance**	
Layout 1	10	19.2	1.92	0.097333	
Layout 2	10	20.8	2.08	0.106222	
Layout 3	10	24.2	2.42	0.037333	
ANOVA					
Source of Variation	**SS**	**df**	**MS**	**F**	**p-value**
Between Groups	1.304	2	0.652	**8.119926**	**0.001734**
Within Groups	2.168	27	0.080296		
Total	3.472	29			

EXERCISES 10.3

Mechanics

44. **FILE** *Exercise_10.44.* Random sampling from three normally distributed populations produced the results in the accompanying data file.
    a. Calculate the grand mean.
    b. Calculate *SSTR* and *MSTR*.
    c. Calculate *SSE* and *MSE*.
    d. Specify the competing hypotheses in order to determine whether some differences exist between the population means.
    e. Calculate the value of the $F_{(df_1, df_2)}$ test statistic and the p-value.
    f. At the 5% significance level, what is the conclusion to the hypothesis test?

45. **FILE** *Exercise_10.45.* Random sampling from four normally distributed populations produced the results in the accompanying data file.
    a. Calculate the grand mean.
    b. Calculate *SSTR* and *MSTR*.

    c. Calculate *SSE* and *MSE*.
    d. Specify the competing hypotheses in order to determine whether some differences exist between the population means.
    e. Calculate the value of the $F_{(df_1, df_2)}$ test statistic and the p-value.
    f. At the 10% significance level, what is the conclusion to the hypothesis test?

46. Given the following information obtained from three normally distributed populations, construct an ANOVA table and perform an ANOVA test of mean differences at the 1% significance level.

    $SSTR = 220.7; SSE = 2252.2; c = 3; n_1 = n_2 = n_3 = 8$

47. Given the following information obtained from four normally distributed populations, construct an ANOVA table and perform an ANOVA test of mean differences at the 5% significance level.

    $SST = 70.47; SSTR = 11.34; c = 4; n_1 = n_2 = n_3 = n_4 = 15$

48. An analysis of variance experiment produced a portion of the accompanying ANOVA table. Assume normality in the underlying populations

Source of Variation	SS	df	MS	F	p-value
Between Groups	25.08	3	?	?	0.000
Within Groups	92.64	76	?		
Total	117.72	79			

a. Specify the competing hypotheses in order to determine whether some differences exist between the population means.

b. Fill in the missing statistics in the ANOVA table.

c. At the 5% significance level, what is the conclusion to the hypothesis test?

Applications

49. A report finds that Asian residents in Boston have the highest average life expectancy of any racial or ethnic group. The report included the following summary statistics:

Asian	Black	Latino	White
$\bar{x}_1 = 83.7$ years	$\bar{x}_2 = 73.5$ years	$\bar{x}_3 = 80.6$ years	$\bar{x}_4 = 79.0$ years
$s_1^2 = 26.3$	$s_2^2 = 27.5$	$s_3^2 = 28.2$	$s_4^2 = 24.8$
$n_1 = 20$	$n_2 = 20$	$n_3 = 20$	$n_4 = 20$

a. Specify the competing hypotheses to test whether there are some differences in average life expectancies between the four groups.

b. Construct an ANOVA table. Assume life expectancies are normally distributed.

c. At the 5% significance level, what is the conclusion to the hypothesis test?

50. **FILE** *Detergent.* A well-known conglomerate claims that its detergent "whitens and brightens better than all the rest." In order to compare the cleansing action of the top three brands of detergents, 24 swatches of white cloth were soiled with red wine and grass stains and then washed in front-loading machines with the respective detergents. The accompanying data file shows the results.

a. Specify the competing hypotheses to test whether there are some differences in the average whitening effectiveness of the three detergents.

b. At the 5% significance level, what is the conclusion to the hypothesis test? Assume whiteness readings are normally distributed.

51. A survey finds that the cost of long-term care in the United States varies significantly, depending on where an individual lives. An economist collects data from the five states with the highest

annual costs (Alaska, Massachusetts, New Jersey, Rhode Island, and Connecticut), in order to determine if his sample data are consistent with the survey's conclusions. The economist provides the following portion of the relevant ANOVA table:

Source of Variation	SS	df	MS	F	p-value
Between Groups	635.0542	4	?	?	?
Within Groups	253.2192	20	?		
Total	888.2734	24			

a. Specify the competing hypotheses to test whether some differences exist in the mean long-term care costs in these five states.

b. Complete the ANOVA table. Assume that long-term care costs are normally distributed.

c. At the 5% significance level, do mean costs differ? Explain.

52. **FILE** *Sports.* An online survey finds that household income of recreational athletes varies by sport. In order to verify this claim, an economist samples five sports enthusiasts participating in each of four different recreational sports and obtains each enthusiast's income (in $1,000s), as shown in the accompanying data file.

a. Specify the competing hypotheses in order to test the survey's claim.

b. Do some average incomes differ depending on the recreational sport? Explain. Assume incomes are normally distributed.

53. The following output summarizes the results of an analysis of variance experiment in which the treatments were three different hybrid cars and the variable measured was the miles per gallon (mpg) obtained while driving the same route. Assume mpg is normally distributed.

Source of Variation	SS	df	MS	F	p-value
Between Groups	1034.51	2	517.26	19.86	4.49E-07
Within Groups	1302.41	50	26.05		
Total	2336.92	52			

At the 5% significance level, can we conclude that average mpg differs between the hybrids? Explain.

54. Do energy costs vary dramatically depending on where you live in the United States? Annual energy costs are collected from 25 households in four regions in the United States. A portion of the ANOVA table is shown.

Source of Variation	SS	df	MS	F	p-value
Between Groups	7531769	3	?	?	7.13E-24
Within Groups	3492385	96	?		
Total	11024154	99			

a. Complete the ANOVA table. Assume energy costs are normally distributed.

b. At the 1% significance level, can we conclude that average annual energy costs vary by region? Explain.

55. **FILE** *Buggies.* Wenton Powersports produces dune buggies. They have three assembly lines, "Razor," "Blazer," and "Tracer," named after the particular dune buggy models produced on those lines. Each assembly line was originally designed using the same target production rate. However, over the years, various changes have been made to the lines. Accordingly, management wishes to determine whether the assembly lines are still operating at the same average hourly production rate. The accompanying data file shows the production data (in dune buggies/hour) for the last eight hours.

a. Specify the competing hypotheses to test whether there are some differences in the mean production rates across the three assembly lines.

b. At the 5% significance level, what is the conclusion to the hypothesis test? What about the 10% significance level? Assume production rates are normally distributed.

56. **FILE** *Fill_Volumes.* In the carbonated beverage industry, dispensing pressure can be an important factor in achieving accurate fill volumes. Too little pressure can slow down the dispensing process. Too much pressure can create excess "fizz" and, thus, inaccurate fill volumes. Accordingly, a leading beverage manufacturer wants to conduct an experiment at three different pressure settings to determine if differences exist in the mean fill volumes. Forty bottles with a target fill volume of 12 ounces were filled at each pressure setting, and the resulting fill volumes (in ounces) are shown in the accompanying data file.

a. Specify the competing hypotheses to test whether there are differences in the mean fill volumes across the three pressure settings.

b. At the 5% significance level, what is the conclusion to the hypothesis test? What about the 1% significance level?

57. **FILE** *Exam_Scores.* A statistics instructor wonders whether significant differences exist in her students' final exam scores in her three different sections. She randomly selects the scores from 10 students in each section. The accompanying data file shows the results. Assume exam scores are normally distributed. Do these data provide enough evidence at the 5% significance level to indicate that there are some differences in final exam scores among these three sections?

58. **FILE** *Patronage.* The accompanying data file shows the number of customers that frequent a restaurant on weekend days over the past 52 weeks. At the 5% significance level, can we conclude that the average number of customers that frequent the restaurant differs by weekend day?

59. **FILE** *Revenues.* The accompanying data file shows the quarterly revenues (in $ millions) for a large firm over the past 10 years. Assume revenues are normally distributed. Conduct an ANOVA test to determine if the data provide enough evidence at the 5% significance level to indicate that there are quarterly differences in the firm's revenue.

60. **FILE** *Field_Score.* A human resource specialist wants to determine whether the average job satisfaction score (on a scale of 0 to 100) differs depending on a person's field of employment. The accompanying data file shows the scores that she collects from 30 employees in three different fields. At the 10% significance level, can we conclude that the average job satisfaction differs by field?

61. **FILE** *Foodco.* The Marketing Manager at Foodco, a large grocery store, wants to determine if store display location influences sales of a particular grocery item. She instructs employees to rotate the display location of that item every week and then tallies the weekly sales at each location over a 24-week period (8 weeks per location). The sample information is in the accompanying data file.

a. Specify the competing hypotheses to test whether there are some differences in the mean weekly sales across the three store display locations.

b. At the 5% significance level, what is the conclusion to the hypothesis test? Assume sales are normally distributed.

62. **FILE** *Generic.* A consumer advocate in California is concerned with the price of a common generic drug. Specifically, he feels that one region of the state has significantly different prices for the drug compared to two other regions. He divides the state into three regions and collects the generic drug's price (in $) from 10 pharmacies in each region. The sample information is in the accompanying data file. At the 5% significance level, do differences exist between the mean drug prices in the three regions? Explain. Assume that prices are normally distributed.

63. **FILE** *Concrete_Mixing.* Compressive strength of concrete is affected by several factors, including composition (sand, cement, etc.), mixer type (batch vs. continuous), and curing procedure. Accordingly, a concrete company is conducting an experiment to determine how mixing technique affects the resulting compressive strength. Four potential mixing techniques have been identified. Subsequently, samples of 20 specimens have been subjected to each mixing technique, and the resulting compressive strengths (in pounds per square inch, psi) were measured. The sample information is in the accompanying data file.

a. Specify the competing hypotheses to test whether there are some differences in the mean compressive strengths across the four mixing techniques.

b. At the 5% significance level, what is the conclusion to the hypothesis test? What about the 1% significance level? Assume that compressive strengths are normally distributed.

64. **FILE** *Plywood.* An engineer wants to determine whether the average strength of plywood boards (in pounds per square inch, psi) differs depending on the type of glue used. For three types of glue, she measures the strength of 20 plywood boards. The sample information is in the accompanying data file. At the 5% significance level, can she conclude that the average strength of the plywood boards differs by the type of glue used? Explain. Assume that the strength of plywood boards is normally distributed.

65. **FILE** *Route.* An employee of a small software company in Minneapolis bikes to work during the summer months. He can travel to work using one of three routes and wonders whether the average commute times (in minutes) differ between the three routes. He uses each route for one week and records the commute times. The sample information is in the accompanying data file. Determine at the 1% significance level whether the average commute times differ between the three routes. Assume that commute times are normally distributed.

66. **FILE** *Website.* A data analyst for an online store wonders whether average customer visits to the store's website vary by day of the week. He collects daily unique visits to the website for a 12-week period. The sample information is in the accompanying data file. At the 5% significance level, what conclusion can the data analyst make? Discuss any assumptions that you make for the analysis.

67. **FILE** *Battery_Times.* Electrobat, a battery manufacturer, is investigating how storage temperature affects the performance of one of its popular deep-cell battery models used in recreational vehicles. Samples of 30 fully charged batteries were subjected to a light load under each of four different storage temperature levels. The hours until deep discharge (meaning ≤ 20% of charge remaining) were measured. The sample information is in the accompanying data file. At the 5% significance level, can you conclude that mean discharge times differ across the four storage temperature levels? What about the 1% significance level?

10.4 WRITING WITH DATA

Comstock/Stockbyte/Getty Images

Case study

A study finds that the average U.S. driver languished in rush-hour traffic for 36.1 hours. This congestion also wasted approximately 2.81 billion gallons in fuel, or roughly three weeks' worth of gas per traveler. Omar Najm, a research analyst at an environmental firm, is stunned by some of the report's conclusions. Omar is asked to conduct an independent study in order to see if differences exist in congestion depending on the city where the commuter drives. He selects 25 commuters from each of the five cities that suffered from the worst congestion and asks each commuter to approximate the time spent in traffic (in hours) over the last calendar year. Omar assumes that the underlying populations are normally distributed. Table 10.10 shows a portion of his sample results.

FILE
Congestion

TABLE 10.10 Annual Hours of Delay per Commuter in Five Cities

Los Angeles	Washington, DC	Atlanta	Houston	San Francisco
71	64	60	58	57
60	64	58	56	56
⋮	⋮	⋮	⋮	⋮
68	57	57	59	56

Does traffic congestion vary by city? A study is conducted to determine if traffic congestion, measured by annual hours of delay per commuter, differs in the worst-congested cities: Los Angeles; Washington, D.C.; Atlanta; Houston; and San Francisco. Twenty-five commuters in each of these cities were asked how many hours they wasted in traffic over the past calendar year. Table 10.11 reports the summary statistics. The sample data indicate that Los Angeles residents waste the most time sitting in traffic, with an average of 69.2 hours per year. Washington, DC, residents rank a close second, spending an average of 62 hours per year in traffic. Residents in Atlanta, Houston, and San Francisco spend on average, 57.0, 56.5, and 55.6 hours per year in traffic, respectively.

TABLE 10.11 Summary Statistics for Traffic Congestion

Los Angeles	Washington, DC	Atlanta	Houston	San Francisco
$\bar{x}_1 = 69.24$	$\bar{x}_2 = 61.96$	$\bar{x}_3 = 57.00$	$\bar{x}_4 = 56.52$	$\bar{x}_5 = 55.56$
$s_1 = 4.60$	$s_2 = 4.74$	$s_3 = 4.81$	$s_4 = 5.37$	$s_5 = 3.66$

An ANOVA test was conducted to determine if significant differences exist in the average number of hours spent in traffic in these five worst-congested cities. The value of the test statistic is $F_{(4,120)} = 37.251$ with a p-value of approximately zero. Therefore, at the 5% level of significance, traffic congestion does vary by city.

Although the ANOVA test allows us to conclude that congestion varies by city, it does not allow us to compare congestion between any two cities. For instance, we cannot conclude that Los Angeles commuters face significantly higher delays compared to San Francisco commuters. Further analysis of the difference between paired population means is advised.

Suggested Case Studies

Report 10.1 Recent data report that the average salary is $61,261 in Denver and $63,381 in Chicago. Suppose these data were based on 100 employees in each city where the population standard deviation is $16,000 in Denver and $14,500 in Chicago. In a report, use the sample information to determine whether the average starting salary in Chicago is greater than Denver's average starting salary.

Report 10.2 Go to https://finance.yahoo.com/ to extract two years of monthly adjusted close price data for two of Fidelity's mutual funds. For each fund, calculate monthly returns as the percentage change in adjusted close prices from the previous month, giving 23 months of return data. Use summary measures to compare the risk and reward for each fund. At the 5% significance level, determine whether the mean returns differ. (*Hint:* This is a matched-pairs sample.) Discuss any assumptions that you make for the analysis.

Report 10.3 **FILE** *Industry_Returns.* The accompanying data file contains annual stock returns (in %) for 10 firms in the energy industry, 13 firms in the retail industry, and 16 firms in the utilities industry. In a report, use the sample information to determine whether significant differences exist in the annual returns for the three industries. Use a reasonable level of significance for the tests and state your assumptions clearly.

11

Comparisons Involving Proportions

LEARNING OBJECTIVES

After reading this chapter you should be able to:

LO **11.1** Make inferences about the difference between two population proportions based on independent sampling.

LO **11.2** Conduct a goodness-of-fit test for a multinomial experiment.

LO **11.3** Conduct a test for independence.

In Chapter 10, we used numerical variables to make inferences regarding the means of two or more populations. In this chapter, we focus on categorical variables. We first compare the difference between two population proportions. For instance, marketing executives and advertisers are often interested in the different preferences between male and female customers when determining where to target advertising dollars.

We then introduce a goodness-of-fit test that is commonly used with a frequency distribution for a categorical variable. For instance, we may want to substantiate a claim that market shares in the automotive industry have changed dramatically over the past 10 years.

We conclude the chapter with a test of independence. While a goodness-of-fit test focuses on a single categorical variable, a test for independence is used to compare two categorical variables. For example, doctors might want to investigate whether or not a new vaccine is equally effective for people of all age groups.

Shutterstock

INTRODUCTORY CASE

Sportswear Brands

In the introductory case to Chapter 4, Janet Mwangi, a manager at 24/7 Fitness Center, wishes to develop a data-driven strategy for selecting which new open house attendees to contact. From 400 past open house attendees, she knows the enrollment outcome (Enroll or Not Enroll) of a follow-up phone call regarding a club membership. In addition, she has information on the age of attendees in years, where age is binned into groups: Under 30, Between 30 and 50, and Over 50.

Janet uses the data to construct a contingency table, shown in Table 11.1, that is cross-classified by enrollment outcome and age group. A cursory look at the relevant empirical probabilities concerning age and enrollment seems to suggest that the probability of enrollment depends on the age of the attendees. Before she uses this information to identify individual open house attendees who are likely to purchase a gym membership, Janet wants to ensure that the results are backed by a thorough statistical analysis.

TABLE 11.1 Enrollment and Age Frequencies of Attendees

Enrollment Outcome	Age Group		
	Under 30 (U)	Between 30 and 50 (B)	Over 50 (O)
Enroll (E)	24	72	44
Not Enroll (N)	84	88	88

Janet wants to use the above sample information to

1. Determine whether the two variables (Age Group and Enrollment Outcome) are related at the 5% significance level.

2. Discuss how the findings from the test for independence can be used.

A synopsis of this case will be provided in Section 11.3.

11.1 INFERENCE CONCERNING THE DIFFERENCE BETWEEN TWO PROPORTIONS

In Chapter 10, we focused on numerical variables, where we compared the means of two or more populations. Now we turn our attention to categorical variables. In this section, we provide statistical inference concerning the difference between two population proportions under independent sampling. This technique has many practical applications.

Consider an investor who may want to determine if the bankruptcy rate is the same in the technology and construction industries. The resulting analysis will help determine the relative risk of investing in these two industries. Or perhaps a marketing executive maintains that the proportion of male customers who buy a firm's product is greater than the proportion of female customers who buy the product. If this claim is supported by the data, it provides information as to where the firm should advertise. In another case, a consumer advocacy group may state that the proportion of young adults who carry health insurance is less than the proportion of older adults. Health and government officials might be particularly interested in this type of information.

All of the above examples deal with comparing two population proportions. Our parameter of interest is $p_1 - p_2$, where p_1 and p_2 denote the proportions in the first and second populations, respectively. The estimator for the difference between two population proportions is $\bar{P}_1 - \bar{P}_2$.

Confidence Interval for $p_1 - p_2$

Because the population proportions p_1 and p_2 are unknown, we estimate them by $\bar{p}_1$ and $\bar{p}_2$, respectively. The first sample proportion is computed as $\bar{p}_1 = x_1/n_1$ where x_1 denotes the number of successes in n_1 observations drawn from population 1. Similarly, the second sample proportion is computed as $\bar{p}_2 = x_2/n_2$ where x_2 is the number of successes in n_2 observations drawn from population 2. In both cases, the outcome of interest is labeled as success. The difference $\bar{p}_1 - \bar{p}_2$ is a point estimate of $p_1 - p_2$.

Recall from Chapter 7 that the standard errors for the estimators $\bar{P}_1$ and $\bar{P}_2$ are $se(\bar{P}_1) = \sqrt{\frac{p_1(1-p_1)}{n_1}}$ and $se(\bar{P}_2) = \sqrt{\frac{p_2(1-p_2)}{n_2}}$, respectively. Therefore, for two independently drawn samples, the standard error, $se(\bar{P}_1 - \bar{P}_2) = \sqrt{\frac{p_1(1-p_1)}{n_1} + \frac{p_2(1-p_2)}{n_2}}$. Because p_1 and p_2 are unknown, we estimate the standard error by $\sqrt{\frac{\bar{p}_1(1-\bar{p}_1)}{n_1} + \frac{\bar{p}_2(1-\bar{p}_2)}{n_2}}$. Finally, when both n_1 and n_2 are sufficiently large, the sampling distribution of $\bar{P}_1 - \bar{P}_2$ can be approximated by the normal distribution.

We construct a confidence interval for the difference between two population proportions using the formula in the following definition box.

CONFIDENCE INTERVAL FOR $p_1 - p_2$

A $(1 - \alpha)$ 100% confidence interval for the difference between two population proportions $p_1 - p_2$ is given by:

$$(\bar{p}_1 - \bar{p}_2) \pm z_{\alpha/2} \sqrt{\frac{\bar{p}_1(1-\bar{p}_1)}{n_1} + \frac{\bar{p}_2(1-\bar{p}_2)}{n_2}}.$$

As noted, the above formula is valid only when the two samples are sufficiently large; the general guideline is that $n_1 p_1$, $n_1(1 - p_1)$, $n_2 p_2$, and $n_2(1 - p_2)$ must all be greater than or equal to 5, where p_1 and p_2 are evaluated at $\bar{p}_1$ and $\bar{p}_2$, respectively.

EXAMPLE 11.1

Despite his inexperience, Candidate A appears to have gained support among the electorate. Three months ago, in a survey of 120 registered voters, 55 said that they would vote for Candidate A. Today, 41 registered voters in a sample of 80 said that they would vote for Candidate A. Construct the 95% confidence interval for the difference between the two population proportions.

SOLUTION: Let p_1 and p_2 represent the population proportion of the electorate who support the candidate today and three months ago, respectively. In order to calculate the 95% confidence interval for $p_1 - p_2$, we use the formula $(\bar{p}_1 - \bar{p}_2) \pm z_{\alpha/2} \sqrt{\frac{\bar{p}_1(1-\bar{p}_1)}{n_1} + \frac{\bar{p}_2(1-\bar{p}_2)}{n_2}}$. We compute the sample proportions as

$$\bar{p}_1 = x_1/n_1 = 41/80 = 0.5125 \quad \text{and} \quad \bar{p}_2 = x_2/n_2 = 55/120 = 0.4583.$$

Note that the normality condition is satisfied because $n_1\bar{p}_1$, $n_1(1-\bar{p}_1)$, $n_2\bar{p}_2$, and $n_2(1-\bar{p}_2)$ all exceed 5. For the 95% confidence interval, $\alpha = 0.05$ and $\alpha/2 = 0.05/2 = 0.025$. Using Excel we enter =NORM.INV(0.975, 0, 1) and find that $z_{0.025} = 1.96$. Substituting the values into the formula, we find

$$(0.5125 - 0.4583) \pm 1.96 \sqrt{\frac{0.5125(1 - 0.5125)}{80} + \frac{0.4583(1 - 0.4583)}{120}}$$

$$= 0.0542 \pm 0.1412 \text{ or } [-0.0871, 0.1954].$$

With 95% confidence, we can report that the percentage change of support for the candidate is between –8.71% and 19.54%.

Hypothesis Test for $p_1 - p_2$

The null and alternative hypotheses for testing the difference between two population proportions under independent sampling will take one of the following forms:

Two-Tailed Test	Right-Tailed Test	Left-Tailed Test
$H_0: p_1 - p_2 = d_0$	$H_0: p_1 - p_2 \le d_0$	$H_0: p_1 - p_2 \ge d_0$
$H_A: p_1 - p_2 \ne d_0$	$H_A: p_1 - p_2 > d_0$	$H_A: p_1 - p_2 < d_0$

We use the symbol d_0 to denote a given hypothesized difference between the unknown population proportions p_1 and p_2. In most cases, d_0 is set to zero. For example, when testing if the population proportions differ—that is, if $p_1 \ne p_2$—we use a two-tailed test, with the competing hypotheses defined as $H_0: p_1 - p_2 = 0$ versus $H_A: p_1 - p_2 \ne 0$. If, on the other hand, we wish to determine whether or not the proportions differ by some amount, say 0.20, we set $d_0 = 0.20$ and define the competing hypotheses as $H_0: p_1 - p_2 = 0.20$ versus $H_A: p_1 - p_2 \ne 0.20$. One-tailed tests are defined similarly.

EXAMPLE 11.2

Let's revisit Example 11.1. Specify the competing hypotheses in order to determine whether the proportion of those who favor Candidate A has changed over the three-month period. Using the 95% confidence interval, what is the conclusion to the test? Explain.

SOLUTION: In essence, we would like to determine whether $p_1 \neq p_2$, where p_1 and p_2 represent the population proportion of the electorate who support the candidate today and three months ago, respectively. We formulate the competing hypotheses as

$$H_0 : p_1 - p_2 = 0$$

$$H_A : p_1 - p_2 \neq 0$$

In Example 11.1, we constructed the 95% confidence interval for the difference between the population proportions as [−0.0870, 0.1954]. We note that the interval contains zero, the value hypothesized under the null hypothesis. Therefore, we are unable to reject the null hypothesis. In other words, from the given sample data, we cannot conclude at the 5% significance level that the support for Candidate A has changed.

We now introduce the standard four-step procedure for conducting one- or two-tailed hypothesis tests concerning the difference between two proportions $p_1 - p_2$. We transform its estimate $\bar{p}_1 - \bar{p}_2$ into a corresponding z statistic by subtracting the hypothesized difference d_0 from this estimate and dividing by the standard error of the estimator $se(\bar{P}_1 - \bar{P}_2)$. When we developed the confidence interval for $p_1 - p_2$, we assumed $se(\bar{P}_1 - \bar{P}_2) = \sqrt{\frac{\bar{p}_1(1-\bar{p}_1)}{n_1} + \frac{\bar{p}_2(1-\bar{p}_2)}{n_2}}$. However, if d_0 is zero—that is, $H_0 : p_1 = p_2$—both $\bar{p}_1$ and $\bar{p}_2$ are essentially the estimates of the same unknown population proportion. For this reason, the standard error can be improved upon by computing the pooled estimate $\bar{p} = (x_1 + x_2)/(n_1 + n_2)$ for the unknown population proportion, which is now based on a larger sample.

The following definition box shows the formula for the test statistic when testing $p_1 - p_2$ under two scenarios. As in the case of the confidence interval, the formulas are valid only when the two samples are sufficiently large.

TEST STATISTIC FOR TESTING $p_1 - p_2$

The value of the test statistic for a hypothesis test concerning the difference between two proportions $p_1 - p_2$ is computed using one of the following two formulas:

1. If the hypothesized difference d_0 is zero, then the value of the test statistic is

$$z = \frac{\bar{p}_1 - \bar{p}_2}{\sqrt{\bar{p}(1-\bar{p})\left(\frac{1}{n_1} + \frac{1}{n_2}\right)}},$$

where $\bar{p}_1 = \frac{x_1}{n_1}, \bar{p}_2 = \frac{x_2}{n_2}$, and $\bar{p} = \frac{x_1 + x_2}{n_1 + n_2}$.

2. If the hypothesized difference d_0 is not zero, then the value of the test statistic is

$$z = \frac{(\bar{p}_1 - \bar{p}_2) - d_0}{\sqrt{\frac{\bar{p}_1(1-\bar{p}_1)}{n_1} + \frac{\bar{p}_2(1-\bar{p}_2)}{n_2}}}.$$

EXAMPLE 11.3

An analyst claims that the proportion of men who regularly make online purchases is greater than the proportion of women. Of the 6,000 men that the analyst surveyed, 5,400 of them said they regularly make online purchases, compared with 8,600 of the 10,000 women surveyed. [There are no non-binary observations in this data set.] Test the analyst's claim at the 5% significance level.

SOLUTION: Let p_1 and p_2 denote the population proportions of men and of women who make online purchases, respectively. We wish to test whether the proportion of men who make online purchases is greater than the proportion of women; that is, $p_1 - p_2 > 0$. Therefore, we construct the competing hypotheses as

$$H_0: p_1 - p_2 \leq 0$$

$$H_A: p_1 - p_2 > 0$$

Because the hypothesized difference is zero, or $d_0 = 0$, we compute the value of the

test statistic as $z = \dfrac{\bar{p}_1 - \bar{p}_2}{\sqrt{\bar{p}(1-\bar{p})\left(\frac{1}{n_1} + \frac{1}{n_2}\right)}}$. We first compute the sample proportions

$\bar{p}_1 = x_1/n_1 = 5{,}400/6{,}000 = 0.90$ and $\bar{p}_2 = x_2/n_2 = 8{,}600/10{,}000 = 0.86$. The normal-

ity condition is satisfied because $n_1\bar{p}_1, n_1(1-\bar{p}_1), n_2\bar{p}_2$, and $n_2(1-\bar{p}_2)$ all exceed 5. Next

we calculate the pooled estimate of the population proportion $\bar{p} = \frac{x_1 + x_2}{n_1 + n_2} = \frac{5{,}400 + 8{,}600}{6{,}000 + 10{,}000} =$

0.875. Thus,

$$z = \frac{\bar{p}_1 - \bar{p}_2}{\sqrt{\bar{p}(1-\bar{p})\left(\frac{1}{n_1} + \frac{1}{n_2}\right)}} = \frac{(0.90 - 0.86)}{\sqrt{0.875(1 - 0.875)\left(\frac{1}{6{,}000} + \frac{1}{10{,}000}\right)}} = 7.4066.$$

In Excel, in order to find the *p*-value for this right-tailed test, or equivalently $P(Z \geq 7.4066)$, we enter `=1-NORM.DIST(7.4066, 0, 1, TRUE)`. Excel returns 6.48E-14, which is approximately zero. Because the *p*-value $< \alpha = 0.05$, we reject H_0. At the 5% significance level, the analyst's claim is supported by the sample data; that is, the proportion of men who regularly make online purchases is greater than the proportion of women. The results appear consistent with the decision by retailers to redesign their websites to attract male customers.

EXAMPLE 11.4

While we expect relatively expensive wines to have more desirable characteristics than relatively inexpensive wines, people are often confused in their assessment of the quality of wine in a blind test (npr.com, May 24, 2016). In a recent experiment at a local winery, the same wine is served to two groups of people but with different price information. In the first group, 60 people are told that they are tasting a $25 wine, of which 48 like the wine. In the second group, only 20 of 50 people like the wine when they are told that it is a $10 wine. The experiment is conducted to determine if the proportion of people who like the wine in the first group is more than 20 percentage points higher than in the second group. Conduct this test at the 5% significance level.

SOLUTION: Let p_1 and p_2 denote the proportions of people who like the wine in groups 1 and 2, respectively. We want to test if the proportion of people who like the wine in the first group is more than 20 percentage points higher than in the second group. Thus, we construct the competing hypotheses as

$$H_0: p_1 - p_2 \leq 0.20$$

$$H_A: p_1 - p_2 > 0.20$$

We first compute the sample proportions as $\bar{p}_1 = x_1/n_1 = 48/60 = 0.80$ and $\bar{p}_2 = x_2/n_2 = 20/50 = 0.40$, and we note that the normality condition is satisfied because $n_1\bar{p}_1$, $n_1(1 - \bar{p}_1)$, $n_2\bar{p}_2$, and $n_2(1 - \bar{p}_2)$ all exceed 5.

Because $d_0 = 0.20$, the value of the test statistic is computed as

$$z = \frac{(\bar{p}_1 - \bar{p}_2) - d_0}{\sqrt{\dfrac{\bar{p}_1(1 - \bar{p}_1)}{n_1} + \dfrac{\bar{p}_2(1 - \bar{p}_2)}{n_2}}} = \frac{(0.80 - 0.40) - 0.20}{\sqrt{\dfrac{0.80(1 - 0.80)}{60} + \dfrac{0.40(1 - 0.40)}{50}}} = 2.3146.$$

In Excel, in order to find the p-value for this right-tailed test, or equivalently $P(Z \geq 2.3146)$, we enter =1-NORM.DIST(2.3146, 0, 1, TRUE). Excel returns 0.0103. Because the p-value $< \alpha = 0.05$, we reject the null hypothesis. At the 5% significance level, we conclude that the proportion of people who like the wine in the first group is more than 20 percentage points higher than in the second group. Overall, this result is consistent with scientific research, which has demonstrated the power of suggestion in wine tasting.

EXERCISES 11.1

Mechanics

1. Given $\bar{p}_1 = 0.85$, $n_1 = 400$, $\bar{p}_2 = 0.90$, $n_2 = 350$, construct the 90% confidence interval for the difference between the population proportions. Is there a difference between the population proportions at the 10% significance level? Explain.

2. Given $x_1 = 50$, $n_1 = 200$, $x_2 = 70$, $n_2 = 250$, construct the 95% confidence interval for the difference between the population proportions. Is there a difference between the population proportions at the 5% significance level? Explain.

3. Consider the following competing hypotheses and accompanying sample data.

$$H_0: p_1 - p_2 \geq 0$$
$$H_A: p_1 - p_2 < 0$$
$$x_1 = 250 \qquad x_2 = 275$$
$$n_1 = 400 \qquad n_2 = 400$$

a. Calculate the value of the test statistic.
b. Find the p-value.
c. At the 5% significance level, what is the conclusion to the hypothesis test? Is p_1 less than p_2?

4. Consider the following competing hypotheses and accompanying sample data.

$$H_0: p_1 - p_2 = 0$$
$$H_A: p_1 - p_2 \neq 0$$
$$x_1 = 100 \qquad x_2 = 172$$
$$n_1 = 250 \qquad n_2 = 400$$

a. Calculate the value of the test statistic.
b. Find the p-value.
c. At the 5% significance level, what is the conclusion to the hypothesis test? Do the population proportions differ?

5. Consider the following competing hypotheses and accompanying sample data.

$$H_0: p_1 - p_2 = 0$$
$$H_A: p_1 - p_2 \neq 0$$
$$x_1 = 300 \qquad x_2 = 325$$
$$n_1 = 600 \qquad n_2 = 500$$

a. Calculate the value of the test statistic.
b. Find the p-value.
c. At the 5% significance level, what is the conclusion to the hypothesis test? Do the population proportions differ?

6. Consider the following competing hypotheses and accompanying sample data.

$$H_0: p_1 - p_2 = 0.20$$
$$H_A: p_1 - p_2 \neq 0.20$$
$$x_1 = 150 \qquad x_2 = 130$$
$$n_1 = 250 \qquad n_2 = 400$$

a. Calculate the value of the test statistic.
b. Find the p-value.
c. At the 5% significance level, what is the conclusion to the hypothesis test? Can you conclude that the difference between the population proportions differs from 0.20?

Applications

7. Suppose in a representative sample, 344 of 430 girls and 369 of 450 boys score at proficient or advanced levels on a standardized math test.

a. Construct the 95% confidence interval for the difference between the population proportions of girls and boys who score at proficient or advanced levels.

b. Develop the appropriate null and alternative hypotheses to test whether the proportion of girls who score at proficient or advanced levels differs from the proportion of boys.

c. At the 5% significance level, what is the conclusion to the hypothesis test? Do the results suggest that the proportions differ?

8. Reducing scrap of 4-foot planks of hardwood is an important factor in reducing cost at a wood-flooring manufacturing company. Accordingly, engineers at Lumberworks are investigating a potential new cutting method involving lateral sawing that may reduce the scrap rate. To examine its viability, samples of planks were examined under the old and new methods. Sixty-two of the 500 planks were scrapped under the old method, whereas 36 of the 400 planks were scrapped under the new method.

a. Construct the 95% confidence interval for the difference between the population scrap rates between the old and new methods.

b. Specify the null and alternative hypotheses to test for differences in the population scrap rates between the old and new cutting methods.

c. Using the results from part (a), can we conclude at the 5% significance level that the scrap rate of the new method is different than that of the old method?

9. A recent report finds that 14.6% of newly married couples had a spouse of a different race or ethnicity. In a similar survey in 1980, only 6.8% of newlywed couples reported marrying someone of a different race or ethnicity. Suppose both of these surveys were conducted on 500 newly married couples.

a. Specify the competing hypotheses to test the claim that there has been an increase in the proportion of people who marry someone of a different race or ethnicity.

b. Calculate the value of the test statistic and the p-value.

c. At the 5% level of significance, what is the conclusion to the hypothesis test?

10. In order to landscape its grounds, a bank purchased 500 tulip bulbs from Nursery A of which 135 failed to bloom. The bank also purchased 500 tulip bulbs from Nursery B of which 70 failed to bloom.

a. Develop the hypotheses to test whether the proportion of bulbs that failed to bloom from Nursery A is more than that from Nursery B.

b. Conduct the hypothesis in part (a) at the 5% significance level.

c. At the 5% significance level, determine whether the proportion of bulbs that failed to bloom from Nursery A is more than 0.10 than that from Nursery B.

11. From an employment perspective, jobseekers are no longer calling up friends for help with job placement, as they can now get help online. In a recent survey of 150 jobseekers, 67 said they used LinkedIn to search for jobs. A similar survey of 140 jobseekers, conducted three years ago, had found that 58 jobseekers had used LinkedIn for their job search. Is there sufficient evidence to suggest that more people are now using LinkedIn to search for jobs as compared to three years ago? Use a 5% level of significance for the analysis.

12. The director of housekeeping at *Elegante,* a luxury resort hotel with two locations (*Seaside* and *Oceanfront*), wants to evaluate housekeeping performance at those two locations. Random samples of 100 rooms were inspected at each location for defects (e.g., missing towels, missing soap, dirty floors or showers, dusty tables) after being cleaned. It was found that 21 of the rooms at *Seaside* had some housekeeping defects, and 28 rooms at *Oceanfront* had some housekeeping defects.

a. Develop the hypotheses to test whether the proportion of housekeeping defects differs between the two hotel locations.

b. Calculate the value of the test statistic and the p-value.

c. Do the results suggest that the proportion of housekeeping defects differs between the two hotel locations at the 5% significance level?

d. Construct the 95% confidence interval for the difference between the population housekeeping defect rates at the two hotel locations. How can this confidence interval be used to reach the same conclusion as in part (c)?

13. In an effort to make children's toys safer and more tamper-proof, toy packaging has become cumbersome for parents to remove in many cases. Accordingly, the director of marketing at Toys4Tots, a large toy manufacturer, wants to evaluate the effectiveness of a new packaging design that engineers claim will reduce customer complaints by more than 10 percentage points. Customer satisfaction surveys were sent to 250 parents who registered toys packaged under the old design and 250 parents who registered toys packaged under the new design. Of these, 85 parents expressed dissatisfaction with packaging of the old design, and 40 parents expressed dissatisfaction with packaging of the new design.

a. Specify the null and alternative hypotheses to test whether customer complaints have been reduced by more than 10 percentage points under the new packaging design.

b. Calculate the value of the test statistic and the p-value.

c. At the 5% significance level, do the results support the engineers' claim?

d. At the 1% significance level, do the results support the engineers' claim?

14. A study finds that 14% of females suffer from asthma as opposed to 6% of males. Suppose 250 females and 200 males responded to the study.

a. Develop the appropriate null and alternative hypotheses to test whether the proportion of females suffering from asthma is greater than the proportion of males.

b. Calculate the value of the test statistic and the p-value.

c. At the 5% significance level, what is the conclusion? Do the data suggest that females suffer more from asthma than males?

15. A report finds that only 26% of psychology majors are satisfied with their career paths as compared to 50% of accounting majors. Suppose these results were obtained from a survey of 300 psychology majors and 350 accounting majors.

    a. Develop the null and alternative hypotheses to test whether the proportion of accounting majors satisfied with their career paths is higher than that of psychology majors by more than 20 percentage points.

    b. Calculate the value of the test statistic and the *p*-value.

    c. At the 5% significance level, what is the conclusion?

16. Due to late delivery problems with an existing supplier, the director of procurement at ElectroTech began to place orders for electrical switches with a new supplier as part of a "dual-source" (two-supplier) strategy. Now she wants to revert to a "single-source" (i.e., one supplier) strategy to simplify purchasing activities. She wishes to conduct a test to infer whether the new supplier will continue to outperform the old supplier. Based on recent sample data, she found that 27 of 150 orders placed with the old supplier arrived late, whereas 6 of 75 orders placed with the new supplier arrived late.

    a. Specify the null and alternative hypotheses to test for whether the proportion of late deliveries with the new supplier is less than that of the old supplier.

    b. Calculate the value of the test statistic and the *p*-value.

    c. At the 5% significance level, what is the conclusion to the hypothesis test? Can the director conclude that the new supplier outperforms the old supplier?

17. A report suggests that business majors spend the least amount of time on course work than all other college students. A provost of a university decides to conduct a survey where students are asked if they study hard, defined as spending at least 20 hours per week on course work. Of 120 business majors included in the survey, 20 said that they studied hard, as compared to 48 out of 150 nonbusiness majors who said that they studied hard. At the 5% significance level, can we conclude that the proportion of business majors who study hard is less than that of nonmajors? Provide the details.

18. Two hundred patients agree to participate in a new drug trial. They were randomly assigned to either an experimental group or a control group. Of the 100 patients in the experimental group, 57% saw improvement. Of the 100 patients in the control group, 32% saw improvement. At the 5% significance level, is the proportion of patients who see improvement after taking the experimental drug more than 10 percentage points greater than the proportion of patients who see improvement after taking the placebo? Provide the details.

19. Millions of Americans experience depression every day. A study finds that 10.9% of adults aged 18–24 identified with some level of depression versus 6.8% of adults aged 65 or older. Suppose 1,000 young adults (18–24 years old) and 1,000 older adults (65 years old and older) responded to the study.

    a. Develop the appropriate null and alternative hypotheses to test whether the proportion of young adults who experience depression is greater than the proportion of older adults who experience depression.

    b. Calculate the value of the test statistic and the *p*-value.

    c. At the 5% significance level, do the sample data suggest that young adults experience depression more than older adults?

20. A transportation analyst is interested in comparing the performance at two major international airports, namely Kennedy International (JFK) in New York and O'Hare International in Chicago. She finds that 70% of the flights were on time at JFK compared with 63% at O'Hare. Suppose these proportions were based on 200 flights at each of these two airports. The transportation analyst believes that the proportion of on-time flights at JFK is more than five percentage points higher than that of O'Hare.

    a. Develop the competing hypotheses to test the transportation analyst's belief.

    b. Calculate the value of the test statistic and the *p*-value.

    c. At the 5% significance level, do the data support the transportation analyst's belief? Explain.

11.2 GOODNESS-OF-FIT TEST FOR A MULTINOMIAL EXPERIMENT

LO 11.2

Conduct a goodness-of-fit test for a multinomial experiment.

In the last section, we compared the difference between two population proportions. Here we extend the analysis to test if two or more population proportions differ from each other or any predetermined (hypothesized) set of values. There are many instances where we may want to make inferences of this type. For instance, in a heavily concentrated industry consisting of five firms, we may want to determine whether market shares differ between the firms. Or, in a political contest, we may want to contest the prediction that Candidates A, B, C, and D will receive 40%, 30%, 20%, and 10% of the vote, respectively. Before conducting a test of this type, we must first ensure that the random experiment satisfies the conditions of a **multinomial experiment,** which is simply a generalization of the Bernoulli process first introduced in Chapter 5.

Recall that a Bernoulli process, also referred to as a binomial experiment, is a series of n independent and identical trials of an experiment, where each trial has only two possible outcomes, conventionally labeled "success" and "failure." For the binomial experiment, we generally denote the probability of success as p and the probability of failure as $1 - p$. Alternatively, we could let p_1 and p_2 represent these probabilities, where $p_1 + p_2 = 1$. Now let us assume that the number of outcomes per trial is k where $k \geq 2$.

A MULTINOMIAL EXPERIMENT

A multinomial experiment consists of a series of n independent and identical trials, such that for each trial:

- There are k possible outcomes or categories, where $k \geq 2$.
- The probability p_i associated with the ith category remains the same.
- The sum of the probabilities is one; that is, $p_1 + p_2 + \ldots + p_k = 1$.

Note that when $k = 2$, the multinomial experiment specializes to a binomial experiment.

Numerous experiments fit the conditions of a multinomial experiment. For instance,

- As compared to the previous day, a stockbroker records whether the price of a stock rises, falls, or stays the same. This example has three possible categories ($k = 3$).
- A consumer rates service at a restaurant as excellent, good, fair, or poor ($k = 4$).
- The admissions office records which of the six business concentrations a student picks ($k = 6$).

When setting up the competing hypotheses for a multinomial experiment, we have essentially two choices. We can set all population proportions equal to the same specific value or, equivalently, equal to one another. For instance, if we want to judge on the basis of sample data whether the proportion of voters who favor four different candidates is not the same, the competing hypotheses would take the following form:

$$H_0: p_1 = p_2 = p_3 = p_4 = 0.25$$
$$H_A: \text{Not all population proportions are equal to } 0.25.$$

Note that the hypothesized value under the null hypothesis is 0.25 because the population proportions must sum to one. We can also set each population proportion equal to a different predetermined (hypothesized) value. Suppose we want to contest the prediction that 40% of the voters favor Candidate 1, 30% favor Candidate 2, 20% favor Candidate 3, and 10% favor Candidate 4. The competing hypotheses are formulated as

$$H_0: p_1 = 0.40, p_2 = 0.30, p_3 = 0.20, \text{ and } p_4 = 0.10$$
$$H_A: \text{Not all population proportions equal their hypothesized values.}$$

When conducting a test, we take a random sample and determine whether the sample proportions are significantly different from the hypothesized population proportions. For this reason, this type of test is called a **goodness-of-fit test.** Under the usual assumption that the null hypothesis is true, we derive the expected frequencies of the categories in a multinomial experiment and compare them with observed frequencies. The objective is to determine whether we can reject the null hypothesis in favor of the alternative hypothesis. To see how to conduct a goodness-of-fit test, consider the following example.

One year ago, the management at a restaurant chain surveyed its patrons to determine whether changes should be made to the menu. One question on the survey asked patrons to rate the quality of the restaurant's entrées. The percentages of the patrons responding Excellent, Good, Fair, or Poor are listed in the following table:

Excellent	Good	Fair	Poor
15%	30%	45%	10%

Based on responses to the overall survey, management decided to revamp the menu. Recently, the same question concerning the quality of entrées was asked of a random sample of 250 patrons. Their responses are shown below:

Excellent	Good	Fair	Poor
46	83	105	16

At the 5% significance level, we want to determine whether there has been any change in the population proportions calculated one year ago. In order to conduct this hypothesis test, we first explain the intuition behind the calculation of the test statistic and introduce a new distribution.

Finding Expected Frequencies

The first step in calculating the value of the test statistic for a multinomial experiment is to calculate the expected frequency for each category. That is, we need to estimate the frequencies that we would expect to get if the null hypothesis is true. In general, in order to calculate the expected frequency e_i for category i, we multiply the sample size n by the respective hypothesized value of the population proportion p_i. For example, consider the category Excellent. If the null hypothesis is true—that is, there is no change in the proportion from a year earlier—then we expect that 15% ($p_1 = 0.15$) of 250 patrons will find the quality of entrées to be excellent. Therefore, the expected frequency of Excellent responses is 37.5 (= 250 × 0.15). The expected frequencies for the other responses are found similarly and are shown in Table 11.2.

TABLE 11.2 Calculation of Expected Frequency for Restaurant Example

	Hypothesized Proportion, p_i	Expected Frequency, $e_i = np_i$
Excellent	0.15	250 × 0.15 = 37.5
Good	0.30	250 × 0.30 = 75.0
Fair	0.45	250 × 0.45 = 112.5
Poor	0.10	250 × 0.10 = 25.0
		$\Sigma e_i = 250$

As a check on the calculations, the sum of the expected frequencies Σe_i must equal the sample size n, which in this example equals 250. A condition of the goodness-of-fit test is that each expected frequency e_i must equal five or more. This condition is satisfied here, but we will see shortly that sometimes it is necessary to combine observations from two or more categories to achieve this result. Once the expected frequencies are calculated, we are ready to calculate the value of the test statistic.

The χ^2 Distribution

The test statistic for a goodness-of-fit test compares expected frequencies with observed frequencies. The test statistic follows a new distribution, called the χ^2 **(chi-square) distribution.** Like the t distribution, the χ^2 distribution is characterized by a family of distributions, where each distribution depends on its particular degrees of freedom df. It is common, therefore, to refer to it as the χ^2_{df} distribution. The χ^2_{df} distribution is positively skewed, where the extent of skewness depends on the degrees of freedom. As the *df* grow larger, the χ^2_{df} distribution approaches the normal distribution. For instance, in Figure 11.1, the χ^2_{20} distribution resembles the shape of the normal distribution.

FIGURE 11.1 The χ^2_{df} distribution with various degrees of freedom

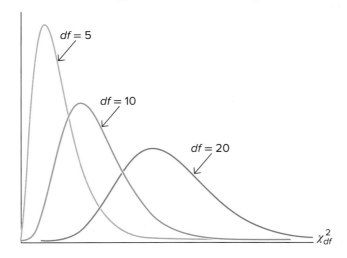

SUMMARY OF THE X^2_{df} DISTRIBUTION

- The χ^2_{df} distribution is characterized by a family of distributions, where each distribution depends on its particular degrees of freedom *df*.
- The χ^2_{df} distribution is positively skewed, and the extent of skewness depends on the *df*. As the *df* grow larger, the χ^2_{df} distribution approaches the normal distribution.
- The values of the χ^2_{df} distribution range from zero to infinity.

The χ^2_{df} test statistic measures how much the observed frequencies deviate from the expected frequencies. In particular, χ^2_{df} is computed as the sum of the standardized squared deviations. The smallest value that χ^2_{df} can assume is zero—this occurs when each observed frequency equals its expected frequency. Rejection of the null hypothesis occurs when χ^2_{df} is significantly greater than zero. As a result, these tests of hypotheses regarding multiple population proportions ($p_1, p_2, p_3, \ldots$) are always implemented as right-tailed tests. However, because the alternative hypothesis states that not all population proportions equal their hypothesized values, rejection of the null hypothesis does not indicate which proportions differ from these values. The following definition box provides the formula for the test statistic for the goodness-of-fit test.

TEST STATISTIC FOR GOODNESS-OF-FIT TEST

For a multinomial experiment with *k* categories, the value of the test statistic is calculated as

$$\chi^2_{df} = \Sigma \frac{(o_i - e_i)^2}{e_i},$$

where $df = k - 1$, o_i is the observed frequency of the *i*th category, $e_i = np_i$ is the expected frequency of the *i*th category, and *n* is the number of observations.

Note: The test is valid when the expected frequencies for each category are five or more.

We are now in a position to conduct a four-step hypothesis test for the restaurant example at the 5% significance level.

Step 1. Specify the null and alternative hypotheses. In the restaurant example, we want to determine whether the responses of the 250 patrons are inconsistent with the earlier proportions. Thus, we let the earlier population proportions denote the hypothesized proportions for the test. We denote p_1, p_2, p_3, and p_4 as the population proportions of those who responded Excellent, Good, Fair, or Poor, respectively, and construct the following competing hypotheses.

$$H_0: p_1 = 0.15, \ p_2 = 0.30, \ p_3 = 0.45, \ \text{and} \ p_4 = 0.10$$
$$H_A: \text{Not all population proportions equal their hypothesized values.}$$

Step 2. Specify the significance level. We conduct the hypothesis test at the 5% significance level, so $\alpha = 0.05$.

Step 3. Calculate the value of the test statistic and the p-value. In the restaurant example, there are four categories ($k = 4$), so $df = k - 1 = 3$. The value of the test statistic is calculated as

$$\chi^2_{df} = \chi^2_3 = \Sigma \frac{(o_i - e_i)^2}{e_i}$$
$$= \frac{(46 - 37.5)^2}{37.5} + \frac{(83 - 75)^2}{75} + \frac{(105 - 112)^2}{112} + \frac{(16 - 25)^2}{25}$$
$$= 6.4575$$

Because the goodness-of-fit test is always implemented as a right-tailed test, we find the p-value as $P(\chi^2_3 \geq 6.4575)$. We could use Excel's CHISQ.DIST function, which, like the NORM.DIST and T.DIST functions, returns a cumulative probability. We would need to subtract the cumulative probability from one in order to find the p-value for this right-tailed test. Instead, we use Excel's CHISQ.DIST.RT function because it directly returns the probability in the right tail of the distribution. This function requires two inputs: the value of the test statistic and df. For the restaurant example, we enter =CHISQ.DIST.RT(6.4575, 3), and Excel returns 0.091. Figure 11.2 graphically depicts the test statistic and the p-value for the restaurant example.

FIGURE 11.2 Graphical depiction of restaurant example

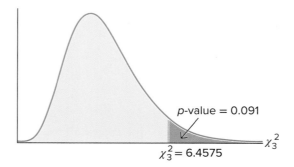

p-value = 0.091

$\chi^2_3 = 6.4575$

χ^2_3

Step 4. State the conclusion and interpret the results. Because the p-value is greater than 0.05, we do not reject H_0. We cannot conclude that the proportions differ from the ones from one year ago at the 5% significance level. Management may find this news disappointing if the goal of the menu change was to improve customer satisfaction. Responses to other questions on the survey may shed more light on whether the goals of the menu change met or fell short of expectations.

As mentioned earlier, the chi-square test is valid when the expected frequencies for each category are five or more. Sometimes it is necessary to combine two or more categories to achieve this result, as illustrated in Example 11.5.

EXAMPLE 11.5

Table 11.3 lists the market shares in 2021 for the five firms that manufacture a particular product. A marketing analyst wonders whether the market shares have changed since 2021. He surveys 200 customers. The last column of Table 11.3 shows the number of customers who recently purchased the product at each firm.

TABLE 11.3 Market Share of Five Firms

Firm	Market_Share	Recent_Customers
1	0.40	70
2	0.32	60
3	0.24	54
4	0.02	10
5	0.02	6

a. Specify the competing hypotheses to test whether the market shares have changed since 2021.

b. Calculate the value of the test statistic.

c. Use $a = 0.05$ to determine if the market shares have changed since 2021.

SOLUTION:

a. Let p_i denote the market share for the ith firm. In order to test whether the market shares have changed since 2021, we *initially* set up the competing hypotheses as

$$H_0: p_1 = 0.40, \ p_2 = 0.32, \ p_3 = 0.24, \ p_4 = 0.02, \text{ and } p_5 = 0.02$$
$$H_A: \text{Not all market shares equal their hypothesized values.}$$

b. The value of the test statistic is calculated as $\chi^2_{df} = \Sigma \frac{(o_i - e_i)^2}{e_i}$. The last column of Table 11.3 shows each firm's observed frequency o_i. Before applying the formula, we first calculate each firm's expected frequency e_i:

$$\begin{aligned} e_1 &= 200 \times 0.40 = 80 \\ e_2 &= 200 \times 0.32 = 64 \\ e_3 &= 200 \times 0.24 = 48 \\ \left.\begin{aligned} e_4 &= 200 \times 0.02 = 4 \\ e_5 &= 200 \times 0.02 = 4 \end{aligned}\right\} 8 \end{aligned}$$

We note that the expected frequencies for Firm 4 and Firm 5 are less than five. For the test to be valid, the expected frequencies in each category must be five or more. In order to achieve this result, we combine the expected frequencies for Firm 4 and Firm 5 to obtain a combined frequency of eight ($e_4 + e_5 = 8$). We could have made other combinations, say e_4 with e_1 and e_5 with e_2, but we preferred to maintain a category for the less dominant firms. Table 11.4 shows the reconfigured market shares. For ease of exposition, we denote the combination of Firm 4 and Firm 5 as Firm 4*.

TABLE 11.4 Reconfigured Market Shares

Firm	Market_Share	Recent_Customers
1	0.40	70
2	0.32	60
3	0.24	54
4*	0.04	16

After making this combination, we now respecify the competing hypotheses as

$$H_0: p_1 = 0.40,\ p_2 = 0.32,\ p_3 = 0.24,\ \text{and}\ p_4 = 0.04$$
$$H_A: \text{Not all market shares equal their hypothesized values.}$$

With $df = k - 1 = 3$, we calculate the value of the test statistic as

$$\chi_3^2 = \sum \frac{(o_i - e_i)^2}{e_i} = \frac{(70 - 80)^2}{80} + \frac{(60 - 64)^2}{64} + \frac{(54 - 48)^2}{48} + \frac{(16 - 8)^2}{8}$$
$$= 10.250.$$

c. We calculate the p-value as $P(\chi_3^2 \geq 10.250)$. In Excel, we enter =CHISQ.DIST. RT(10.250, 3), and Excel returns 0.017. Because the p-value is less than 0.05, we reject H_0. At the 5% significance level, we conclude that market shares have changed.

As mentioned earlier, one limitation of this type of chi-square test is that we cannot tell which proportions differ from their hypothesized values. However, given the divergence between the observed and expected frequencies for the less-dominant firms, it appears that they may be making some headway in this industry. Further analysis is needed to determine if this is the case.

EXERCISES 11.2

Mechanics

21. Consider a multinomial experiment with $n = 250$ and $k = 4$. The null hypothesis to be tested is $H_0: p_1 = p_2 = p_3 = p_4 = 0.25$. The observed frequencies resulting from the experiment are:

Category	1	2	3	4
Frequency	70	42	72	66

a. Specify the alternative hypothesis.
b. Calculate the value of the test statistic and the p-value.
c. At the 5% significance level, what is the conclusion to the hypothesis test?

22. Consider a multinomial experiment with $n = 400$ and $k = 3$. The null hypothesis is $H_0: p_1 = 0.60, p_2 = 0.25$, and $p_3 = 0.15$. The observed frequencies resulting from the experiment are:

Category	1	2	3
Frequency	250	94	56

a. Specify the alternative hypothesis.
b. Calculate the value of the test statistic and the p-value.
c. At the 5% significance level, what is the conclusion to the hypothesis test?

23. A multinomial experiment produced the following results:

Category	1	2	3	4	5
Frequency	57	63	70	55	55

Can we conclude at the 1% significance level that not all population proportions are equal to 0.20?

24. A multinomial experiment produced the following results:

Category	1	2	3
Frequency	128	87	185

At the 1% significance level, can we reject $H_0: p_1 = 0.30, p_2 = 0.20$, and $p_3 = 0.50$?

Applications

25. You suspect that an unscrupulous employee at a casino has tampered with a die; that is, he is using a loaded die. In order to test this claim, you roll the die 200 times and obtain the following frequencies:

Category	1	2	3	4	5	6
Frequency	40	35	33	30	33	29

   a. Specify the null and alternative hypotheses in order to test your claim.
   b. Calculate the value of the test statistic and the p-value.
   c. At the 10% significance level, can you conclude that the die is loaded?

26. A study found that fewer than half of employers who hired fresh college graduates last academic year plan to definitely do so again. Suppose the hiring intentions of the respondents were as follows:

Definitely Hire	Likely to Hire	Hire Uncertain	Will not Hire
37%	17%	28%	18%

   Six months later, a sample of 500 employers were asked their hiring intentions and gave the following responses:

Definitely Hire	Likely to Hire	Hire Uncertain	Will not Hire
170	100	120	110

   a. Specify the competing hypotheses to test whether the proportions from the initial study have changed.
   b. Calculate the value of the test statistic and the p-value.
   c. At the 5% significance level, what is the conclusion to the hypothesis test? Interpret your results.

27. A rent-to-own (RTO) agreement allows immediate access to merchandise, and by making all payments, the consumer acquires the merchandise. At the same time, goods can be returned at any point without penalty. Suppose a recent study documents that 65% of RTO contracts are returned, 30% are purchased, and the remaining 5% default. In order to test the validity of this study, an RTO researcher looks at the transaction data of 420 RTO contracts, of which 283 are returned, 109 are purchased, and the rest defaulted.
   a. Set up the competing hypothesis to test whether the return, purchase, and default probabilities of RTO contracts differ from 0.65, 0.30, and 0.05, respectively.
   b. Compute the value of the test statistic.
   c. Conduct the hypothesis test at the 5% level of significance, and interpret the test results.

28. Thousands of tourists visit Zimbabwe every year. Main attractions include the magnificent Victoria Falls, the ruins of Great Zimbabwe, and herds of roaming wildlife. A tourism director claims that Zimbabwe visitors are equally represented by Europe, North America, and the rest of the world. Records show that of the 380 tourists who recently visited Zimbabwe, 148 were from Europe, 106 were from North America, and 126 were from the rest of the world.
   a. A recent visitor to Zimbabwe believes that the tourism director's claim is wrong. Set up the competing hypotheses to test the visitor's belief.
   b. Conduct the test at the 5% significance level. Do the sample data support the visitor's belief?

29. In 2003, the distribution of the world's people worth $1 million or more was as follows:

Region	Millionaires
Europe	35.7%
North America	31.4%
Asia Pacific	22.9%
Latin America	4.3%
Middle East	4.3%
Africa	1.4%

A recent sample of 500 global millionaires produces the following results:

Region	Number of Millionaires
Europe	153
North America	163
Asia Pacific	139
Latin America	20
Middle East	20
Africa	5

   a. Test whether the distribution of millionaires today is different from the distribution in 2003 at $\alpha = 0.05$.
   b. Would the conclusion change if we tested it at $\alpha = 0.10$?

30. A couple of years ago, a survey found that 38% of American drivers favored U.S. cars, while 33% preferred Japanese brands, with the remaining 29% going for other imported cars. A researcher wonders whether today's preferences for cars have changed. He surveys 200 Americans and finds that the number of respondents who prefer American, Japanese, and other imported cars are 66, 70, and 64, respectively. At the 5% significance level, can the researcher conclude that today's preferences have changed?

31. The quality department at an electronics company has noted that, historically, 92% of the units of a specific product pass a test operation, 6% fail the test but are able to be repaired, and 2% fail the test and need to be scrapped. Due to recent process improvements, the quality department would like to test if the rates have changed. A recent sample of 500 parts revealed that 475 parts passed the test, 18 parts failed the test but were repairable, and 7 parts failed the test and were scrapped.

a. State the null and alternative hypotheses to test if the current proportions are different than the historical proportions.

b. Calculate the value of the test statistic and the p-value.

c. At the 5% significance level, what is the conclusion to the hypothesis test? Would the conclusion change at the 1% significance level?

32. An agricultural grain company processes and packages various grains purchased from farmers. A high-volume conveyor line contains four chutes at the end, each of which is designed to receive and dispense equal proportions of grain into bags. Each bag is then stamped with a date code and the number of the chute from which it came. If the chute output proportions are not relatively equal, then a bottleneck effect is created upstream and the conveyor cannot function at peak output. Recently, a series of repairs and modifications have led management to question whether the grains still are being equally distributed among the chutes. Packaging records from 800 bags yesterday indicate that 220 bags came from Chute 1, 188 bags from Chute 2, 218 bags from Chute 3, and 174 bags from Chute 4.

a. State the null and alternative hypotheses to test if the proportion of bags filled by any of the chutes is different from 0.25.

b. Calculate the value of the test statistic and the p-value.

c. What is the conclusion to the hypothesis test at the 10% significance level? Would the conclusion change at the 5% significance level?

33. A study suggests that airlines have increased restrictions on cheap fares by raising overnight requirements. This forces business travelers to pay more for their flights, because they tend to need the most flexibility and want to be home on weekends. A year ago, the overnight stay requirements were as follows:

One night	Two nights	Three nights	Saturday night
37%	17%	28%	18%

A recent sample of 644 flights found the following restrictions:

One night	Two nights	Three nights	Saturday night
117	137	298	92

a. Specify the competing hypotheses to test whether the proportions cited by the study have changed.

b. Calculate the value of the test statistic.

c. At the 5% significance level, what is the conclusion to the hypothesis test? Interpret your results.

34. In a survey by Facebook, young users were asked about their preference for delivering the news about breaking up a relationship. One of the shocking results was that only 47% of users preferred to break the news in person. A researcher decides to verify the survey results of Facebook by taking her own sample of 200 young Facebook users. The preference percentages from Facebook and the researcher's survey are presented in the following table.

Delivery Method	Facebook Results	Researcher's Results
In Person	47%	55%
Phone	30%	25%
E-mail	4%	6%
Facebook	5%	5%
Text	14%	9%

At the 5% level of significance, test if the researcher's results are inconsistent with the survey results conducted by Facebook. Provide the details.

35. A local TV station claims that 60% of people support Candidate A, 30% support Candidate B, and 10% support Candidate C. A survey of 500 registered voters is taken. The accompanying table indicates how they are likely to vote.

Candidate A	Candidate B	Candidate C
350	125	25

a. Specify the competing hypotheses to test whether the TV station's claim can be rejected by the survey results.

b. Test the hypothesis at the 1% significance level.

36. The following table lists the market shares of the four firms in a particular industry in 2019 and total sales (in $ billions) for each firm in 2020.

Firm	Market Share in 2019	Total Sales in 2020
1	0.40	200
2	0.30	180
3	0.20	100
4	0.10	70

a. Specify the competing hypotheses to test whether the market shares in 2019 are not valid in 2020.

b. Calculate the value of the test statistic and the p-value.

c. At the 1% significance level, do the sample data suggest that the market shares changed from 2019 to 2020?

11.3 CHI-SQUARE TEST FOR INDEPENDENCE

Conduct a test for independence.

In this section, we conduct a **test for independence**—also called a **chi-square test of a contingency table**—to assess the relationship between two categorical variables. Many examples of the use of this test arise, especially in marketing, biomedical research, and courts of law. For instance, a politician may be trying to determine whether there is a relationship between voting preferences and income brackets. Doctors might want to investigate whether or not a new vaccine is equally effective for people of all age groups. Or one party in a discrimination lawsuit may be trying to show that a person's gender and promotion are related. All of these examples lend themselves to applications of the hypothesis test discussed in this section.

Recall from Chapters 2 and 4 that a contingency table shows the frequencies for two categorical variables, x and y, where each cell represents a mutually exclusive combination of the pair of x and y values. In the introductory case study, we are presented with a contingency table cross-classified by the variables Age Group and Enrollment Outcome. Specifically, we want to determine whether the likelihood of gym enrollment depends on the age group of open house attendees. We will conduct this test at the 5% significance level.

The competing hypotheses for a statistical test for independence are formulated such that rejecting the null hypothesis leads to the conclusion that the two categorical variables are dependent. In the gym example, the criteria upon which we classify the variables are Age Group and Enrollment Outcome; thus, we write the competing hypotheses as

H_0: Age Group and Enrollment Outcome are independent.

H_A: Age Group and Enrollment Outcome are dependent.

Table 11.5 reproduces Table 11.1 of the introductory case. The variable Enrollment Outcome has two categories: (1) Enroll (E) and (2) Not Enroll (N). The variable Age Group has three categories: (1) Under 30 (U), (2) Between 30 and 50 (B), and (3) Over 50 (O). Each cell in this table represents an observed frequency o_{ij}, where the subscript ij refers to the ith row and the jth column. For example, o_{13} refers to the observed frequency in the first row and the third column. Here, $o_{13} = 44$, or, equivalently, there are 44 open house attendees who are over 50 years of age and enrolled in the gym.

TABLE 11.5 Enrollment and Age Frequencies of Attendees

Enrollment Outcome	Age Group		
	Under 30 (*U*)	Between 30 and 50 (*B*)	Over 50 (*O*)
Enroll (*E*)	24	72	44
Not Enroll (*N*)	84	88	88

Finding Expected Frequencies

We will use the independence assumption postulated under the null hypothesis to derive an expected frequency for each cell from the sample data. In other words, we first find expected frequencies as if no relationship exists between age group and enrollment outcome. Then we compare these expected frequencies with the observed frequencies to compute the value of the test statistic.

Table 11.6 shows the sum of the frequencies for each column and row in Table 11.5. For instance, the sum of the frequencies for event E is 140 ($= 24 + 72 + 44$). Totals for the other rows and columns are found similarly.

TABLE 11.6 Row and Column Totals

Enrollment Outcome	Age Group			Row Total
	U	*B*	*O*	
E	e_{11}	e_{12}	e_{13}	140
N	e_{21}	e_{22}	e_{23}	260
Column Total	108	160	132	400

Our goal is to calculate the expected frequency e_{ij} for each cell, where the subscript ij refers to the ith row and the jth column. Thus, e_{13} refers to the expected frequency in the first row and the third column, or the expected number of open house attendees who are over 50 years of age and enrolled in the gym.

Before we can arrive at the expected frequencies, we first calculate marginal row probabilities (the proportion of open house attendees who enrolled in the gym and those who did not enroll in the gym) and marginal column probabilities (the proportion of open house attendees who are under 30, between 30 and 50, and over 50 years of age). We calculate a marginal row (column) probability by dividing the row (column) sum by the total sample size:

Marginal Row Probabilities:

$$P(E) = \frac{140}{400} \text{ and } P(N) = \frac{260}{400}$$

Marginal Column Probabilities:

$$P(U) = \frac{108}{400}, P(B) = \frac{160}{400}, \text{ and } P(O) = \frac{132}{400}$$

We can now calculate each cell probability by applying the multiplication rule for independent events from Chapter 4. That is, if two events are independent, say events E and U (our assumption under the null hypothesis), then their joint probability is

$$P(E \cap U) = P(E)P(U) = \left(\frac{140}{400}\right)\left(\frac{108}{400}\right) = 0.0945.$$

Multiplying this joint probability by the sample size yields the expected frequency for e_{11}; that is, the expected number of customers who are under 30 years of age and enroll in the gym is

$$e_{11} = 400 \times 0.0945 = 37.80.$$

The following definition box provides a simple formula for finding the expected frequency for each cell in a contingency table.

CALCULATING THE EXPECTED FREQUENCY FOR EACH CELL IN A CONTINGENCY TABLE

The expected frequency e_{ij} for each cell in a contingency table is calculated as

$$e_{ij} = \frac{(\text{Row } i \text{ total})(\text{Column } j \text{ total })}{\text{Sample Size}},$$

where the subscript ij refers to the ith row and the jth column of the contingency table.

Applying the formula, we calculate each expected frequency as

$$e_{11} = \frac{(140)(108)}{400} = 37.80 \qquad e_{12} = \frac{(140)(160)}{400} = 56.00 \qquad e_{13} = \frac{(140)(132)}{400} = 46.20$$

$$e_{21} = \frac{(260)(108)}{400} = 70.20 \qquad e_{22} = \frac{(260)(160)}{400} = 104.00 \qquad e_{23} = \frac{(260)(132)}{400} = 85.80$$

Table 11.7 shows the expected frequency e_{ij} for each cell. In order to satisfy subsequent assumptions, each expected frequency e_{ij} *must equal five or more*. This condition is satisfied here. As we saw in Example 11.5, it may be necessary to combine two or more rows or columns to achieve this result in other applications.

TABLE 11.7 Expected Frequencies for Contingency Table

Enrollment Outcome	Age Group			Row Total
	U	B	O	
E	37.80	56.00	46.20	140
N	70.20	104.00	85.80	260
Column Total	108	160	132	400

When conducting a test for independence, we calculate the value of the chi-square test statistic χ^2_{df}. Analogous to the discussion in Section 11.2, χ^2_{df} measures how much the observed frequencies deviate from the expected frequencies. The smallest value that χ^2_{df} can assume is zero—this occurs when each observed frequency equals its expected frequency. Thus, a test for independence is also implemented as a *right-tailed test*. The following definition box provides the formula for the test statistic for the test for independence.

TEST STATISTIC FOR A TEST FOR INDEPENDENCE

For a test for independence applied to a contingency table with r rows and c columns, the value of the test statistic is calculated as

$$\chi^2_{df} = \sum_i \sum_j \frac{(o_{ij} - e_{ij})^2}{e_{ij}},$$

where $df = (r - 1)(c - 1)$, and o_{ij} and e_{ij} are the observed frequency and the expected frequency, respectively, for each cell in a contingency table.

Note: This test is valid when the expected frequencies for each cell are five or more.

With two rows and three columns in the contingency table, degrees of freedom are calculated as $df = (r - 1)(c - 1) = (2 - 1)(3 - 1) = 2$. We apply the formula to compute the value of the test statistic as

$$\chi^2_2 = \frac{(24 - 37.80)^2}{37.80} + \frac{(72 - 56.00)^2}{56.00} + \frac{(44 - 46.20)^2}{46.20}$$
$$+ \frac{(84 - 70.20)^2}{70.20} + \frac{(88 - 104.00)^2}{104.00} + \frac{(88 - 85.80)^2}{85.80}$$
$$= 14.945.$$

For $df = 2$, we calculate the p-value as $P(\chi^2_2 \geq 14.945)$. In Excel, we enter =CHISQ.DIST. RT(14.945, 2), and Excel returns 0.001. Because the p-value is less than 0.05, we reject H_0. At the 5% significance level, we conclude that the two categorical variables are dependent; that is, there is a relationship between the age group of open house attendees and the enrollment outcome.

SYNOPSIS OF INTRODUCTORY CASE

Janet Mwangi, a manager at 24/7 Fitness Center, analyzes data from the gym's past open house. She wants to gain a better insight into which attendees are likely to purchase a gym membership after attending this event.

Halfpoint/Shutterstock

After careful analysis of the contingency table representing frequencies for age groups and enrollment outcome of attendees, several interesting observations are made. From a sample of 400 past attendees, 35% ended up enrolling in the gym. Further inspection revealed that 45% of the attendees in the 30 to 50 age group enrolled in the gym compared to only 22% for under 30 years old and 33% for over 50 years old. While these results seem to indicate that the probability of enrollment depends on the age of the attendees, Janet wants to ensure that the results are backed by a thorough statistical analysis.

A formal test for independence is conducted to determine if there is a relationship between the age of an attendee and their decision to enroll in the gym. At the 5% significance level, it is concluded that the variables, age group and enrollment outcome, are dependent; that is, there is a statistically significant relationship between the two. Janet uses this information to identify individual open house attendees who are likely to purchase a gym membership.

EXAMPLE 11.6

In general, Latinx and white Americans use social media networks equally, but there are some differences in their preferences for specific social media sites (www.pewresearch.org, February 5, 2015). In particular, Instagram is more popular among Latinx while Pinterest is more popular among white Americans. Aarti Vardan, a junior in college, decides to test if similar differences exist among students on her campus. She collects data on 400 students cross-classified by Ethnicity (Latinx versus white Americans) and Social Media Preference (Instagram versus Pinterest). The results are shown in Table 11.8. At the 10% significance level, determine whether the sample data support ethnic differences in social media preferences.

FILE
Social_Media

TABLE 11.8 Social Media Preference by Ethnicity

Ethnicity	Social Media Preference		Row Total
	Instagram	Pinterest	
Latinx	50	60	110
White Americans	120	170	290
Column Total	170	230	400

SOLUTION: In order to determine whether social media preference depends on ethnicity, we specify the competing hypotheses as

H_0: Ethnicity and Social Media Preference are independent.

H_A: Ethnicity and Social Media Preference are dependent.

The value of the test statistic is calculated as $\chi^2_{df} = \sum_i \sum_j \frac{(o_{ij} - e_{ij})^2}{e_{ij}}$. Table 11.8 provides each cell's observed frequency o_{ij}, so before applying the formula, we first calculate each cell's expected frequency e_{ij}:

$$e_{11} = \frac{(110)(170)}{400} = 46.75 \qquad e_{12} = \frac{(110)(230)}{400} = 63.25$$

$$e_{21} = \frac{(290)(170)}{400} = 123.25 \qquad e_{22} = \frac{(290)(230)}{400} = 166.75$$

With two rows and two columns in the contingency table, degrees of freedom are calculated as $df = (r-1)(c-1) = (2-1)(2-1) = 1$. The value of the test statistic is calculated as

$$\chi^2_1 = \frac{(50 - 46.75)^2}{46.75} + \frac{(60 - 63.25)^2}{63.25} + \frac{(120 - 123.25)^2}{123.25} + \frac{(170 - 166.75)^2}{166.75}$$
$$= 0.2259 + 0.1670 + 0.0857 + 0.0633 = 0.542.$$

In order to find the p-value in Excel, we enter =CHISQ.DIST.RT(0.542, 1), and Excel returns 0.462. Because the p-value is greater than 0.10, we do not reject H_0. At the 10% significance level, the sample data do not support ethnic differences in social media preferences.

EXERCISES 11.3

Mechanics

37. Given the following contingency table, conduct a test for independence at the 5% significance level.

Variable B	Variable A 1	Variable A 2
1	23	47
2	32	53

38. Given the following contingency table, conduct a test for independence at the 1% significance level.

Variable B	Variable A 1	Variable A 2	Variable A 3	Variable A 4
1	120	112	100	110
2	127	115	120	124
3	118	115	110	124

Applications

39. According to an online survey, more than half of IT workers say they have fallen asleep at work. The same is also true for government workers. Assume that the following contingency table is representative of the survey results.

Slept on the Job?	Job Category IT Professional	Job Category Government Professional
Yes	155	256
No	145	144

a. Specify the competing hypotheses to determine whether sleeping on the job is associated with job category.

b. Calculate the value of the test statistic.

c. Find the p-value.

d. At the 5% significance level, can you conclude that sleeping on the job depends on job category?

40. A market researcher for an automobile company suspects differences in preferred color between male and female buyers. Advertisements targeted to different groups should take such differences into account, if they exist. The researcher examines the most recent sales information of a particular car that comes in three colors.

Color	Gender of Automobile Buyer Male	Gender of Automobile Buyer Female
Silver	470	280
Black	535	285
Red	495	350

a. Specify the competing hypotheses to determine whether color preference depends on the automobile buyer's gender.

b. Calculate the value of the test statistic and the p-value.

c. At the 1% significance level, does the conclusion to the hypothesis test suggest that the company should target advertisements differently for males versus females? Explain.

41. The following sample data reflect shipments received by a large firm from three different vendors and the quality of those shipments.

Vendor	Defective	Acceptable
1	14	112
2	10	70
3	22	150

a. Specify the competing hypotheses to determine whether quality is associated with the source of the shipments.

b. Conduct the hypothesis test at the 1% significance level.

c. Should the firm be concerned about the source of the shipments? Explain.

42. A marketing agency would like to determine if there is a relationship between union membership and type of vehicle owned (domestic or foreign brand). The goal is to develop targeted advertising campaigns for particular vehicle brands likely to appeal to specific groups of customers. A survey of 500 potential customers revealed the following results.

	Union Member	Not Union Member
Domestic brand	133	147
Foreign brand	67	153

a. Specify the competing hypotheses to determine whether vehicle brand (domestic, foreign) is associated with union membership.

b. Conduct the test at the 10% significance level. What is the conclusion to the hypothesis test?

c. Is the conclusion reached in part (b) sensitive to the choice of significance level?

43. A quality manager believes there may be a relationship between the experience level of an inspector and whether a product passes or fails inspection. Inspection records were reviewed for 630 units of a particular product, and the number of units that passed and failed inspection was determined based on three inspector experience levels. The results are shown in the following table.

	Experience Level		
Decision	Low (< 2 years)	Medium (2–8 years)	High (> 8 years)
Pass	152	287	103
Fail	16	46	26

a. Specify the competing hypotheses to determine whether the inspector pass/fail decision depends on experience level.

b. Calculate the value of the test statistic.

c. Find the p-value.

d. At the 5% significance level, what is the conclusion to the hypothesis test? Does your conclusion change at the 1% significance level?

44. Firms routinely conduct surveys to gauge their customer satisfaction levels. The marketing manager of a firm wants to know if the satisfaction level depends on the customer's age. Survey responses are tabulated in the following table.

Age	Very Happy	Somewhat Happy	Not Happy
20 up to 40	23	50	18
40 up to 60	51	38	16
60 and older	19	45	20

a. Specify the competing hypotheses to test the claim that satisfaction level depends on the age of the customer.

b. Calculate the value of the test statistic.

c. Find the p-value.

d. At the 1% level of significance, can we infer that satisfaction level of customers is dependent on age?

45. **FILE** *CarCrash.* The California Highway Patrol (CHP) routinely compiles car crash data in California. The accompanying data file shows the data for Santa Clara county. It shows information on the type of car crash (Head-On or Not Head-On) and light (Daylight or Not Daylight).

a. Use the data to construct a contingency table.

b. Specify the competing hypotheses to determine whether crash type is related to light.

c. Conduct the hypothesis test at the 1% significance level and make a conclusion.

46. In a survey of 3,000 Facebook users, a researcher looked at why Facebook users break up in a relationship.

Reasons for Breakup	Sex of Respondent	
	Percentage of Men	Percentage of Women
Nonapproval	3	4
Distance	21	16
Cheating	18	22
Lost Interest	28	26
Other	30	32

Suppose the survey consisted of 1,800 men and 1,200 women. Use the data to determine whether the reasons for breakup depend on one's gender at the 1% significance level. Provide the details.

47. **FILE** *Happiness.* There have been numerous attempts that relate happiness with income. In a recent survey, 290 individuals were asked to evaluate their state of happiness (Happy or Not Happy) and income (Low, Medium, or High). The accompanying data file shows the results.

   a. Use the data to construct a contingency table.

   b. Specify the competing hypotheses to determine whether happiness is related to income.

   c. Conduct the test at the 5% significance level and make a conclusion.

48. Given a shaky economy and high heating costs, more and more households are struggling to pay utility bills. Particularly hard hit are households with homes heated with propane or heating oil. A representative sample of 500 households was taken to investigate if the type of heating influences whether or not a household is delinquent in paying its utility bill. The following table reports the results.

Delinquent in Payment?	Type of Heating			
	Natural Gas	Electricity	Heating Oil	Propane
Yes	50	20	15	10
No	240	130	20	15

   At the 5% significance level, test whether the type of heating influences a household's delinquency in payment. Interpret your results.

49. An analyst is trying to determine whether the prices of certain stocks on the NASDAQ are independent of the industry to which they belong. She examines four industries and, within each industry, categorizes each stock according to its price (high-priced, average-priced, low-priced).

Stock Price	Industry			
	I	II	III	IV
High	16	8	10	14
Average	18	16	10	12
Low	7	8	4	9

   a. Specify the competing hypotheses to determine whether stock price depends on the industry.

   b. Calculate the value of the test statistic and the p-value.

   c. At the 1% significance level, what can the analyst conclude?

50. The human resources department would like to consolidate the current set of retirement plan options offered to specific employee pay groups into a single plan for all pay groups (salaried, hourly, or piecework). A sample of 585 employees of various pay groups were asked which of three potential plans they preferred (A, B, or C). The results are shown in the accompanying table. The human resources department is hoping to conclude that the retirement plan preferred by the majority of employees is independent of pay group, in order to avoid the impression that the preferred plan may favor a particular group.

Preferred Plan	Employee Pay Group		
	Salaried	Hourly	Piecework
A	78	98	37
B	121	95	30
C	51	57	18

   a. Specify the competing hypotheses to determine whether the preferred retirement plan depends on employee pay group.

   b. Calculate the value of the test statistic and the p-value.

   c. What is the conclusion to the hypothesis test at the 10% significance level? What about the 5% significance level?

51. A poll asked 3,228 Americans aged 16 to 21 whether they are likely to serve in the U.S. military. The following table, cross-classified by a person's gender and ethnicity, reports those who responded that they are likely or very likely to serve in the active-duty military.

Gender	Ethnicity		
	Hispanic	Black	White
Male	1,098	678	549
Female	484	355	64

   a. State the competing hypotheses to test whether gender and ethnicity are dependent when making a choice to serve in the military.

   b. Conduct the hypothesis test at the 5% significance level.

52. The operations manager at ElectroTech, an electronics manufacturing company, believes that workers on particular shifts may be more likely to phone in "sick" than those on other shifts. To test this belief, she has compiled the following table containing frequencies based on work shift and days absent over the past year.

	First Shift	Second Shift	Third Shift
0–2 days absent	44	20	10
3–6 days absent	38	25	12
7–10 days absent	14	9	13
11 or more days absent	4	6	5

   a. Specify the competing hypotheses to determine whether days absent depend on work shift.

   b. Calculate the value of the test statistic and the p-value.

   c. What is the conclusion to the hypothesis test at the 5% significance level? What about the 1% significance level?

Peathegee Inc/Getty Images

Shannon Fagan/Image Source

11.4 WRITING WITH DATA

Case study

Online dating has made it as likely for would-be couples to meet via email or other virtual matchmaking services as through friends and family. One study found that women put greater emphasis on the cultural background and financial stability of a partner, while men mostly look for physical attractiveness. It is reported that 13% of women and 8% of men want their partner to be of the same cultural background. Moreover, 36% of women and 13% of men would like to meet someone who makes as much money as they do.

Anka Wilder, working for a small matchmaking service in Cincinnati, Ohio, wants to know if a similar pattern also exists with her customers. She has access to the preferences of 160 female and 120 male customers. In this sample, she finds that 28 female and 12 male customers want their partner to be of the same cultural background. Also, 50 women and 10 men want their partner to make as much money as they do.

Anka wants to use this sample information to determine whether the proportion of women who want their partner to be of the same cultural background is greater than that of men. In addition she wants to determine whether the proportion of women who want their partner to make as much money as they do is more than 20 percentage points greater than that of men.

Sample Report— Online Dating Preferences

With the advent of the internet, there has been a surge in online dating services that connect individuals with similar interests, religions, and cultural backgrounds for personal relationships. In 1992, when the internet was still in its infancy, less than 1% of Americans met their partners through online dating services. Today, about 39% of heterosexual couples reported meeting online (stanford.edu, August 21, 2019). A recent survey suggested that a higher proportion of women than men would like to meet someone with a similar cultural background. Also, the difference between the proportion of women and men who would like to meet someone who makes as much money as they do is greater than 20%.

A couple of hypothesis tests were performed to determine if similar gender differences existed for online dating customers in Cincinnati, Ohio. The sample consisted of responses from 160 women and 120 men. The summary of the test results is presented in Table 11.9.

TABLE 11.9 Test Statistics and p-values for Hypothesis Tests

Hypotheses	Test Statistic	p-value
$H_0: p_1 - p_2 \leq 0$ $H_A: p_1 - p_2 > 0$	$z = \dfrac{0.175 - 0.10}{\sqrt{0.1429(1 - 0.1429)\left(\dfrac{1}{160} + \dfrac{1}{120}\right)}} = 1.7748$	0.038
$H_0: p_1 - p_2 \leq 0.20$ $H_A: p_1 - p_2 > 0.20$	$z = \dfrac{0.3125 - 0.0833 - 0.20}{\sqrt{\dfrac{0.3125(1 - 0.3125)}{160} + \dfrac{0.0833(1 - 0.0833)}{120}}} = 0.6556$	0.256

First, it was tested if the proportion of women, denoted p_1, who want their partner to have the same cultural background is greater than that of men, denoted p_2. It was found that 28 out of 160 women valued this trait, yielding a sample proportion of $\bar{p}_1 = 28/160 = 0.175$; a similar proportion for men was calculated as $\bar{p}_2 = 12/120 = 0.10$. The first row of Table 11.9 shows the competing hypotheses, the value of the test statistic, and the p-value for this test. At the 5%

significance level, the proportion of women who want the same cultural background was greater than that of men. In the second test, p_1 and p_2 denoted the proportion of women and men, respectively, who would like their partner to make as much money as they do; here $\bar{p}_1 = 50/160 = 0.3125$ and $\bar{p}_2 = 10/120 = 0.0833$. The second row of Table 11.9 shows the competing hypotheses, the value of the test statistic, and the p-value for this test. At the 5% significance level, the proportion of women who want their partner to make as much income as they do is not more than 20 percentage points greater than that of men. Online dating is a relatively new market, and any such information is important for individuals looking for relationships as well as for service providers.

Suggested Case Studies

Report 11.1 Repeat the analysis performed in this section, but collect your own survey data on dating preferences or any other issue of your choice.

Report 11.2 FILE *Color.* Color coding is often used in manufacturing operations to display production status or to identify/prioritize materials. For example, suppose "green" status indicates that an assembly line is operating normally, "yellow" indicates it is down waiting on personnel for set up or repair, "blue" indicates it is down waiting on materials to be delivered, and "red" indicates an emergency condition. Management has set realistic goals whereby the assembly line should be operating normally 80% of the time, waiting on personnel 9% of the time, waiting on materials 9% of the time, and in an emergency condition 2% of the time. The data in the accompanying file shows the recent assembly line status for 250 records. Construct a frequency distribution for the color code. Determine if the proportions of the assembly line statuses differ from the goals set by management. Use a reasonable significance level for the test.

Report 11.3 FILE *Machine.* Being able to predict machine failures before they happen can save millions of dollars. This allows manufacturers to perform preventive maintenance or repairs in advance to minimize machine downtime. A manager wants to explore the effect of percentage humidity (Low, Medium, or High) on machine failure (Yes or No). In a report, use the data in the accompanying file to construct a contingency table and interpret the results. Further, determine if machine failure is significantly related to humidity levels. Use a reasonable significance level for the test.

12

Regression Analysis

In this chapter, we introduce regression analysis, which is one of the most widely used statistical techniques in business, engineering, and the social sciences. We use regression analysis for two primary purposes: (1) to assess the relationship between variables and (2) to predict the outcome of a target variable on the basis of several input variables. For example, if a firm increases advertising expenditures by $100,000, then we may want to know the likely impact on sales. Or we may want to predict the price of a house based on its size and location. Regression analysis can be applied in both of these scenarios.

We explore the ordinary least squares (OLS) method for estimating a linear regression model, where the relationship between the target and the input variables is assumed to be linear. We first discuss a model using one input variable, referred to as the simple linear regression model. We then extend the model to the case involving several input variables, referred to as the multiple linear regression model. For both models, we use the estimates to make predictions about the target variable. We then examine a number of goodness-of-fit measures and conduct hypothesis tests in order to assess the effectiveness of the input variables.

Finally, we examine the importance of the assumptions on the statistical properties of the OLS estimator, as well as the validity of the testing procedures. We address common violations to the model assumptions, discuss the consequences when these assumptions are violated, and offer some remedial measures.

Rawpixel.com/Shutterstock

INTRODUCTORY CASE

College Scorecard

With college costs and student debt on the rise, the choices that families make when searching for and selecting a college have never been more important. Yet, students and parents struggle to find clear, reliable data on critical questions of college affordability and value. For these reasons, the Department of Education published a redesigned College Scorecard that reports the most reliable national data on college costs and students' outcomes at specific colleges.

Layla Khaled, a college counselor, believes that the information from the College Scorecard can help her as she advises families. Layla wonders what college factors influence post-college earnings and wants answers to the following questions: If a college costs more or has a higher graduation rate, should a student expect to earn more after graduation? If a greater percentage of the students are paying down debt after college, does this somehow influence post-college earnings? And finally, does the location of a college affect post-college earnings?

To address these questions, Layla gathers information from 116 colleges on annual post-college earnings (Earnings in $), the average annual cost (Cost in $), the graduation rate (Grad in %), the percentage of students paying down debt (Debt in %), and the location variable (Location = City or Non-city). Table 12.1 shows a portion of the data.

TABLE 12.1 College Scorecard Data, May 2016

School	Earnings	Cost	Grad	Debt	Location
St. Ambrose Univ.	44800	22920	62	88	City
Albion College	45100	23429	73	92	Non-city
⋮	⋮	⋮	⋮	⋮	⋮
Wittenburg Univ.	42700	26616	64	90	City

FILE
College

Layla would like to use the information in Table 12.1 to:

1. Make predictions for post-college earnings using regression analysis.
2. Interpret goodness-of-fit measures for the post-college earnings model.
3. Determine which factors are statistically significant in explaining post-college earnings.

A synopsis of this case is provided at the end of Section 12.3.

12.1 THE SIMPLE LINEAR REGRESSION MODEL

Regression analysis is one of the most widely used statistical techniques to examine the relationship between two or more variables. Recall from Chapter 3 that the correlation coefficient is used to measure the strength of the linear relationship between two variables of interest. A regression model extends the analysis by relating the outcome of a target variable, called the **response variable,** to one or more other input variables, called the **predictor variables.** It also allows us to make predictions regarding the response variable for given values of the predictor variables.

In the introductory case, Layla would like to analyze post-college earnings (response variable) based on several college factors (predictor variables). In another scenario, we may want to predict a firm's sales based on its advertising; estimate an individual's salary based on education and years of experience; predict the selling price of a house based on its square footage and the number of bedrooms and bathrooms; or describe auto sales with respect to consumer income, interest rates, and price discounts. In all these examples, we can use regression analysis to describe and/or predict changes in the response variable.

It is important to point out that regression models are known to perform well for making predictions. Oftentimes, however, they fail to establish a cause-and-effect relationship between the variables because business data are not randomized in a lab setting. A regression model may appear to search for causality when it basically detects correlation. Causality can only be established through randomized experiments and/or advanced statistical models, which are outside the scope of this text.

No matter the response variable that we choose to examine, we cannot expect to predict its exact (unique) value. If the value of the response variable is uniquely determined by the values of the predictor variables, we say that the relationship between the variables is **deterministic.** This is often the case in the physical sciences. For example, momentum p is the product of the mass m and velocity v of an object; that is, $p = mv$. In most business applications, however, we tend to find that the relationship between the predictor variables and the response variable is **stochastic,** due to the omission of relevant variables (sometimes not measurable) that influence the response variable. For example, we cannot predict the exact value of a house based on its square footage and the number of bedrooms and bathrooms. There are always other predictor variables, such as the condition and the location of the house, that are not included in the model.

DETERMINISTIC VERSUS STOCHASTIC RELATIONSHIPS

The relationship between the response variable and the predictor variables is deterministic if the value of the response variable is uniquely determined by the predictor variables; otherwise, the relationship is stochastic.

In order to develop a linear regression model, we start with a deterministic component that approximates the relationship we want to model, and then add a random error term to it, making the relationship stochastic. In this section, we focus on the **simple linear regression model,** which uses one predictor variable, denoted x, to explain the variation in the response variable, denoted y. In Section 12.2, we will extend the model to include multiple predictor variables.

Model Development and Estimation

A fundamental assumption underlying the simple linear regression model is that the expected value of y lies on a straight line, denoted by $\beta_0 + \beta_1 x$, where β_0 and β_1 (the Greek letters read as beta zero and beta one, respectively) are the unknown intercept and slope parameters, respectively. (You have actually seen this relationship before, but you just used different notation. Recall the equation for a line: $y = mx + b$, where b and m are the intercept and the slope, respectively, of the line.)

The expression $\beta_0 + \beta_1 x$ is the deterministic component of the simple linear regression model, which can be thought of as the expected value of y for a given value of x. In other words, conditional on x, $E(y) = \beta_0 + \beta_1 x$. The slope parameter β_1 determines whether the linear relationship between x and $E(y)$ is positive ($\beta_1 > 0$) or negative ($\beta_1 < 0$); $\beta_1 = 0$ indicates that there is no linear relationship. Figure 12.1 shows the expected value of y for various values of the intercept β_0 and the slope β_1 parameters.

FIGURE 12.1 Various examples of a simple linear regression model

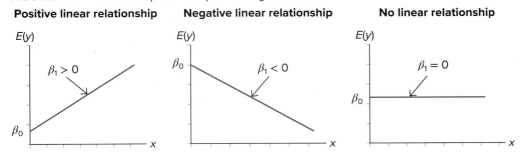

As noted earlier, the observed value y may differ from the expected value $E(y)$. Therefore, we add a random error term ε (the Greek letter read as epsilon) to develop a simple linear regression model.

THE SIMPLE LINEAR REGRESSION MODEL

The simple linear regression model is specified as

$$y = \beta_0 + \beta_1 x + \varepsilon,$$

where y and x are the response variable and the predictor variable, respectively, and ε is the random error term. The coefficients β_0 and β_1 are the unknown parameters to be estimated.

The population parameters β_0 and β_1 used in the simple linear regression model are unknown and, therefore, must be estimated. As always, we use sample data to estimate the population parameters of interest. Here, sample data consist of n pairs of observations on y and x.

Let b_0 and b_1 represent the estimates of β_0 and β_1, respectively. We form the sample regression equation as $\hat{y} = b_0 + b_1 x$, where $\hat{y}$ (read as y-hat) is the predicted value of the response variable given a specified value of the predictor variable x. We refer to the difference between the observed and the predicted values of y, that is $y - \hat{y}$, as the **residual** e.

THE SAMPLE REGRESSION EQUATION FOR THE SIMPLE LINEAR REGRESSION MODEL

The sample regression equation for the simple linear regression model is denoted as

$$\hat{y} = b_0 + b_1 x,$$

where b_0 and b_1 are the estimates of β_0 and β_1, respectively.

The difference between the observed and the predicted values of y represents the residual e—that is, $e = y - \hat{y}$.

Before estimating a simple linear regression model, it is useful to visualize the relationship between y and x by constructing a scatterplot. Here, we explicitly place y on the vertical axis and x on the horizontal axis. In Figure 12.2, we use the data from the introductory case to show a scatterplot of Earnings against Cost. We then superimpose a linear trendline through the points on the scatterplot. Shortly, we will provide Excel instructions for replicating Figure 12.2.

FIGURE 12.2 Scatterplot of Earnings against Cost

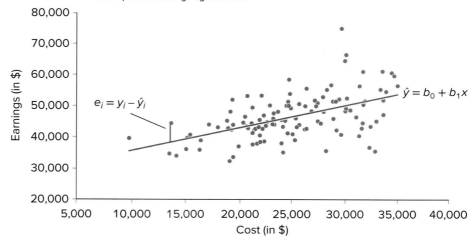

The superimposed line in Figure 12.2 is the sample regression equation, $\hat{y} = b_0 + b_1 x$, where y and x represent Earnings and Cost, respectively. The upward slope of the line suggests that as the average cost of a college increases, predicted post-college earnings also increase. Also, the vertical distance between any data point on the scatterplot (y) and the corresponding point on the line ($\hat{y}$) represents the residual, $e = y - \hat{y}$.

A common approach to fitting a line to the scatterplot is the **method of least squares,** also referred to as **ordinary least squares (OLS).** In other words, we use OLS to estimate the parameters β_0 and β_1. The OLS method chooses the line whereby the **error sum of squares, SSE,** is minimized, where $SSE = \Sigma(y_i - \hat{y}_i)^2 = \Sigma e_i^2$. SSE is the sum of the squared difference between the observed value y and its predicted value $\hat{y}$ or, equivalently, the sum of the squared residuals. Thus, the OLS method produces the best model in that the straight line is "closest" to the data. In the context of Figure 12.2, the superimposed line has been estimated by OLS.

Using calculus, equations have been developed for b_0 and b_1 that satisfy the OLS criterion. These equations, or formulas, are as follows.

CALCULATING THE REGRESSION COEFFICIENTS b_1 AND b_0

The slope b_1 and the intercept b_0 of the sample regression equation are calculated as

$$b_1 = \frac{\Sigma(x_i - \bar{x})(y_i - \bar{y})}{\Sigma(x_i - \bar{x})^2} \text{ and}$$

$$b_0 = \bar{y} - b_1\bar{x}.$$

Fortunately, virtually every statistical software package produces values for b_1 and b_0. So we can focus on interpreting these regression coefficients rather than performing the grueling calculations. The slope estimate b_1 represents the change in $\hat{y}$ when x increases by one unit. As we will see in the following example, it is not always possible to provide an economic interpretation of the intercept estimate b_0; mathematically, however, it represents the predicted value of $\hat{y}$ when x has a value of zero.

EXAMPLE 12.1

Use the *College* data file from the introductory case to estimate a simple linear regression model, using Earnings and Cost as the response and predictor variables, respectively.

a. What is the sample regression equation?

b. Interpret the estimated slope coefficient b_1.

c. Interpret the estimated intercept coefficient b_0.

d. Predict post-college earnings if a college's average cost is $25,000.

SOLUTION: Table 12.2 shows the Excel-produced output from estimating the model: Earnings $= \beta_0 + \beta_1$ Cost $+ \varepsilon$. We will provide Excel instructions at the end of this example.

TABLE 12.2 Regression Results for Example 12.1

SUMMARY OUTPUT					
Regression Statistics					
Multiple R	0.5260				
R Square	0.2767				
Adjusted R Square	0.2703				
Standard Error	6271.44				
Observations	116				
ANOVA					
	df	SS	MS	F	Significance F
Regression	1	1715131265	171513265	43.6077	1.33E-09
Residual	114	4483730459	39330969		
Total	115	6198861724			
	Coefficients	Standard error	t stat	p-value	Lower 95%	Upper 95%
Intercept	**28375.4051**	2802.4173	10.125	1.41E-17	22823.84	33926.97
Cost	**0.7169**	0.1086	6.604	1.33E-09	0.50	0.93

a. As Table 12.2 shows, Excel produces quite a bit of information. In order to formulate the sample regression equation, we need the regression coefficient estimates, which are found at the bottom of the table (see values in boldface). We address the remaining information in later sections of this chapter. We find that $b_0 = 28,375.4051$ and $b_1 = 0.7169$. Thus, the sample regression equation is $\overline{\text{Earnings}} = 28,375.4051 + 0.7169\text{Cost}$.

b. The estimated slope coefficient of 0.7169 suggests a positive relationship between Earnings and Cost. If the average annual cost increases by $1, then predicted post-college earnings increase by about $0.72. This result suggests that spending more on college pays off.

c. The estimated intercept coefficient of 28,375.4051 suggests that if a college's average cost equals zero, then predicted post-college earnings are about $28,375. In this application, we may be tempted to make this conclusion because someone who pays no annual cost will have positive earnings. However, we should be careful about predicting the response variable when we use a value for the predictor variable that is not included in its sample range. In the *College* data set, the lowest and highest values for Cost are

$9,938 and $35,159, respectively. Unless we assume that Earnings and Cost will maintain the same linear relationship for observations of Cost less than $9,938 and more than $35,159, we should refrain from making predictions based on observations of the predictor variable outside the sample range.

d. If the average cost is $25,000, then predicted post-college earnings are

$$\widehat{\text{Earnings}} = 28,375.4051 + 0.7169 \times 25,000 = 46,297.16, \text{ or about } \$46,297.$$

Using Excel to Estimate a Simple Linear Regression Model

In order to obtain the regression output in Table 12.2 using Excel, we follow these steps.

A. Open the *College* data file.

B. For model estimation, we choose **Data > Data Analysis > Regression** from the menu.

C. See Figure 12.3. In the *Regression* dialog box, click on the box next to *it Input Y Range,* and then select the data for Earnings. Click on the box next to *Input X Range,* and then select the data for Cost. Select *Labels* because we are using Earnings and Cost as headings. Click **OK.** The resulting output should be similar to Table 12.2.

FIGURE 12.3
Excel's regression dialog box for Example 12.1

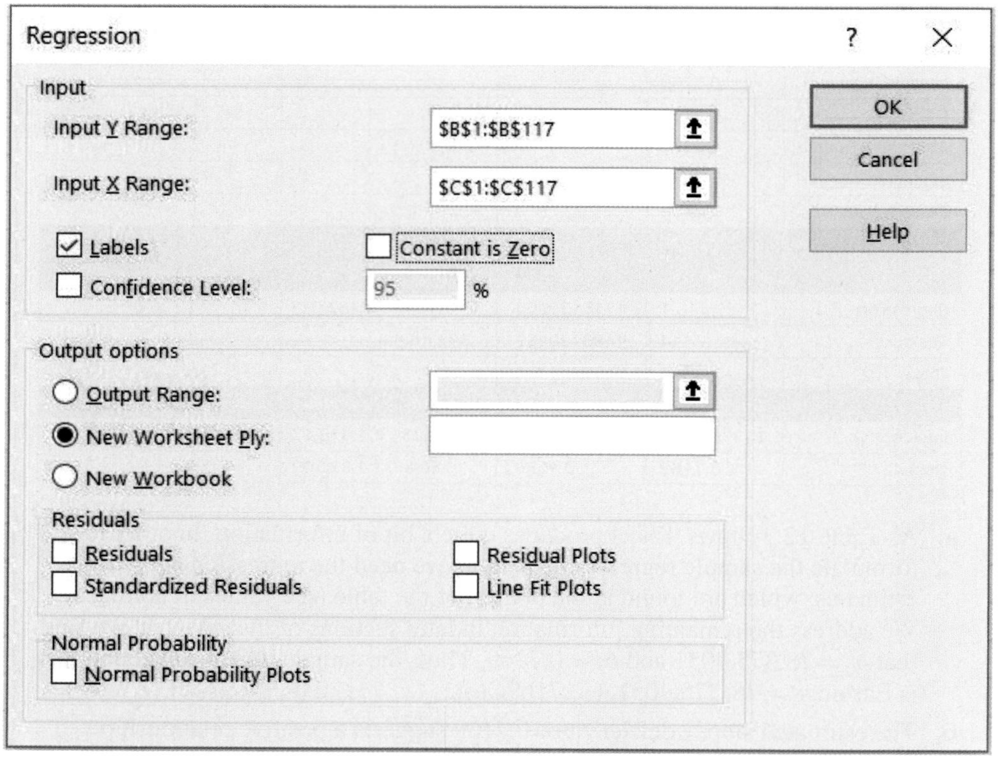

Microsoft Excel

Detailed instructions to construct a scatterplot were provided in Example 2.4 of Chapter 2. In this example, because we want to plot Earnings (*y*-axis) against Cost (*x*-axis), we first copy and paste the data so that the observations for Cost are in the left column and the observations for Earnings are in the right column. We then simultaneously select the observations for Cost and Earnings and choose **Insert > Insert Scatter or Bubble Chart > Scatter.** To superimpose a line to the scatterplot, we select the "+" sign at the top right of the chart (or select **Add Chart Elements** from the menu) and check the box next to *Trendline* in the *Chart Elements* pop-up box. The resulting scatterplot and the superimposed line should be similar to Figure 12.2.

EXERCISES 12.1

Applications

1. If a firm spends more on advertising, is it likely to increase sales? Data on annual sales (in $100,000s) and advertising expenditures (in $10,000s) were collected for 20 firms in order to estimate the model Sales $= \beta_0 + \beta_1$Advertising $+ \varepsilon$. A portion of the regression results is shown in the accompanying table.

	Coefficients	Standard Error	t Stat	p-value
Intercept	−7.42	1.46	−5.09	7.66E-05
Advertising	0.42	0.05	8.70	7.26E-08

   a. Interpret the estimated slope coefficient.
   b. What is the sample regression equation?
   c. Predict the sales for a firm that spends $500,000 annually on advertising.

2. The owner of several used-car dealerships believes that the selling price of a used car can best be predicted using the car's age. He uses data on the recent selling price (in $) and age of 20 used sedans to estimate Price $= \beta_0 + \beta_1$Age $+ \varepsilon$. A portion of the regression results is shown in the accompanying table.

	Coefficients	Standard Error	t Stat	p-value
Intercept	21187.94	733.42	28.89	1.56E-16
Age	−1208.25	128.95	−9.37	2.41E-08

   a. What is the estimate for β_1? Interpret this value.
   b. What is the sample regression equation?
   c. Predict the selling price of a 5-year-old sedan.

3. **FILE** *Education.* A social scientist would like to analyze the relationship between educational attainment (in years of higher education) and annual salary (in $1,000s). The accompanying data file contains relevant data.
   a. Find the sample regression equation for the model: Salary $= \beta_0 + \beta_1$Education $+ \varepsilon$.
   b. Interpret the coefficient for Education.
   c. What is the predicted salary for an individual who completed 7 years of higher education?

4. **FILE** *GPA.* The director of graduate admissions at a large university is analyzing the relationship between scores on the math portion of the Graduate Record Examination (GRE) and subsequent performance in graduate school, as measured by a student's grade point average (GPA). She uses a sample of 24 students who graduated within the past five years. The accompanying data file contains relevant data.
   a. Find the sample regression equation for the model: GPA $= \beta_0 + \beta_1$GRE $+ \varepsilon$.
   b. What is the predicted GPA of a student who scored 710 on the math portion of the GRE?

5. **FILE** *Pitchers.* A sports analyst for Major League Baseball wonders whether there is a relationship between a pitcher's salary (in $ millions) and his earned run average (ERA). The accompanying file contains data that she collected for 10 pitchers.
   a. Estimate the model: Salary $= \beta_0 + \beta_1$ERA $+ \varepsilon$ and interpret the coefficient of ERA.
   b. Use the estimated model to predict the salary for each player, given his ERA. For example, use the sample regression equation to predict the salary for Pitcher 1 with ERA $= 2.53$.
   c. Derive the corresponding residuals for each player.

6. **FILE** *Consumption.* The consumption function, first developed by John Maynard Keynes, captures one of the key relationships in economics. It expresses consumption as a function of disposable income, where disposable income is income after taxes. The accompanying file contains quarterly data for these seasonally adjusted variables, measured in billions of dollars.
   a. Find the sample regression equation for the model, Consumption $= \beta_0 + \beta_1$Income $+ \varepsilon$.
   b. In this model, the slope coefficient is called the marginal propensity to consume. Interpret its meaning.
   c. What is predicted consumption if disposable income is $15,000 billion?

7. **FILE** *Happiness_Age.* Refer to the accompanying data file on happiness and age to answer the following questions.
   a. Estimate Happiness as a function of Age in a simple linear regression model. What is the sample regression equation?
   b. Use the sample regression equation to predict Happiness when Age equals 25, 50, and 75.
   c. Construct a scatterplot of Happiness against Age. Discuss why your predictions might not be accurate.

8. **FILE** *Test_Scores.* The accompanying data file contains the scores that 32 students obtained on the final and the midterm in a course in statistics.
   a. Estimate the sample regression equation that enables us to predict a student's final score on the basis of their midterm score.
   b. Predict the final score of a student who received an 80 on the midterm.

9. **FILE** *Taxes.* The accompanying data file contains the property taxes owed by a homeowner (in $) and the size of the home (in square feet).
   a. Estimate the sample regression equation that enables us to predict property taxes on the basis of the size of the home.
   b. Interpret the slope coefficient.
   c. Predict the property taxes for a 1,500-square-foot home.

10. **FILE** *Dexterity.* Finger dexterity, the ability to make precisely coordinated finger movements to grasp or assemble very small objects, is important in jewelry making. Thus, the manufacturing manager at Gemco, a manufacturer of high-quality watches, wants to develop a regression model to predict the productivity (in watches per shift) of new employees based on dexterity. He has subjected a sample of 20 current employees to the O'Connor dexterity test in which the time required to place 3 pins in each of 100 small holes using tweezers is measured in seconds. The accompanying file contains relevant data.

  a. Estimate the model: Watches $= \beta_0 + \beta_1 \text{Time} + \varepsilon$.
  b. Interpret the coefficient of Time.
  c. Explain why the y-intercept makes no practical sense in this particular problem.
  d. Suppose a new employee takes 550 seconds on the dexterity test. How many watches per shift is she expected to produce?

11. **FILE** *Fertilizer.* A horticulturist is studying the relationship between tomato plant height and fertilizer amount. Thirty tomato plants grown in similar conditions were subjected to various amounts of fertilizer (in ounces) over a four-month period, and then their heights (in inches) were measured. The accompanying data file contains relevant data.

  a. Estimate the model: Height $= \beta_0 + \beta_1 \text{Fertilizer} + \varepsilon$.
  b. Interpret the coefficient of Fertilizer. Does the y-intercept make practical sense?
  c. Use the estimated model to predict, after four months, the height of a tomato plant that received 3.0 ounces of fertilizer.

12.2 THE MULTIPLE LINEAR REGRESSION MODEL

Estimate and interpret a multiple linear regression model.

In Section 12.1, we introduced a simple linear regression model using one predictor variable. We can easily extend the simple linear regression to include more than one predictor variable. The resulting model is referred to as a **multiple linear regression model** and is specified as $y = \beta_0 + \beta_1 x_1 + \beta_2 x_2 + \cdots + \beta_k x_k + \varepsilon$, where $x_1, x_2, \ldots, x_k$ are the k predictor variables. For simplicity, we will refer to the simple linear regression model or the multiple linear regression model as the linear regression model. We use economic theory, intuition, and statistical measures to determine which predictor variables might best explain the response variable.

The population parameters $\beta_0, \beta_1, \beta_2, \ldots, \beta_k$ used in the linear regression model are unknown and, therefore, must be estimated. As always, we use sample data to estimate the population parameters of interest. Here, sample data consist of n observations on $y, x_1, x_2, \ldots, x_k$.

THE MULTIPLE LINEAR REGRESSION MODEL

The multiple linear regression model is specified as
$$y = \beta_0 + \beta_1 x_1 + \beta_2 x_2 + \cdots + \beta_k x_k + \varepsilon,$$
where y is the response variable; $x_1, x_2, \ldots, x_k$ are the k predictor variables; and ε is the random error term. The coefficients $\beta_0, \beta_1, \beta_2, \ldots, \beta_k$ are the unknown parameters to be estimated.

Let $b_0, b_1, b_2, \ldots, b_k$ represent the estimates of $\beta_0, \beta_1, \beta_2, \ldots, \beta_k$, respectively. We form the **sample regression equation** as $\hat{y} = b_0 + b_1 x_1 + b_2 x_2 + \cdots + b_k x_k$, where $\hat{y}$ is the predicted value of the response variable given specified values of the predictor variables. As in the simple linear regression model, the residual e represents the difference between the observed and the predicted values of y; that is, $e = y - \hat{y}$.

It is important to be able to interpret the estimated regression coefficients. Mathematically, the intercept estimate b_0 represents the predicted value of $\hat{y}$ when each predictor variable x_j ($j = 1, \ldots, k$) assumes a value of zero. As noted in Section 12.1, in many applications it is not possible to provide a meaningful interpretation for the intercept. For each predictor variable x_j ($j = 1, \ldots, k$), the corresponding slope coefficient b_j is the estimate of β_j. The slope coefficient b_j measures the change in the predicted value of the response variable $\hat{y}$ given a unit increase in the associated predictor variable x_j, *holding all other predictor variables constant.* In other words, it represents the partial influence of x_j on $\hat{y}$.

Using Dummy Variables in Regression

It is common in regression for the response variable to be influenced by numerical as well as categorical predictor variables. Recall from Chapter 1 that the observations of a categorical variable represent categories, whereas the observations of a numerical variable represent meaningful numbers. For example, marital status is a categorical variable, whereas income is a numerical variable. Although a categorical variable can have several categories, it is commonly described by only two categories. Examples include email (legitimate or spam), homeownership (own or do not own), and loan default (yes or no). In the introductory case, Layla would like to analyze post-college earnings where, in addition to the average cost, predictor variables include the graduation rate, the percentage of students paying down debt, and location. Here, location is a categorical variable with two categories (City or Non-city).

A categorical variable requires special attention in regression analysis because, unlike a numerical variable, the observations of a categorical variable cannot be used in their original form—that is, in a non-numerical format. We convert a categorical variable into a **dummy variable,** also referred to as an **indicator variable.** A dummy variable d is defined as a variable that assumes a value of 1 for one of the categories and 0 for the other. For example, when categorizing location, we can define d as 1 for city and 0 for non-city. Alternatively, we can define d as 1 for non-city and 0 for city, with no change in inference.

For a predictor dummy variable, we refer to the category that assumes a value of 0 as the **reference category** or the **benchmark category.** All comparisons are made in relation to the reference category. Continuing with the dummy variable example to categorize location, if we define 1 for city and 0 for non-city , the reference category would be non-city. Here, the estimated coefficient of the dummy variable would capture the predicted difference in earnings between city and non-city, holding other predictor variables constant.

A DUMMY VARIABLE

A dummy variable d is defined as a variable that takes on values of 1 or 0. It is commonly used to describe a categorical variable with two categories.

For the sake of simplicity, we will first consider a model containing one numerical predictor variable and one dummy variable. As we will see shortly, the model can easily be extended to include additional variables.

Consider the following model:

$$y = \beta_0 + \beta_1 x + \beta_2 d + \varepsilon,$$

where x is a numerical variable and d is a dummy variable with values of 1 or 0. We can use sample data to estimate the model as

$$\hat{y} = b_0 + b_1 x + b_2 d.$$

For a given x and $d = 1$, we can compute the predicted value as

$$\hat{y} = b_0 + b_1 x + b_2 = (b_0 + b_1) + b_1 x.$$

Similarly, for $d = 0$,

$$\hat{y} = b_0 + b_1 x.$$

Figure 12.4 shows the two regression lines, one for each category, when $b_2 > 0$. Observe that $\hat{y} = (b_0 + b_2) + b_1 x$ and $\hat{y} = b_0 + b_1 x$, have the same slope b_1. In other words, the dummy variable d accommodates a shift of the intercept but not of the slope. The difference between the intercepts is b_2 when d changes from 0 to 1.

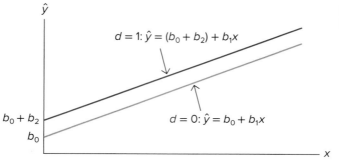

FIGURE 12.4
Using d for an intercept shift

In Example 12.2, we estimate and interpret a multiple linear regression model that includes a dummy variable.

EXAMPLE 12.2

College

Using the data from Table 12.1, estimate the linear regression model, Earnings $= \beta_0 + \beta_1 \text{Cost} + \beta_2 \text{Grad} + \beta_3 \text{Debt} + \beta_4 \text{City} + \varepsilon$, where Earnings is annual post-college earnings (in \$), Cost is the average annual cost (in \$), Grad is the graduation rate (in %), Debt is the percentage of students paying down debt (in %), and City assumes a value of 1 if the college is located in a city, 0 otherwise.

a. What is the sample regression equation?

b. Interpret the slope coefficients.

c. Predict annual post-college earnings if a college's average annual cost is \$25,000, its graduation rate is 60%, its percentage of students paying down debt is 80%, and it is located in a city.

SOLUTION: Table 12.3 shows the Excel output from estimating this model, where the dummy variable City equals 1 for city and 0 otherwise. We will provide Excel instructions right after this example.

TABLE 12.3 Regression Results for Example 12.2

Regression statistics						
Multiple R	0.6552					
R Square	0.4292					
Adjusted R Square	0.4087					
Standard Error	5645.831					
Observations	116					
ANOVA						
	df	SS	MS	F	Significance F	
Regression	4	2660691959	665172990	20.868	7.56E-13	
Residual	111	3538169765	31875403			
Total	115	6198861724				
	Coefficients	Standard error	t stat	p-value	Lower 95%	Upper 95%
Intercept	**10004.9665**	7634.3338	1.311	0.1927	−5122.98	25132.91
Cost	**0.4349**	0.1110	3.917	0.0002	0.21	0.65
Grad	**178.0989**	69.1940	2.574	0.0114	40.99	315.21
Debt	**141.4783**	117.2120	1.207	0.2300	−90.79	373.74
City	**2526.7888**	1103.4026	2.290	0.0239	340.32	4713.25

a. In order to answer the questions in Example 12.2, we only need the estimated coefficients, which we have put in boldface in the lower portion of the table. We will address the remaining information in later sections of this chapter. The coefficient estimates, rounded to four decimal places, are $b_0 = 10{,}004.9665$, $b_1 = 0.4349$, $b_2 = 178.0989$, $b_3 = 141.4783$, and $b_4 = 2{,}526.7888$. Thus, the sample regression equation is

$$\widehat{Earnings} = 10{,}004.9665 + 0.4349Cost + 178.0989Grad + 141.4783Debt + 2{,}526.7888City.$$

b. All coefficients are positive, suggesting a positive influence of each predictor variable on the response variable. Specifically:

- Holding all other predictor variables constant, if average annual costs increase by \$1, then predicted earnings increase by b_1; that is, by about \$0.43. This result suggests that spending more on college pays off.

- If the graduation rate increases by 1%, then predicted earnings increase by \$178.10, holding the other predictor variables constant. Policymakers often debate whether graduation rate can be used as a proxy for a college's academic quality. Perhaps it is not the academic quality but the case that colleges with a higher graduation rate have more motivated students, which translates into higher earnings for these students.

- A one percentage point increase in the percentage of students paying down debt increases predicted earnings by approximately \$141.48, holding the other three predictor variables constant. As it turns out, Debt is not statistically significant at any reasonable level; we will discuss tests of significance in Section 12.4.

- All else constant, predicted earnings are \$2,526.79 higher for graduates of colleges located in a city relative to the reference category of non-city. This difference is not surprising seeing that students who attend college in a city likely have more internship opportunities, which then often translate into higher-paying jobs after graduation.

c. If a college's average annual cost is \$25,000, its graduation rate is 60%, its percentage of students paying down debt is 80%, and it is located in a city, then predicted post-college earnings for its students are

$$\widehat{Earnings} = 10{,}004.9665 + 0.4349 \times 25{,}000 + 178.0989 \times 60 + 141.4783 \times 80 + 2{,}526.7888 \times 1 = 45{,}408.7991, \text{ or approximately } \$45{,}409.$$

Using Excel to Estimate a Multiple Linear Regression Model

In order to obtain the regression output in Table 12.3 using Excel, we follow these steps.

A. Open the ***College*** data file.

B. Choose **Data > Data Analysis > Regression** from the menu.

C. Insert a blank column between Debt and Location so that we can place the dummy variable together with other predictor variables. Note that column F is now blank and column G has data on Location. We use the **IF** function to create a City dummy variable for the Location variable. Enter the column heading City in cell F1. In cell F2, enter the formula =IF(G2="City", 1, 0). Copy and paste the formula from cell F2 to cells F3 through F117.

D. In the *Regression* dialog box, click on the box next to *Input Y Range,* and then select the data for Earnings. Click on the box next to *Input X Range,* and then *simultaneously* select the data for Cost, Grad, Debt, and City. Select *Labels* because we are using Earnings, Cost, Grad, Debt, and City as headings. Click **OK.**

Note: In Section 13.1 of Chapter 13, we estimate and interpret regression models where the categorical variable has multiple categories.

EXERCISES 12.2

Applications

12. A sociologist hypothesizes that the crime rate is higher in areas with higher poverty rate and lower median income. She collects data on the crime rate (crimes per 100,000 residents), the poverty rate (in %), and the median income (in $1,000s) from 41 New England cities. A portion of the regression results is shown in the following table.

	Coefficients	Standard error	t stat	p-value
Intercept	−301.62	549.71	−0.55	0.5864
Poverty	53.16	14.22	3.74	0.0006
Income	4.95	8.26	0.60	0.5526

a. Are the signs as expected on the slope coefficients?

b. Predict the crime rate in an area with a poverty rate of 20% and a median income of $50,000.

13. Using data from 50 workers, a researcher estimates Wage = $\beta_0 + \beta_1$Education + β_2Experience + β_3Age + ε, where Wage is the hourly wage rate and Education, Experience, and Age are the years of higher education, the years of experience, and the age of the worker, respectively. A portion of the regression results is shown in the following table.

	Coefficients	Standard error	t stat	p-value
Intercept	7.87	4.09	1.93	0.0603
Education	1.44	0.34	4.24	0.0001
Experience	0.45	0.14	3.16	0.0028
Age	−0.01	0.08	−0.14	0.8920

a. Interpret the estimated coefficients for Education and Experience.

b. Predict the hourly wage rate for a 30-year-old worker with four years of higher education and three years of experience.

14. Osteoporosis is a degenerative disease that primarily affects people over the age of 60. A medical researcher wants to forecast sales of StrongBones, a prescription drug for treating this debilitating disease. She uses the model Sales = $\beta_0 + \beta_1$Population + β_2Income + ε, where Sales is the sales of StrongBones (in $1,000,000s), Population is the number of people over the age of 60 (in millions), and Income is the average income of people over the age of 60 (in $1,000s). She collects data on 38 cities across the United States and obtains the following regression results:

	Coefficients	Standard error	t stat	p-value
Intercept	10.35	4.02	2.57	0.0199
Population	8.47	2.71	3.12	0.0062
Income	7.62	6.63	1.15	0.2661

a. Interpret the slope coefficients.

b. Predict sales if a city has 1.5 million people over the age of 60 and their average income is $44,000.

15. House price y is estimated as a function of the square footage of a house x and a dummy variable d that equals 1 if the house has ocean views. The estimated house price, measured in $1,000s, is given by $\hat{y} = 118.90 + 0.12x + 52.60d$

a. Compute the predicted price of a house with ocean views and square footage of 2,000 and 3,000, respectively.

b. Compute the predicted price of a house without ocean views and square footage of 2,000 and 3,000, respectively.

c. Discuss the impact of ocean views on the house price.

16. A researcher wants to better understand the factors that explain differences in salaries for college graduates. He decides to estimate two models: $y = \beta_0 + \beta_1 d_1 + \varepsilon$ (Model 1) and $y = \beta_0 + \beta_1 d_1 + \beta_2 d_2 + \varepsilon$ (Model 2). Here, y represents salary, d_1 is a dummy variable that equals 1 for business majors, and d_2 is a dummy variable that equals 1 for employees with an MBA.

a. What is the reference group in Model 1?

b. What is the reference group in Model 2?

c. In these two models, would it matter if d_1 equaled 1 for non-business majors?

17. **FILE** *Car_Prices.* The accompanying data file shows the price, the age, and the mileage for 20 used sedans.

a. Estimate the sample regression equation that enables us to predict the price of a sedan on the basis of its age and mileage.

b. Interpret the slope coefficient of Age.

c. Predict the price of a five-year-old sedan with 65,000 miles.

18. **FILE** *Engine.* The maintenance manager at a trucking company wants to build a regression model to forecast the time until the first engine overhaul (Time in years) based on four predictor variables: (1) annual miles driven (Miles in 1,000s), (2) average load weight (Load in tons), (3) average driving speed (Speed in mph), and (4) oil change interval (Oil in 1,000s of miles). The accompanying data file shows the results for 25 trucks.

a. Find the sample regression equation for the regression model (use all four predictor variables).

b. Predict the time before the first engine overhaul for a particular truck driven 60,000 miles per year with an average load of 22 tons, an average driving speed of 57 mph, and 18,000 miles between oil changes.

19. **FILE** *MCAS.* Education reform is one of the most hotly debated subjects on both state and national policymakers' list of socioeconomic topics. Consider a linear regression model that relates school expenditures and family background to student performance in Massachusetts. The response variable is the mean score on the MCAS (Massachusetts Comprehensive Assessment System) exam given to 10th graders. Four predictor variables are used: (1) STR is the student-to-teacher ratio (2) TSAL is the average teacher's salary in $1,000s, (3) INC is the median household income in $1,000s, and (4) SGL is the percentage of single-parent households. The accompanying data file shows the results for 224 school districts.

   a. For each predictor variable, discuss whether it is likely to have a positive or negative influence on Score.

   b. Find the sample regression equation. Are the signs of the slope coefficients as expected?

   c. What is the predicted score if STR = 18, TSAL = 50, INC = 60, and SGL = 5?

   d. What is the predicted score if everything else is the same as in part c except INC = 80?

20. **FILE** *Electricity_Cost.* The facility manager at a pharmaceutical company wants to build a regression model to forecast monthly electricity cost. Three main variables are thought to dictate electricity cost (Cost in $): (1) average outdoor temperature (Temp in °F), (2) working days per month (Work), and (3) tons of product produced (Tons). The accompanying data file shows the results for the past 12 months.

   a. For each predictor variable, discuss whether it is likely to have a positive or negative influence on monthly electricity cost.

   b. Find the sample regression equation for the regression model (use all three predictor variables).

   c. What is the predicted electricity cost in a month during which the average outdoor temperature is 65°, there are 23 working days, and 76 tons are produced?

21. **FILE** *SAT_1.* The SAT has gone through many revisions over the years. The accompanying data file shows a student's score on the writing and math sections of the SAT (Writing and Math, respectively), the student's GPA, and the student's gender (Female or Non-female). Use the gender variable to create the Female dummy variable that equals 1 if the student is female, 0 otherwise.

   a. Estimate a linear regression model with Writing as the response variable and GPA and Female as the predictor variables. Compute the predicted writing score for a non-female student with a GPA of 3.5. Repeat the computation for a female student.

   b. Estimate a linear regression model with Math as the response variable and GPA and Female as the predictor variables. Compute the predicted math score for a non-female student with a GPA of 3.5. Repeat the computation for a female student.

22. **FILE** *Franchise.* A president of a large chain of fast-food restaurants collects data on 100 franchises. The accompanying data file shows relevant data.

   a. Estimate the model: $y = \beta_0 + \beta_1 x_1 + \beta_2 x_2 + \varepsilon$, where y is net profit, x_1 is counter sales, and x_2 is drive-through sales. All variables are measured in millions of dollars.

   b. Interpret the coefficient attached to drive-through sales.

   c. Predict net profit if counter sales are $6 million and drive-through sales are $4 million.

23. **FILE** *Houses.* A Realtor is analyzing the relationship between the sale price of a home (Price in $), its square footage (Sqft), the number of bedrooms (Beds), the number of bathrooms (Baths), and Style (Colonial or Non-colonial). Use the Style variable to create a Colonial dummy variable that equals 1 for colonial, 0 otherwise. The accompanying data file shows information on 36 recent home sales.

   a. Estimate the model: $\text{Price} = \beta_0 + \beta_1\text{Sqft} + \beta_2\text{Beds} + \beta_3\text{Baths} + \beta_4\text{Colonial} + \varepsilon$.

   b. Interpret the coefficients attached to Beds and Colonial.

   c. Predict the price for a 2,500-square-foot, colonial-style home with three bedrooms and two bathrooms.

24. **FILE** *Startups.* Many of today's leading companies, including Google, Microsoft, and Facebook, are based on technologies developed within universities. Lisa Fisher is a business school professor who would like to analyze university factors that enhance innovation. The accompanying data file shows information that she has collected on 143 universities for a regression where the response variable is the number of startups (Startups), which is used as a measure for innovation. The predictor variables include the university's research expenditure (Research in $ millions), the number of patents issued (Patents), and the age of its technology transfer office (Duration in years).

   a. Estimate: $\text{Startups} = \beta_0 + \beta_1\text{Research} + \beta_2\text{Patents} + \beta_3\text{Duration} + \varepsilon$.

   b. Predict the number of startups for a university that spent $120 million on research, was issued eight patents, and has had a technology transfer office for 20 years.

   c. How much more research expenditure is needed for the university to have an additional predicted startup, with everything else being the same?

25. **FILE** *Quarterbacks.* American football is the highest-paying sport on a per-game basis. Given that the quarterback is considered the most important player on the team, he is typically well compensated. A sports statistician examines the factors that influence a quarterback's salary. He believes that a quarterback's pass completion rate is the most important variable affecting salary. He also wonders how total touchdowns scored and a quarterback's age might impact salary. The accompanying data file shows information that he has collected on salary (Salary in $ millions), pass completion rate (PC in %), total touchdowns scored (TD), and age for 32 quarterbacks during a recent season.

a. Estimate: Salary $= \beta_0 + \beta_1 PC + \beta_2 TD + \beta_3 Age + \varepsilon$.
b. Interpret the slope coefficient attached to TD.
c. Player 8 earned 12.9895 million dollars during the season. According to the model, what is his predicted salary if PC $= 70.6$, TD $= 34$, and Age $= 30$?
d. Player 16 earned 8.0073 million dollars during the season. According to the model, what is his predicted salary if PC $= 65.5$, TD $= 28$, and Age $= 32$?
e. Compute and interpret the residual salary for Player 8 and Player 16.

12.3 MODEL SELECTION

By simply observing the sample regression equation, we cannot assess how well the predictor variables explain the variation in the response variable. In this section, we discuss objective "goodness-of-fit" measures that summarize how well the sample regression equation fits the data. We also conduct hypothesis tests to assess the statistical significance of predictor variables.

LO 12.3

Goodness-of-Fit Measures

Interpret goodness-of-fit measures.

Recall that in the introductory case study, we are interested in analyzing factors that may influence post-college annual earnings (Earnings) for 116 colleges. Here, we will estimate three models, using a combination of four predictor variables, to determine which sample regression equation 'best' explains Earnings. The four predictor variables are the average annual cost (Cost), the graduation rate (Grad), the percentage of students paying down debt (Debt), and whether or not a college is located in a city (City equals 1 if a city location and 0 otherwise). Let the models be specified as follows:

Model 1: Earnings $= \beta_0 + \beta_1 Cost + \varepsilon$
Model 2: Earnings $= \beta_0 + \beta_1 Cost + \beta_2 Grad + \beta_3 Debt + \varepsilon$
Model 3: Earnings $= \beta_0 + \beta_1 Cost + \beta_2 Grad + \beta_3 Debt + \beta_4 City + \varepsilon$

(To simplify, we use the same notation to refer to the coefficients in Models 1, 2, and 3. The coefficients and their estimates may have a different meaning depending on which model we reference.)

If you had to choose one of these models to predict annual post-college earnings, which model would you choose? It may be that by using more predictor variables, you can better describe the response variable. However, for a given sample, more is not always better. In order to select the preferred model, we examine several goodness-of-fit measures: the standard error of the estimate, the coefficient of determination, and the adjusted coefficient of determination. We first discuss these measures in general, and then determine whether Model 1, Model 2, or Model 3 is the preferred model.

The Standard Error of the Estimate, s_e

To simplify, we describe goodness-of-fit measures in the context of a simple linear regression model (Model 1). Refer to Figure 12.2 for a scatterplot of Earnings (y) against Cost (x), as well as the superimposed sample regression line. Recall that the residual e_i represents the difference between the observed value and the predicted value of the response variable for the ith observation—that is, $e_i = y_i - \hat{y}_i$. If all the data points had fallen on the line, then each residual would be zero; in other words, there would be no dispersion between the observed and the predicted values. Because in practice we rarely, if ever, obtain this result, we evaluate models on the basis of the relative magnitude of the residuals. The sample regression equation provides a good fit when the dispersion of the residuals is relatively small.

A numerical measure that gauges the dispersion from the sample regression equation is the sample variance of the residual, denoted s_e^2. This measure is defined as the error (residual) sum of squares, $SSE = \Sigma(y_i - \hat{y}_i)^2 = \Sigma e_i^2$, divided by its respective degrees of freedom $n - k - 1$. Recall that k denotes the number of predictor variables in the linear regression model; thus, for a simple linear regression model, k equals one. Instead of s_e^2, we generally report the standard deviation of the residual, denoted s_e, more commonly referred to as the **standard error of the estimate.** As usual, s_e is the positive square root of s_e^2. When comparing models with the same response variable, we prefer the model with a smaller s_e. A smaller s_e implies that there is less dispersion of the observed values from the predicted values.

THE STANDARD ERROR OF THE ESTIMATE

The standard error of the estimate s_e is calculated as

$$s_e = \sqrt{\frac{\Sigma e_i^2}{n - k - 1}},$$

where e_i is the residual for the ith observation.

Theoretically, s_e can assume any value between zero and infinity, $0 \leq s_e < \infty$. When comparing models, the model with the smaller s_e is preferred.

For a given sample size n, increasing the number of predictor variables k reduces both the numerator (Σe_i^2) and the denominator ($n - k - 1$) in the formula for s_e. The net effect, shown by the value of s_e, allows us to determine if the added predictor variables improve the fit of the model. Virtually all statistical software packages report s_e. Excel reports s_e in the *Regression Statistics* portion of the regression output and refers to it as "Standard Error."

The Coefficient of Determination, R^2

Like the standard error of the estimate, the **coefficient of determination R^2** evaluates how well the sample regression equation fits the data. In particular, R^2 quantifies the sample variation in the response variable y that is explained by the sample regression equation. It is computed as the ratio of the explained variation of the response variable to its total variation. For example, if $R^2 = 0.72$, we say that 72% of the sample variation in y is explained by the sample regression equation. Other predictor variables, which have not been included in the model, account for the remaining 28% of the sample variation.

We denote the total variation in y as $\Sigma(y_i - \bar{y})^2$, which is the numerator in the formula for the variance of y. This value, called the total sum of squares, *SST,* can be broken down into two components: explained variation and unexplained variation.

Explained variation is the variation in y that can be explained by the sample regression equation. It is often referred to as the regression sum of squares, $SSR = \Sigma(\hat{y}_i - \bar{y})^2$. Unexplained variation is the variation in y that cannot be explained by the sample regression equation. It is the familiar error sum of squares, $SSE = \Sigma(y_i - \hat{y}_i)^2 = \Sigma e_i^2$.

Thus, the total variation in y can be decomposed into explained and unexplained variation as follows:

$$SST = SSR + SSE.$$

We derive the formula for R^2 by dividing both sides by *SST* and rearranging:

$$R^2 = SSR/SST = 1 - SSE/SST.$$

In other words, R^2 is the proportion of the total variation in y that is explained by the sample regression equation.

THE COEFFICIENT OF DETERMINATION, R^2

The coefficient of determination R^2 is the proportion of the sample variation in the response variable that is explained by the sample regression equation. We compute R^2 as

$$R^2 = \frac{SSR}{SST} = \frac{\Sigma(\hat{y}_i - \bar{y})^2}{\Sigma(y_i - \bar{y})^2}.$$

Equivalently, $R^2 = 1 - \dfrac{SSE}{SST} = 1 - \dfrac{\Sigma e_i^2}{\Sigma(y_i - \bar{y})^2}.$

The value of R^2 falls between zero and one; the closer the value is to one, the better the fit.

Virtually all statistical software packages report R^2. Excel reports R^2 in the *Regression Statistics* section of the regression output and refers to it as R Square.

Our objective in adding another predictor variable to a linear regression model is to increase the model's usefulness. It turns out that we cannot use R^2 for model comparison when the competing models do not include the same number of predictor variables. This occurs because R^2 never decreases as we add more predictor variables to the model. A popular model selection method in such situations is to choose the model that has the highest adjusted R^2 value, a topic that we discuss next.

The Adjusted R^2

Because R^2 never decreases as we add more predictor variables to the linear regression model, it is possible to increase its value unintentionally by including a group of predictor variables that may have no economic or intuitive foundation in the linear regression model. This is true especially when the number of predictor variables k is large relative to the sample size n. In order to avoid the possibility of R^2 creating a false impression, virtually all software packages include **adjusted R^2.** Unlike R^2, adjusted R^2 explicitly accounts for the sample size n and the number of predictor variables k. It is common to use adjusted R^2 for model selection because it imposes a penalty for any additional predictor variable included in the analysis. In other words, it penalizes overfitting. When comparing models, we prefer the model with the higher adjusted R^2.

ADJUSTED R^2

The adjusted coefficient of determination is calculated as

$$\text{Adjusted } R^2 = 1 - (1 - R^2)\left(\frac{n-1}{n-k-1}\right)$$

Adjusted R^2 is used to compare competing linear regression models with different numbers of predictor variables; the higher the adjusted R^2, the better the model.

If the error sum of squares (SSE) is substantially greater than zero and k is large compared to n, then adjusted R^2 will differ substantially from R^2. Adjusted R^2 may be negative if the correlation between the response variable and the predictor variables is sufficiently low. Both the standard error of the estimate s_e and the adjusted R^2 impose a penalty for overfitting. Adjusted R^2, however, is the more commonly used criterion for model selection when comparing linear regression models with different numbers of predictor variables.

EXAMPLE 12.3

Let's revisit the three models that were introduced in the beginning of this section:

FILE
College

Model 1: Earnings $= \beta_0 + \beta_1 \text{Cost} + \varepsilon$
Model 2: Earnings $= \beta_0 + \beta_1 \text{Cost} + \beta_2 \text{Grad} + \beta_3 \text{Debt} + \varepsilon$
Model 3: Earnings $= \beta_0 + \beta_1 \text{Cost} + \beta_2 \text{Grad} + \beta_3 \text{Debt} + \beta_4 \text{City} + \varepsilon$

Recall that Model 1 and Model 3 were estimated in Section 12.1 and Section 12.2, respectively. We have also estimated Model 2, but we do not show all of its regression output for the sake of brevity. As mentioned earlier, Excel reports goodness-of-fit measures in the top portion of the regression output. Table 12.4 shows the goodness-of-fit measures from estimating the three models.

TABLE 12.4 Goodness-of-Fit Measures for Models 1, 2, and 3

	Model 1	Model 2	Model 3
Standard error of the estimate s_e	6,271.4407	5,751.8065	5,645.8306
Coefficient of determination R^2	0.2767	0.4023	0.4292
Adjusted R^2	0.2703	0.3862	0.4087

a. Based on two goodness-of-fit measures, which of the three models is the preferred model?

b. Interpret the coefficient of determination for the preferred model.

c. What percentage of the sample variation in annual post-college earnings is unexplained by the preferred model?

SOLUTION:

a. Model 3 has the lowest standard error of the estimate ($s_e = 5,645.8306$) as compared to Model 1 and Model 2. Model 3 also has the highest adjusted R^2 (adjusted $R^2 = 0.4087$). Thus, Model 3 is the preferred model. Note that we cannot use the coefficient of determination R^2 to compare the three models because the models have different numbers of predictor variables.

b. The coefficient of determination R^2 for Model 3 is 0.4292, which means that 42.92% of the sample variation in Earnings is explained by the estimated regression model.

c. If 42.92% of the sample variation in Earnings is explained by changes in the predictor variables, then 57.08% (100 − 42.92) is unexplained by the regression model. It should not come as a surprise that the regression model leaves quite a bit of the sample variation in annual post-college earnings unexplained; there are many factors (grade-point average, field of emphasis, natural ability, etc.) that are likely to explain earnings that have not been included in the model.

Tests of Significance

LO **12.4**

We continue our assessment of the linear regression model by turning our attention to hypothesis tests about the unknown parameters (coefficients) $\beta_0, \beta_1, \ldots, \beta_k$. In particular, we test for joint and individual significance to determine whether there is evidence of a linear relationship between the response variable and the predictor variables.

Conduct tests of significance.

Test of Joint Significance

Consider the following linear regression model, which links the response variable y with k predictor variables $x_1, x_2, \ldots, x_k$:

$$y = \beta_0 + \beta_1 x_1 + \beta_2 x_2 + \cdots + \beta_k x_k + \varepsilon.$$

If the slope coefficients $\beta_1, \beta_2, \ldots, \beta_k$ equal zero, then all of the predictor variables drop out of the model; this implies that none of the predictor variables has a linear relationship with the response variable. Conversely, if at least one of the slope coefficients does not equal zero, then at least one predictor variable influences the response variable.

When we assess a linear regression model, a test of joint significance is often regarded as a test of its overall usefulness. This test determines whether the predictor variables $x_1, x_2, \ldots, x_k$ have a joint statistical influence on y. Following the hypothesis testing methodology introduced in Chapter 9, if we reject the null hypothesis that all slope coefficients equal zero, then we are able to conclude that at least one predictor variable influences the response variable. The competing hypotheses for a test of joint significance take the following form:

$$H_0 : \beta_1 = \beta_2 = \cdots = \beta_k = 0$$
$$H_A : \text{At least one } \beta_i \neq 0$$

The test statistic for a test of joint significance follows the $F_{(df_1, df_2)}$ distribution, which was first introduced in Chapter 10. It is calculated as $F_{(df_1, df_2)} = \frac{SSR/k}{SSE/(n-k-1)} = \frac{MSR}{MSE}$; refer to the definition box below for details. The $F_{(df_1, df_2)}$ test statistic is a ratio of the mean square regression MSR to the mean square error MSE, and it measures how well the regression equation explains the variability in the response variable. We always employ a right-tailed F test when conducting a test of joint significance because a larger value of $F_{(df_1, df_2)}$ provides us with more evidence to reject the null hypothesis.

A TEST OF JOINT SIGNIFICANCE

For the linear regression model $y = \beta_0 + \beta_1 x_1 + \beta_2 x_2 + \cdots + \beta_k x_k + \varepsilon$, the following competing hypotheses are used for a test of joint significance:

$$H_0 : \beta_1 = \beta_2 = \cdots = \beta_k = 0$$
$$H_A : \text{At least one } \beta_i \neq 0$$

The value of the test statistic is calculated as:

$$F_{(df_1, df_2)} = \frac{SSR/k}{SSE/(n-k-1)} = \frac{MSR}{MSE}$$

where $df_1 = k$, $df_2 = n - k - 1$, SSR is the regression sum of squares $(= \Sigma(y_i - \bar{y}^2))$, SSE is the error sum of squares $(= \Sigma e_i^2)$, MSR is the mean square regression, and MSE is the mean square error.

- The F test of joint significance is always implemented as a right-tailed test.
- If the null hypothesis is not rejected, then the predictor variables are not jointly significant in explaining the response variable; the model is not useful.
- If the null hypothesis is rejected, then the predictor variables are jointly significant in explaining the response variable; the model is useful.

Most statistical computer packages, including Excel, produce an ANOVA table that decomposes the total variability of the response variable y into two components: (1) the variability explained by the regression and (2) the variability that is unexplained. In addition, the value for the $F_{(df_1, df_2)}$ test statistic and its p-value are also provided. Table 12.5 shows the general format of an ANOVA table. Excel explicitly provides an ANOVA table with its regression output, with the p-value reported under the heading Significance F.

TABLE 12.5 General Format of an ANOVA Table for Regression

ANOVA	df	SS	MS	F	Significance F
Regression	k	SSR	$MSR = \dfrac{SSR}{k}$	$F_{(df_1, df_2)} = \dfrac{MSR}{MSE}$	$P\left(F_{(df_1, df_2)} \geq \dfrac{MSR}{MSE}\right)$
Residual	$n - k - 1$	SSE	$MSE = \dfrac{SSE}{n - k - 1}$		
Total	$n - 1$	SST			

EXAMPLE 12.4

Let's revisit Model 3.

$$\text{Model 3: Earnings} = \beta_0 + \beta_1 \text{Cost} + \beta_2 \text{Grad} + \beta_3 \text{Debt} + \beta_4 \text{City} + \varepsilon$$

Recall that we chose Model 3 to predict annual post-college earnings because it had the lowest standard error of the estimate and the highest adjusted R^2. We reproduce the ANOVA portion of the regression results in Table 12.6. Conduct a test to determine if the predictor variables are jointly significant in explaining Earnings at $\alpha = 0.05$.

TABLE 12.6 ANOVA portion of Regression Results for Model 3

ANOVA	df	SS	MS	F	Significance F
Regression	4	2660691959	665172990	20.868	7.56E-13
Residual	111	3538169765	31875403		
Total	115	6198861724			

SOLUTION: When testing whether the predictor variables are jointly significant in explaining Earnings, we set up the following competing hypotheses:

$$H_0: \beta_1 = \beta_2 = \beta_3 = \beta_4 = 0$$
$$H_A: \text{At least one } \beta_i \neq 0.$$

Given $n = 116$ and $k = 4$, we find that $df_1 = k = 4$ and $df_2 = n - k - 1 = 111$. From Table 12.6, we find that

$$F_{(4, 111)} = \frac{2{,}660{,}691{,}959/4}{3{,}538{,}169{,}765/111} = \frac{665{,}172{,}990}{31{,}875{,}403} = 20.868.$$

The p-value, $P(F_{(4, 111)} \geq 20.868) = 7.56 \times 10^{-13}$. Because the p-value is less than $\alpha = 0.05$, we reject H_0. At the 5% significance level, the predictor variables are jointly significant in explaining Earnings.

Note: Although not necessary, we could use Excel's F.DIST.RT function to derive the p-value for this right-tailed test. We enter =F.DIST.RT(20.868, 4, 111), and Excel returns 7.56×10^{-13}.

Test of Individual Significance

In addition to testing all slope coefficients jointly, we often want to conduct tests on a single coefficient. Again consider the following linear regression model, which links the response variable y with k predictor variables $x_1, x_2, \ldots, x_k$:

$$y = \beta_0 + \beta_1 x_1 + \beta_2 x_2 + \cdots + \beta_k x_k + \varepsilon.$$

If, for example, the slope coefficient β_1 equals zero, then the predictor variable x_1 drops out of the equation, implying that x_1 does not influence y. In other words, if β_1 equals zero, then there is no linear relationship between x_1 and y. Conversely, if β_1 does not equal zero, then x_1 influences y.

In general, when we want to test whether the population coefficient β_j is different from, greater than, or less than β_{j0}, where β_{j0} is the hypothesized value of β_j, then the competing hypotheses take one of the following forms:

Two-tailed test	Right-tailed test	Left-tailed test
$H_0: \beta_j = \beta_{j0}$	$H_0: \beta_j \leq \beta_{j0}$	$H_0: \beta_j \geq \beta_{j0}$
$H_A: \beta_j \neq \beta_{j0}$	$H_A: \beta_j > \beta_{j0}$	$H_A: \beta_j < \beta_{j0}$

When testing whether x_j significantly influences y, we set $\beta_{j0} = 0$ and specify a two-tailed test as $H_0: \beta_j = 0$ and $H_A: \beta_j \neq 0$. We could easily specify one-tailed competing hypotheses for a positive linear relationship ($H_0: \beta_j \leq 0$ and $H_A: \beta_j > 0$) or a negative linear relationship ($H_0: \beta_j \geq 0$ and $H_A: \beta_j < 0$).

Although tests of significance are commonly based on $\beta_{j0} = 0$, in some situations we might wish to determine whether the slope coefficient differs from a nonzero value. For instance, if we are analyzing the relationship between students' exam scores on the basis of hours studied, we may want to determine if an extra hour of review before the exam will increase a student's score by more than five points. Here, we formulate the hypotheses as $H_0: \beta_j \leq 5$ and $H_A: \beta_j > 5$. Finally, although in most applications we are interested in conducting hypothesis tests on the slope coefficient(s), there are instances where we may also be interested in testing the intercept, β_0. The testing framework for the intercept remains the same; that is, if we want to test whether the intercept differs from zero, we specify the competing hypotheses as $H_0: \beta_0 = 0$ and $H_A: \beta_0 \neq 0$.

The following definition box elaborates on a test of individual significance.

TEST OF INDIVIDUAL SIGNIFICANCE

For the linear regression model $y = \beta_0 + \beta_1 x_1 + \beta_2 x_2 + \cdots + \beta_k x_k + \varepsilon$, we use the t test to conduct a one- or a two-tailed test of individual significance based on the regression coefficient β_j. The value of the test statistic is calculated as

$$t_{df} = \frac{b_j - \beta_{j0}}{se(b_j)},$$

where $df = n - k - 1$, b_j is the estimate for β_j, $se(b_j)$ is the standard error of the estimator b_j, and β_{j0} is the hypothesized value of β_j. If $\beta_{j0} = 0$, the value of the test statistic reduces to $t_{df} = \frac{b_j}{se(b_j)}$.

Suppose the competing hypotheses are $H_0: \beta_j = 0$ versus $H_A: \beta_j \neq 0$.

- If the null hypothesis is not rejected, then x_j is not significant in explaining y.
- If the null hypothesis is rejected, then x_j is significant in explaining y.

Inferences for one-tailed tests and/or nonzero β_{j0} can be made similarly.

We would like to note that while the F test of joint significance is important for a multiple linear regression model, it is redundant for a simple linear regression model. In fact, for a simple linear regression model, the p-value of the F test is identical to that of the t test on the single slope coefficient. We advise you to verify this fact.

EXAMPLE 12.5

Let's again revisit Model 3.

FILE
College

$$\text{Model 3: Earnings} = \beta_0 + \beta_1\text{Cost} + \beta_2\text{Grad} + \beta_3\text{Debt} + \beta_4\text{City} + \varepsilon$$

We produce a portion of the regression results in Table 12.7. Conduct a hypothesis test to determine whether Cost influences Earnings at the 5% significance level.

TABLE 12.7 Portion of Regression Results for Model 3

	Coefficients	Standard error	*t* stat	*p*-value
Intercept	10004.9665	7634.3338	1.311	0.1927
Cost	0.4349	0.1110	3.917	0.0002
Grad	178.0989	69.1940	2.574	0.0114
Debt	141.4783	117.2120	1.207	0.2300
City	2526.7888	1103.4026	2.290	0.0239

SOLUTION: We set up the following competing hypotheses in order to determine whether Cost influences Earnings:

$$H_0: \beta_1 = 0$$
$$H_A: \beta_1 \neq 0$$

From Table 12.7, we find that $b_1 = 0.4349$ and $se(b_1) = 0.1110$. Given earlier information that $n = 116$, we find $df = n - k - 1 = 116 - 4 - 1 = 111$. So, using unrounded calculations, we find the value of the test statistic as $t_{111} = \frac{b_j - \beta_{j0}}{se(b_j)} = \frac{0.4349 - 0}{0.1110} = 3.917$. Recall from Chapter 9 that we can easily find the corresponding *p*-value in Excel using the **T.DIST** function. For the two-tailed test, we enter =2*(1-T.DIST(3.917, 111, TRUE)), and Excel returns a *p*-value of 0.0002. Note that these calculations are not necessary because virtually all statistical computer packages automatically provide the value of the test statistic and its associated *p*-value for a two-tailed test. As usual, the decision rule is to reject H_0 if the *p*-value $< \alpha$. Because the reported *p*-value is 0.0002, we reject H_0. At the 5% significance level, Cost is significant in explaining Earnings.

It is important to note that the computer-generated results are valid only in a standard case where a two-tailed test is implemented to determine whether a regression coefficient differs from zero. In Example 12.5, we could use the computer-generated value of the test statistic as well as the corresponding *p*-value because it represented a standard case. For a one-tailed test with $\beta_{j0} = 0$, the value of the test statistic is valid, but the *p*-value is not; in most cases, the computer-generated *p*-value must be divided in half. For a one- or two-tailed test to determine if the regression coefficient differs from a nonzero value, both the computer-generated value of the test statistic and the *p*-value become invalid. These facts are summarized as follows:

COMPUTER-GENERATED TEST STATISTIC AND THE *p*-VALUE

Virtually all statistical packages report a value of the test statistic and its associated *p*-value for a two-tailed test that assesses whether the regression coefficient differs from zero.

- If we specify a one-tailed test, then we need to divide the computer-generated *p*-value in half.
- If we test whether the coefficient differs from a nonzero value, then we cannot use the value of the computer-generated test statistic and its *p*-value.

We would also like to point out that for a one-tailed test with $\beta_{j0} = 0$, there are rare instances when the computer-generated p-value is invalid. This occurs when the sign of b_j (and the value of the accompanying test statistic) is not inconsistent with the null hypothesis. For example, for a right-tailed test, $H_0: \beta_j \leq 0$ and $H_A: \beta_j > 0$, the null hypothesis cannot be rejected if the estimate b_j (and the value of the accompanying test statistic t_{df}) is negative. Similarly, no further testing is necessary if $b_j > 0$ (and thus $t_{df} > 0$) for a left-tailed test. In these rare instances, the reported p-value is invalid.

A Test for a Nonzero Slope Coefficient

In Example 12.5, the null hypothesis included a zero value for the slope coefficient—that is, $\beta_{j0} = 0$. We now motivate a test where the hypothesized value is not zero by using a renowned financial application referred to as the **capital asset pricing model (CAPM).**

Let R represent the return on a stock or portfolio of interest. Given the market return R_M and the risk-free return R_f, the CAPM expresses the risk-adjusted return of an asset, $R - R_f$, as a function of the risk-adjusted market return, $R_M - R_f$. It is common to use the return of the S&P 500 index for R_M and the return on a Treasury bill for R_f. For empirical estimation, we express the CAPM as

$$R - R_f = \alpha + \beta(R_M - R_f) + \varepsilon.$$

We can rewrite the model as $y = \alpha + \beta x + \varepsilon$, where $y = R - R_f$ and $x = R_M - R_f$. Note that this is essentially a simple linear regression model that uses α and β, in place of the usual β_0 and β_1, to represent the intercept and the slope coefficients, respectively. The slope coefficient β, called the stock's **beta,** measures how sensitive the stock's return is to changes in the level of the overall market. When β equals 1, any change in the market return leads to an identical change in the given stock return. A stock for which $\beta > 1$ is considered more "aggressive" or riskier than the market, whereas one for which $\beta < 1$ is considered "conservative" or less risky. We also give importance to the intercept coefficient α, called the stock's **alpha.** The CAPM theory predicts α to be zero, and thus a nonzero estimate indicates abnormal returns. The abnormal return, also called excess return, is the difference between the actual return of an investment and its expected return. Abnormal returns are often the results of events such as announcements of higher-than-expected earnings, which may lead to positive abnormal returns, or being named in lawsuits, which may lead to negative abnormal returns. Abnormal returns are positive when $\alpha > 0$ and negative when $\alpha < 0$.

EXAMPLE 12.6

Johnson & Johnson (J&J) was founded more than 130 years ago on the premise that doctors and nurses should use sterile products to treat people's wounds. Since that time, J&J products have become staples in most people's homes. Consider the CAPM where the J&J risk-adjusted stock return (JJ_Adj) is used as the response variable and the risk-adjusted market return (Market_Adj) is used as the predictor variable. A portion of 60 months of data is shown in Table 12.8.

TABLE 12.8 Risk-Adjusted Return for J&J and Market

Month	Year	JJ_Adj	Market_Adj
Jan	2016	0.0044	−0.0071
Feb	2016	0.0328	0.0629
⋮	⋮	⋮	⋮
Dec	2020	0.0359	−0.0118

a. Because consumer staples comprise many of the products sold by J&J, its stock is often considered less risky; that is, people need these products whether the economy is good or bad. At the 5% significance level, is the beta coefficient less than one?

b. At the 5% significance level, are there abnormal returns? In other words, is the alpha coefficient significantly different from 0?

SOLUTION: Using the CAPM notation, we estimate the model, JJ_Adj = α + β(Market_Adj) + ε; the relevant portion of the regression output is presented in Table 12.9.

TABLE 12.9 Portion of CAPM Regression Results for J&J

	Coefficients	Standard error	t stat	p-value
Intercept	−0.0007	0.0050	−0.139	0.8899
Market_Adj	0.7306	0.1091	6.694	9.57E-09

a. The estimate for the beta coefficient is 0.7306 and its standard error is 0.1091. In order to determine whether the beta coefficient is significantly less than one, we formulate the hypotheses as

$$H_0: \beta \geq 1$$
$$H_A: \beta < 1$$

Given 60 data points, $df = n - k - 1 = 60 - 1 - 1 = 58$. We cannot use the test statistic value or the p-value reported in Table 12.9 because the hypothesized value of β is not zero. Using unrounded calculations, we find the value of the test statistic as $t_{58} = \frac{b_j - \beta_{j0}}{se(b_j)} = \frac{0.7306 - 1}{0.1091} = -2.468$. In Excel, in order to find the p-value for this left-tailed test, or equivalently $P(T_{58} \leq -2.468)$, we enter =T.DIST(-2.468, 58, TRUE). Excels returns 0.008. Because the p-value $< \alpha =$ 0.05, we reject H_0 and conclude that β is significantly less than one; that is, the return on J&J stock is less risky than the return on the market.

b. Abnormal returns exist when α is significantly different from zero. Thus, the competing hypotheses are $H_0: \alpha = 0$ versus $H_A: \alpha \neq 0$. Because it is a standard case, where the hypothesized value of the coefficient is zero, we can use the reported test statistic value of −0.139 with an associated p-value of 0.8899. We cannot reject H_0 at any reasonable level of significance. Therefore, we cannot conclude that there are abnormal returns for J&J stock.

A Note on Tests of Significance with Big Data

When using regression analysis with big data, we often do not place much value on tests of significance. Why is this the case? It turns out that if the sample size is sufficiently large, then the relationship between each predictor variable and the response variable will be statistically significant even when the relationship is not economically meaningful.

What occurs in these instances is that there is little difference in the estimates of β_j generated by different large random samples. Recall that we use $se(b_j)$ to gauge the variability in b_j and this variability depends on two factors: (1) how closely the members of the population mirror the relationship between x_j and y that is implied by β_j and (2) the size of the sample on which the value of the estimator b_j is based. If the sample size is sufficiently large, then the variability virtually disappears, or, equivalently, $se(b_j)$ approaches zero. As $se(b_j)$ approaches zero, the value of the t_{df} test statistic [calculated as $t_{df} = b_j / se(b_j)$] increases, leading to a small p-value, and thus rejection of the null hypothesis of insignificance.

Therefore, if the sample size is sufficiently large, statistical significance does not necessarily imply that a relationship is economically meaningful. It is for this reason that when confronted with big data and assessing various models, we tend to rely on economic intuition and model validation rather than tests of significance.

Reporting Regression Results

Regression results are often reported in a "user-friendly" table. Table 12.10 reports the regression results for the three models that attempt to explain annual post-college earnings (Earnings). For Model 1, the predictor variable is the average annual cost (Cost); for Model 2, the predictor variables are Cost, the graduation rate (Grad), and the percentage of students paying down debt (Debt); and for Model 3, the predictor variables are Cost, Grad, Debt, and whether or not a college is located in a city (City equals 1 if a city location, 0 otherwise). If we were supplied with only this table, we would be able to compare these models, construct the sample regression equation of the chosen model, and perform a respectable assessment of the model with the statistics provided. Many tables contain a Notes section at the bottom explaining some of the notation. We choose to put the p-values in parentheses under all the estimated coefficients; however, some analysts place the standard errors of the coefficients or the values of the test statistics in parentheses. Whichever format is chosen, it must be made clear to the reader in the Notes section.

TABLE 12.10 Estimates of Alternative Regression Models to Explain Earnings, $n = 116$

	Model 1	Model 2	Model 3
Intercept	28,375.4051*	11819.4747	10,004.9665
	(0.000)	(0.129)	(0.193)
Cost	0.7169*	0.5050*	0.4349*
	(0.000)	(0.000)	(0.000)
Grad	NA	192.6664*	178.0989*
		(0.007)	(0.011)
Debt	NA	104.6573	141.4783
		(0.378)	(0.230)
City	NA	NA	2,526.7888*
			(0.024)
s_e	6,271.4407	5,751.8065	5,645.8306
R^2	0.2767	0.4023	0.4292
Adjusted R^2	0.2703	0.3862	0.4087
F statistic (p-value)	43.608 (0.000)	25.124 (0.000)	20.868(0.000)

Notes: Parameter estimates are in the top half of the table with the p-values in parentheses; * represents significance at the 5% level. NA denotes not applicable. The lower part of the table contains goodness-of-fit measures.

SYNOPSIS OF INTRODUCTORY CASE

The Department of Education published a redesigned College Scorecard that reports the most reliable national data on college costs and students' outcomes at specific colleges. The availability of clear, reliable data was welcomed by families who are searching for answers to critical questions concerning college affordability and value.

In an attempt to determine which college factors "best" explain annual post-college earnings, three regression models were estimated. A combination of four predictor variables was used in the analysis. The four predictor variables were the average annual cost (Cost), the graduation rate (Grad), the percentage of students paying down debt (Debt), and a City dummy variable that equals 1 if the college is located in a city, 0 otherwise. Goodness-of-fit measures suggested that the model that included all

Africa Studio/Shutterstock

four predictor variables provided the best overall fit, as measured by its lowest standard error of the estimate and its highest adjusted R^2 value. The sample regression equation was $\overline{Earnings} = 10{,}004.9665 + 0.4349Cost + 178.0989Grad + 141.4783Debt + 2{,}526.7888City$. This regression equation implies that if a college's average annual cost is \$25,000, its graduation rate is 60%, its percentage of students paying down debt is 80%, and it is located in a city, then average post-college earnings for its students are \$45,409.

Further testing of this preferred model revealed that the four predictor variables were jointly significant. Individual tests of significance showed that Cost, Grad, and City were significant at the 5% level; Debt was not significant in explaining Earnings. The coefficient of determination, or R^2, revealed that approximately 43% of the sample variability in annual post-college earnings is explained by the model. Thus, 57% of the sample variability in annual post-college earnings remains unexplained. This is not entirely surprising because factors not included in the model, such as field of emphasis, grade point average, and natural ability, also influence annual post-college earnings.

EXERCISES 12.3

Applications

26. The director of college admissions at a local university is trying to determine whether a student's high school GPA or SAT score is a better predictor of the student's subsequent college GPA. She formulates two models:

    Model 1. College GPA $= \beta_0 + \beta_1$High School GPA $+ \varepsilon$
    Model 2. College GPA $= \beta_0 + \beta_1$SAT Score $+ \varepsilon$

    She estimates these models and obtains the following goodness-of-fit measures.

	Model 1	Model 2
R^2	0.5595	0.5322
Adjusted R^2	0.5573	0.5298
s_e	40.3684	41.6007

    Which model provides a better fit for y? Justify your response with two goodness-of-fit measures.

27. **FILE** *Test_Scores.* The accompanying data file shows the midterm and final scores for 32 students in a statistics course.
    a. Estimate a student's final score as a function of their midterm score.
    b. Find the standard error of the estimate.
    c. Find and interpret the coefficient of determination.

28. **FILE** *Property_Taxes.* The accompanying data file shows the square footage and associated property taxes for 20 homes.
    a. Estimate a home's property taxes as a linear function of the size of the home (measured by its square footage).
    b. What proportion of the sample variation in property taxes is explained by the home's size?
    c. What proportion of the sample variation in property taxes is unexplained by the home's size?

29. **FILE** *Football.* Is it defense or offense that wins football games? The accompanying data file includes a team's winning record (Win in %), the average number of yards gained, and the average number of yards allowed during a recent NFL season.
    a. Compare two simple linear regression models where Model 1 predicts Win as a function of Yards_Gained and Model 2 predicts Win as a function of Yards_Allowed.
    b. Estimate a linear regression model, Model 3, that applies both Yards_Gained and Yards_Allowed to forecast Win. Is this model an improvement over the other two models? Explain.

30. **FILE** *Ownership.* In order to determine if the homeownership rate in the U.S. is linked with income, state-level data on the homeownership rate (Ownership in %) and median household income (Income in \$) were collected. The accompanying data file shows the results.
    a. Estimate and interpret the model Ownership $= \beta_0 + \beta_1$Income $+ \varepsilon$. Is the coefficient attached to Income as expected? Explain.
    b. What is the standard error of the estimate?
    c. Interpret the coefficient of determination. Does this seem like a promising model? Explain.

31. **FILE** *Return.* A research analyst is trying to determine whether a firm's price-earnings (P/E) and price-sales (P/S) ratios can explain the firm's stock performance over the past year. A P/E ratio is calculated as a firm's share price compared to the income or profit earned by the firm per share. Generally, a high P/E ratio suggests that investors are expecting higher earnings growth in the future compared to companies with a lower P/E ratio. The P/S ratio is calculated by dividing a firm's share price by the firm's revenue per share for the trailing 12 months. In short, investors can use the P/S ratio to determine how much they are paying for a dollar of the firm's sales rather than a

dollar of its earnings (P/E ratio). In general, the lower the P/S ratio, the more attractive the investment. The accompanying data file includes the year-to-date returns (Return in %) and the P/E and P/S ratios for 30 firms.

a. Estimate Return $= \beta_0 + \beta_1 \text{ P/E} + \beta_2 \text{ P/S} + \varepsilon$. Are the signs on the coefficients as expected? Explain.

b. Interpret the slope coefficient of the P/S ratio.

c. What is the predicted return for a firm with a P/E ratio of 10 and a P/S ratio of 2?

d. What is the standard error of the estimate?

e. Interpret R^2.

32. **FILE** *SAT_2.* It is generally believed that students from wealthier families do well on the Scholastic Aptitude Test (SAT) because of their time and money resources. Another commonly used predictor for SAT scores is the student's grade point average (GPA). The accompanying data file shows the SAT score, household income (Income in $), and the GPA for 24 students.

a. Estimate three models:

(i) $\text{SAT} = \beta_0 + \beta_1 \text{Income} + \varepsilon$,

(ii) $\text{SAT} = \beta_0 + \beta_1 \text{GPA} + \varepsilon$, and

(iii) $\text{SAT} = \beta_0 + \beta_1 \text{Income} + \beta_2 \text{GPA} + \varepsilon$.

b. Use goodness-of-fit measures to select the best-fitting model.

c. Use the preferred model to predict SAT given the mean value of the predictor variable(s).

33. In order to examine the relationship between the selling price of a used car and its age, an analyst uses data from 20 recent transactions and estimates Price $= \beta_0 + \beta_1 \text{Age} + \varepsilon$. A portion of the regression results is shown in the accompanying table.

	Coefficients	Standard error	t stat	p-value
Intercept	21187.94	733.42	28.889	1.56E-16
Age	−1208.25	128.95		2.41E-08

a. Specify the competing hypotheses in order to determine whether the selling price of a used car and its age are linearly related.

b. Calculate the value of the test statistic.

c. At the 5% significance level, is the age of a used car significant in explaining its selling price?

d. Conduct a hypothesis test at the 5% significance level in order to determine if β_1 differs from $-1,000$. Show all of the relevant steps.

34. For a sample of 20 New England cities, a sociologist studies the crime rate in each city (crimes per 100,000 residents) as a function of its poverty rate (in %) and its median income (in $1,000s). She estimates the following model: Crime $= \beta_0 + \beta_1 \text{Poverty} + \beta_2 \text{Income} + \varepsilon$. A portion of the regression results is shown in the accompanying table.

ANOVA	df	SS	MS	F	Significance F
Regression	2	188246.8	94123.40	35.20	9.04E-07
Residual	17	45457.32	2673.96		
Total	19	233704.1			

	Coefficients	Standard error	t stat	p-value
Intercept	−301.7927	549.7135	−0.549	0.590
Poverty	53.1597	14.2198	3.738	0.002
Income	4.9472	8.2566	0.599	0.557

a. Specify the sample regression equation.

b. At the 5% significance level, are the poverty rate and income jointly significant in explaining the crime rate?

c. At the 5% significance level, show whether the poverty rate and the crime rate are linearly related.

d. Determine whether income influences the crime rate at the 5% significance level.

35. Akiko Hamaguchi is a manager at a small sushi restaurant in Phoenix, Arizona. Akiko is concerned that the weak economic environment has hampered foot traffic in her area, thus causing a dramatic decline in sales. In order to offset the decline in sales, she has pursued a strong advertising campaign. She believes advertising expenditures have a positive influence on sales. To support her claim, Akiko estimates the following linear regression model: Sales $= \beta_0 + \beta_1 \text{Unemployment} + \beta_2 \text{Advertising} + \varepsilon$. A portion of the regression results is shown in the accompanying table.

ANOVA	df	SS	MS	F	Significance F
Regression	2	72.6374	36.3187	8.760	0.003
Residual	14	58.0438	4.1460		
Total	16	130.681			

	Coefficients	Standard error	t stat	p-value
Intercept	17.5060	3.9817	4.397	0.007
Unemployment	−0.6879	0.2997	−2.296	0.038
Advertising	0.0266	0.0068	3.932	0.002

a. At the 5% significance level, test whether the predictor variables jointly influence sales.

b. At the 1% significance level, test whether the unemployment rate is negatively related with sales.

c. At the 1% significance level, test whether advertising expenditures are positively related with sales.

36. **FILE** *Dexterity.* Finger dexterity, the ability to make precisely coordinated finger movements to grasp or assemble very small objects, is important in jewelry making. Thus, the manufacturing manager at Gemco, a manufacturer of high-quality watches, has developed a regression model to predict the productivity, measured by watches per shift, of new employees based on the time required (in seconds) to place three pins in each of 100 small holes using tweezers. The accompanying file contains relevant data.

a. Estimate the regression model:
Watches $= \beta_0 + \beta_1$Time $+ \varepsilon$.

b. The manager claims that for every extra second taken on placing the pins, the number of watches produced decreases by more than 0.02. Test this claim at the 5% significance level. Show the relevant steps of the test.

37. **FILE** *Fertilizer.* A horticulturist is studying the relationship between tomato plant height and fertilizer amount. Thirty tomato plants grown in similar conditions were subjected to various amounts of fertilizer (in ounces) over a four-month period, and then their heights (in inches) were measured. The accompanying file contains relevant data.

a. Estimate the regression model:
Height $= \beta_0 + \beta_1$Fertilizer $+ \varepsilon$.

b. At the 5% significance level, determine if an ounce of fertilizer increases height by more than three inches. Show the relevant steps of the test.

38. **FILE** *Electricity_Cost.* The facility manager at a pharmaceutical company wants to build a regression model to forecast monthly electricity cost. Three main variables are thought to dictate electricity cost: (1) average outdoor temperature (Temp in °F), (2) working days per month (Days), and (3) tons of product produced (Tons). The accompanying file contains relevant data.

a. Estimate the regression model.

b. At the 10% significance level, are the predictor variables jointly significant? Show the relevant steps of the test.

c. Are the predictor variables individually significant at the 10% significance level? Show the relevant steps of the test.

39. **FILE** *Engine.* The maintenance manager at a trucking company wants to build a regression model to forecast the time until the first engine overhaul (Time in years) based on four predictor variables: (1) annual miles driven (Miles in 1,000s), (2) average load weight (Load in tons), (3) average driving speed (Speed in mph), and (4) oil change interval (Oil in 1,000s miles). Based on driver logs and onboard computers, data have been obtained for a sample of 25 trucks. The accompanying file contains relevant data.

a. Estimate the time until the first engine overhaul as a function of all four predictor variables.

b. At the 10% significance level, are the predictor variables jointly significant? Show the relevant steps of the test.

c. Are the predictor variables individually significant at the 10% significance level? Show the relevant steps of the test.

40. **FILE** *Houses.* A Realtor is analyzing the relationship between the sale price of a house (Price in $), its square footage (Sqft), the number of bedrooms (Beds), the number of bathrooms (Baths), and a Colonial dummy variable (Colonial equals 1 if a colonial-style house, 0 otherwise). The accompanying data file shows information on 36 recent sales.

a. Estimate Price $= \beta_0 + \beta_1$Sqft $+ \beta_2$Beds $+ \beta_3$Baths $+ \beta_4$Colonial $+ \varepsilon$. Show the regression results in a well-formatted table.

b. At the 5% significance level, are the predictor variables jointly significant in explaining Price?

c. At the 5% significance level, are all predictor variables individually significant in explaining Price?

41. **FILE** *Caterpillar.* Caterpillar, Inc., manufactures and sells heavy construction equipment worldwide. The performance of Caterpillar's stock is likely to be strongly influenced by the economy. For example, during the Great Recession, the value of Caterpillar's stock plunged dramatically. The accompanying data file shows Caterpillar's monthly risk-adjusted return (Cat_Adj) and the risk-adjusted market return (Market_Adj) for a five-year period ($n = 60$).

a. Estimate the CAPM model for Caterpillar, Inc. Show the regression results in a well-formatted table.

b. At the 5% significance level, determine if investment in Caterpillar is riskier than the market (beta greater than 1).

c. At the 5% significance level, is there evidence of abnormal returns (alpha differs from zero)?

42. **FILE** *Final_Test.* On the first day of class, an economics professor administers a test to gauge the math preparedness of her students. She believes that the performance on this math test and the number of hours studied per week on the course are the primary factors that predict a student's score on the final exam. The accompanying data file shows information on 60 students.

a. Estimate the sample regression equation that enables us to predict a student's final exam score (Final) on the basis of their math score (Math) and the number of hours studied per week (Hours).

b. At the 5% significance level, are a student's math score and the number of hours studied per week jointly significant in explaining a student's final exam score?

c. At the 5% significance level, is each predictor variable individually significant in explaining a student's final exam score?

43. **FILE** *Union_Pay.* An automotive workers union, in conjunction with top management, is negotiating a new hourly pay policy for union workers based on three variables: (1) job class, (2) years with the company, and (3) years as a union member at any company. The goal is to develop an equitable model that can objectively specify hourly pay, thereby reducing pay disparity grievances. The accompanying data file shows information on 50 union workers.

a. Report the sample regression equation of the appropriate model.

b. At the 5% significance level, are the predictor variables jointly significant? Are they individually significant?

c. Predict hourly pay for a worker in Job Class 48 with 18 years of experience at the company and 14 years with the union.

44. **FILE** *Yields.* While the Federal Reserve controls short-term interest rates, long-term interest rates essentially depend on supply/demand dynamics, as well as longer-term interest rate expectations. In order to examine the relationship between short-term and long-term interest rates, monthly data were collected on the three-month Treasury yield (Three_month, in %) and the 10-year Treasury yield (Ten_year, in %). The accompanying data file shows the results.

   a. Estimate and interpret a sample regression equation using the 10-year yield as the response variable and the three-month yield as the predictor variable.

   b. Interpret the coefficient of determination.

   c. At the 5% significance level, is the three-month yield significant in explaining the 10-year yield?

   d. Many wonder whether a change in the three-month yield implies the same change in the 10-year yield. At the 5% significance level, is this belief supported by the data?

45. **FILE** *Wage.* A consumer group activist is concerned about sex discrimination at a firm. The accompanying data file shows the hourly wage (Wage in $), years of education (Educ), years of experience (Exper), age (Age), and a Male dummy variable that equals 1 if cisgender male, 0 otherwise, for 50 employees.

   a. Estimate $Wage = \beta_0 + \beta_1 Educ + \beta_2 Exper + \beta_3 Age + \beta_4 Male + \varepsilon$.

   b. Predict the hourly wage of a 40-year-old cisgender male employee with 10 years of education and five years of experience. Find the corresponding wage for a non-cisgender male.

   c. Is the variable Male significant at the 5% level? Do the data suggest that sex discrimination exists at this firm?

46. **FILE** *BMI.* According to the World Health Organization, obesity has reached epidemic proportions globally. While obesity has generally been linked with chronic disease and disability, researchers argue that it may also affect salaries. In other words, the body mass index (BMI) of an employee is a predictor for salary. The accompanying data file shows Salary (in $1,000s), BMI, and a College dummy variable that equals 1 for a college-educated person.

   a. Estimate a model for Salary using BMI and College as the predictor variables. Determine if BMI influences salary at the 5% level of significance.

   b. What is the estimated salary for a college-educated person with a BMI of 30? Compute the corresponding salary for a non-college-educated person with a BMI of 300.

47. **FILE** *Ice_Cream.* A manager at an ice cream store is trying to determine how many customers to expect on any given day. Overall business has been relatively steady over the past several years, but the customer count seems to have ups and downs. The accompanying data file shows the number of customers, the high temperature (Temperature in degrees Fahrenheit), and whether the day fell on a weekend (Weekend equals 1 if weekend, 0 otherwise) over the past 30 days.

   a. Estimate $Customers = \beta_0 + \beta_1 Temperature + \beta_2 Weekend + \varepsilon$.

   b. How many customers should the manager expect on a Sunday with a forecasted high temperature of 80°?

   c. Interpret the estimated coefficient for Weekend. Is it significant at the 5% level? How might this affect the store's staffing needs?

48. **FILE** *Quotations.* The labor estimation group at Sturdy Electronics, a contract electronics manufacturer of printed circuit boards, wants to simplify the process it uses to quote production costs to potential customers. It has identified the primary drivers for production time (and thus production cost) as being the number of electronic parts that can be machine-installed and the number of parts that must be manually installed. Accordingly, it wishes to develop a multiple regression model to predict production time, measured as minutes per board. The accompanying data file shows information on 25 recent product quotations.

   a. What is the sample regression equation?

   b. Predict production time for a circuit board with 475 machine-installed components and 16 manually installed components.

   c. What proportion of the sample variability in production time is explained by the two predictor variables?

   d. At the 5% significance level, are the predictor variables jointly significant? Are they individually significant?

49. **FILE** *Longevity.* According to the Centers for Disease Control and Prevention, life expectancy at age 65 in the United States is about 18.7 years. Medical researchers have argued that while excessive drinking is detrimental to health, drinking a little alcohol every day, especially wine, may be associated with an increase in life expectancy. Others have also linked longevity with income and a person's gender. The accompanying data file shows information relating to the length of life after 65; average income (in $1,000s) at a retirement age of 65; a Female dummy variable that equals 1 if the individual is female, 0 if male; and the average number of alcoholic drinks consumed per day. In this data set, information on non-binary cases is not available.

   a. Use the data to model life expectancy at 65 on the basis of Income, Female, and Drinks.

   b. Conduct a one-tailed test at $a = 0.01$ to determine if females live longer than males.

   c. Predict the life expectancy at 65 of a male with an income of $40,000 and an alcohol consumption of two drinks per day; repeat the prediction for a female.

50. **FILE** *QuickFix.* The general manager of QuickFix, a chain of quick-service, no-appointment auto repair shops, wants to develop a model to forecast monthly vehicles served at any particular shop based on four factors: garage bays, population

within five-mile radius (Population in 1,000s), interstate highway access (Access equals 1 if convenient, 0 otherwise), and time of year (Winter equals 1 if winter, 0 otherwise). He believes that, all else equal, shops near an interstate will service more vehicles and that more vehicles will be serviced in the winter due to battery and tire issues. The accompanying data file shows information on 19 locations.

a. Estimate the regression equation relating vehicles serviced to the four predictor variables.

b. Interpret each of the slope coefficients.

c. At the 5% significance level, are the predictor variables jointly significant? Are they individually significant? What about at the 10% significance level?

d. What proportion of the variability in vehicles served is explained by the four predictor variables?

e. Predict vehicles serviced in a nonwinter month for a particular location with five garage bays, a population of 40,000, and convenient interstate access.

12.4 MODEL ASSUMPTIONS AND COMMON VIOLATIONS

LO 12.5

So far we have focused on the estimation and the assessment of linear regression models. It is important to understand that the statistical properties of the ordinary least squares (OLS) estimator, as well as the validity of the testing procedures, depend on the assumptions of the classical linear regression model. In this section, we discuss these assumptions. We also address common violations to the assumptions, discuss the consequences when the assumptions are violated, and, where possible, offer some simple remedies.

Address common violations of the OLS assumptions.

Under the assumptions of the classical linear regression model, the OLS estimators have desirable properties. In particular, the OLS estimators of the regression coefficients β_j are unbiased; that is, $E(b_j) = \beta_j$. Moreover, among all linear unbiased estimators, they have minimum variations between samples. These desirable properties of the OLS estimators become compromised as one or more model assumptions are violated. Aside from coefficient estimates, the validity of the significance tests is also impacted by the assumptions. For certain violations, the estimated standard errors of the OLS estimators are inappropriate; in these cases it is not possible to make meaningful inferences from the t and the F test results.

Residual Plots

The assumptions of the classical linear regression model are, for the most part, based on the error term ε. Because the residuals, or the observed error term, $e = y - \hat{y}$, contain useful information regarding ε, it is common to use the residuals to investigate the assumptions. In this section, we will rely on **residual plots** to detect some of the common violations to the assumptions. These graphical plots are easy to use and provide informal analysis of the estimated regression models. Formal tests are beyond the scope of this text.

RESIDUAL PLOTS

For the regression model $y = \beta_0 + \beta_1 x_1 + \beta_2 x_2 + \cdots + \beta_k x_k + \varepsilon$, the residuals are computed as $e = y - \hat{y}$, where $\hat{y} = b_0 + b_1 x_1 + b_2 x_2 + \cdots + b_k x_k$. These residuals can be plotted sequentially over time or against a predictor variable x_j or against predicted values $\hat{y}$ to look for model inadequacies.

Residual plots can also be used to detect outliers. Recall that outliers are observations that stand out from the rest of the data. For an outlier observation, the resulting residual will appear distinct in a plot; it will stand out from the rest. While outliers can greatly impact the estimates, it is not always clear what to do with them. As mentioned in Chapter 3, outliers may indicate bad data due to incorrectly recorded (or included) observations in the data set. In such cases, the relevant observation should be corrected or simply deleted. Alternatively, outliers may just be due to random variations, in which case the relevant observations should remain. In any event, residual plots help us identify potential outliers so that we can take corrective actions, if needed.

It is common to plot the residuals e sequentially over time or against a predictor variable x_j or against predicted values $\hat{y}$. In Figure 12.5, we present a hypothetical residual plot where the residuals are plotted against one of the predictor variables. Note that all the points are randomly dispersed around the zero value of the residuals. This suggests that none of the assumptions has been violated. Also, there is no evidence of outliers because no residual stands out from the rest. Any discernible pattern of the residuals indicates that one or more assumptions have been violated.

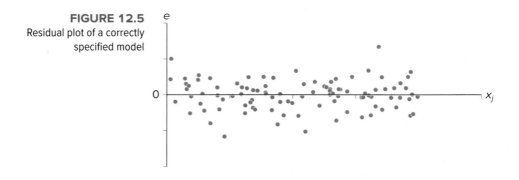

FIGURE 12.5
Residual plot of a correctly specified model

Next we discuss the OLS assumptions, describe common violations, and offer remedies. At the end of this section, we outline how to obtain residual plots in Excel.

> **Assumption 1.** The regression model given by $y = \beta_0 + \beta_1 x_1 + \beta_2 x_2 + \cdots + \beta_k x_k + \varepsilon$ is linear in the parameters and is correctly specified.

Note that Assumption 1 requires linearity in the parameters $(\beta_0, \beta_1, \ldots, \beta_k)$, but not the variables $(y, x_1, x_2, \ldots, x_k)$. Assumption 1 also requires that we correctly specify the model. The model should make economic and intuitive sense, include all relevant predictor variables, and incorporate any nonlinearities between the response and predictor variables.

Detecting Nonlinearities

We can use residual plots to identify nonlinear patterns. Linearity is justified if the residuals are randomly dispersed across the observations of a predictor variable. A discernible trend in the residuals is indicative of a nonlinear pattern.

EXAMPLE 12.7

Arun Jain is a sociologist who wishes to study the relationship between age and happiness. He interviews 24 individuals and collects data on each person's age and happiness, where happiness is measured on a scale from 0 to 100. A portion of the data is shown in Table 12.11. Use a residual plot to determine whether the regression model, Happiness $= \beta_0 + \beta_1$Age $+ \varepsilon$, is correctly specified.

TABLE 12.11 Happiness and Age

Happiness	Age
62	46
66	51
⋮	⋮
72	69

SOLUTION: We start the analysis with a scatterplot of Happiness against Age. Figure 12.6 shows the scatterplot and the superimposed trend line, which is based on the sample regression equation $\widehat{Happiness} = 56.18 + 0.28Age$. It is clear from the figure that the model does not appropriately capture the relationship between Happiness and Age. In other words, it is misleading to conclude that a person's happiness increases by 0.28 unit every year.

FIGURE 12.6 Scatterplot and the superimposed trendline

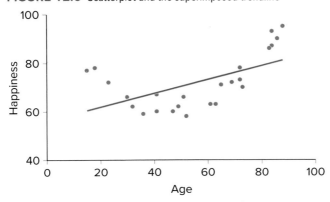

Figure 12.7 shows a residual plot against Age. It highlights the nonlinear, U-shaped relationship between Happiness and Age. The residuals decrease until the age of 50 and steadily increase thereafter. The model is inappropriate as it underestimates at lower and higher age levels and overestimates in the middle.

FIGURE 12.7 Residual plot against Age

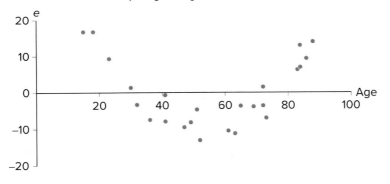

Remedy

If the residual plot exhibits strong nonlinear patterns, then we should accommodate non-linearity by making simple transformations of the predictor variable. In Chapter 13, we will discuss how we can easily capture a quadratic relationship within a linear regression model framework.

Assumption 2. There is no exact linear relationship among the predictor variables; or, in statistical terminology, there is no perfect multicollinearity.

Perfect **multicollinearity** exists when two or more predictor variables have an exact linear relationship. Consider the model $y = \beta_0 + \beta_1 x_1 + \beta_2 x_2 + \varepsilon$, where y is the bonus earned by a car salesperson, x_1 is the proportion of cars sold, and x_2 is the proportion of cars remaining in the lot. This represents a case of *perfect* multicollinearity because $x_1 + x_2 = 1$. Perfect multicollinearity is easy to detect because the model cannot be estimated. However, if x_2 represents the proportion of positive reviews from customers, we have *some* multicollinearity because the proportion of cars sold and the proportion of positive reviews are likely to be correlated. In most applications, some degree of correlation exists between the predictor variables.

The problem with (nonperfect) multicollinearity is similar to that of small samples. *Multicollinearity does not violate any of the assumptions;* however, its presence results in imprecise estimates of the slope coefficients. In other words, multicollinearity makes it difficult to disentangle the separate influences of the predictor variables on the response variable. If multicollinearity is severe, we may find insignificance of important predictor variables; some coefficient estimates may even have the wrong signs.

Detecting Multicollinearity

The detection methods for multicollinearity are mostly informal. The presence of a high R^2 coupled with individually insignificant predictor variables can indicate multicollinearity. Sometimes researchers examine the correlations between the predictor variables to detect severe multicollinearity. One such guideline suggests that multicollinearity is severe if the sample correlation coefficient between any two predictor variables is more than 0.80 or less than -0.80. Seemingly wrong signs of the estimated regression coefficients may also indicate multicollinearity.

EXAMPLE 12.8

Examine the multicollinearity issue in a linear regression model that uses median home values (Home_Value in $) as the response variable and median household incomes (HH_Income in $), per capita incomes (Per_Cap_Inc in $), and the proportion of owner-occupied homes (Pct_Owner_Occ in %) as the predictor variables. A portion of the data for all states in the United States is shown in Table 12.12.

TABLE 12.12 Home Values and Other Factors

State	Home_Value	HH_Income	Per_Cap_Inc	Pct_Owner_Occ
Alabama	117600	42081	22984	71.1
Alaska	229100	66521	30726	64.7
⋮	⋮	⋮	⋮	⋮
Wyoming	174000	53802	27860	70.2

SOLUTION: We estimate three models to examine the multicollinearity issue; Table 12.13 presents the regression results.

TABLE 12.13 Summary of Model Estimates (Example 12.8)

Variable	Model 1	Model 2	Model 3
Intercept	417,892.04*	348,187.14*	285,604.08
	(0.001)	(0.002)	(0.083)
HH_Income	9.04*	7.74*	NA
	(0.000)	(0.000)	
Per_Cap_Inc	−3.27	NA	13.21*
	(0.309)		(0.000)
Pct_Owner_Occ	−8,744.30*	−8,027.90*	−6,454.08*
	(0.000)	(0.000)	(0.001)
Adjusted R^2	0.8071	0.8069	0.6621

Notes: The table contains parameter estimates with *p*-values in parentheses; * represents significance at the 5% level. NA denotes not applicable. Adjusted R^2, reported in the last row, is used for model selection.

Model 1 uses all three predictor variables to explain home values. Surprisingly, the per capita income variable shows a negative influence on home values. With the estimated coefficient of −3.27 and a *p*-value of 0.31, it is not even statistically significant at the 5% level. Multicollinearity might be the reason for this surprising result because household income and per capita income are likely to be correlated. We compute the sample correlation coefficient between these two variables as 0.8582, which suggests that multicollinearity is severe.

We estimate two more models where one of these collinear variables is removed; Model 2 removes per capita income and Model 3 removes household income. Note that per capita income in Model 3 now exerts a positive and significant influence on home values. Between these two models, Model 2 is preferred to Model 3 because of its higher adjusted R^2 (0.8069 > 0.6621). The choice between Model 1 and Model 2 is unclear. In general, Model 1, with the highest adjusted R^2 value of 0.8071, is preferred if the sole purpose of the analysis is to make predictions. However, if the coefficient estimates need to be evaluated, then Model 2 is the preferred choice.

Remedy

Inexperienced researchers tend to include too many predictor variables in their quest not to omit anything important, and in doing so may include redundant variables that essentially measure the same thing. When confronted with multicollinearity, a good remedy is to drop one of the collinear variables. The difficult part is to decide which of the collinear variables is redundant and, therefore, can safely be removed. Another option is to obtain more data because the sample correlation may get weaker as we include more observations. Sometimes it helps to express the predictor variables differently so that they are not collinear. At times, the best approach may be to *do nothing* when there is a justification to include all predictor variables. This is especially so if the estimated model yields a high R^2, which implies that the estimated model is good for making predictions.

> **Assumption 3.** Conditional on $x_1, x_2, \ldots, x_k$, the variance of the error term ε is the same for all observations (constant variability); or in statistical terminology, there is no heteroskedasticity.

The assumption of constant variability of observations often breaks down in studies with cross-sectional data. Consider the model $y = \beta_0 + \beta_1 x + \varepsilon$, where y is a household's consumption expenditure and x is its disposable income. It may be unreasonable to assume that the variability of consumption is the same across a cross-section of household incomes. For example, we would expect higher-income households to have a higher variability in consumption as compared to lower-income households. Similarly, home prices tend to vary more as homes get larger, and sales tend to vary more as firm size increases.

In the presence of **changing variability,** the OLS estimators are still unbiased. However, the estimated standard errors of the OLS estimators are inappropriate. Consequently, we cannot put much faith in the standard t or F tests because they are based on these estimated standard errors.

Detecting Changing Variability

We can use residual plots to gauge changing variability. The residuals are generally plotted against each predictor variable x_j; for a multiple regression model, we can also plot them against the predicted value $\hat{y}$. There is no violation if the residuals are randomly dispersed across the values of x_j. On the other hand, there is a violation if the variability increases or decreases over the values of x_j.

EXAMPLE 12.9

Consider a simple regression model that relates a store's monthly sales (Sales in $1,000s) to its square footage (Sqft) for a chain of convenience stores. A portion of the data used for the analysis is shown in Table 12.14. Estimate the model and use a residual plot to determine if the observations have a changing variability.

TABLE 12.14

Sales and Square Footage of Convenience Stores

Sales	Sqft
140	1810
160	2500
⋮	⋮
110	1470

SOLUTION: The sample regression is given by

$$\widehat{\text{Sales}} = 22.0795 + 0.0591\text{Sqft}.$$

A residual plot of the estimated model is shown in Figure 12.8. Note that the residuals seem to fan out across the horizontal axis. Therefore, we conclude that changing variability is a likely problem in this application relating sales to square footage. This result is not surprising because you would expect sales to vary more as square footage increases. For instance, a small convenience store is likely to include only bare essentials for which there is a fairly stable demand. A larger store, on the other hand, may include specialty items, resulting in more fluctuation in sales.

FIGURE 12.8 Residual plot against square footage

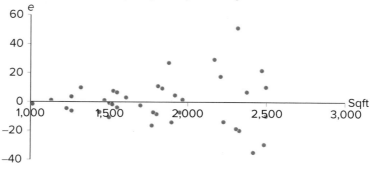

Remedy

As mentioned earlier, in the presence of changing variability, the OLS estimators are unbiased, but their estimated standard errors are inappropriate. Therefore, while the estimated model may be good for making predictions, the t and the F tests are no longer valid. This has prompted some researchers to use the OLS estimates along with a correction for the standard errors, referred to as robust standard errors. Unfortunately, the current version of Excel does not include a correction for the standard errors.

Assumption 4. Conditional on $x_1, x_2, \ldots, x_k$, the error term ε is uncorrelated across observations; or in statistical terminology, there is no serial correlation.

When obtaining the OLS estimators, we assume that the observations are uncorrelated. This assumption often breaks down in studies with time series data. Variables such as GDP, employment, and asset returns exhibit business cycles. As a consequence, successive observations are likely to be correlated.

In the presence of **correlated observations,** the OLS estimators are unbiased, but their estimated standard errors are inappropriate. Generally, these standard errors are distorted downward, making the model look better than it really is with a spuriously high R^2. Furthermore, the t and F tests may suggest that the predictor variables are individually and jointly significant when this is not true.

Detecting Correlated Observations

We can plot the residuals sequentially over time to look for correlated observations. If there is no violation, then the residuals should show no pattern around the horizontal axis. A violation is indicated when a positive residual in one period is followed by positive residuals in the next few periods, followed by negative residuals for a few periods, then positive residuals, and so on. Although not as common, a violation is also indicated when a positive residual is followed by a negative residual, then a positive residual, and so on.

EXAMPLE 12.10

Consider $y = \beta_0 + \beta_1 x_1 + \beta_2 x_2 + \varepsilon$, where y represents sales (in \$1,000s) at a sushi restaurant and x_1 and x_2 represent advertising costs (in \$) and the unemployment rate (in %), respectively. Data for these variables are collected for 17 consecutive months, a portion of which is shown in Table 12.15. Inspect the behavior of the residuals in order to comment on serial correlation.

FILE
Sushi

TABLE 12.15 Sales, Advertising Costs, and Unemployment Data

Month	y	x_1	x_2
1	27.0	550	4.6
2	24.2	425	4.3
⋮	⋮	⋮	⋮
17	27.4	550	9.1

SOLUTION: The model is estimated as

$$\hat{y} = 17.5060 + 0.0266 x_1 - 0.6879 x_2.$$

In order to detect serial correlation, we plot the residuals sequentially against time t, where t is given by 1, 2, . . . , 17 for the 17 months of time series data.

Figure 12.9 shows a wavelike movement in the residuals over time, first clustering below the horizontal axis, then above the horizontal axis, and so on. Given this pattern around the horizontal axis, we conclude that the observations are correlated.

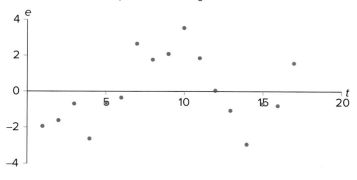

FIGURE 12.9 Scatterplot of residuals against time t

Remedy

As mentioned earlier, in the presence of correlated observations, the OLS estimators are unbiased, but their standard errors are inappropriate and generally distorted downward, making the model look better than it really is. Therefore, while the estimated model may be good for making predictions, the t and the F tests are no longer valid. This has prompted some researchers to use the OLS estimates along with a correction for the standard errors, referred to as robust standard errors. As in the case of changing variability, the current version of Excel does not include this correction.

> **Assumption 5.** The error term ε is not correlated with any of the predictor variables $x_1, x_2, \ldots, x_k$; or in statistical terminology, there is no endogeneity.

Another crucial assumption in a linear regression model is that the error term is not correlated with the predictor variables; that is, the predictor variables are exogenous. In general, this assumption breaks down when important predictor variables are excluded. If one or more of the relevant predictor variables are excluded, then the resulting OLS estimators are biased. The extent of the bias depends on the degree of the correlation between the included and the excluded predictor variables.

Suppose we want to estimate $y = \beta_0 + \beta_1 x + \varepsilon$, where y is salary and x is years of education. This model excludes innate ability, which is an important ingredient for salary. Because ability is omitted, it gets incorporated in the error term, and the resulting error term is likely to be correlated with years of education. Now consider someone who is highly educated and also commands a high salary. The model will associate high salary with education, when, in fact, it may be the person's unobserved high level of innate ability that has raised both education and salary. In sum, the violation of Assumption 5 leads to unreliable coefficient estimates and, therefore, the estimated model is unable to establish causality.

Remedy

It is important that we include all relevant predictor variables in the regression model. An important first step before running a regression model is to compile a comprehensive list of potential predictor variables. We can then build down to perhaps a smaller list of predictor variables using the adjusted R^2 criterion. Sometimes, due to data limitations, we are unable to include all relevant variables. For example, innate ability may be an important predictor variable for a model that explains salary, but we are unable to include it because innate ability is not observable. Specialized models that can be used to establish causality are outside the scope of this text.

> **Assumption 6.** Conditional on $x_1, x_2, \ldots, x_k$, the error term ε is normally distributed.

Given Assumptions 1 through 5, the OLS estimators are unbiased and, among all linear unbiased estimators, they have minimum variations between samples. Assumption 6 allows us to construct interval estimates and conduct tests of significance. If the error term ε is not normally distributed, then the interval estimates and the hypothesis tests are valid only for large samples.

Summary of Regression Modeling

Regression models are an integral part of statistical analysis. It takes practice to become an effective user of the regression methodology. We should think of regression modeling as an iterative process. We start with a clear understanding of what the regression model is supposed to do. We define the relevant response variable and compile a comprehensive list of potential predictor variables. The emphasis should be to pick a model that makes economic and intuitive sense and avoid predictor variables that more or less measure the same thing, thus causing multicollinearity. We then apply this model to data and refine and improve its fit. Specifically, from the comprehensive list, we build down to perhaps a smaller list of predictor variables using significance tests and goodness-of-fit measures such as the standard error of the estimate and the adjusted R^2. It is important that we explore residual plots to look for signs of changing variability and correlated observations in cross-sectional and time series studies, respectively. If we identify any of these two violations, we can still use the estimated model to make predictions. However, we cannot place much faith in the standard t or F tests of significance unless we employ the necessary correction.

Using Excel to Construct Residual Plots

Using Excel to Replicate Figure 12.8

A. Open the *Stores* data file.

B. From the menu, choose **Data > Data Analysis > Regression.**

C. For *Input Y Range,* select the Sales observations, and for *Input X Range,* select the Sqft observations. Select *Residual Plots.* Click **OK.** You should see a graph very similar to Figure 12.8. Formatting (regarding colors, axes, etc.) can be done by selecting **Format** from the menu.

FILE
Stores

Using Excel to Replicate Figure 12.9

A. Open the *Sushi* data file.

B. From the menu, choose **Data > Data Analysis > Regression.** For *Input Y Range,* select the y observations, and for *Input X Range,* simultaneously select the x1 and x2 observations. Select *Residuals.* Click **OK.**

C. Below the regression output, you will see a column labeled Residuals. Select the Residuals observations (with heading), and from the menu, select **Insert.** In the Charts group, expand the selection by clicking on the arrow at the bottom right. Select the All **Charts** tab and then select **XY (Scatter).** You should see a graph very similar to Figure 12.9. Formatting (regarding colors, axes, etc.) can be done by selecting **Format** from the menu.

FILE
Sushi

EXERCISES 12.4

Mechanics

51. Using 20 observations, the multiple regression model $y = \beta_0 + \beta_1 x_1 + \beta_2 x_2 + \varepsilon$ was estimated. A portion of the regression results is as follows:

	df	SS	MS	F	Significance F
Regression	2	2.12E+12	1.06E+12	56.556	3.07E-08
Residual	17	3.19E+11	1.88E+10		
Total	19	2.44E+12			

	Coefficients	Standard error	t stat	p-value	Lower 95%	Upper 95%
Intercept	−987557	131583	−7.505	0.000	−1265173	−709941
x_1	29233	32653	0.895	0.383	−39660	98125
x_2	30283	32645	0.928	0.367	−38592	99158

a. At the 5% significance level, are the predictor variables jointly significant?

b. At the 5% significance level, is each predictor variable individually significant?

c. What is the likely problem with this model?

52. **FILE** *Exercise_12.52.* A simple linear regression, $y = \beta_0 + \beta_1 x + \varepsilon$, is estimated with cross-sectional data. The resulting residuals e along with the values of the predictor variable x are shown in the accompanying data file.

a. Graph the residuals e against the values of the predictor variable x and look for any discernible pattern.

b. Which assumption is being violated? Discuss its consequences and suggest a possible remedy.

53. **FILE** *Exercise_12.53.* A simple linear regression, $y = \beta_0 + \beta_1 x + \varepsilon$, is estimated with time series data. The resulting residuals e and the time variable t are shown in the accompanying data file.

a. Graph the residuals against time and look for any discernible pattern.

b. Which assumption is being violated? Discuss its consequences and suggest a possible remedy.

Applications

54. **FILE** *Television.* Numerous studies have shown that watching too much television hurts school grades. Others have argued that television is not necessarily a bad thing for children. Like books and stories, television not only entertains, it also exposes a child to new information about the world. While watching too much television is harmful, a little bit may actually help. The accompanying data file shows information on the grade point average (GPA) of 28 middle-school children and the number of hours of television they watched per week. Estimate the model GPA $= \beta_0 + \beta_1$Hours $+ \varepsilon$ and plot the residuals against the predictor variable. Does the model appear correctly specified? Explain.

55. **FILE** *Delivery.* Quick2U, a delivery company, would like to standardize its delivery charge model for shipments (Charge in $) such that customers will better understand their delivery costs. Three predictor variables are used: (1) distance (in miles), (2) shipment weight (in lbs), and (3) number of boxes. The accompanying data file shows information on 30 recent deliveries.

a. Estimate the model Charge $= \beta_0 + \beta_1$Distance $+ \beta_2$Weight $+ \beta_3$Boxes $+ \varepsilon$ and examine the joint and individual significance of the predictor variables at the 1% level.

b. Is there any evidence of multicollinearity?

c. Graph the residuals against the predicted values and determine if there is any evidence of changing variability.

56. Consider the results of a survey where students were asked about their GPA and also to break down their typical 24-hour day into study, leisure (including work), and sleep. Consider the model GPA $= \beta_0 + \beta_1$Study $+ \beta_2$Leisure $+ \beta_3$Sleep $+ \varepsilon$.

a. What is wrong with this model?

b. Suggest a simple way to reformulate the model.

57. **FILE** *Rental.* The accompanying file shows the monthly rent (Rent in $) of an apartment as a function of the number of bedrooms (Beds), the number of bathrooms (Baths), and square footage (Sqft).

a. Estimate: Rent $= \beta_0 + \beta_1$Beds $+ \beta_2$Baths $+ \beta_3$Sqft $+ \varepsilon$.

b. Which of the predictor variables might cause changing variability? Explain.

c. Use residual plots to verify your economic intuition.

58. **FILE** *Work_Experience.* The accompanying file shows the data on salary (in $) and work experience (in years) of 100 employees in a marketing firm. Estimate the model: Salary $= \beta_0 + \beta_1$Experience $+ \varepsilon$.

a. Explain why you would be concerned about changing variability in this application.

b. Use a residual plot to confirm your economic intuition.

59. **FILE** *Healthy_Living.* Healthy living has always been an important goal for any society. Consider a regression model that conjectures that fruits and vegetables (FV) and regular exercising have a positive effect on health and smoking has a negative effect on health. The accompanying data file shows the percentage of these variables observed in various states in the United States.

a. Estimate the model Healthy $= \beta_0 + \beta_1$FV $+ \beta_2$Exercise $+ \beta_3$Smoke $+ \varepsilon$.

b. Analyze the data to determine if multicollinearity and changing variability are present.

60. **FILE** *J&J.* Estimate the capital asset pricing model (CAPM) for Johnson & Johnson where the risk-adjusted stock return (JJ_Adj) is the response variable and the risk-adjusted market return (Market_Adj) is the predictor variable. Because serial correlation may occur with time series data, it is prudent to

inspect the behavior of the residuals. Use the accompanying data file to construct a scatterplot of the residuals against time to comment on correlated observations.

61. **FILE** *Consumption.* The consumption function is one of the key relationships in economics, where consumption *y* depends on disposable income *x*. The accompanying data file shows quarterly data for these seasonally adjusted variables, measured in billions of dollars.

    a. Estimate $y = \beta_0 + \beta_1 x + \varepsilon$. Plot the residuals against time to determine if there is a possibility of correlated observations.

    b. Discuss the consequences of correlated observations and suggest a possible remedy.

62. **FILE** *Mowers.* The marketing manager at Turfco, a lawn mower company, believes that monthly sales across all outlets (stores, online, etc.) are influenced by three key variables: (1) outdoor temperature (in °F), (2) advertising expenditures (in $1,000s), and (3) promotional discounts (in %). The accompanying data file shows monthly sales data over the past two years.

    a. Estimate the model Sales $= \beta_0 + \beta_1$Temperature $+ \beta_2$Advertising $+ \beta_3$Discount $+ \varepsilon$, and test for the joint and individual significance of the predictor variables at the 5% level.

    b. Examine the data for evidence of multicollinearity. Provide two reasons why it might be best to do nothing about multicollinearity in this application.

    c. Examine the residual plots for evidence of changing variability.

12.5 WRITING WITH DATA

Case Study

Your objective in the following report is to develop a predictive model for the price of a house in the college town of Ames, Iowa. Before evaluating various models, you first have to filter out the *House_Price* data to get the appropriate subset of observations for selected variables. After you have obtained the preferred model, summarize your findings and predict the price of a house in Ames, Iowa, given typical values of the predictor variables.

House_Price

Investing in college town real estate can be a smart move. First, students offer a steady stream of rental demand as many cash-strapped public universities are unable to house their students beyond freshman year. Second, this demand is projected to grow. The National Center for Education Statistics predicts that college enrollment in the U.S. will reach 19.8 million students by 2025, an increase of 14% from its 2014 enrollment of 17.3 million.

A regression analysis is conducted to determine the factors that influence

Dmytro Zinkevych/Shutterstock

Sample Report— Investing In College Town Real Estate

the sale price of a single-family house in Ames, Iowa—home to Iowa State University. For a sample of 209 single-family houses in 2016, the following data are collected: the house's sale price (Price in $), the number of bedrooms (Beds), the number of bathrooms (Baths), the square footage (Sqft), and the lot size (LSize in square feet). Table 12.16 shows the mean values of the relevant variables for newer houses (those built in 2000 or after), for older houses (those built prior to 2000), and for all houses in the sample. Median values are shown in parentheses.

TABLE 12.16 The Mean (Median) of Variables for New, Old, and All Houses

Variables	New houses	Old houses	All houses
Price	326,134 (292,000)	209,552 (190,500)	230,191 (215,000)
Beds	3.68 (4.00)	3.22 (3.00)	3.30 (3.00)
Baths	3.06 (3.00)	2.20 (2.00)	2.35 (2.00)
Sqft	1,867 (1,691)	1,596 (1,444)	1,644 (1,515)
LSize	18,137 (10,361)	19,464 (10,123)	19,229 (10,171)
Number of Observations	37	172	209

The average sale price for the newer houses is substantially more than that for the older houses. For all houses, given that the mean is higher than the median, the house price distribution is positively skewed, indicating that a few expensive houses have pulled up the mean above the median. The square footage and the lot size are also positively skewed. Finally, relatively newer houses have more bedrooms, bathrooms, and square footage but a smaller lot size. This is consistent with a 2017 article in *Building* magazine that found that newer houses have become 24% bigger over the past 15 years, while lot sizes have shrunk 16%.

In order to analyze the factors that may influence the price of a house, the following linear regression model with all the referenced predictor variables is considered:

$$Price = \beta_0 + \beta_1 Beds + \beta_2 Baths + \beta_3 Sqft + \beta_4 Lsize + \beta_5 New + \varepsilon$$

where New is a dummy variable that equals 1 if the house was built in 2000 or after, 0 otherwise. It is expected that Beds, Bath, Sqft, and Lsize will have a positive relationship with Price; that is, a house with more bedrooms and bathrooms is expected to cost more than one with fewer bedrooms and bathrooms. Similarly, a bigger house, or one on a bigger lot, is expected to be more expensive. A newer house, one with all the latest updates, is expected to cost more than an older house that is likely in need of work. Column 2 of Table 12.17 shows the regression results from estimating this complete model.

TABLE 12.17 Estimates of Alternative Regression Models to Predict House Price, $n = 209$

Variables	Complete model	Restricted model
Intercept	95.82 (0.996)	5,815.38 (0.672)
Beds	3,124.63 (0.623)	NA
Baths	30,971.41* (0.000)	31,985.61* (0.000)
Sqft	76.98* (0.000)	78.36* (0.000)
Lsize	0.43* (0.000)	0.43* (0.000)
New	68,248.89* (0.000)	68,415.54* (0.000)
s_e	64,610	64,490
R^2	0.6689	0.6685
Adjusted R^2	0.6608	0.6620
F statistic (p-value)	82.03* (0.000)	102.86* (0.000)

Notes: Parameter estimates are in the top half of the table with the *p*-values in parentheses; * represents significance at the 5% level. NA denotes not applicable. The lower part of the table contains goodness-of-fit measures.

All predictor variables with the exception of Beds are correctly signed and statistically significant. Perhaps the lack of significance of Beds is due to multicollinearity because the number of bedrooms is likely to be correlated with the number of bathrooms as well as square footage.

An alternative explanation might be that additional bedrooms add value only in houses with large square footage. For comparison, a restricted model is estimated that omits Beds from the list of predictor variables; see Column 3 of Table 12.17 for the results.

The following observations are made:

- The restricted model is preferred because it has the lower standard error of the estimate s_e and the higher adjusted R^2.

- Holding other factors constant, an additional bathroom adds about \$31,986 in value. Similarly, a 100-square-foot increase in a house adds \$7,836 in value and a 1,000-square-foot increase in the lot size adds \$430 in value. Finally, there is a premium of \$68,416 for a relatively newer house.

- The coefficient of determination reveals that 66.85% of the variability in sale price is explained by the predictor variables, implying that approximately 33.15% is unexplained. This is not surprising because other factors, such as the condition of the house or its proximity to nearby amenities, are likely to influence the sale price.

- Suppose a 1,600-square-foot house with two bathrooms sits on a 15,000-square-foot lot. Given the preferred model, its predicted sale price is \$269,969 for a relatively newer house and \$201,553 for an older house.

Suggested Case Studies

Many different regression models can be estimated and assessed with the big data that accompany this text. Here are some suggestions.

Report 12.1 FILE *House_Price.* Choose two comparable college towns. Find the model that best predicts the sale price of a house. Make sure to include a dummy variable that accounts for the possibility of differences in the sale price due to the location.

Report 12.2 FILE *College_Admissions.* Choose a college of interest and use the sample of enrolled students to best predict a student's college grade point average. Use goodness-of-fit measures and significance tests to find the best predictive model. In order to estimate these models, you have to first filter the data to include only the enrolled students.

Report 12.3 FILE *TechSales_Reps.* Develop a linear regression model for predicting the salary of a sales representative for the software industry. Use goodness-of-fit measures and significance tests to find the best predictive model for salary.

13 More Topics in Regression Analysis

LEARNING OBJECTIVES

After reading this chapter, you should be able to:

LO **13.1** Estimate and interpret regression models using predictor variables with multiple categories.

LO **13.2** Estimate and interpret regression models with interaction variables.

LO **13.3** Estimate and interpret a quadratic regression model.

In Chapter 12, we discussed regression models using numerical predictor variables along with a dummy variable used to describe two categories of a categorical variable. For example, we can use regression models to analyze the salary of employees using predictor variables such as education, experience, and gender. In the absence of non-binary cases, gender is a categorical variable with two categories (male or female) that can be described by a dummy variable. Sometimes, a categorical predictor variable has more than two categories. In the salary example, we may also want to include the employee's personality type, which we separate into four possible categories: analyst, diplomat, explorer, or sentinel. In this chapter, we estimate and interpret regression models using predictor variables with multiple categories.

In addition, the linear regression models discussed in Chapter 12 assumed that the partial effect of a predictor variable on the response variable does not depend on the values of other predictor variables. Continuing with the salary example, we assumed that males, for example, enjoy the same salary premium regardless of their experience. In this chapter, we introduce an interaction variable that allows the partial effect of a predictor variable to depend on the value of another variable. In the salary example, it is possible that gender interacts with experience in that for every year of experience, males get a higher increase in salary than their female counterparts.

Finally, we turn our attention to quadratic regression models. These models are useful when the relationship between the predictor variable and the response variable cannot be represented by a straight line. In the salary example, it is possible that salaries increase with experience up to a certain number of years, beyond which they begin to fall. By using experience along with squared experience as predictor variables, we capture a quadratic relationship.

JrCasas/Shutterstock

INTRODUCTORY CASE

Gender Gap in Manager Salaries

The salary difference between males and females has shrunk over the years, particularly among younger workers, but it still persists. According to payscale, females earned 82% of what males earned in 2021. Ara Lily is completing her MBA degree from Bentley University, located just outside Boston. She is upset that the gender gap in salaries continues to exist in the American workplace. For a class project, she decides to analyze the gender gap in salaries of project managers. Ara gains access to the salary (in $1,000s) for 200 project managers in small- to middle-sized firms in the Boston area. In addition, she has data on the firm size, the manager's experience (in years), whether the manager is a female (Female equals 1 if female, 0 otherwise), and whether the manager has a graduate degree (Grad equals 1 if graduate degree, 0 otherwise). In this data set, information on non-binary gender cases is not available. Table 13.1 shows a portion of the data.

TABLE 13.1 Salary and Other Information on Project Managers ($n = 200$)

Salary	Size	Experience	Female	Grad
111	233	11	0	1
137	327	18	0	0
⋮	⋮	⋮	⋮	⋮
117	202	19	0	0

Ara would like to use the information in Table 13.1 to:

1. Analyze the determinants of a project manager's salary.

2. Estimate and interpret a regression model with relevant interaction variables.

3. Determine whether there is evidence of a gender gap in salaries.

A synopsis of this case is provided at the end of Section 13.2.

13.1 CATEGORICAL VARIABLE WITH MULTIPLE CATEGORIES

In Chapter 12, we discussed how a categorical variable is used as an important predictor variable in regression. Recall that the observations of a categorical variable cannot be used in their original form—that is, in a non-numerical format. We convert a categorical variable into a dummy variable with values 1 or 0 to describe two categories of the variable. It is common to refer to the category that assumes a value of 0 as the reference (benchmark) category. All comparisons are made in relation to the reference category. For example, in the case of a dummy variable categorizing a person's employment status, we can define 1 for employed and 0 for unemployed. In this case, the reference category would be unemployed. Alternatively, we can define 1 for unemployed and 0 for employed, where employed would be the reference category. The prediction is not impacted by the choice of the reference category.

So far, we have used dummy variables to describe predictor variables with two categories. Sometimes, a categorical predictor variable may be defined by more than two categories. In such cases, we use multiple dummy variables to capture all categories. For example, the mode of transportation used to commute to work may be described by three categories: Public Transportation, Driving Alone, and Car Pooling. We can then define two dummy variables d_1 and d_2, where d_1 equals 1 for Public Transportation, 0 otherwise, and d_2 equals 1 for Driving Alone, 0 otherwise. For this three-category case, we need to define only two dummy variables; Car Pooling is indicated when $d_1 = d_2 = 0$.

Consider the following regression model:

$$y = \beta_0 + \beta_1 x + \beta_2 d_1 + \beta_3 d_2 + \varepsilon,$$

where y represents commuting expenditure, x represents distance to work, and d_1 and d_2 represent the Public Transportation and Driving Alone dummy variables, respectively. We can use sample data to estimate the model as

$$\hat{y} = b_0 + b_1 x + b_2 d_1 + b_3 d_2.$$

For $d_1 = 1, d_2 = 0$ (Public Transportation), $\hat{y} = b_0 + b_1 x + b_2 = (b_0 + b_2) + b_1 x$.

For $d_1 = 0, d_2 = 1$ (Driving Alone), $\hat{y} = b_0 + b_1 x + b_3 = (b_0 + b_3) + b_1 x$.

For $d_1 = d_2 = 0$ (Car Pooling), $\hat{y} = b_0 + b_1 x$.

Here Car Pooling is used as the reference category with the intercept b_0. The intercept changes to $(b_0 + b_2)$ for Public Transportation and $(b_0 + b_3)$ for Driving Alone. Therefore, we account for all three categories with just two dummy variables.

Given the intercept term, we exclude one of the dummy variables from the regression, where the excluded variable represents the reference category against which the others are assessed. If we include as many dummy variables as there are categories, then their sum will equal one. For instance, if we add a third dummy variable d_3 that equals 1 to denote Car Pooling, then for all observations, $d_1 + d_2 + d_3 = 1$. This creates the problem of perfect multicollinearity, which we discussed in Chapter 12; recall that such a model cannot be estimated. This situation is sometimes referred to as the **dummy variable trap.**

AVOIDING THE DUMMY VARIABLE TRAP

Assuming that the linear regression model includes an intercept, the number of dummy variables representing a categorical variable should be *one less than the number of categories* of the variable.

In Examples 13.1 and 13.2, we explain how a predictor variable with multiple categories is used in estimation and in conducting tests of significance.

EXAMPLE 13.1

A human resources manager at a software development firm would like to analyze the net promoter score (NPS) of sales representatives at the company. The NPS is a key indicator of customer satisfaction and loyalty, measuring how likely a customer would recommend a product or company to others on a scale of 0 (unlikely) to 10 (very likely). The manager believes that NPS is linked with the sales representative's personality type (Analyst, Diplomat, Explorer, and Sentinel) and the number of professional certifications (Certificates) they have earned. The manager collects data on NPS, four personality types, and certificates for 120 sales representatives. A portion of the data is shown in Table 13.2.

TABLE 13.2 NPS, Certificates, and Personality Types; $n = 120$

NPS	Certificates	Analyst	Diplomat	Explorer	Sentinel
8	1	0	0	1	0
7	5	0	1	0	0
⋮	⋮	⋮	⋮	⋮	⋮
5	0	0	1	0	0

FILE
NPS

a. Estimate and interpret a linear regression model using NPS as the response variable and certificates along with three dummy variables representing Analyst, Diplomat, and Explorer as the predictor variables. Note that Sentinel is used as the reference category.

b. Find the predicted NPS for a diplomat and a sentinel with three certificates.

c. Test if NPS differs between diplomats and sentinels at the 5% significance level.

SOLUTION:

a. We estimate the following model: $NPS = \beta_0 + \beta_1 Certificates + \beta_2 Analyst + \beta_3 Diplomat + \beta_4 Explorer + \varepsilon$. Table 13.3 shows a portion of the regression results.

TABLE 13.3 Regression Results for Example 13.1

	Coefficients	Standard Error	t Stat	p-Value
Intercept	3.0998	0.461	6.721	0.000
Certificates	0.6123	0.103	5.971	0.000
Analyst	−0.1485	0.582	−0.255	0.799
Diplomat	2.5029	0.488	5.124	0.000
Explorer	1.9483	0.459	4.245	0.000

In addition to certificates, we find that personality types are linked with NPS. Relative to sentinels and with the same number of certificates, NPS is 0.1485 lower for analysts and 2.5029 and 1.9483 higher for diplomats and explorers, respectively.

b. To predict NPS for a diplomat with three certificates, we set Certificates = 3, Analyst = 0, Diplomat = 1, and Explorer = 0 and calculate $\widehat{NPS} = 3.0998 + 0.6123 \times 3 + 2.5029 = 7.44$. The corresponding NPS for a sentinel is $\widehat{NPS} = 3.0998 + 0.6123 \times 3 = 4.94$. The difference of 2.50 (7.44 − 4.94) can also be deduced from the estimated coefficient of 2.5029 for a diplomat.

c. In order to test if NPS differs between diplomats and sentinels with Sentinel as the reference category, we set up the following competing hypotheses: $H_0: \beta_3 = 0$ versus $H_A: \beta_3 \neq 0$. The p-value for the Diplomat variable is approximately zero. Therefore, at the 5% significance level, we conclude that NPS differs between diplomats and sentinels.

In Example 13.1, we used Sentinel as the reference category. As noted earlier, predictions do not change if a different personality type is used as the reference category. The choice of the reference category is sometimes dictated by specific tests of significance. This is illustrated in Example 13.2.

EXAMPLE 13.2

Use the *NPS* data file to determine if NPS differs between diplomats and explorers. Conduct the test at the 5% significance level.

SOLUTION: We note that the regression results reported in Table 13.3 cannot be used to determine if NPS differs between diplomats and explorers. To conduct the relevant test, we must use either Diplomat or Explorer as the reference category against which the other is assessed. Using Explorer as the reference category, we estimate the following model: $NPS = \beta_0 + \beta_1 Certificates + \beta_2 Analyst + \beta_3 Diplomat + \beta_4 Sentinel + \varepsilon$. Table 13.4 shows a portion of the regression results.

TABLE 13.4 Regression Results for Example 13.2

	Coefficients	Standard Error	t Stat	p-Value
Intercept	5.0481	0.348	14.511	0.000
Certificates	0.6123	0.103	5.971	0.000
Analyst	−2.0968	0.501	−4.183	0.000
Diplomat	0.5546	0.388	1.428	0.156
Sentinel	−1.9483	0.459	−4.245	0.000

For a diplomat with three certificates, we set Certificates = 3, Analyst = 0, Diplomat = 1, and Sentinel = 0 and calculate $\widehat{NPS} = 5.0481 + 0.6123 \times 3 + 0.5546 = 7.44$, which is the same as the value obtained in Example 13.1. In fact, we can show that all predicted NPS values are identical to the corresponding values derived in Example 13.1. This shows that the choice of the reference category does not matter for making predictions.

In order to test if NPS differs between diplomats and explorers with Explorer as the reference category, we set up the following competing hypotheses: $H_0: \beta_3 = 0$ versus $H_A: \beta_3 \neq 0$. The p-value of 0.156 for the Diplomat variable is more than $\alpha = 0.05$. Therefore, we cannot conclude that NPS differs between diplomats and explorers at the 5% significance level.

EXERCISES 13.1

Mechanics

1. **FILE** *Exercise_13.1.* The accompanying data file contains 120 observations for y and x along with dummy variables d_1, d_2, d_3, and d_4 to describe four categories of a variable. For example, d_1 equals 1 for the first category and 0 otherwise. Other dummy variables are defined similarly.

   a. Estimate a linear regression model using y as the response variable and x, d_1, d_2, d_3 as the predictor variables. Here, the fourth category is used as the reference category.

   b. At the 5% level, which categories, relative to the fourth category, have a significantly different influence on the response variable y?

   c. Use the estimated model to find the predicted y for categories 1 and 4. Use x = 20 for making predictions.

   d. Would the predictions in part c change if we used the first category as the reference category?

2. **FILE** *Exercise_13.2.* The accompanying data file contains 90 observations for y and x along with dummy variables d_1, d_2,

and d_3 to describe three categories of a variable. For example, d_1 equals 1 for the first category and 0 otherwise. Other dummy variables are defined similarly.

a. Estimate a linear regression model using y as the response variable and x, d_1, and d_2 as the predictor variables. Here, the third category is used as the reference category.

b. Use the estimated model to find the predicted y for all three categories. Use $x = 60$ for making predictions.

c. At the 5% level, do the first and the third categories have a significantly different influence on the response variable y?

d. Which reference category will you use to test if the first and the second categories have a significantly different influence on the response variable y.

Applications

3. In an attempt to "time the market," a financial analyst studies the quarterly returns of a stock. Consider the model $y = \beta_0 + \beta_1 d_1 + \beta_2 d_2 + \beta_3 d_3 + \varepsilon$ where y is the quarterly return of a stock, d_1 is a dummy variable that equals 1 if quarter 1 and 0 otherwise, d_2 is a dummy variable that equals 1 if quarter 2 and 0 otherwise, and d_3 is a dummy variable that equals 1 if quarter 3 and 0 otherwise. The following table shows a portion of the regression results.

	Coefficients	Standard Error	t Stat	p-Value
Intercept	10.62	5.81	1.83	0.08
d_1	−7.26	8.21	−0.88	0.38
d_2	−1.87	8.21	−0.23	0.82
d_3	−9.31	8.21	−1.13	0.27

a. At the 5% significance level, are the dummy variables individually significant? Explain.

b. Explain how you would reformulate the model to determine if the quarterly return is higher in quarter 2 than in quarter 3, still accounting for all quarters.

4. **FILE** *Study.* A researcher wants to determine if the number of hours that business students study per week at a state university varies by term. He conducts a survey where business students are asked how much they study per week in each of the three terms. He defines a Fall dummy variable that equals 1 if the survey was conducted in the fall term and 0 otherwise. The Winter and Spring dummy variables are defined similarly. The accompanying data file contains the data for 120 students.

a. Estimate the appropriate model to determine, at the 5% significance level, if students study more in Fall and Winter as compared to Spring.

b. Find the predicted number of hours that students study per week in the fall, winter, and spring terms.

5. **FILE** *Return.* A financial analyst would like to determine whether the return on a mutual fund varies depending

on the quarter; that is, if there is a seasonal component describing return. He collects 10 years of quarterly return data. The accompanying data file contains the data.

a. Estimate $y = \beta_0 + \beta_1 d_1 + \beta_2 d_2 + \beta_3 d_3 + \varepsilon$, where y is the mutual fund's quarterly return, d_1 is a dummy variable that equals 1 if quarter 1 and 0 otherwise, d_2 is a dummy variable that equals 1 if quarter 2 and 0 otherwise, and d_3 is a dummy variable that equals 1 if quarter 3 and 0 otherwise.

b. Interpret the slope coefficients of the dummy variables.

c. Predict the mutual fund's return in quarters 2 and 4.

6. **FILE** *LDL.* According to the American Heart Association, race/ethnicity is an important risk factor for developing cardiovascular diseases. For otherwise healthy people, the suggested level of low-density lipoprotein (LDL) cholesterol is less than 100 mg/dl. Recent research has shown that LDL cholesterol levels are particularly high among Hispanic men and white women. The accompanying data file contains LDL cholesterol, weight, and ethnicity for 200 American adult cis-gender males. There are four categories of the ethnicity variable that are appropriately captured by the white, Black, Asian, and Hispanic dummy variables.

a. Estimate a linear regression model using LDL as the response variable and Weight, White, Black, and Asian as the predictor variables. Here, Hispanic is used as the reference category.

b. Test if the LDL levels for white men and Hispanic men differ significantly at the 5% level.

c. Which reference category will you use to test if the LDL levels for white men and Asian men differ significantly at the 5% level?

7. **FILE** *Industry.* The issues regarding executive compensation have received extensive media attention. Consider a regression model that links CEO compensation (in $ millions) with the total assets of the firm (in $ billions) and the firm's industry. Dummy variables are used to represent four industries: Manufacturing Technology d_1, Manufacturing Other d_2, Financial Services d_3, and Nonfinancial Services d_4. The accompanying data file contains data for 455 CEOs.

a. Estimate the model $y = \beta_0 + \beta_1 x + \beta_2 d_1 + \beta_3 d_2 + \beta_4 d_3 + \varepsilon$, where y and x denote compensation and assets, respectively. Here the reference category is the nonfinancial services industry.

b. Use a 5% level of significance to determine which industries, relative to the nonfinancial services industry, have different executive compensation.

c. Reformulate the model to determine, at the 5% significance level, if compensation is higher in Manufacturing Other than in Manufacturing Technology. Your model must account for total assets and all industry types.

8. **FILE** *Retail.* A government researcher is analyzing the relationship between retail sales (in $ millions) and the gross

national product (GNP in $ billions). He also wonders whether there are significant differences in retail sales related to the quarters of the year. The accompanying data file contains 10 years of quarterly data.

a. Estimate $y = \beta_0 + \beta_1 x + \beta_2 d_1 + \beta_3 d_2 + \beta_4 d_3 + \varepsilon$ where y is retail sales, x is GNP, d_1 is a dummy variable that equals 1 if quarter 1 and 0 otherwise, d_2 is a dummy variable that equals 1 if quarter 2 and 0 otherwise, and d_3 is a dummy variable that equals 1 if quarter 3 and 0 otherwise. Here the reference category is quarter 4.

b. Predict retail sales in quarters 2 and 4 if GNP equals $13,000 billion.

c. Which of the quarterly sales are significantly different from those of the 4th quarter at the 5% level?

d. Reformulate the model to determine, at the 5% significance level, if sales differ between quarter 2 and quarter 3. Your model must account for all quarters.

13.2 REGRESSION MODELS WITH INTERACTION VARIABLES

LO 13.2

Estimate and interpret regression models with interaction variables.

Consider a linear regression model $y = \beta_0 + \beta_1 x_1 + \beta_2 x_2 + \cdots + \beta_k x_k + \varepsilon$. We estimate the model to derive the sample regression equation as $\hat{y} = b_0 + b_1 x_1 + b_2 x_2 + \cdots + b_k x_k$. For each predictor variable x_j $(j = 1, \ldots, k)$, the corresponding slope coefficient b_j measures the change in $\hat{y}$ given a one-unit increase in x_j, *holding all other predictor variables constant*. In other words, b_j represents the partial (or marginal) effect of x_j on $\hat{y}$. (Note that the partial effect is simply the partial derivative of $\hat{y}$ with respect to x_j.)

It is important to note that the partial effect of a predictor variable in the above regression model does not depend on the values of any other predictor variable. Consider, for example, a regression model using salary as the response variable and education, experience, and a male dummy variable as predictor variables. A positive coefficient for male implies that males get the same salary premium regardless of their education or experience. Here, the partial effect of male does not depend on the value of another predictor variable. It is feasible that for every year of experience, males get a higher increase in salary than their non-male counterparts. In other words, there is an **interaction effect** between male and experience. We capture this effect by incorporating interaction variables in the regression model, where each **interaction variable** is a product of two interacting predictor variables.

> ### INTERACTION EFFECT IN A REGRESSION MODEL
> The interaction effect in a regression model occurs when the partial effect of a predictor variable on the response variable depends on the value of another predictor variable.

Recall that the predictor variables can be both numerical and dummy variables, denoted by x and d, respectively. We will consider two types of interactions: (a) the interaction of two dummy variables and (b) the interaction of a dummy variable and a numerical variable.

The Interaction of Two Dummy Variables

Consider a regression model with two dummy variables, d_1 and d_2, along with an interaction variable $d_1 d_2$: $y = \beta_0 + \beta_1 d_1 + \beta_2 d_2 + \beta_3 d_1 d_2 + \varepsilon$. This model is estimated as $\hat{y} = b_0 + b_1 d_1 + b_2 d_2 + b_3 d_1 d_2$. The partial effect of d_1 on $\hat{y}$, given by $b_1 + b_3 d_2$, equals b_1 if $d_2 = 0$ and $b_1 + b_3$ if $d_2 = 1$. Similarly, the partial effect of d_2 on $\hat{y}$ is $b_2 + b_3 d_1$, which depends on the value of d_1. Models with the interaction variables are easy to estimate. In addition, tests of significance can be conducted on all variables, including the interaction variable. Example 13.3 illustrates the interaction between two dummy variables.

EXAMPLE 13.3

The field of business analytics has exploded over the years. This has led to an increased demand for business graduates who have a concentration in management information systems (MIS) and/or a minor in statistics. Consider the data on the starting salary of business graduates (Salary in $1,000s) along with their cumulative GPA, whether they have an MIS concentration (MIS = 1 if yes, 0 otherwise), and whether they have a statistics minor (Statistics = 1 if yes, 0 otherwise). A portion of the data is shown in Table 13.5.

TABLE 13.5 Starting Salary of Business Majors (n =120)

Salary	GPA	MIS	Statistics
72	3.53	1	0
66	2.86	1	0
⋮	⋮	⋮	⋮
66	3.65	0	0

a. Estimate and interpret the effect of GPA, MIS, and Statistics on Salary. Predict the salary of a business graduate with and without the MIS concentration and the statistics minor. Use a GPA of 3.5 for making predictions.

b. Extend the model from part a to include the interaction between MIS and Statistics. Predict the salary of a business graduate with and without the MIS concentration and the statistics minor. Use a GPA of 3.5 for making predictions.

SOLUTION: We estimate two models:

Model 1: Salary $= \beta_0 + \beta_1 \text{GPA} + \beta_2 \text{MIS} + \beta_3 \text{Statistics} + \varepsilon.$

Model 2: Salary $= \beta_0 + \beta_1 \text{GPA} + \beta_2 \text{MIS} + \beta_3 \text{Statistics} + \beta_4 (\text{MIS} \times \text{Statistics}) + \varepsilon.$

Note that for Model 2, we first create an interaction variable in Excel that is the product of MIS and Statistics. Given MIS = 1 and Statistics = 0, the first observation for the interaction variable equals $1 \times 0 = 0$; other observations are computed similarly.

Table 13.6 shows the regression results of the estimated models.

TABLE 13.6 Regression Results of the Starting Salary of Business Graduates

Variable	Model 1	Model 2
Constant	44.0072*	44.0993*
	(0.000)	(0.000)
GPA	6.6227*	6.7109*
	(0.000)	(0.000)
MIS	6.6071*	5.3250*
	(0.000)	(0.000)
Statistics	6.7309*	5.5350*
	(0.000)	(0.000)
MIS × Statistics	NA	3.4915*
		(0.004)
Adjusted R^2	0.7901	0.8029

Notes: Parameter estimates are followed with the *p*-values in parentheses; NA denotes not applicable; * represents significance at the 5% level.

a. We estimate Model 1 as $\widehat{Salary} = 44.0072 + 6.6227GPA + 6.6071MIS + 6.7309Statistics$. Note that with the positive coefficients and the p-values of approximately 0, all predictor variables exert a positive and significant influence on the starting salary of business graduates. For a GPA of 3.5, we compute the predicted salary for a business graduate with neither an MIS concentration nor a Statistics minor as $44.0072 + 6.6227 \times 3.5 + 6.6071 \times 0 + 6.7309 \times 0 = 67.187$, or \$67,187. Similarly, the predicted salaries for business graduates are \$73,794 with an MIS concentration only, \$73,918 with a Statistics minor only, and \$80,525 with both an MIS concentration and a Statistics minor.

b. We estimate Model 2 as $\widehat{Salary} = 44.0993 + 6.7109GPA + 5.325MIS + 5.5350Statistics + 3.4915(MIS \times Statistics)$. Like before, all predictor variables, including the interaction variable, are positive and statistically significant at the 5% level. All else constant, the slope coefficient attached to the interaction variable implies that the value of an MIS concentration is enhanced by about \$3,492 when it is accompanied with a Statistics minor. Likewise, the value of a Statistics minor is enhanced by \$3,492 when accompanied with an MIS concentration.

Model 2 provides a better fit because it has a higher value of the adjusted R^2 than Model 1 (0.8029 > 0.7901). For a GPA of 3.5, we compute the predicted salary for a business graduate who has neither an MIS concentration nor a Statistics minor as $44.0993 + 6.7109 \times 3.5 + 5.3250 \times 0 + 5.5350 \times 0 + 3.4915(0 \times 0) = 67.588$, or \$67,588. Similarly, the predicted salaries for business graduates are \$72,913 with an MIS concentration only, \$73,123 with a Statistics minor only, and \$81,939 with both an MIS concentration and a Statistics minor.

The Interaction of a Dummy Variable and a Numerical Variable

In Chapter 12, we discussed how a dummy variable d allows the intercept of the estimated linear regression line to vary between the two categories of a predictor variable. The interaction variable is a product term xd that captures the interaction between a numerical variable x and a dummy variable d. Together, the variables d and xd allow the intercept as well as the slope of the estimated linear regression line to vary between the two categories of a predictor variable.

Consider the following regression model:

$$y = \beta_0 + \beta_1 x + \beta_2 d + \beta_3 xd + \varepsilon.$$

We can use sample data to estimate the model as

$$\hat{y} = b_0 + b_1 x + b_2 d + b_3 xd.$$

For a given x and $d = 1$, we can compute the predicted value as

$$\hat{y} = b_0 + b_1 x + b_2 + b_3 x = (b_0 + b_2) + (b_1 + b_3)x.$$

Similarly, for $d = 0$,

$$\hat{y} = b_0 + b_1 x.$$

The dummy variable d along with the interaction variable xd affects the intercept as well as the slope of the estimated regression line. Note that the estimated intercept b_0 and slope b_1 when $d = 0$ shift to $(b_0 + b_2)$ and $(b_1 + b_3)$, respectively, when $d = 1$. Figure 13.1 shows a shift in the intercept and the slope of the estimated regression line when $d = 0$ changes to $d = 1$, given $b_2 > 0$ and $b_3 > 0$.

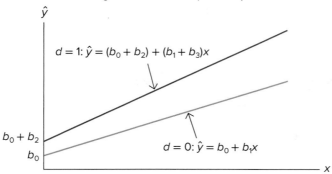

FIGURE 13.1 Using *d* and *xd* for intercept and slope shifts

$d = 1: \hat{y} = (b_0 + b_2) + (b_1 + b_3)x$

$d = 0: \hat{y} = b_0 + b_1x$

$b_0 + b_2$

b_0

EXAMPLE 13.4

Important risk factors for high blood pressure reported by the National Institutes of Health include weight and race. High blood pressure is common in adults who are overweight and Black American. According to the American Heart Association, the systolic pressure (top number) should be below 120. In a recent study, a public policy researcher surveyed 110 adult men about 5′10″ in height and in the 55–60 age group. Data were collected on their systolic pressure, weight (in pounds), and race; a portion of the data is shown in Table 13.7.

TABLE 13.7 Systolic Pressure of Adult Men (*n* = 110)

Systolic	Weight	Race
196	254	Black
151	148	Non-Black
⋮	⋮	⋮
170	228	Non-Black

FILE
BP_Race

a. Use Race to create a dummy variable, labeled Black, with values 1 for Black men and 0 for non-Black men. Estimate and interpret the effect of Weight and Black on systolic pressure. Predict the systolic pressure for Black and non-Black men with a weight of 180 pounds.

b. Extend the model to include the interaction between Weight and Black. Predict the systolic pressure for Black and non-Black men with a weight of 180 pounds.

SOLUTION: We estimate two models.

Model 1: Systolic $= \beta_0 + \beta_1$ Weight $+ \beta_2$ Black $+ \varepsilon$.

Model 2: Systolic $= \beta_0 + \beta_1$ Weight $+ \beta_2$ Black $+ \beta_3$ (Weight × Black) $+ \varepsilon$.

Note that we first use the **IF** function in Excel to create the dummy variable Black. Also, for Model 2, we create an interaction variable that is the product of Weight and Black. Given Weight = 254 and Black = 1, the first observation of the interaction variable equals 254 × 1 = 254; other observations are computed similarly. Table 13.8 shows the regression results of the estimated models.

TABLE 13.8 Regression Results of the Systolic Pressure of Adult Men

Variable	Model 1	Model 2
Constant	80.2085*	70.8312*
	(0.000)	(0.000)
Weight	0.3901*	0.4362*
	(0.000)	(0.000)
Black	6.9082*	30.2482*
	(0.001)	(0.006)
Weight × Black	NA	−0.1118*
		(0.029)
Adjusted R^2	0.7072	0.7175

Notes: Parameter estimates are followed with the *p*-values in parentheses; NA denotes not applicable; * represents significance at the 5% level.

a. We estimate Model 1 as $\widehat{\text{Systolic}} = 80.2085 + 0.3901\,\text{Weight} + 6.9082\text{Black}$. Both predictor variables are statistically significant at the 5% level (*p*-values < 0.05). For any given weight, Black men are predicted to have about 6.91 units of higher systolic pressure than their non-Black counterparts. This result is consistent with the National Institutes of Health report. For a weight of 180 pounds, the predicted systolic pressure for a Black man is $80.2085 + 0.3901 \times 180 + 6.9082 \times 1 = 157$. The corresponding systolic pressure for a non-Black man is 150.

b. We estimate Model 2 as $\widehat{\text{Systolic}} = 70.8312 + 0.4362\text{Weight} + 30.2482\text{Black} - 0.1118(\text{Weight} \times \text{Black})$. The interaction variable is negative and statistically significant at the 5% level, implying that the partial effect of weight on systolic pressure is lower for Black men than their non-Black counterparts. Model 2 is more suitable for prediction because it has a higher value of the adjusted R^2 than Model 1 (0.7175 > 0.7072). For a weight of 180 pounds, the predicted systolic pressure for a Black man is $70.8312 + 0.4362 \times 180 + 30.2482 \times 1 - 0.1118(180 \times 1) = 159$. The corresponding systolic pressure for a non-Black man is 149.

EXAMPLE 13.5

The objective outlined in the introductory case is to analyze a possible gender gap in the salaries of project managers. Use the data in Table 13.1 for the following analysis.

a. Evaluate the determinants of a project manager's salary. Estimate and interpret a regression model with relevant interaction variables.

b. Determine whether there is evidence of a gender gap in salaries.

Gender_Gap

SOLUTION:

a. In addition to the predictor variables Size, Experience, Female, and Grad, we also consider two interactions. By interacting Female with Experience and Female with Grad, the influence of experience on salary or a graduate degree on salary now depends on whether the manager is female or male. We estimate the following model:

$$\text{Salary} = \beta_0 + \beta_1 \text{Size} + \beta_2 \text{Experience} + \beta_3 \text{Female} + \beta_4 \text{Grad} + \beta_5(\text{Female} \times \text{Experience}) + \beta_6(\text{Female} \times \text{Grad}) + \varepsilon.$$

As noted earlier, in this data set, information on non-binary gender cases is not available. Table 13.9 shows the regression results of the estimated model.

TABLE 13.9 Regression Results for the Project Manager's Salary; $n = 200$

Variable	Coefficient	*p*-value
Constant	2.9941	0.627
Size	0.1126*	0.000
Experience	4.5932*	0.000
Female	−3.6791	0.712
Grad	15.1040*	0.000
Female × Experience	−1.4976*	0.019
Female × Grad	4.5685	0.241
R^2	0.7302	
F-test (*p*-value)	87.04* (0.000)	

Notes: * represents significance at the 5% level.

Overall, 73.02% of the sample variations in salaries is explained by the sample regression equation. The predictor variables are jointly significant at any significance level, given the *F*-statistic value of 87.04 with an approximate *p*-value of 0. Because Female is not individually significant at the 5% level, one may be tempted to infer that there are no salary differences between males and females. This inference, however, is erroneous as it ignores the significance of the interaction variable Female × Experience, whose negative coefficient implies that for every year of experience, the gender gap increases by about $1,498. Project managers with a graduate degree make about $15,104 more in salaries than their non-graduate degree counterparts; with *p*-value = 0.241 > 0.05, this additional salary is not statistically different between male and female managers at the 5% level

To better understand the gender gap, Figure 13.2 shows the predicted salary for male and female managers with experience ranging between 0 and 20 years. We assume a graduate degree and the sample average firm size of 244.72 employees. (Qualitatively, the results will not change if we reference a different sized firm and/or a manager without a graduate degree.) Initially, the salary gap between male and female managers is minimal. For example, with one year of experience, the predicted salaries for male and female managers are $50,258 and $49,650, respectively, amounting to a difference of $608. However, with 20 years of experience, the predicted salaries for male and female managers are $137,530 and $108,467, respectively, amounting to a difference of over $29,000.

FIGURE 13.2 Salary of male and female managers

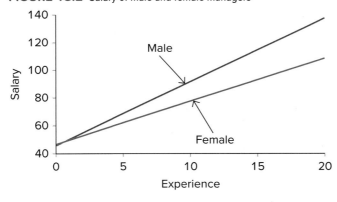

b. We find evidence of a gender gap in the salaries of project managers despite the fact that the Female variable is insignificant at the 5% level. The significance of the interaction of Female and Experience implies that for every year of experience, the gender gap increases by about $1,498. While the difference is under $1,000 after one year, it jumps to over $29,000 after 20 years of experience.

SYNOPSIS OF INTRODUCTORY CASE

Millennial women are closing the salary gap with men; however, the gender gap in the United States still persists. It is well documented that women are less likely than men to hold management roles, and those who do make about 20% less than men. In this report, the gender gap in salaries of project managers is analyzed for small- to middle-sized firms in the Boston area. The predictor variables used for the analysis include firm size, work experience, female and graduate degree dummy variables, and interactions between female with experience, and female with graduate degree. Overall, 73.02% of the sample variations in salaries is explained by the sample regression equation, and the predictor variables are jointly significant at any level.

Elnur/Shutterstock

Several interesting results emerge from the regression analysis. We find that, over the course of their career, salaries of both male and female managers increase, but not at the same rate. For every year of experience, male managers get about $1,498 more than their female counterparts. Therefore, while the estimated difference in salaries between male and female managers is under $1,000 after one year of experience, it jumps to about $14,000 after 10 years and to about $29,000 after 20 years. This result is consistent with the notion that the salary difference between men and women continues to persist in America. We also find that project managers with a graduate degree make about $15,104 more in salaries, and this premium for a graduate degree is not statistically different between male and female managers.

EXERCISES 13.2

Mechanics

9. Consider a linear regression model where y represents the response variable and x, d_1, and d_2 are the predictor variables. Both d_1 and d_2 are dummy variables, each assuming values 1 or 0. A regression model with x, d_1, d_2, and d_1d_2, where d_1d_2 is the interaction variable, is estimated as $\hat{y} = -1.34 + 1.02x + 3.08d_1 - 1.29d_2 + 0.58d_1d_2$.
   a. Compute $\hat{y}$ for $x = 5$, $d_1 = 1$, and d_2 equal to 0 and 1.
   b. Compute $\hat{y}$ for $x = 5$, $d_1 = 0$, and d_2 equal to 0 and 1.

10. Consider a linear regression model where y represents the response variable and x and d are the predictor variables; d is a dummy variable assuming values 1 or 0. A model with x, d, 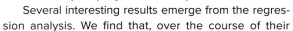 and the interaction variable xd is estimated as $\hat{y} = 5.2 + 0.9x + 1.4d + 0.2xd$.
   a. Compute $\hat{y}$ for $x = 10$ and $d = 1$.
   b. Compute $\hat{y}$ for $x = 10$ and $d = 0$.

11. **FILE** *Exercise_13.11.* The accompanying data file contains 20 observations on the response variable y along with the predictor variables x, d_1, and d_2.
   a. Estimate a regression model with the predictor variables x, d_1, and d_2, and then extend it to also include the interaction variable d_1d_2.
   b. Use the preferred model to compute $\hat{y}$ given $x = 20$, $d_1 = 1$, and d_2 equal to 0 and 1.

12. **FILE** *Exercise_13.12.* The accompanying data file contains 20 observations on the response variable y along with the predictor variables x and d.

a. Estimate a regression model with the predictor variables x and d, and then extend it to also include the interaction variable xd.

b. Use the preferred model to compute $\hat{y}$ given $x = 15$ and d equal to 0 and 1.

Applications

13. **FILE** *Overweight.* It is well documented that Black Americans experience socioeconomic barriers with regard to health care and nutrition that white Americans do not experience. According to the U.S. Department of Health and Human Services, Black women have the highest rates of being overweight compared to other groups in the United States. Individuals are considered overweight if their body mass index (BMI) is 25 or greater. The accompanying data file includes 120 individuals with each individual's BMI; a Female dummy variable that equals 1 for female, 0 otherwise; and a Black dummy variable that equals 1 for Black, 0 otherwise.

a. Estimate the model BMI $= \beta_0 + \beta_1$Female $+ \beta_2$Black $+ \beta_3$(Female $\times$ Black) $+ \varepsilon$ to predict the BMI for white males, white females, Black males, and Black females.

b. Is the difference between white females and white males statistically significant at the 5% level?

c. Is the difference between white males and Black males statistically significant at the 5% level?

14. **FILE** *Diversity_Silicon.* Silicon Valley tech companies recognize the positive need for diversity, equity, and inclusion (DEI) in the workplace. The majority of the employees in these companies, however, are white and Asian men. Use the accompanying data on the percentage of white and Asian men (Majority Male) in Silicon Valley tech companies and whether the founding members included a woman (Female) and/or a Black or Hispanic man (Minority Male).

a. Estimate a model for predicting Majority Male. Predictor variables include Female, Minority Male, and the interaction between Female and Minority Male.

b. Predict Majority Male if the founding members included a female but no minority male. Repeat the analysis if the founding members included a female and a minority male.

15. **FILE** *IceCream.* In a recent survey, ice cream truck drivers in Cincinnati, Ohio, reported that they make about $280 in income on a typical summer day. The income was generally higher on days with longer work hours, particularly hot days, and on holidays. The accompanying data file includes five weeks of the driver's daily income (Income), number of hours on the road (Hours), whether it was a particularly hot day (Hot = 1 if the high temperature was above 85°F, 0 otherwise), and whether it was a Holiday (Holiday = 1, 0 otherwise).

a. Estimate and interpret the effect of Hours, Hot, and Holidays on Income. Predict the income of a driver working 6 hours on a hot holiday. What if it was not a holiday?

b. Extend the above model to include the interaction between Hot and Holiday. Predict the income of a driver working 6 hours on a hot holiday. What if it was not a holiday?

16. **FILE** *Mobile_Devices.* Americans are addicted to smartphones and other mobile devices to connect to the world of digital information. The usage of mobile devices is especially high for affluent, college-educated urban/suburban dwellers. The accompanying data file contains survey results of customers in the 50-mile radius of Chicago. Participants were asked the average daily time they spent on mobile devices (Usage, in minutes), their household income (Income, in $1,000s), if they lived in a rural area (Rural =1 if rural, 0 otherwise), and if they had a college degree (College = 1 if college graduate, 0 otherwise).

a. Estimate a regression model for the mobile device usage based on Income, Rural, College, and the interaction between Rural and College. Explain the rationale for using the interaction variable.

b. Predict the mobile device usage for a college-educated person with a household income of $120,000 and living in a rural area. What would be the corresponding usage for someone living in an urban/suburban area?

c. Discuss the impact of a college degree on salary.

17. **FILE** *Urban.* A sociologist is looking at the relationship between consumption expenditures of families in the United States (Consumption in $), family income (Income in $), and family location (Urban or Rural). The accompanying data file includes relevant information for 50 families.

a. Estimate Consumption $= \beta_0 + \beta_1$Income $+ \varepsilon$. Compute the predicted consumption expenditures of a family with income of $75,000.

b. Extend the model in part a to include a dummy variable, labeled Urban, with values 1 for urban and 0 otherwise, to predict consumption for a family with income of $75,000 in urban and rural communities.

c. Extend the model in part a to include a dummy variable Urban and an interaction variable (Income $\times$ Urban) to predict consumption for a family with income of $75,000 in urban and rural communities.

d. Which of the preceding models is most suitable for the data? Explain.

18. **FILE** *Pick_Errors.* The distribution center for an online retailer has been experiencing quite a few "pick errors" (i.e., retrieving the wrong item). Although the warehouse manager thinks most errors are due to inexperienced workers, the manager believes that a training program also may help to reduce them. Before sending all employees to training,

she examines data from a pilot study of 30 employees. The accompanying data file includes information on the employee's annual pick errors (Errors), experience (Exper in years), and whether or not the employee attended training (Train equals 1 if the employee attended training, 0 otherwise).

a. Estimate two models:

$Errors = \beta_0 + \beta_1 Exper + \beta_2 Train + \varepsilon$, and

$Errors = \beta_0 + \beta_1 Exper + \beta_2 Train + \beta_3 (Exper \times Train) + \varepsilon$.

b. Which model provides a better fit in terms of adjusted R^2 and the significance of the predictor variables at the 10% level?

c. Use the chosen model to predict the number of pick errors for an employee with 10 years of experience who attended the training program, and for an employee with 20 years of experience who did not attend the training program.

d. Give a practical interpretation for the positive interaction coefficient.

19. **FILE** *BMI.* According to the World Health Organization, obesity has reached epidemic proportions globally. While obesity has generally been linked with chronic disease and disability, researchers argue that it may also affect wages. In other words, the body mass index (BMI) of an employee is a predictor for salary. The accompanying data file includes salary (in $1,000s), BMI, and a College dummy variable that equals 1 for a college-educated person and 0 otherwise.

a. Estimate a model for Salary with BMI and College as the predictor variables.

b. Reestimate the model with BMI, College and a product of BMI and College as the predictor variables.

c. Which of the models is more suitable? Explain. Use this model to estimate the salary for a college-educated person with a BMI of 30. Compute the corresponding salary for a non–college educated person.

20. **FILE** *Compensation.* To encourage performance, loyalty, and continuing education, the human resources department

at a large company wants to develop a regression-based compensation model (Comp in $ per year) for midlevel managers based on three variables: (1) business-unit profitability (Profit in $1000s per year), (2) years with the company (Years), and (3) whether or not the manager has a graduate degree (Grad equals 1 if graduate degree, 0 otherwise). The accompanying data file contains information for 36 managers.

a. Estimate the following model for compensation:

$Comp = \beta_0 + \beta_1 Profit + \beta_2 Years + \beta_3 Grad + \beta_4 (Profit \times Grad) + \beta_5 (Years \times Grad) + \varepsilon$.

b. At the 5% significance level, is the overall regression model significant?

c. Which predictor variables and interaction terms are significant at $\alpha = 0.05$?

d. Use the (full) model to determine compensation for a manager having 15 years with the company, a graduate degree, and a business-unit profit of $4,800 thousand last year.

21. **FILE** *IPO.* One of the theories regarding initial public offering (IPO) pricing is that the initial return (Return) on an IPO depends on Ethe price revision (Revision). Another factor that may influence the initial return is whether or not the firm is high-tech. The accompanying data file includes information on 264 IPO firms.

a. Estimate a model with the initial return as the response variable and Revision and Tech as the predictor variables, where Tech equals 1 for high tech and 0 otherwise.

b. Extend the model to include an interaction of Revision and Tech.

c. Determine the preferred model and use it to predict the initial return for a high-tech firm with a 15% price revision. Compute the corresponding initial return for a firm that is not high-tech.

13.3 THE QUADRATIC REGRESSION MODEL

Estimate and interpret a quadratic regression model.

Linear regression models are often justified based on their computational simplicity. An implication of a simple linear regression model, $y = \beta_0 + \beta_1 x + \varepsilon$, is that if x goes up by one unit, the expected value of y changes by β_1, irrespective of the value of x. However, in many applications, the relationship between the variables cannot be represented by a straight line.

If you ever studied microeconomics, you may have learned that a firm's (or industry's) average cost curve tends to be "U-shaped." Due to economies of scale, the average cost y of a firm initially decreases as output x increases. However, as x increases beyond a certain point, its impact on y turns positive. Other applications show the influence of the predictor variable initially positive but then turning negative, leading to an "inverted U-shape." The **quadratic regression model** is appropriate when the slope, which captures the influence of x on y, changes in magnitude as well as sign.

A quadratic regression model with one predictor variable is specified as $y = \beta_0 + \beta_1 x + \beta_2 x^2 + \varepsilon$; we can easily extend it to include multiple predictor variables. Figure 13.3 shows two scatterplots of sample data with superimposed quadratic trendlines. Although the linear trendline is not superimposed in either panel, it is clear that the quadratic regression model provides a better fit for both scatterplots.

FIGURE 13.3 Scatterplot of y against x with trendline generated from estimating the quadratic regression model

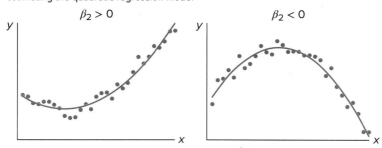

In order to estimate the quadratic regression model $y = \beta_0 + \beta_1 x + \beta_2 x^2 + \varepsilon$, we have to first create a new variable x^2 that contains the squared values of x. The quadratic model is estimated in the usual way as $\hat{y} = b_0 + b_1 x + b_2 x^2$, where b_1 and b_2 are the estimates of β_1 and β_2, respectively.

We can formally determine whether a quadratic regression model provides a better fit than the linear regression model. Recall that we cannot compare these models on the basis of their respective R^2 values because the quadratic regression model uses one more parameter than the linear regression model. For comparison purposes, we use adjusted R^2, which imposes a penalty for the additional x^2 variable.

It is important to evaluate the change in $\hat{y}$ due to a one-unit increase in x. In the estimated linear regression equation $\hat{y} = b_0 + b_1 x$ the partial effect is constant, estimated by the slope coefficient b_1. In a quadratic regression model, it can be shown that the partial effect of x on $\hat{y}$ can be approximated by $b_1 + 2b_2 x$. This partial effect, unlike in the case of a linear regression model, depends on the value at which x is evaluated. In addition, $\hat{y}$ reaches a maximum ($b_2 < 0$) or minimum ($b_2 > 0$) when the partial effect equals zero. The value of x when this happens is obtained from solving the equation $b_1 + 2b_2 x = 0$, as $x = \frac{-b_1}{2b_2}$. (Note that the optimum is obtained where the first derivative, $b_1 + 2b_2 x$, equals zero, and the second derivative, $2b_2$, is negative for a maximum and positive for a minimum.)

THE QUADRATIC REGRESSION MODEL

In a quadratic regression model $y = \beta_0 + \beta_1 x + \beta_2 x^2 + \varepsilon$, the coefficient β_2 determines whether the relationship between x and y is U-shaped ($\beta_2 > 0$) or inverted U-shaped ($\beta_2 < 0$).

Predictions with a quadratic model are made by $\hat{y} = b_0 + b_1 x + b_2 x^2$, where $\hat{y}$ reaches a maximum ($b_2 < 0$) or minimum ($b_2 > 0$) when $x = \frac{-b_1}{2b_2}$. It is advisable to use unrounded coefficients for making predictions.

Note: Sometimes a regression model includes multiple predictor variables of which only one has a quadratic effect on the response variable. In order to determine the value at which the response variable is maximized or minimized with respect to the variable that has a quadratic effect, we substitute b_1 and b_2 in the above formula with the estimated coefficients for this variable and its corresponding squared variable.

EXAMPLE 13.6

It is widely believed that worker wages decline as they get older. A young worker can expect wages to rise with age only up to a certain point, beyond which wages begin to fall. Consider the hourly wages (Wage) of independent workers for short-term engagements in the construction industry. The data also include information on whether the worker has graduated from college (Graduate equals 1 if graduate, 0 otherwise) and the worker's age (Age). A portion of the data is shown in Table 13.10.

TABLE 13.10 Independent Workers Information ($n = 160$)

Wage	Graduate	Age
53	1	57
47	0	42
⋮	⋮	⋮
44	1	30

a. Plot Wage against Age and evaluate whether the linear or the quadratic regression model better captures the relationship.

b. In order to verify your answer in part a, estimate two models. In Model 1, estimate Wage as a function of Grad and Age. In Model 2, estimate Wage as a function of Grad, Age, and Age^2. Which model provides a better fit?

c. Use the preferred model to predict hourly wages of a college graduate with age equal to 30, 50, or 70 years.

d. According to the model, at what age will a college graduate attain the highest wage?

SOLUTION:

a. In Figure 13.4 we superimpose linear and quadratic trendlines on the scatterplot. Clearly, the quadratic regression model provides a better fit for the data as compared to the linear regression model.

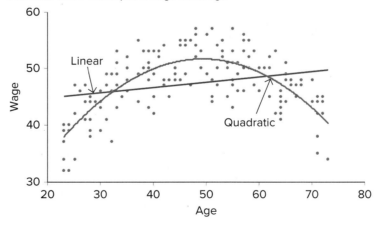

FIGURE 13.4 Scatterplot of wage versus age

b. We estimate two models.

$$\text{Model 1: Wage} = \beta_0 + \beta_1 \text{Graduate} + \beta_2 \text{Age} + \varepsilon$$
$$\text{Model 2: Wage} = \beta_0 + \beta_1 \text{Graduate} + \beta_2 \text{Age} + \beta_3 \text{Age}^2 + \varepsilon$$

Note that for Model 2, we first create the predictor variable Age^2. The first observation for Age^2 equals $57^2 = 3{,}249$; other observations are computed similarly. Table 13.11 shows the regression results of the estimated models.

TABLE 13.11 Regression Model Estimates, Example 13.6

Variable	Model 1	Model 2
Intercept	39.1580* (0.000)	−1.5014 (0.4153)
Graduate	5.9517* (0.000)	6.1988* (0.000)
Age	0.0935* (0.000)	2.0058* (0.000)
Age^2	NA	−0.0204* (0.000)
Adjusted R^2	0.3309	0.8509

Notes: Parameter estimates are in the main body of the table with the *p*-values in parentheses; NA denotes not applicable; *represents significance at the 5% level. The last row presents adjusted R^2 for model comparison.

With *p*-values of approximately 0, all predictor variables are statistically significant at the 5% level for both models. The adjusted R^2 is higher for Model 2 (0.8509 > 0.3309), making it a better choice for making prediction. This conclusion is consistent with our visual inspection of the scatterplot in part a.

c. The predicted hourly wage for a 30-year-old college graduate is

$\widehat{Wage} = -1.5014 + 6.1988 \times 1 + 2.0058 \times 30 - 0.0204 \times 30^2 = \$46.52$.
Similarly, the predicted hourly wages for a 50- and a 70-year-old college graduate are \$54.00 and \$45.17, respectively.

d. The age at which a college graduate attains the highest wage is found as $Age = \frac{-b_2}{2b_3} = \frac{-2.0058}{2 \times -0.0240} = 49.18$ years. It is important to note that a non-college graduate would also attain the highest wage at 49.18 years.

EXERCISES 13.3

Mechanics

22. Consider the following two estimated models:

$$\hat{y} = 25 + 1.2x$$
$$\hat{y} = 30 + 1.4x - 0.12x^2$$

For each of the estimated models, predict *y* when *x* equals 5 and 10.

23. Consider the estimated quadratic model $\hat{y} = 20 + 1.9x - 0.05x^2$.

a. Predict *y* when *x* equals 10, 20, and 30.

b. Find the value of *x* at which the predicted *y* is optimized. At this *x* value, is the predicted *y* maximized or minimized?

24. Consider the following sample regressions for the linear and quadratic models along with their respective R^2 and adjusted R^2.

	Linear	Quadratic
Intercept	13.3087	1.7656
x	0.3392	4.0966
x^2	NA	−0.2528
R^2	0.1317	0.5844
Adjusted R^2	0.0232	0.4657

a. Use the appropriate goodness-of-fit measure to justify which model fits the data better.

b. Given the best-fitting model, predict *y* for *x* = 4, 8, and 12.

25. **FILE** *Bids.* Consider a sample comprised of firms that were targets of tender offers. Conduct an analysis where the response variable represents the number of bids (Bids) received prior to the takeover of the firm. The predictor

variables include the bid premium (Premium) and firm size (Size in $ billions). It is generally believed that a high initial bid premium, defined as the percentage excess of the firm's stock price, would deter subsequent bids. Moreover, while tender offers for large firms are likely to receive more media coverage and thereby attract the attention of opportunistic bidders, it also is a wealth constraint to potential bidders. The accompanying file contains relevant data.

a. Estimate the model, Bids $= \beta_0 + \beta_1 \text{Premium} + \beta_2 \text{Size} + \beta_3 \text{Size}^2 + \varepsilon$.

b. Justify the inclusion of the quadratic term in the model.

c. What firm size is likely to get the highest number of bids?

26. **FILE** *Crew_Size.* The project manager at a construction company is evaluating how crew size affects the productivity of framing jobs. She has experimented with varying crew size (Crew, the number of workers) over the past 27 weeks and has recorded productivity (Jobs, jobs/week). The accompanying file contains relevant data.

a. Create a scatterplot of the data. Based on the scatterplot alone, what crew size seems optimal?

b. Estimate the linear and the quadratic regression models. Evaluate the two models in terms of variable significance and adjusted R^2. Which model provides the best fit?

c. Use the best-fitting model to predict how many jobs a crew of 5 could be expected to complete in a week.

Applications

27. **FILE** *Television.* It has been argued that like books and stories, television not only entertains, it also exposes a child to new information about the world. While watching too much television is harmful, a little bit may actually help. The accompanying data file contains information on the grade point average (GPA) of 28 middle school children and the number of hours of television they watched per week.

a. Estimate a quadratic regression model where the GPA of middle school children is regressed on hours and hours-squared.

b. Is the quadratic term in this model justified? Explain.

c. Find the optimal number of weekly hours of TV for middle school children.

28. **FILE** *Sales_Reps.* The accompanying data file includes the salary information of 300 sales reps along with their age and the net promoter score (NPS) that indicates customer satisfaction. Also included is a Female dummy variable that equals 1 for female and 0 otherwise.

a. Estimate and interpret a quadratic model using the salary as the response variable and Age, Age^2, Female, and NPS as the predictor variables.

b. Determine the optimal level of age at which the salary is maximized.

c. At the optimal age, predict the salary of female and non-female sales reps with NPS $= 8$.

29. **FILE** *Fertilizer2.* A horticulturist is studying the relationship between tomato plant height and fertilizer amount. Thirty tomato plants grown in similar conditions were subjected to various amounts of fertilizer (in ounces) over a four-month period, and then their heights (in inches) were measured. The accompanying file contains relevant data.

a. Estimate the linear regression model Height $= \beta_0 + \beta_1 \text{Fertilizer} + \varepsilon$.

b. Estimate the quadratic regression model Height $= \beta_0 + \beta_1 \text{Fertilizer} + \beta_2 \text{Fertilizer}^2 + \varepsilon$. Find the fertilizer amount at which the height reaches a minimum or maximum.

c. Use the best-fitting model to predict, after a four-month period, the height of a tomato plant that received 3.0 ounces of fertilizer.

30. **FILE** *Circuit_Boards.* The operations manager at an electronics company believes that the time required for workers to build a circuit board is not necessarily proportional to the number of parts on the board. The manager wants to develop a regression model to predict time (in minutes) based on part quantity. The accompanying file contains relevant data.

a. Estimate the linear regression model to predict time as a function of the number of parts (Parts). Then estimate the quadratic regression model to predict time as a function of Parts and Parts squared.

b. Evaluate the two models in terms of variable significance ($\alpha = 0.05$) and adjusted R^2.

c. Use the best-fitting model to predict how long it would take to build a circuit board consisting of 48 parts.

31. **FILE** *Inventory_Cost.* The inventory manager at a warehouse distributor wants to predict inventory cost (Cost in $) based on order quantity (Quantity in units). She thinks it may be a nonlinear relationship because its two primary components move in opposite directions: (1) order processing cost (costs of procurement personnel, shipping, transportation), which *decreases* as order quantity increases (due to fewer orders needed), and (2) holding cost (costs of capital, facility, warehouse personnel, equipment), which *increases* as order quantity increases (due to more inventory held). The accompanying data file includes monthly inventory costs and order quantities for the past 36 months.

a. Create a scatterplot of inventory cost as a function of quantity. Superimpose the linear trendline and the quadratic trendline.

b. Estimate the linear regression model to predict inventory cost as a function of order quantity. Then estimate the quadratic regression model to predict inventory cost as a function of order quantity and order quantity squared.

c. Evaluate the two models in terms of significance tests ($\alpha = 0.05$) and adjusted R^2.

d. Use the best-fitting model to predict monthly inventory cost for an order quantity of 800 units.

13.4 WRITING WITH DATA

Case Study

It is well documented that salaries depend on the education level and experience of working professionals. Lately, there has also been interest in analyzing the impact of noncognitive factors such as a professional's gender, age, and personality traits. Pedro Braga is a human resources manager at a major technology firm that produces software and hardware products. He would like to analyze the salary of the company's sales representatives in the software division. The following report summarizes major findings.

Labor market success has historically been linked with human capital aspects such as education and job training. There has also been interest in examining the impact of noncognitive factors such as a worker's gender, age, and personality trait. In this report, a regression model is developed for predicting the salary of a sales representative in the software division of a high-tech company, where salary is used as a proxy for labor market success. Predictor variables include a sales representative's age,

fizkes/Shutterstock

gender (Female equals 1 if female, 0 if male), whether they have a college degree (College equals 1 if college graduate, 0 otherwise), the number of professional certifications earned (Certificates), and their personality trait. Non-binary gender classifications are not included in this data set.

The four personality traits analyzed in this report are based on the Myers-Briggs personality assessment.

- **Analysts,** comprising 12.13% of sales representatives, exemplify rationality. They are known to make decisions using their heads rather than their hearts.

- **Diplomats,** comprising 35.62% of sales representatives, exemplify cooperation and diplomacy. They have a lot of empathy toward others.

- **Explorers,** comprising 37.07% of sales representatives, exemplify practicality. They are good at making quick decisions in difficult situations.

- **Sentinels,** comprising 15.19% of sales representatives, exemplify order, security, and stability. They tend to be hard working and meticulous.

The sample consists of 12,130 sales representatives, of which about 42% are female. The average values of the relevant variables for male and female sales representatives are shown in Table 13.12.

TABLE 13.12 Averages for Male and Female Sales Representatives

Variable	Male	Female
College	81.14%	81.52%
Certificates	2.74	2.77
Age	39.07	38.91
Analyst	12.08%	12.19%
Diplomat	35.91%	35.23%
Explorer	36.76%	37.49%
Sentinel	15.25%	15.10%
Salary	$74,964	$68,317
Observations	7,043	5,087

Sample Report– Analyzing Salaries of Sales Representatives

Table 13.12 shows that about 81% of sales representatives have a college degree and have earned an average of about 2.7 professional certifications. It is important to note that while the cognitive and noncognitive skills of females are almost identical to those of males, their salaries are lower ($68,317 < $74,964).

Regression models are used to conduct a more formal analysis of the salaries. Several models are explored even though the results of only the final model is reported in Table 13.13. The analyst, diplomat, and explorer dummy variables are used with sentinel as the reference category.

TABLE 13.13 Estimated Regression Model for Salaries

Variable	Coefficient	p-Value
Constant	−43798.41*	0.00
College	11554.11*	0.00
Certificates	6307.07*	0.00
Age	3734.62*	0.00
Age-squared	−39.55*	0.00
Female	−6765.41*	0.00
Analyst	123.16	0.83
Diplomat	14704.38*	0.00
Explorer	14969.16*	0.00

Notes: *represents significance at the 5% level.

Note that except for the analyst variable, all other predictor variables are statistically significant at any reasonable level. The R^2 value of 0.48 suggests that 48% of the sample variations in salaries are explained by the estimated regression model. The estimated coefficients for the college and female variables imply that there is a $11,554 premium for college graduates and females make $6,765 lower salaries than their male counterparts.

The negative coefficient for the age-squared variable implies that age has an inverted U-shaped effect on salaries, consistent with the view that worker salaries decline after a certain age. We use the coefficient estimates for the age and age-squared variables to determine that the predicted salary reaches a peak at 47.21 years of age.

The estimated model also shows that diplomats and explorers make $14,704 and $14,969 higher salaries, respectively, than sentinels. Salaries for analysts are not statistically different than those of sentinels. Table 13.14 shows the predicted salaries for 40-year-old employees with a college degree and three certificates broken down by personality type and gender.

TABLE 13.14 Predicted Salaries for Male and Female Employees

Personality	Male	Female
Analyst	$72,906	$66,141
Diplomat	$87,477	$80,722
Explorer	$87,752	$80,987
Sentinel	$72,783	$66,018

Table 13.14 shows that explorers and diplomats are very well rewarded when compared with other personality traits. It seems that the company culture is set up to promote sales representatives who thrive on uncertainty as well as those who strive for cooperation and harmony in the workplace. The discrepancy in salaries between male and female sales representatives for the same level of cognitive and noncognitive skills is troubling. It is advised that top management address the gender gap in the company.

Suggested Case Studies

Many predictive models can be estimated and assessed with the big data that accompany this text. Here are some suggestions.

Report 13.1 `FILE` *House_Price.* Choose two comparable college towns. Develop a predictive, model for the sale price of a house for each college town. Explore relevant predictor variables, including the type variable with three categories. Use model selection criteria to select the best predictive model. Interpret your results with reference to well-formatted figures and tables.

Report 13.2 `FILE` *College_Admissions.* Choose a college of interest and use the sample of enrolled students to best predict a student's college grade point average. Explore interactions of the relevant predictor variables and use model selection criteria to select the best predictive model. In order to estimate these models, you have to first filter the data to include only the enrolled students. Interpret your results with reference to well-formatted figures and tables.

Report 13.3 `FILE` *TechSales_Reps.* The net promoter score (NPS) is a key indicator of customer satisfaction and loyalty. Use data on employees in the hardware product group with a college degree to develop a regression model that analyzes the effect of cognitive and noncognitive factors on NPS. Use model selection criteria to find the appropriate model for the analysis. Interpret your results with reference to well-formatted figures and tables.

14

Forecasting with Time Series Data

Observations of any variable recorded over time in sequential order are considered a time series. Forecasting with time series is an important aspect of statistics, providing guidance for decisions in all areas of business. Sound forecasts not only improve the quality of business plans, but also help identify and evaluate potential risks. Examples include forecasting product sales, product defects, the inflation rate, cyber attacks, and cash flows.

In this chapter, we focus on the trend, the seasonal, and the random components of a time series. Several models are introduced that capture one or more of these components. In particular, we use simple smoothing techniques for making forecasts when short-term fluctuations in the data represent random departures from the overall pattern with no discernible trend or seasonal fluctuations. Linear and polynomial regression models are introduced when trend and seasonal fluctuations are present in the time series. Finally, we discuss regression models that use lagged variables for making forecasts.

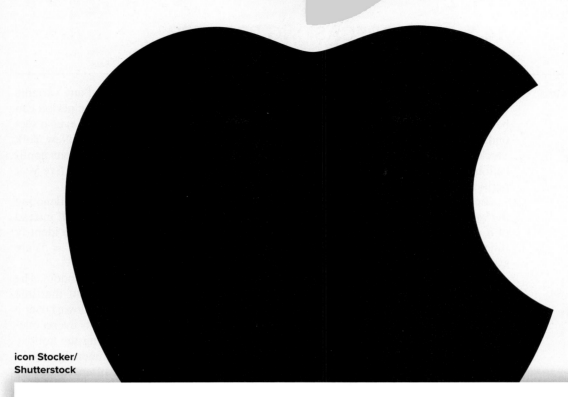

icon Stocker/
Shutterstock

INTRODUCTORY CASE

Apple Revenue Forecast

Apple Inc. is an American multinational technology company that designs, develops, and sells consumer electronics, computer software, and online services. On October 29, 2020, Apple announced revenue of $64.7 billion for its fiscal 2020 fourth quarter. The revenue was boosted by stronger-than-expected sales for smartphones and for telecommuting devices amid a work-from-home trend due to the pandemic. According to CEO Tim Cook, "Despite the ongoing impacts of COVID-19, Apple is in the midst of our most prolific product introduction period ever, and the early response to all our new products, led by our first 5G-enabled iPhone lineup, has been tremendously positive."

    Cadence Johnson, a research analyst at a small investment firm, is evaluating Apple's performance by analyzing the firm's revenue. She is aware that Apple could be seeing some resistance to its newly revamped and high-priced line of iPhones, stoking fears among investors that demand for iPhones is waning. Cadence hopes that Apple's past performance will aid in predicting its future performance. She collects quarterly data on Apple's revenue for the fiscal years 2010 through 2020, with the fiscal year concluding at the end of September.

    A portion of the data is shown in Table 14.1.

TABLE 14.1 Quarterly Revenue for Apple Inc. (in $ millions)

Year	Quarter	Revenue
2010	1	15,683
2010	2	13,499
⋮	⋮	⋮
2020	4	64,698

Revenue_Apple

Cadence would like to use the information in Table 14.1 to

1. Explore models that capture the trend and seasonal components of Apple's revenue.

2. Forecast Apple's revenue for fiscal year 2021.

A synopsis of this case is provided at the end of Section 14.4.

14.1 THE FORECASTING PROCESS FOR TIME SERIES

LO 14.1

Describe the time series forecasting process.

In this chapter, we focus our attention on time series data. Observations of any variable recorded over time in sequential order are considered a time series. The time period can be expressed in terms of a year, a quarter, a month, a week, a day, an hour, or even a second. Examples of time series include the *hourly* volume of stocks traded on the New York Stock Exchange (NYSE) on five consecutive trading days, the *daily* number of loan applications over the months of June and July, the *monthly* sales for a retailer over a five-year period, and the *annual* growth rate of a country over the past 30 years.

Let $y_1, y_2, \ldots, y_T$ represent a sample of T observations of a variable y with y_t denoting the value of y at time t. With time series data, it is customary to use the notation T, instead of n, to represent the number of sample observations and to use a subscript t to identify time. For instance, if the numbers of daily loan applications over five days ($T = 5$) are 100, 94, 98, 110, 102, then $y_1 = 100$, $y_2 = 94$, $\ldots$, $y_5 = 102$.

There are four components of a time series: trend, seasonal, cyclical, and random. The **trend** component represents long-term upward or downward movements of the time series. For example, product sales or a firm's stock price may go up (or go down) over a certain time period. The **seasonal** component typically represents repetitions over a one-year period. For example, every year, sales of retail goods increase during the holiday season, and the number of vacation packages sold goes up during the summer. The **cyclical** component represents wavelike fluctuations or business cycles, often caused by expansion and contraction of the economy. The main distinction between seasonal and cyclical patterns is that seasonal patterns tend to repeat within periods of one year or less, whereas cyclical patterns last for one to several years—plus, the duration of a cycle differs from one cycle to the next. In addition, the magnitude of the up-and-down swings of the time series is more predictable with seasonal patterns as opposed to cyclical patterns. The **random** component is difficult to identify as it captures the unexplained movements of the time series. For example, there may be an increase or decrease in customers at a retail store for no apparent reason. In this text, we will focus on the trend, the seasonal, and the random components of a time series when making forecasts.

> ### TIME SERIES
> A time series is a set of sequential observations of a variable over time. It is generally characterized by the trend, the seasonal, the cyclical, and the random components.

FILE
Revenue_Apple

In the introductory case, we considered Apple's quarterly revenue from 2010 through 2020, with the fiscal year concluding at the end of September. Figure 14.1 is a scatterplot of the series, with the dots connected, where we have relabeled the 11 years of quarterly observations from 1 to 44.

FIGURE 14.1 Scatterplot of Apple's quarterly revenue (in $ millions)

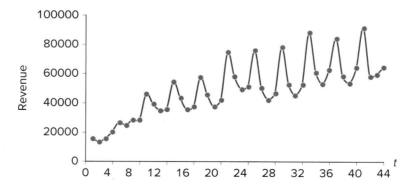

The graph highlights some important characteristics of Apple's revenue. First, there is a persistent upward movement with the series plateauing near the end of the observation period. Second, a seasonal pattern repeats itself year after year. For instance, revenue is consistently higher in the first quarter as compared to the other quarters. Note that given Apple's fiscal calendar, the first quarter, ending in December, encompasses the holiday period with usual strong sales.

Forecasting Methods

Forecasting methods are broadly classified as qualitative or quantitative. **Qualitative forecasting** methods are based on the judgment of the forecaster, who uses prior experience and expertise to make forecasts. On the other hand, **quantitative forecasting** methods use a formal model along with historical data for the variable of interest.

Qualitative forecasting is especially attractive when historical data are not available. For instance, a manager may use qualitative forecasts when attempting to project sales for a new product. Similarly, we rely on qualitative forecasts when future results are suspected to depart markedly from results in prior periods, and, therefore, cannot be based on historical data. For example, a major recession or a pandemic or a war will render the analysis from historical data misleading.

Although attractive in certain scenarios, qualitative forecasts are often criticized on the grounds that they are prone to some well-documented biases such as optimism and overconfidence. Decisions based on the judgment of an overly optimistic manager may prove costly to the business. Furthermore, qualitative forecasting is difficult to document, and its quality is totally dependent on the judgment and skill of the forecaster. Two people with access to similar information may offer different qualitative forecasts.

> ### FORECASTING METHODS
> Forecasting methods are broadly classified as qualitative or quantitative. Qualitative methods are based on the judgment of the forecaster, whereas quantitative methods use a formal model to project historical data.

In this chapter, we focus on quantitative models to project historical data, where each model is specially designed to capture one or more components of a time series.

Model Selection Criteria

Numerous models can be used to make a forecast, with each model well-suited to capture a particular feature of the time series. It would be easy to choose the right model if we knew for certain which feature describes the given time series. Unfortunately, such certainty rarely exists in the business world. Because we do not know which of the competing models is likely to provide the best forecast, it is common to explore several models. Model selection is one of the most important steps in forecasting. Therefore, it is important to understand model selection criteria before we even introduce any of the formal models.

Two types of model selection criteria are used to compare the performance of competing models. These are broadly defined as in-sample criteria and out-of-sample criteria. These criteria give rise to two important questions: How well does a model explain the given sample data? And how well does a model make out-of-sample forecasts? Ideally, the chosen model is best in terms of its in-sample predictability *and* its out-of-sample forecasting ability. In this chapter, we will focus on in-sample criteria.

Model selection, using in-sample criteria, is based on the forecast errors (residuals) $e_t = y_t - \hat{y}_t$, where y_t denotes the value of the series at time t and $\hat{y}_t$ denotes its forecast (prediction). Because there is no "primary" model selection criterion, multiple performance measures are often used for model selection. Commonly used performance measures are the mean square error (*MSE*), the mean absolute deviation (*MAD*), and the mean absolute percentage error (*MAPE*). Ideally, the preferred model will have the lowest *MSE, MAD,* and *MAPE* values. The following definition box provides the formulas for these measures.

PERFORMANCE MEASURES

Performance measures are based on the forecast error (residuals) $e_t = y_t - \hat{y}_t$, where y_t denotes the value of the series at time t and $\hat{y}_t$ denotes its forecast (prediction). We compute these measures as

$$MSE = \frac{1}{n}\sum e_t^2,$$

$$MAD = \frac{1}{n}\sum |e_t|, \text{ and}$$

$$MAPE = \frac{1}{n}\left(\sum \left|\frac{e_t}{y_t}\right|\right) \times 100,$$

where n is the number of e_t values used in the computation. Ideally, the preferred model will have the lowest values for *MSE, MAD,* and *MAPE*.

MSE heavily penalizes models with large forecast errors because of squaring, and, therefore, is preferred if relatively large forecast errors are particularly undesirable. Another popular measure is the root mean square error (*RMSE*), which is simply the square root of *MSE*. A large *RMSE* relative to *MAD* is indicative of relatively large errors in the forecast. The main attraction of using *MAPE* is that it shows the error as a percentage of the actual value, giving a sense of the magnitude of the errors.

We cannot use *MSE, MAD,* and *MAPE* to compare regression-based forecasting models that do not employ the same number of predictor variables. The problem is similar to the one encountered when using R^2. For comparing regression-based forecasting models with different numbers of predictor variables, we use adjusted R^2, which imposes a penalty for overfitting.

14.2 SIMPLE SMOOTHING TECHNIQUES

Use smoothing techniques to make forecasts.

As mentioned earlier, a time series is a sequence of observations that are ordered in time. Inherently, any data collected over time are likely to exhibit some form of random variation. For instance, the checkout time at a campus bookstore or the weekly sales at a convenience store encounter random variations for no apparent reason. In this section we focus on applications where the time series is described primarily by random variations around an unknown level. In other words, there are no variations due to trend and/or seasonality.

A simple plot of the time series provides insights into its components. A jagged appearance, caused by abrupt changes in the series, indicates random variations. **Smoothing techniques** are employed to reduce the effect of the random fluctuations. These techniques can also be used to provide forecasts if short-term fluctuations represent random departures from the structure, with no discernible patterns. Smoothing techniques are especially attractive when forecasts of multiple variables need to be updated frequently. For example, consider a manager of a convenience store who has to update the inventories of numerous items on a weekly basis. It is not practical in such situations to develop complex forecasting models for each item. We discuss two distinct smoothing techniques: the moving average technique and the simple exponential smoothing technique.

The Moving Average Technique

The **moving average** ranks among the most popular techniques for smoothing a time series. It is defined as the average of the most recent m observations, where m is a fixed integer. For instance, a three-period moving average is formed by averaging the three most recent observations. We can use this moving average as a forecast for the next period.

> ### MOVING AVERAGES FORECASTS
>
> A moving average forecast, using a fixed integer value m, is derived as:
>
> $$\hat{y}_{t+1} = \frac{\text{sum of the } m \text{ most recent observations}}{m}.$$

The term "moving" is used because as a new observation becomes available, the average is updated by including the newest observation and dropping the oldest observation. The moving average technique for making forecasts is described in Example 14.1.

EXAMPLE 14.1

In preparation for staffing during the upcoming summer months, an online retailer reviews the number of customer service calls received over the past three weeks (21 days). Table 14.2 shows a portion of the time series.

TABLE 14.2 Daily Customer Service Calls

Day	Calls
1	309
2	292
3	284
4	294
5	292
⋮	⋮
19	326
20	327
21	309

a. Construct a 3-period moving average series for making forecasts.

b. Plot the time series and its corresponding 3-period moving average forecasts against days. Comment on any differences.

c. Make a forecast for the number of customer service calls for the 22nd day.

d. Use the in-sample forecast errors to calculate *MSE, MAD,* and *MAPE.*

SOLUTION: We would like to point out that the calculations are based on unrounded values even though we show rounded values in the text. For notational simplicity, let Calls be denoted by y_t and the corresponding forecast be denoted by $\hat{y}_t$.

a. We form a 3-period moving average series by averaging all sets of three consecutive values of the original series. The first in-sample forecast, using the average for days 1 through 3, is derived as

$$\hat{y}_4 = \frac{y_3 + y_2 + y_1}{3} = \frac{284 + 292 + 309}{3} = 295.$$

Note that the forecasts start from period 4 because we are using a 3-period moving average. (If it were a 5-period moving average, the first forecast would be for period 6.) Similarly, the forecast for period 5 is derived as

$$\hat{y}_5 = \frac{y_4 + y_3 + y_2}{3} = \frac{294 + 284 + 292}{3} = 290.$$

Other forecasts are presented in column 3 of Table 14.3.

TABLE 14.3 3-Period Moving Average Forecasts and Errors

Day (1)	y (2)	$\hat{y}$ (3)	$e = y - \hat{y}$ (4)
1	309	—	—
2	292	—	—
3	284	—	—
4	294	295	−1
5	292	290	2
⋮	⋮	⋮	⋮
19	326	304	22
20	327	309	18
21	309	320.67	−11.67

b. In Figure 14.2, we plot the time series and its corresponding 3-period moving average forecasts against days. Note that the original time series has a jagged appearance, suggesting the presence of an important random component of the series. The moving average forecasts, on the other hand, present a much smoother picture.

FIGURE 14.2
Number of customer service calls and 3-period moving average forecasts

c. We compute the forecast for day 22 as

$$\hat{y}_{22} = \frac{y_{21} + y_{20} + y_{19}}{3} = \frac{309 + 327 + 326}{3} = 320.67.$$

Therefore, the forecast for the number of customer service calls for the 22nd day is 321 calls. Note that all future forecasts are the same because the moving average cannot be updated; that is, the forecast for the 23rd day is also 321 calls.

d. To calculate *MSE, MAD,* and *MAPE,* we first compute the forecast errors (residuals), $e_t = y_t - \hat{y}_t$, as shown in column 4 of Table 14.3.

$$MSE = \frac{1}{n}\sum e_t^2 = \frac{(-1)^2 + (2)^2 + \cdots + (-11.67)^2}{18} = 208.90,$$

$$MAD = \frac{1}{n}\sum |e_t| = \frac{|-1| + |2| + \cdots + |-11.67|}{18} = 11.85, \text{ and}$$

$$MAPE = \frac{1}{n}\left(\sum \left|\frac{e_t}{y_t}\right|\right) \times 100 = \frac{1}{18}\left(\left|\frac{-1}{294}\right| + \left|\frac{2}{292}\right| + \cdots + \left|\frac{-11.67}{309}\right|\right) \times 100 = 3.92.$$

These performance measures prove useful when comparing alternative models.

The Simple Exponential Smoothing Technique

Although the moving average technique is popular, it has some shortcomings. First, the choice of the order m is arbitrary, although we can use trial and error to choose the value of m that results in the smallest values for *MSE, MAD,* and *MAPE*. Second, it may not be appropriate to give equal weight to all recent m observations. Whereas the moving average technique weighs all recent observations equally, the method called **simple exponential smoothing** assigns exponentially decreasing weights as the observations get older. As in the case of moving averages, exponential smoothing is a procedure for continually revising a forecast in light of more recent observations.

Let $\hat{y}_{t+1}$ be the forecast for the series at time $t + 1$. Using simple exponential smoothing, we derive the forecast as

$$\hat{y}_{t+1} = \alpha y_t + \alpha(1 - \alpha)y_{t-1} + \alpha(1 - \alpha)^2 y_{t-2} + \alpha(1 - \alpha)^3 y_{t-3} + \cdots, \text{ where } 0 < \alpha < 1.$$

That is, y_{t+1} is a weighted average of exponentially declining weights, with α dictating the speed of decline. For example, with $\alpha = 0.8$,

$$\hat{y}_{t+1} = 0.8 y_t + 0.16 y_{t-1} + 0.032 y_{t-2} + 0.0064 y_{t-3} + \cdots.$$

Similarly, with $\alpha = 0.2$,

$$\hat{y}_{t+1} = 0.2 y_t + 0.16 y_{t-1} + 0.128 y_{t-2} + 0.1024 y_{t-3} + \cdots.$$

Note that the speed of decline is higher when $\alpha = 0.8$ as compared to when $\alpha = 0.2$.

Using algebra, it can be shown that the forecast equation simplifies to

$$\hat{y}_{t+1} = \alpha y_t + (1 - \alpha)\hat{y}_t.$$

Note that the above expression can also be written as $\hat{y}_{t+1} = \hat{y}_t + \alpha(y_t - \hat{y}_t)$, implying that the forecast for the next period, $\hat{y}_{t+1}$, equals the forecast from the last period, $\hat{y}_t$, plus $\alpha(y_t - \hat{y}_t)$, where α is a 'weight' on the forecast error from the last period.

SIMPLE EXPONENTIAL SMOOTHING FORECASTS

The simple exponential smoothing forecast is derived as

$$\hat{y}_{t+1} = \alpha y_t + (1 - \alpha)\hat{y}_t,$$

where α $(0 < \alpha < 1)$ represents the speed of decline.

In order to implement this technique, we need α and the initial value $\hat{y}_1$ to make forecasts for period 2 and beyond. It is common to set $\hat{y}_1 = y_1$; the choice of the initial value is less important if the number of observations is large. The optimal value for α is determined by a trial-and-error method. We evaluate various values of α and choose the one that results in the smallest values for *MSE, MAD, MAPE,* or some other selection criteria.

EXAMPLE 14.2

Revisit the *Service_Calls* data from Example 14.1.

a. Construct the simple exponential smoothing forecasts with $\alpha = 0.20$ and $\hat{y}_1 = y_1$.

Service_Calls

b. Plot the time series and its corresponding forecasts against days. Comment on any differences.

c. Make a forecast for the number of customer service calls for the 22nd day.

d. Use the in-sample forecast errors to calculate *MSE, MAD,* and *MAPE*. Compare these values with those obtained using the 3-period moving average technique in Example 14.1.

SOLUTION: Again, the calculations are based on unrounded values even though we show rounded values in the text.

a. In Column 3 of Table 14.4, we present the forecasts for period 2 and beyond using $\hat{y}_1 = y_1 = 309$ and $\alpha = 0.2$. Note that $\hat{y}_2 = \alpha y_1 + (1 - \alpha)\hat{y}_1 = \alpha y_1 + (1 - \alpha)y_1 = y_1$. Therefore, the forecast for period 2 equals $y_1 = 309$. The forecasts for periods 3 and 4 are derived as

$$\hat{y}_3 = 0.20 \times 292 + 0.80 \times 309 = 305.60, \text{ and}$$
$$\hat{y}_4 = 0.20 \times 284 + 0.80 \times 305.60 = 301.28.$$

Forecasts for the remaining periods are derived similarly.

TABLE 14.4 Exponential Smoothing Forecasts and Errors with $\alpha = 0.20$

Day (1)	y (2)	$\hat{y}$ (3)	$e = y - \hat{y}$ (4)
1	309	—	—
2	292	309.00	−17.00
3	284	305.60	−21.60
⋮	⋮	⋮	⋮
20	327	306.93	20.07
21	309	310.95	−1.95

b. In Figure 14.3, we plot the original time series and its corresponding forecasts against days. Again, while the original time series has the jagged appearance, the exponential smoothing forecasts remove most of the sharp points and, like the moving average series, present a much smoother picture.

FIGURE 14.3
Number of customer service calls and exponential smoothing forecasts

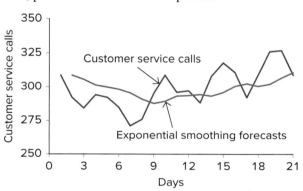

c. We compute the forecast for the 22nd day as $\hat{y}_{22} = 0.20 \times 309 + 0.80 \times 310.95 = 310.56$, or 311 customer service calls. As with the moving average technique, any further out-of-sample forecasts also assume this same value; that is, the forecast for the 23rd day is also 311 customer service calls.

d. To calculate *MSE, MAD,* and *MAPE,* we first compute the forecast errors (residuals), $e_t = y_t - \hat{y}_t$, as shown in column 4 of Table 14.4.

$$MSE = \frac{1}{n}\sum e_t^2 = \frac{(-17.00)^2 + (-21.60)^2 + \cdots + (-1.95)^2}{20} = 217.16,$$

$$MAD = \frac{1}{n}\sum |e_t| = \frac{|-17.00| + |-21.60| + \cdots + |-1.95|}{20} = 12.91, \text{ and}$$

$$MAPE = \frac{1}{n}\left(\sum \left|\frac{e_t}{y_t}\right|\right) \times 100 = \frac{1}{20}\left(\left|\frac{-17.00}{292}\right| + \left|\frac{-21.60}{284}\right| + \cdots + \left|\frac{-1.95}{309}\right|\right) \times 100 = 4.32.$$

Comparing these values with those derived in Example 14.1, we prefer the moving average technique because it has lower values for all three performance measures.

There is nothing special about $\alpha = 0.2$; we used this value primarily to illustrate the exponential smoothing technique. As we noted earlier, it is common to evaluate various values of α and choose the one that produces the smallest *MSE, MAD,* or *MAPE* values. To illustrate how α is chosen, we generate *MSE, MAD,* and *MAPE* with α values ranging from 0.1 to 0.9 with increments of 0.1. The results are summarized in Table 14.5.

TABLE 14.5 Various Values of α and the Resulting *MSE, MAD,* and *MAPE*

α	0.1	0.2	0.3	0.4	0.5	0.6	0.7	0.8	0.9
MSE	257.20	217.16	192.44	180.42	175.40	173.61	172.82	171.79	169.97
MAD	13.60	12.91	12.18	11.42	11.10	11.11	11.25	11.41	11.43
MAPE	4.57	4.32	4.07	3.81	3.70	3.70	3.75	3.81	3.82

In this example, the choice of α depends on whether we employ *MSE, MAD,* or *MAPE* for model comparison. It may be appropriate to select $\alpha = 0.5$ because it leads to the smallest value for two out of three performance measures (*MAD* and *MAPE*). With $\alpha = 0.5$, the simple exponential smoothing forecasts outperform the moving average forecasts because of their lower *MSE, MAD,* and *MAPE* values.

Using Excel for Moving Averages and Exponential Smoothing

FILE
Service_Calls

To obtain the Moving Average Forecasts in Table 14.3:

A. Open the ***Service_Calls*** data file.

B. From the menu, choose **Data > Data Analysis > Moving Average.** Click **OK.**

C. Click on the box next to *Input Range,* select the Calls data (including the heading), and then check the box in front of *Labels in First Row.* Next to *Interval,* enter 3 because we want to generate a 3-period moving average. Finally, indicate an *Output Range;* we enter D3. Click **OK.** Column D replicates the forecasts shown in column 3 of Table 14.3; it also includes the forecast for the 22nd period.

To obtain the Exponential Smoothing Forecasts in Table 14.4:

A. Open the ***Service_Calls*** data file.

B. From the menu, choose **Data > Data Analysis > Exponential Smoothing.** Click **OK.**

C. Click on the box next to *Input Range,* select the Calls data (including the heading), and then check the box in front of *Labels.* Select the box next to *Damping Factor.* If we want to construct an exponentially smoothed series with $\alpha = 0.2$, then for *Damping Factor* we enter $1 - \alpha = 0.8$. Finally, indicate an *Output Range;* we enter D2, thus replicating the forecasts shown in column 3 of Table 14.4. Click **OK.** In order to get the forecast for the 22nd day, copy and paste the formula in cell D22 into cell D23.

EXERCISES 14.2

Mechanics

1. **FILE** *Exercise_14.1.* The accompanying data file contains 20 observations for t and y_t.
   a. Use the 3-period moving average for making forecasts.
   b. Use the in-sample forecast errors to compute *MSE, MAD,* and *MAPE.*
   c. Make a forecast for period 21.

2. **FILE** *Exercise_14.2.* The accompanying data file contains 20 observations for t and y_t.
   a. Use simple exponential smoothing with $\alpha = 0.2$ for making forecasts.
   b. Use the in-sample forecast errors to compute *MSE, MAD,* and *MAPE.*
   c. Make a forecast for period 21.

Applications

3. **FILE** *Convenience_Store.* The owner of a convenience store near Salt Lake City in Utah has been tabulating weekly sales at the store, excluding gas. The accompanying data file contains the sales for 30 weeks.
   a. Use the 3-period moving average to forecast sales for the 31st week.
   b. Use simple exponential smoothing with $\alpha = 0.3$ to forecast sales for the 31st week.
   c. Which is the preferred technique for making the forecast based on *MSE, MAD,* and *MAPE?*

4. **FILE** *Spotify.* Spotify is a music streaming platform that gives access to songs from artists all over the world. The accompanying data file contains the monthly stock price of Spotify for 11 months after it started trading on the New York Stock Exchange.
   a. Use the 3-period moving average to forecast Spotify's stock price for the 12th month.
   b. Use simple exponential smoothing with $\alpha = 0.2$ to forecast Spotify's stock price for the 12th month.
   c. Which is the preferred technique for making the forecast based on *MSE, MAD,* and *MAPE?*

5. **FILE** *FoodTruck.* Food trucks have become a common sight on American campuses. They serve scores of hungry students strolling through campus and looking for trendy food served fast. The accompanying data file contains the number of students served on weekdays on a small campus in California.
   a. Use the 3-period moving average to make a forecast for weekday 41.
   b. Use the 5-period moving average to make a forecast for weekday 41.
   c. Which is the preferred technique for making the forecast based on *MSE, MAD,* and *MAPE?*

6. **FILE** *Exchange_Rate.* Consider the exchange rate of the $ (USD) with € (Euro) and $ (USD) with £ (Pound). The accompanying data file contains the exchange rates for 25 weeks.
   a. Find the 3-period and the 5-period moving averages for Euro. Based on *MSE, MAD,* and *MAPE,* use the preferred model to forecast Euro for the 26th week.
   b. Find the simple exponential smoothing series for Pound with possible α values of 0.2, 0.4, 0.6. Based on *MSE, MAD,* and *MAPE,* use the preferred model to forecast Pound for the 26th week.

7. **FILE** *Downtown_Cafe.* The manager of a trendy downtown café in Columbus, Ohio, collects weekly data on the number of customers it serves. The accompanying file contains the data.
   a. Use the simple exponential smoothing technique with $\alpha = 0.2$ to make a forecast for week 53.
   b. Use the simple exponential smoothing technique with $\alpha = 0.4$ to make a forecast for week 53.
   c. Which is the preferred technique for making the forecast based on *MSE, MAD,* and *MAPE?*

8. **FILE** *Gas_Prices.* It is difficult to predict gas prices given a multitude of factors affecting them. The accompanying data file contains 22 weeks of the average weekly regular gasoline price ($ per gallon) in New England and the West Coast.
   a. Find the 3-period and the 5-period moving averages for gas prices in New England. Based on *MSE, MAD,* and *MAPE,* use the preferred model to forecast gas prices for the 23rd week.
   b. Find the simple exponential smoothing series with possible α values of 0.2, 0.4, 0.6 for gas prices on the West Coast. Based on *MSE, MAD,* and *MAPE,* use the preferred model to forecast gas prices for the 23rd week.

14.3 LINEAR REGRESSION MODELS FOR TREND AND SEASONALITY

LO 14.3

Use linear regression models to make forecasts.

The smoothing techniques discussed in Section 14.2 are used when the time series represent random fluctuations with no discernible trend or seasonal fluctuations. When trend and seasonal variations are present, we need to use special models for the analysis. In this section, we first focus on trend analysis, which extracts long-term upward or downward movements of the series. We then incorporate seasonal dummy variables that extract the repetitive movement of the series within a one-year period.

The Linear Trend Model

We estimate a **linear trend model** using the regression technique described in Chapter 12. Let y_t be the value of the response variable at time t. Here we use t as the predictor variable corresponding to consecutive time periods, such as 1, 2, 3, and so on.

THE LINEAR TREND MODEL

The linear trend model is used for a time series that is expected to increase or decrease by a fixed amount each time period. It is specified as

$$y_t = \beta_0 + \beta_1 t + \varepsilon_t,$$

where y_t is the value of the time series at time t.

- Forecasts with a linear trend model are made by $\hat{y}_t = b_0 + b_1 t$, where b_0 and b_1 are the coefficient estimates.
- It is advisable to use unrounded coefficient estimates for making forecasts.

Example 14.3 provides an application of the linear trend model for making forecasts.

EXAMPLE 14.3

A local organic food store carries several food products for health-conscious consumers. The store has witnessed a steady growth in the sale of chef-designed meals, which are especially popular with college-educated millennials. For planning purposes, the manager of the store would like to extract useful information from the weekly sales of chef-designed meals for the past year, a portion of which is shown in Table 14.6.

TABLE 14.6 Weekly Sales (in $) at Organic Food Store

Week	Sales
1	1925
2	2978
⋮	⋮
52	6281

a. Visually inspect the time series to confirm the existence of a trend.

b. Estimate and interpret the linear trend model for the sale of chef-designed meals.

c. Forecast the sale of chef-designed meals for the next four weeks.

SOLUTION:

a. As a first step, it is advisable to visually inspect the time series. Figure 14.4 is a scatterplot of the weekly sales of chef-designed meals for the past year with a superimposed linear trend line. We see an upward movement of the series over this time period.

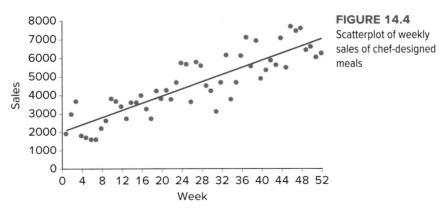

FIGURE 14.4 Scatterplot of weekly sales of chef-designed meals

b. The estimated linear trend model is $\widehat{Sales} = 1998.2285 + 96.8383\text{Week}$, implying that every week, predicted sales increase by about \$96.84. The estimated $R^2 = 0.7538$ suggests that about 75.38% of the sample variations in sales are explained by the sample trend line.

Note: Refer to Chapter 12 for Excel instructions for creating a scatterplot and/or estimating a linear regression model. In this example, we use Week as the time variable t. Sometimes, we have to first create the time variable t with consecutive time periods 1, 2, 3, etc.

c. We use Week = 53 to forecast sales for the next week as $\widehat{Sales} = 1998.2285 + 96.8383 \times 53 = \$7.130.66$. Similarly, we use Week = 54, 55, and 56 to forecast sales for the subsequent three weeks as \$7,227.49, \$7,324.33, and \$7,421.17, respectively.

Trend forecasting models, like the model used in Example 14.3, extract long-term upward or downward movements of a time series. These models are appropriate when the time series does not exhibit seasonal variations or has been stripped of its seasonal variation; that is, it has been deseasonalized. We now move our attention to making forecasts that extract both trend and seasonal variations.

The Linear Trend Model with Seasonality

With seasonal data, we estimate a linear trend model that also includes dummy variables to capture the seasonal variations. Recall that a dummy variable is commonly used to describe a predictor variable with two categories. As discussed in Chapter 13, dummy variables can also be used to describe predictor variables with multiple categories. For quarterly data, we need to define only three dummy variables representing three quarters, using the fourth quarter as reference.

LINEAR TREND MODEL WITH SEASONAL DUMMY VARIABLES

With quarterly data, a linear trend model with seasonal dummy variables can be specified as

$$y_t = \beta_0 + \beta_1 d_1 + \beta_2 d_2 + \beta_3 d_3 + \beta_4 t + \varepsilon,$$

where d_1, d_2, and d_3 are the dummy variables representing the first three quarters.

- Forecasts are made as

Quarter 1 $(d_1 = 1, d_2 = 0, d_3 = 0)$: $\hat{y}_t = (b_0 + b_1) + b_4 t$,
Quarter 2 $(d_1 = 0, d_2 = 1, d_3 = 0)$: $\hat{y}_t = (b_0 + b_2) + b_4 t$,
Quarter 3 $(d_1 = 0, d_2 = 0, d_3 = 1)$: $\hat{y}_t = (b_0 + b_3) + b_4 t$,
Quarter 4 $(d_1 = 0, d_2 = 0, d_3 = 0)$: $\hat{y}_t = b_0 + b_4 t$,

where $b_0, b_1, \ldots b_4$ are the coefficient estimates.

- It is advisable to use unrounded coefficient estimates for making forecasts.

Note: The above equations use the fourth season as reference, which we can modify if we want to use a different season as reference. Forecasts are not impacted by the choice of the reference season. Also, the model for the quarterly data can be modified to make forecasts with monthly or other forms of seasonal data. Example 14.4 provides an application with quarterly data.

EXAMPLE 14.4

With Amazon.com at the lead, e-commerce retail sales have increased substantially over the last decade. Consider quarterly data on e-commerce retail sales in the United States from 2010 to 2019, a portion of which is shown in Table 14.7.

TABLE 14.7 Quarterly e-Commerce Retail Sales (in $ millions)

Year	Quarter	Sales
2010	1	37059
2010	2	38467
⋮	⋮	⋮
2019	4	185700

a. Visually inspect the data to confirm the existence of trend and seasonality.

b. Estimate and interpret the linear trend model with seasonal dummy variables for e-commerce retail sales.

c. Forecast e-commerce retail sales for the first quarter of 2020.

SOLUTION: When using Excel with quarterly data, we first construct the time variable and the seasonal dummy variables for the model. Table 14.8 presents a portion of the data for sales; seasonal dummy variables d_1, d_2, and d_3 representing the first three quarters (using the fourth quarter as reference); and the time variable t representing 10 years of quarterly data.

TABLE 14.8 Constructing Variables for Example 14.4

Year	Quarter	Sales	d_1	d_2	d_3	t
2010	1	37059	1	0	0	1
2010	2	38467	0	1	0	2
2010	3	40075	0	0	1	3
2010	4	54320	0	0	0	4
⋮	⋮	⋮	⋮	⋮	⋮	⋮
2019	3	145474	0	0	1	39
2019	4	185700	0	0	0	40

a. Figure 14.5 is a scatterplot of quarterly sales, with the dots connected, and the quarterly data relabeled from 1 to 40. The graph highlights some important characteristics of e-commerce retail sales. First, there is a persistent upward movement in sales. Second, a seasonal pattern repeats itself year after year. For instance, sales are consistently higher in the fourth quarter as compared to the other quarters. The graph makes a strong case for a model that captures both trend and seasonality.

FIGURE 14.5
Scatterplot of e-commerce retail sales (in $ millions)

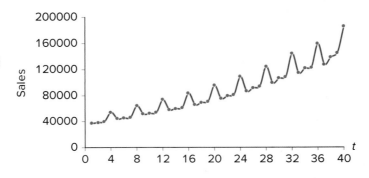

b. The estimated linear trend model with seasonal dummy variables is $\widehat{\text{Sales}} = 45,189.66 - 24,259.97d_1 - 22,874.71d_2 - 23,874.36d_3 + 2,867.84t$

The negative coefficient values for the seasonal dummy variables indicate that, relative to the fourth quarter, e-commerce sales are between \$22,875 and \$24,260 lower in the other three quarters. The estimated coefficient for the time variable suggests that the predicted quarterly sales increase by about \$2,868 million every quarter, in addition to the seasonal variations.

c. For the first quarter of 2020, we use $d_1 = 1$, $d_2 = 0$, $d_3 = 0$, and $t = 41$ to forecast $\widehat{\text{Sales}} = 45,189.66 - 24,259.97 + 2.867.84 \times 41 = \$138,511$ million.

EXERCISES 14.3

Mechanics

9. A linear trend model estimated from 30 days of data is given by $\hat{y} = 80.20 + 0.62t$. Use the estimated model to forecast y for the next two days.

10. Consider the following linear trend models estimated from 10 years of quarterly data with and without seasonal dummy variables d_1, d_2, and d_3. Here, $d_1 = 1$ for quarter 1, 0 otherwise; other dummy variables are defined similarly.

Model 1: $\hat{y} = 48.00 + 0.44t$

Model 2: $\hat{y} = 48.00 + 0.46t - 0.38d_1 - 0.42d_2 - 0.12d_3$

a. Use each model to make a forecast for y for the first and the fourth quarters of the 11th year.

b. Which is the preferred model for forecasting if, relative to Model 1, Model 2 has higher R^2 but lower adjusted R^2?

Applications

11. **FILE** *Inquiries.* Morgan Bank has been encouraging its customers to use its new mobile banking app. While this may be good for business, the bank has to deal with a number of inquiries it receives about the new app. The accompanying data file includes weekly inquiries the bank has received over the past 30 weeks. Estimate the linear trend model to forecast the number of inquiries over the next two weeks.

12. **FILE** *Stock_Price.* An investor seeking to gain from the positive momentum of a company's stock price analyzes 53 weeks of stock price data. The accompanying file includes the data.

a. Estimate and interpret the linear trend model (no seasonality).

b. Make a forecast for the next week (54th week).

13. **FILE** *Hamburger.* A famous hamburger place experiences significantly higher sales on Fridays and Saturdays compared to the other days of the week. The accompanying data file includes the sales for 10 weeks. Estimate a linear trend model along with a weekend dummy variable that captures the higher sales volume for Fridays and Saturdays. Use the estimated model to forecast the sales for Monday and Friday of week 11.

14. **FILE** *Covid.* A county has been battling COVID for the last few months. The accompanying data file includes the daily number of new COVID cases in this county for six weeks. It is known that the number of COVID cases recorded over the weekend, which includes Saturday and Sunday, are lower than they are on weekdays. Estimate a linear trend model along with a weekend dummy variable and forecast the number of COVID cases for Monday and Saturday of week 7.

15. **FILE** *Tax_Revenue.* In Colorado, sales of medical marijuana began in November 2012; however, the Department of Revenue did not report tax collection data until February of 2014. The accompanying data file includes monthly revenue from medical and retail marijuana tax and fee collections as posted in the Colorado state accounting system. Use the linear trend model (no seasonality) to forecast the tax revenue for November and December of 2018.

16. **FILE** *Revenue_Lowes.* Lowe's Companies, Inc., is a home improvement company offering a range of products for maintenance, repair, remodeling, and decorating. The accompanying data file includes quarterly revenue (in \$ millions) for Lowe's with its fiscal year concluding at the end of January.

a. Estimate and interpret the linear trend model with seasonal dummy variables.

b. Use the estimated model to forecast Lowe's revenue for the first quarter of 2021.

17. **FILE** *Vacation.* Vacation destinations often run on a seasonal basis, depending on the primary activities in that location. Amanda Wang is the owner of a travel agency in Cincinnati, Ohio. She has built a database of the number of vacation packages (Vacation) that she has sold over the last 12 years. The accompanying file includes quarterly data on the number of vacation packages sold.

a. Estimate the linear regression models using seasonal dummy variables with and without the trend term. Which is the preferred model?

b. Use the preferred model to forecast the quarterly number of vacation packages sold in the first two quarters of 2020.

14.4 POLYNOMIAL REGRESSION MODELS FOR TREND AND SEASONALITY

LO 14.4

Although the linear models estimated in Section 14.3 may be adequate, there are many cases in which a nonlinear functional form is more suitable. In this section, we discuss the quadratic and the cubic trend models with and without seasonal dummy variables.

Use polynomial regression models to make forecasts.

The Polynomial Trend Model

In Chapter 13, we introduced the quadratic regression model when the relationship between the response variable and the predictor variable is best captured by a U-shape or an inverted U-shape. Similarly, the **quadratic trend model** is specified as

$$y_t = \beta_0 + \beta_1 t + \beta_2 t^2 + \varepsilon_t.$$

The coefficient β_2 determines whether the trend is U-shaped or inverted U-shaped. Figure 14.6 presents a scatterplot of a time series with superimposed linear (blue) and quadratic (green) trend lines. Here, the linear trend line would under forecast future values when $\beta_2 > 0$ and over forecast future values when $\beta_2 < 0$.

FIGURE 14.6
Scatterplots with superimposed linear and quadratic trend lines

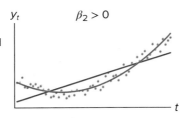 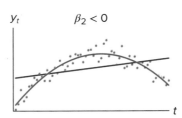

In order to estimate the quadratic trend model, we generate t^2, which is simply the square of t. Then we run a multiple regression model that uses y as the response variable and both t and t^2 as the predictor variables. The estimated model is used to make forecasts as

$$\hat{y}_t = b_0 + b_1 t + b_2 t^2.$$

Higher-order polynomial functions can be estimated similarly. For instance, the **cubic trend model** is specified as

$$y_t = \beta_0 + \beta_1 t + \beta_2 t^2 + \beta_3 t^3 + \varepsilon_t.$$

In the cubic trend model, we basically generate two additional variables, t^2 and t^3, for the regression. A multiple regression model is run that uses y as the response variable and t, t^2, and t^3 as the predictor variables. The estimated model is used to make forecasts as $\hat{y}_t = b_0 + b_1 t + b_2 t^2 + b_3 t^3$.

Note: We cannot use *MSE, MAD, MAPE,* or R^2 to compare polynomial trend models because the number of predictor variables varies with the order of the polynomial. When comparing polynomial trend models, we use adjusted R^2, which imposes a penalty for overfitting.

THE POLYNOMIAL TREND MODEL

The polynomial trend model of order q is estimated as

$$y_t = \beta_0 + \beta_1 t + \beta_2 t^2 + \beta_3 t^3 + \cdots + \beta_q t^q + \varepsilon_t.$$

This model specializes to a linear trend model, quadratic trend model, and cubic trend model for $q = 1, 2$, and 3, respectively.

- Forecasts are made as $\hat{y}_t = b_0 + b_1 t + b_2 t^2 + b_3 t^3 + \ldots + b_q t^q$, where $b_0, b_1,$ $\ldots, b_q$ are the coefficient estimates.
- Adjusted R^2 is used to compare polynomial trend models with different orders.
- It is advisable to use unrounded coefficient estimates for making forecasts.

The Polynomial Trend Model with Seasonality

In Section 14.3, we incorporated seasonality in linear trend models; here we do the same for polynomial trend models. The following definition box specifies the quadratic trend model with quarterly seasonal dummy variables; the cubic trend model with seasonal dummy variables can be specified similarly.

QUADRATIC TREND MODEL WITH SEASONAL DUMMY VARIABLES

With quarterly data, a quadratic trend model with seasonal dummy variables is specified as

$$y_t = \beta_0 + \beta_1 d_1 + \beta_2 d_2 + \beta_3 d_3 + \beta_4 t + \beta_5 t^2 + \varepsilon.$$

- Forecasts are made as

    Quarter 1 $(d_1 = 1, d_2 = 0, d_3 = 0)$: $\hat{y}_t = (b_0 + b_1) + b_4 t + b_5 t^2$,

    Quarter 2 $(d_1 = 0, d_2 = 1, d_3 = 0)$: $\hat{y}_t = (b_0 + b_2) + b_4 t + b_5 t^2$,

    Quarter 3 $(d_1 = 0, d_2 = 0, d_3 = 1)$: $\hat{y}_t = (b_0 + b_3) + b_4 t + b_5 t^2$,

    Quarter 4 $(d_1 = 0, d_2 = 0, d_3 = 0)$: $\hat{y}_t = b_0 + b_4 t + b_5 t^2$,

    where $b_0, b_1, \ldots, b_5$ are the coefficient estimates.
- It is advisable to use unrounded coefficient estimates for making forecasts.

Note: The quadratic trend model with quarterly seasonal dummy variables can be modified to make forecasts with monthly or other forms of seasonal data. As before, we use adjusted R^2 to compare regression models that do not use the same number of predictor variables. Example 14.5 provides an application with quarterly data.

EXAMPLE 14.5

The objective outlined in the introductory case is to use Apple's quarterly revenue, in $ millions, from 2010 to 2020.

a. Estimate the linear and the quadratic trend models with seasonal dummy variables for Apple's revenue.

b. Determine the preferred model and use it to forecast Apple's revenue for fiscal year 2021.

SOLUTION: In Section 14.1, we used Figure 14.1 to highlight important characteristics of Apple's revenue. First, there is a persistent upward movement with the time series plateauing near the end of the observation period, which is suggestive of a quadratic trend model. Second, a seasonal pattern repeats itself year after year. For instance, revenue is consistently higher in the first quarter (September–December), as compared to the other quarters.

a. When using Excel with quarterly data, we first construct relevant variables for the linear and the quadratic trend models with seasonal dummy variables. Table 14.9 presents a portion of the data file for the revenue variable y; three seasonal dummy variables d_1, d_2, and d_3 representing the first three quarters (using the fourth quarter as reference); and the time variable t and its square t^2.

TABLE 14.9 Variables for Example 14.5

Year	Quarter	y	d_1	d_2	d_3	t	t^2
2010	1	15,683	1	0	0	1	1
2010	2	13,499	0	1	0	2	4
2010	3	15,700	0	0	1	3	9
2010	4	20,343	0	0	0	4	16
⋮	⋮	⋮	⋮	⋮	⋮	⋮	⋮
2020	3	59,685	0	0	1	43	1849
2020	4	64,698	0	0	0	44	1936

The estimated trend models with seasonal dummy variables are:

Linear: $\hat{y}_t = 17{,}009.87 + 20{,}665.22d_1 + 2{,}311.03d_2$
$- 3{,}386.08d_3 + 1{,}210.74t$; Adjusted $R^2 = 0.8436$

Quadratic: $\hat{y}_t = 6{,}815.17 + 20{,}665.22d_1 + 2{,}251.75d_2 - 3{,}445.35d_3$
$+ 2{,}544.35t - 29.64t^2$; Adjusted $R^2 = 0.8980$

The coefficients for the seasonal dummy variables indicate that the revenue is about $20,665 million higher in the first quarter as compared to the fourth quarter. The results also suggest that compared to the fourth quarter, the revenue is higher in the second quarter and lower in the third quarter. The positive coefficient for the time variable t in the linear model indicates an upward movement of the revenue. The positive coefficient for t along with a negative coefficient for t^2 in the quadratic model captures the inverted U-shape of the time series.

b. The quadratic trend model with seasonal dummy variables is preferred for making forecasts because of its higher adjusted R^2 value ($0.8980 > 0.8436$). Therefore, the revenue forecasts for fiscal year 2021 are:
$\hat{y}_{2021:01}(d_1 = 1, d_2 = 0, d_3 = 0, t = 45, t^2 = 2{,}025) = \$81{,}963.70$ million
$\hat{y}_{2021:02}(d_1 = 0, d_2 = 1, d_3 = 0, t = 46, t^2 = 2{,}116) = \$63{,}397.73$ million
$\hat{y}_{2021:03}(d_1 = 0, d_2 = 0, d_3 = 1, t = 47, t^2 = 2{,}209) = \$57{,}488.85$ million
$\hat{y}_{2021:04}(d_1 = 0, d_2 = 0, d_3 = 0, t = 48, t^2 = 2{,}304) = \$60{,}663.16$ million

The quarterly forecasts result in a sum of $263,513 million in revenue for fiscal year 2021.

SYNOPSIS OF INTRODUCTORY CASE

Apple Inc. is an American multinational technology company headquartered in Cupertino, California. It designs, manufactures, and markets mobile communication and media devices, personal computers, and portable digital music players. It also sells a range of related software, streaming services, accessories, networking solutions, and third-party digital content and applications.

Shutterstock/Tooykrub

For several years, Apple's smartphone segment has been the company's core source of revenue, resulting in record revenue. A scatterplot of Apple's quarterly revenue for the fiscal years 2010 through 2020 highlights some important characteristics. First, there is a persistent upward movement with the revenue plateauing near the end of the observation period. Second, a seasonal pattern repeats itself. For each year, the revenue is the highest in the first quarter (October–December) followed by the second (January–March), fourth (July–September), and third (April–June) quarters.

The coefficients of the estimated quadratic trend model with seasonal dummy variables suggest that the revenue is about $20.67 billion higher in the first quarter as compared to the fourth quarter. This is not surprising because given Apple's fiscal calendar, the first quarter encompasses the holiday period with usual strong sales. The positive coefficient for the time variable t along with a negative coefficient for t^2 captures the plateauing of the series. This finding is consistent with the concern that while Apple is doing well for now, its future growth may be murky partly because, in terms of the smartphone market, it only sells on the somewhat saturated mid- to high-end range market. The quarterly revenue forecasts for 2021 are $81.96, $63.40, $57.49, and $60.66 billion, respectively, resulting in a whopping $263.51 billion in revenue for fiscal year 2021.

EXERCISES 14.4

Mechanics

20. Consider the following trend models estimated from 20 observations. Use them to make a forecast for y at $t = 21$.
    a. Linear trend: $\hat{y} = 13.54 + 1.08t$
    b. Quadratic trend: $\hat{y} = 18.28 + 0.92t - 0.01t^2$

21. Consider the following trend models estimated from 30 observations.

    Linear model: $\hat{y} = 24 + 0.12t$

    Quadratic model 2: $\hat{y} = 30 + 0.20t - 0.01t^2$

    a. Use each model to make a forecast for y at $t = 31$ and $t = 32$.
    b. Which is the preferred model for forecasting if, relative to the linear model, the quadratic model has higher R^2 but lower adjusted R^2?

Applications

22. **FILE** *White_Americans.* Demographers have reported that deaths outnumber births among white Americans in more than half the states in the U.S. The accompanying data file includes the white American population, in millions, from 2005 through 2017.
    a. Use the scatterplot to explore linear and quadratic trends; the cubic trend is not considered. Which trend model do you think describes the time series better?
    b. Validate your intuition by comparing adjusted R^2 of the two models. Use the preferred model to forecast the white population in 2018 and 2019.

23. **FILE** *Pharma.* Investors are always reviewing past pricing history and using it to influence their future investment decisions. An investor, looking for a promising return, analyzes the monthly stock price data of a pharmaceutical firm from June 2017 to May 2020. The accompanying file contains the data.
    a. Estimate the linear, the quadratic, and the cubic trend models. Which is the preferred model?
    b. Use the preferred model to make a forecast for June 2020.

24. **FILE** *Mayas.* After the pandemic, weekly sales at Maya's street food are showing signs of improvement. The accompanying data file includes the sales for the past 40 weeks.

a. Estimate the quadratic and the cubic trend models. Which is the preferred model?

b. Use the preferred model to forecast sales for week 41.

25. **FILE** *Population_Japan.* For several years, Japan's declining population has led experts and lawmakers to consider its economic and social repercussions. The accompanying data file includes the population data, in millions, for Japan from 1960 to 2019.

a. Estimate the linear and the quadratic trend models for population. Which is the preferred model?

b. Use the preferred model to forecast the population in Japan for 2020 and 2021.

26. **FILE** *House_Price.* The West Census region for the U.S. includes Montana, Wyoming, Colorado, New Mexico, Idaho, Utah, Arizona, Nevada, California, Oregon, and Washington. The accompanying data file contains the median house prices in the West Census region from 2010:01 through 2018:03.

a. Estimate and interpret the quadratic trend model with seasonal dummy variables.

b. Use the estimated model to forecast the median house price in the West Census region for the fourth quarter of 2018.

27. **FILE** *Weekly_Earnings.* Data on weekly earnings are collected as part of the Current Population Survey, a nationwide sample survey of households in which respondents are asked how much each worker usually earns. The accompanying data file includes quarterly data on weekly earnings (Earnings, adjusted for inflation) in the U.S. from 2010 through 2017.

a. Estimate the linear and the quadratic trend models with seasonal dummy variables. Which is the preferred model?

b. Use the preferred model to forecast earnings for the first two quarters of 2018.

14.5 CAUSAL FORECASTING METHODS

The models we have discussed so far are sometimes referred to as noncausal, or purely time series, models. These models do not offer any explanation of the mechanism generating the variable of interest and simply provide a method for projecting historical data. Although this approach can be effective, it provides no guidance on the likely effects of changes in policy (predictor) variables.

Causal forecasting models are based on a regression framework, where the predictor variables are associated with the outcome of the response variable. For example, we can use causal models to forecast product sales y_t using the firm's advertising budget x_t as the predictor variable. Here, we specify the linear regression model as

$$y_t = \beta_0 + \beta_1 x_t + \varepsilon_t.$$

Let the sample observations be denoted by $y_1, y_2, \ldots, y_T$ and $x_1, x_2, \ldots, x_T$, respectively. The model can easily be estimated to make a one-step-ahead forecast as

$$\hat{y}_{T+1} = b_0 + b_1 x_{T+1}.$$

Multi-step-ahead forecasts can be made similarly. Note that this approach works only if we know, or can predict, the future value of the predictor variable x_{T+1}. In this application, we can forecast sales $\hat{y}_{T+1}$ only if we know the advertisement budget, x_{T+1}, for the next period.

Lagged Regression Models

LO 14.5

For forecasting, sometimes we use a causal approach with lagged values of x and y as predictor variables. For instance, consider the model

Use lagged variable models to make forecasts.

$$y_t = \beta_0 + \beta_1 x_{t-1} + \varepsilon_t,$$

where β_1 represents the slope of the lagged predictor variable x. Note that if we have T sample observations, the estimable sample will consist of $T - 1$ observations, where $y_2, y_3, \ldots, y_T$ are matched with $x_1, x_2, \ldots, x_{T-1}$. Here, a one-step-ahead forecast is easily made as

$$\hat{y}_{T+1} = b_0 + b_1 x_T.$$

This forecast does not require the future value of the predictor variable because x_T is its last known sample value. We can generalize this model to include more lags. For example, we can specify a two-period lagged regression model as $y_t = \beta_0 + \beta_1 x_{t-1} + \beta_2 x_{t-2} + \varepsilon_t$. A one-step-ahead forecast is now made as $\hat{y}_{T+1} = b_0 + b_1 x_T + b_2 x_{T-1}$.

Another popular specification for causal forecasting uses lagged values of the response variable as an predictor variable. For instance, consider the model

$$y_t = \beta_0 + \beta_1 y_{t-1} + \varepsilon_t,$$

where the parameter β_1 represents the slope of the lagged response variable y. This regression is also referred to as an **autoregressive model** of order one, or simply an AR(1). Higher-order autoregressive models can be constructed similarly.

Autoregressive models exploit time dependence in the given time series where future behavior can be predicted based on past behavior. A one-period-ahead forecast is made as

$$\hat{y}_{T+1} = b_0 + b_1 y_T.$$

Finally, we can also use lagged values of both x and y as the predictor variables. For instance, consider

$$\hat{y}_t = \beta_0 + \beta_1 x_{t-1} + \beta_2 y_{t-1} + \varepsilon_t.$$

Here, a one-period-ahead forecast is made as

$$\hat{y}_{T+1} = b_0 + b_1 x_T + b_2 y_T.$$

In Example 14.6, we discuss forecasting models based on lagged variables.

EXAMPLE 14.6

Buildings

Table 14.10 shows a portion of data on total dwellings and residential buildings started in the U.S. (Buildings, in 1,000s) and real gross domestic product (GDP, in $ billions). Estimate the following three models and use the most suitable model to make a forecast for buildings in 2020.

Model 1: Buildings$_t = \beta_0 + \beta_1 \text{GDP}_{t-1} + \varepsilon_t$.
Model 2: Buildings$_t = \beta_0 + \beta_1 \text{Buildings}_{t-1} + \varepsilon_t$.
Model 3: Buildings$_t = \beta_0 + \beta_1 \text{GDP}_{t-1} + \beta_2 \text{Buildings}_{t-1} + \varepsilon_t$.

TABLE 14.10 Buildings and GDP Data

Year	Buildings	GDP
1990	99.38	9365.49
1991	84.50	9355.36
1992	99.97	9684.89
⋮	⋮	⋮
2019	107.49	19073.06

SOLUTION: In order to estimate these models, we first have to create lagged variables. This can easily be done in Excel. We create a new variable called LagGDP by copying the GDP observations from 1990 to 2018 and pasting them from 1991 to 2019. Note that the lagged GDP information for 1990 is not available. We repeat the process for the new lagged variable called LagBldg. Table 14.11 shows a portion of the data.

TABLE 14.11 Variables for Example 14.6

Year	Buildings	GDP	LagGDP	LagBldg
1990	99.38	9365.49	—	—
1991	84.50	9355.36	9365.49	99.38
1992	99.97	9684.89	9355.36	84.50
⋮	⋮	⋮	⋮	⋮
2019	107.49	19073.06	18638.16	104.17

When estimating the three regression models in Excel, we make sure that the cell ranges for the response and predictor variable(s) correspond to the years 1991–2019. Table 14.12 summarizes the regression results of the three models.

TABLE 14.12 Regression Models with Lagged Variables

Parameters	Model 1	Model 2	Model 3
Constant	160.2109*	10.9114	27.6681
	(0.000)	(0.254)	(0.157)
LagGDP	−0.0037	NA	−0.0010
	(0.101)		(0.320)
LagBldg	NA	0.9019*	0.8799*
		(0.000)	(0.000)
Adjusted R^2	0.0630	0.8087	0.8089

Notes: The top portion of the table contains parameter estimates with p-values in parentheses; NA denotes not applicable; the symbol * denotes significance at the 5% level.

As discussed earlier, it is preferable to compare competing regression models in terms of adjusted R^2 because it appropriately penalizes for overfitting. We choose Model 3 because it has the highest adjusted R^2 of 0.8089. To make a forecast for 2020, we use the 2019 values for GDP and Buildings, which represent their lagged values for 2020.

$$\widehat{\text{Building}}_{2020} = 27.6681 - 0.0010 \times 19073.06 + 0.8799 \times 107.49 = 102.59.$$

Therefore, we forecast that about 102,590 new dwellings and residential buildings will start in the U.S. in 2020.

EXERCISES 14.5

Mechanics

28. **FILE** *Exercise_14.28.* The accompanying file contains data for y and x. Estimate $y_t = \beta_0 + \beta_1 x_{t-1} + \beta_2 x_{t-2} + \varepsilon_t$ and use it to make a one-step-ahead forecast ($t = 13$) for y.

29. **FILE** *Exercise_14.29.* The accompanying file contains data for y.

   a. Estimate an autoregressive model of order 1, $y_t = \beta_0 + \beta_1 y_{t-1} + \varepsilon_t$, to make a one-step-ahead forecast ($t = 25$) for y.

   b. Estimate an autoregressive model of order 2, $y_t = \beta_0 + \beta_1 y_{t-1} + \beta_2 y_{t-2} + \varepsilon_t$, to make a one-step-ahead forecast ($t = 25$) for y.

30. **FILE** *Exercise_14.30.* The accompanying file contains data for y and x.

   a. Estimate $y_t = \beta_0 + \beta_1 x_{t-1} + \varepsilon_t$ to make a one-step-ahead forecast for period 13.

   b. Estimate $y_t = \beta_0 + \beta_1 y_{t-1} + \varepsilon_t$ to make a one-step-ahead forecast for period 13.

31. **FILE** *Exercise_14.31.* The accompanying file contains data for y and x.

    a. Estimate $y_t = \beta_0 + \beta_1 x_{t-1} + \varepsilon_t$.

    b. Estimate $y_t = \beta_0 + \beta_1 y_{t-1} + \varepsilon_t$.

    c. Estimate $y_t = \beta_0 + \beta_1 x_{t-1} + \beta_2 y_{t-1} + \varepsilon_t$.

    d. Use the most suitable model to make a one-step-ahead forecast ($t = 13$) for y.

Applications

32. Hiroshi Sato, an owner of a sushi restaurant in San Francisco, has been following an aggressive marketing campaign to thwart the effect of rising unemployment rates on business. He used monthly data on sales ($1,000s), advertising costs ($), and the unemployment rate (%) from January 2018 to May 2019 to estimate the following sample regression equation:

$$\widehat{Sales}_t = 17.51 + 0.03 AdCost_{t-1} - 0.69 Unemp_{t-1}.$$

    a. Hiroshi had budgeted $620 toward advertising costs in May 2019. Make a forecast for Sales for June 2019 if the unemployment rate in May 2019 was 9.1%.

    b. What will be the forecast if he raises his advertisement budget to $700?

    c. Reevaluate the above forecasts if the unemployment rate was 9.5% in May 2019.

33. **FILE** *Profits.* The owner of a popular restaurant wants to forecast weekly profits during the peak tourist season. The accompanying data file contains its profits y (in $1,000s) and its marketing expenditure x for 12 weeks. Estimate three

models: (a) $y_t = \beta_0 + \beta_1 x_{t-1} + \varepsilon_t$, (b) $y_t = \beta_0 + \beta_1 y_{t-1} + \varepsilon_t$, and (c) $y_t = \beta_0 + \beta_1 x_{t-1} + \beta_2 y_{t-1} + \varepsilon_t$. Use the most suitable model to forecast the restaurant's profit for Week 13.

34. **FILE** *Phillips_Curve.* The Phillips curve captures the inverse relation between the rate of unemployment and the rate of inflation; the lower the unemployment in an economy, the higher is the inflation rate. The accompanying data file contains monthly data on the seasonally adjusted consumer price index (CPI) and the unemployment rates in the United States from January 2018 to December 2019.

    a. Estimate two models. Model 1 uses CPI as the response variable and the lagged unemployment rate as the predictor variable. Model 2 extends the model by including the lagged CPI as another predictor variable.

    b. Determine the preferred model and use it to forecast CPI for January 2020.

35. **FILE** *Consumption.* The consumption function is one of the key relationships in economics, where consumption (y) depends on disposable income (x). The accompanying data file contains quarterly data on personal consumption expenditure and disposable income for five years. Both variables are measured in billions of dollars and are seasonally adjusted.

    a. Plot the consumption series. Estimate the appropriate polynomial trend model to forecast consumption expenditure for the 1st quarter of year 6.

    b. Estimate $y_t = \beta_0 + \beta_1 x_{t-1} + \varepsilon_t$ to forecast consumption expenditure for the 1st quarter of year 6.

    c. Which of these two models is more appropriate for making forecasts? Explain.

14.6 WRITING WITH DATA

Case Study

feverpitched/123RF

Leading economic indicators, such as the stock market or the housing market, often change prior to large economic adjustments. For example, a rise in stock prices often means that investors are more confident of future growth in the economy. Or a fall in building permits is likely a signal that the housing market is weakening—which is often a sign that other sectors of the economy are on the downturn.

Consider what happened prior to the 2008 recession. As early as October 2006, building permits for new homes were down 28% from October 2005. Analysts use economic indicators to predict future trends and gauge where the economy is heading. The information provided by economic indicators helps firms implement or alter business strategies.

Pooja Nanda is an analyst for a large investment firm in Chicago. She covers the construction industry and has been given the challenging task of forecasting housing starts for June 2019. She has access to seasonally adjusted monthly housing starts in the United States from January 2016 to May 2019. A portion of the data is shown in Table 14.13.

TABLE 14.13 Monthly Housing Starts (in 1,000s)

Date	Housing starts
Jan-16	1114
Feb-16	1208
⋮	⋮
May-19	1269

Pooja would like to use the sample information to identify the best-fitting model to forecast housing starts for June 2019.

Sample Report— Forecasting Monthly Housing Starts

Leading economic indicators are often used to gauge where the economy is heading. The housing market is one of the most important indicators because it is a significant component of the economy. When this sector weakens, just about everyone and everything feels it—from homeowners and construction workers to government municipalities that rely on property taxes to operate. Given the importance of the housing market, this report will employ simple time series models to project historical data on housing starts.

A scatterplot of housing starts from January 2016 to May 2019 is shown in Figure 14.7. A casual observation of the scatterplot suggests quite a bit of random variation and possibly a slight upward trend. There is no concern for seasonality as the housing starts data represent seasonally adjusted annual rates.

FIGURE 14.7 Scatterplot of housing starts (in 1,000s)

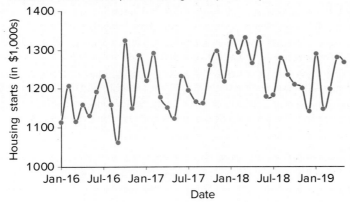

Given the findings from Figure 14.7, three models are estimated:

1. The three-period moving average model.
2. The simple exponential smoothing model.
3. The simple linear trend model, $y_t = \beta_0 + \beta_1 t + \varepsilon_t$, where y_t represents housing starts.

Three performance measures are used for model selection: mean square error (*MSE*), mean absolute deviation (*MAD*), and the mean absolute percentage error (*MAPE*). Ideally, the preferred model will have the lowest values for *MSE, MAD,* and *MAPE*. Table 14.14 shows the values of these three performance measures for the models.

TABLE 14.14 Performance Measures of Competing Models

	3-period moving average model	Exponential smoothing model ($\alpha = 0.2$)*	Linear regression model
MSE	5,069.50	4,798.44	4,091.72
MAD	60.55	57.13	54.24
MAPE	4.96	4.65	4.46

*For the exponential smoothing model, $\alpha = 0.20$ provides the lowest values for *MSE, MAD,* and *MAPE*.

The linear trend model provides the best sample fit, as it has the lowest values for *MSE,* *MAD,* and *MAPE.* Therefore, the estimated linear trend model is used to derive the forecast for June 2019 as

$$\hat{y}_{42} = 1,170.2524 + 2.1413 \times 42 = 1,260.19.$$

Housing starts play a key role in determining the health of the economy and are, therefore, always under scrutiny. The U.S. housing market seems to be on solid ground even though there has been a slowdown from its peak in early 2018.

Suggested Case Studies

Report 14.1 FILE *Fried_Dough.* Fried dough is a popular North American food associated with outdoor food stands at carnivals, amusement parks, fairs, festivals, and so on. Usually dusted with powdered sugar and drenched in oil, it is not particularly healthy, but it sure is tasty! Jose Sanchez owns a small stall at Boston Commons in Boston, Massachusetts, where he sells fried dough and soft drinks. Although business is good, he is apprehensive about the variation in sales for no apparent reason. The accompanying data file contains information on the number of plates of fried dough and soft drinks that he sold over the last 30 days. In a report, use the sample information to explore forecasting models, including moving averages and the simple exponential method, to smooth the time series for fried dough and soft drinks. Use the preferred method to forecast sales of fried dough and soft drinks for the next few days.

Report 14.2 FILE *India_China.* According to United Nations estimates, more than half of the world population live in just seven countries, with China, closely followed by India, leading the pack. The other five countries on the list include the United States, Indonesia, Brazil, Pakistan, and Nigeria. It is believed that India will overtake China to become the world's most populous nation much sooner than previously thought. The accompanying data file, compiled by the World Bank, contains the population data, in millions, for India and China from 1960 to 2019. In a report, use the sample information to explore linear, quadratic, and cubic regression models to capture the population trend for both China and India. Use the preferred model to forecast the population of China and India from 2018–2020.

Report 14.3 FILE *Revenue_Amazon.* Amazon.com, Inc., was a money-losing company when it went public on May 15, 1997, with an IPO valued at a modest $438 million. Amazon has since had an epic run as a public company, worth over a trillion dollars in 2020. An important question for investors and other stakeholders is whether Amazon's growth is sustainable. The accompanying data file contains quarterly data on Amazon's revenue for the fiscal years 2010 through 2020, with the fiscal year concluding at the end of December. In a report, use the sample information to explore linear and quadratic regression models to capture Amazon's revenue trend and seasonality. Use the preferred model to forecast Amazon's revenue for fiscal year 2021.

Report 14.4 COVID-19 disease caused a worldwide pandemic in 2020 and necessitated the need for public health organizations to gather and provide COVID-19 data to study the spread of the disease. Visit https://github.com/owid/covid-19-data/tree/master/public/data to find daily data on confirmed cases, deaths, hospitalizations, testing, and vaccinations as well as other variables of potential interest. Select any two variables for a country of your choice and use the appropriate time series models for making forecasts.

APPENDIX A

Big Data Sets: Variable Description and Data Dictionary

A distinctive feature of the text is the access to big data sets with relevance to several applications to which students can relate. Although the data sets represent a simplified (modified) portion of the actual data, they still retain several features of big data. In Chapters 1, 2, 3, 12, and 13, we use these big data sets in the Writing with Data sections. Data dictionaries for the three big data sets used in the text are described below.

Data 1: College Admissions Data

The **College_Admissions** data contain important college admission and enrollment information related to a selective four-year university in North America. The data shed light on admission and enrollment decisions made by the admissions office and the applicants. Based on the admissions dashboard, there are about 18,000 applicants for fall admissions in three colleges within the university. Also included in the data is the college GPA of enrolled applicants.

TABLE A.1 Data Dictionary for College Admissions Data

Variable name	Description or possible values
Applicant	A modified ID for each applicant
Edu_Parent1 Edu_Parent2	Education for Parent 1 and Parent 2 is defined as: 1 – No High School 2 – Some High School 3 – High School Graduate 4 – Some College 5 – 2-Year College Graduate 6 – 4-Year College Graduate 7 – Postgraduate
Sex	M – Male F – Female
White	1 – White 0 – Not White
Asian	1 – Asian 0 – Not Asian
HSGPA	High school weighted GPA, ranging from 0 to 5.
SAT/ACT	The higher of the SAT/ACT score, where the ACT score is first converted into the equivalent SAT score for English and Math
College	Arts & Letters Business & Economics Math & Science
Admitted	1 – Admitted by College 0 – Not Admitted by College
Enrolled	1 – Applicant enrolled 0 – Applicant not enrolled
College_GPA	College GPA, ranging from 0 to 4, four years after enrollment; blanks for those who did not enroll

Data 2: House Price Data

The **House_Price** data are extracted from Zillow (http://www.zillow.com). The data show information on about 11,000 home sales for 50 campus towns in the U.S. over a one-year period.

TABLE A.2 Data Dictionary for House Price Data

Variable name	Description or possible values
Record	A modified ID for each house
Sale_amount	Sale price of the house in U.S. dollars
Sale_date	Sale date of the house
Beds	Number of bedrooms in the house
Baths	Number of bathrooms in the house
Sqft_home	Square footage of the house
Sqft_lot	Square footage of the lot
Type	Multiple Family Multiple Occupancy Single Family
Build_year	Year the house was built
Town	Name of the campus town
University	Name of the university

Data 3: Tech Sales Reps Data

TechSales_Reps

The *TechSales_Reps* data contain records of 21,990 sales representatives from the hardware and software product groups of a high-tech company. For each employee, the data include socio-demographic and education information, salary, sales performance, and a personality indicator. Also included in the data is the net promoter score, which is an indicator of customer satisfaction with each sales rep.

TABLE A.3 Data Dictionary for Tech Sales Reps Data

Variable name	Description or possible values
Rep	A unique ID for each sales representative
Business	One of the two product groups: Hardware and Software
Age	Employee's age
Female	1 – female 0 – otherwise
Years	The number of years the employee has been employed at the company
College	Whether or not the employee has a four-year college degree (Yes/No)
Personality	Analyst: Analysts tend to be open-minded and strong-willed. They like to work independently and usually approach things from a very practical perspective. Diplomat: Diplomats care about people and tend to have a lot of empathy toward others. They exemplify cooperation and diplomacy. Explorer: Explorers are highly practical and can think on their feet. They tend to be very good at making quick, rational decisions in difficult situations. Sentinel: Sentinels are cooperative and practical. They like stability, order, and security. People with this personality type tend to be hardworking and meticulous.
Certificates	The number of relevant professional certifications each employee has earned
Feedback	The average feedback score that each employee receives from their peers and supervisor on the 360-degree annual evaluation. The possible scores range from 0 (lowest) to 4 (highest).
Salary	Annual base salary of each employee
NPS	The net promoter score (NPS) is a key indicator of customer satisfaction and loyalty.

Getting Started with Excel

Microsoft Excel

Microsoft Excel is arguably the most widely used computer application among business and nonbusiness professionals. In fields such as marketing, finance, health care, sports, and politics, professionals use Excel spreadsheets for everyday tasks. Oftentimes, these tasks involve entering, editing, and formatting data as well as performing data analysis. Excel is used throughout this text as the tool for analytics.

In this appendix, we summarize Excel formulas, references, and functions that are commonly used for calculations and data analysis. We also provide a brief description of Excel's Analysis ToolPak add-in at the end of the appendix; more detailed instructions on the use of this add-in are included in the relevant chapters of the text.

Formulas

In Excel, we use formulas to perform basic calculations. When we enter a formula in a cell, Excel carries out the specified calculation and returns the result in the same cell. We also use formulas to manipulate the cell content such as rounding a number. A formula in Excel always starts with an equal sign (=) and usually includes cell addresses. A cell address or cell reference consists of a column name and a row number. For example, cell reference A1 refers to the top and leftmost cell in column A and row 1. Basic calculations can be performed using arithmetic operations such as addition (+), subtraction (−), multiplication (*), division (/), and exponentiation (^). For example, we select an empty cell and use the formula =A1+B1+C1 to add values from cells A1, B1, and C1, and the formula =A1^2 to square the value in cell A1.

Relative, Absolute, and Mixed References

There are three types of cell references: relative, absolute, and mixed. The three cell reference types behave differently when copied elsewhere on the worksheet. By default, cell addresses in a formula, such as =B1+C1, are relative references and will change when a formula is copied to another cell. For example, if we enter the formula =B1+C1 in cell A1 and copy it to cell D4, the formula in cell D4 will appear as =E4+F4. In other words, references to cells B1 and C1 are relative to where the formula is placed on the worksheet. We use relative references when we want to repeat similar calculations while allowing column names and row numbers to change.

Absolute references allow us to maintain the original cell references when a formula is copied elsewhere. We specify absolute references by adding a dollar sign ($) in front of the column name and row number (e.g., $B$1). From the previous example, if we enter the formula =$B$1+$C$1 in cell A1 and copy it to cell D4, the formula in cell D4 will remain =$B$1+$C$1. Unlike relative references, absolute references remain unchanged when copied elsewhere on the worksheet.

We use mixed references by adding a dollar sign ($) in front of either the column name or the row number (e.g., $B1 or B$1), but not both. This will keep the reference to the specific column name or the row number constant. From the previous example, if we enter the formula =$B1+$C1 in cell A1 and copy it to cell D4, the formula in cell D4 will become =$B4+$C4. Similarly, if we enter the formula =B$1+C$1 in cell A1 and copy it to cell D4, the formula in cell D4 will become =E$1+F$1.

In Table B.1, we summarize the different results when using relative, absolute, and mixed references with the same formula.

TABLE B.1 Relative, Absolute, and Mixed References

Reference	Formula in cell A1	Formula in cell A1 copied to cell D4
Relative	=B1+C1	=E4+F4
Absolute	=$B$1+$C$1	=$B$1+$C$1
Mixed	=$B1+$C1	=$B4+$C4
Mixed	=B$1+C$1	=E$1+F$1

Functions

Functions in Excel are predefined formulas. Like a formula, a function always begins with an equal sign (=) and must be written with the correct syntax enclosed within parentheses. Most functions require at least one input. Inputs are the values or criteria that Excel uses to perform calculations. For example, the COUNT function is used to count the number of cells that contain numerical values and has the syntax =COUNT(A1:A10), where A1:A10 is the input indicating the array of cells to be counted. Table B.2 provides a summary of some of the most basic descriptive functions in Excel. In this table, the notation array in the function's input specifies the range of cell addresses to be included in the calculation.

Note: Due to different fonts and type settings, copying and pasting formulas and functions from this text directly into Excel may cause errors. When such errors occur, you may need to replace special characters such as quotation marks and parentheses or delete extra spaces in the functions.

TABLE B.2 Basic Descriptive Functions in Excel

Function and syntax	Description	Example
=COUNT(array)	Returns the number of cells in the array with numerical values.	=COUNT(A1:A10)
=COUNTA(array)	Returns the number of cells in the array that are not blank.	=COUNTA(A1:A10)
=COUNTBLANK(array)	Returns the number of cells in the array that are blank.	=COUNTBLANK(A1:A10)
=COUNTIF(array, criteria)	Returns the number of cells in the array that meet a specific selection criterion.	=COUNTIF(A1:A10, ">10")
=IF(logical statement, result if the statement is true, result if the statement is false)	Returns a result based on the outcome of the logical statement.	=IF(A1="Yes", 1, 0). If A1 equals Yes, then Excel returns a 1; if not, it returns a 0.
=SUM(array)	Adds and returns the sum of the numbers in the array.	=SUM(A1:A10)

Table B.3 provides a summary of some basic statistical functions in Excel.

TABLE B.3 Basic Statistical Functions in Excel

Function and syntax	Description	Example
=AVERAGE(array)	Returns the arithmetic mean of the array.	=AVERAGE(A1:A10)
=MAX(array)	Returns the largest number in the array.	=MAX(A1:A10)
=MEDIAN(array)	Returns the median of the array.	=MEDIAN(A1:A10)
=MIN(array)	Returns the smallest number in the array.	=MIN(A1:A10)
=RAND( )	Returns a uniformly distributed random number that is greater than or equal to 0 and less than 1.	=RAND( )
=RANDBETWEEN(lowest value, highest value)	Returns a uniformly distributed random number between the specified lowest and highest values, inclusive.	=RANDBETWEEN(1,10) Excel returns a random number between 1 and 10.
=ROUND(cell, decimal digit)	Rounds the numerical value in the referenced cell to the specified decimal digit.	=ROUND(A1,2) Excel returns the numerical value in cell A1 rounded to two decimal places.
=STDEV.S(array)	Estimates and returns the sample standard deviation of the array.	=STDEV.S(A1:A10)

Excel's Analysis ToolPak Add-In

Excel offers a number of add-ins that come preinstalled. The Analysis ToolPak add-in is used for statistical analysis. The following instructions activate the Analysis Toolpak add-in.

Activating the Analysis ToolPak Add-In

A. For Microsoft Windows, in Excel, go to **File > Options > Add-Ins**. For macOS, go to **Tools > Excel Add-ins** and continue to step C.

B. In the Manage Excel Add-ins section (toward the bottom of the screen), click **Go**. . . . .

C. On the *Add-ins* dialog box, check the Analysis ToolPak box and click **OK**.

D. In Excel, go to the **Data** tab and verify that the Data Analysis command button appears in the Analyze (or Analysis) group.

APPENDIX C

Brief Answers to Select Even-Numbered Exercises

Chapter 1

1.2 Estimated; impossible to reach all video game players

1.4. a. All recent graduates with an engineering degree
b. No, computed from a sample

1.6 a. All U.S. citizens born in 2019
b. Sample data

1.8. Cross-sectional data; will vary due to the nature of sampling

1.10 Unstructured data

1.12 Structured; time series data; will vary depending on retrieval date

1.20 a. Nominal scale
b. Interval scale
c. Ratio scale

1.22 a. Interval scale
b. Nominal scale
c. Ratio scale

1.30 a. 1 of the 10
b. 9
c. 5 missing, 2 for Marriage and 3 for Income
d. 281 married, 134 not married
e. 69 married always exercise; 74 unmarried never exercise

1.32 a. Only Travel Plan has missing values
b. 300 observations are removed
c. 2 observations remain in the subset

1.34 a. $3,362.86
b. 3 are homeowners, and 1 is both a home and car owner
c. 3 for OwnHome, 3 for OwnCar, 0 for FoodSpend, and 1 for TravelSpend
d. 133; 88

1.36 a. 614; 616
b. 57.33%; 49.35%
c. 2
d. 6
e. 1599 highest, 1062 lowest; 1600 highest, 1055 lowest

Chapter 2

2.2 a. The proportion of the sales for medium-sized shirts was 0.302.
b. Sales of large-sized shirts had the highest frequency and sales of small-sized shirts had the lowest frequency.

2.4 a. 19.3% of people in the Midwest are living below the poverty level.
b. The South has the highest relative frequency as compared to the other three regions, which are roughly equal.

2.6 a. A rating of 5 has the highest frequency.
b. The higher ratings have the higher frequencies.

2.8 a. Not Religious is the most common response.
b. 35% responded Not Religious which is consistent with the earlier study.

2.10 a. 220; 0.10
b. The majority of respondents, 55%, felt that parents do too much for their adult children; only 10% of respondents felt that parents do too little for their adult children.

2.12 a. 0.317
b. 104
c. 0.867; 0.133

2.18 a. 47
b. 0.31; 0.13

2.20 a. 125
b. The distribution is symmetric.

2.24 a. No. The distribution is not symmetric. It is positively skewed.
b. Over this time period, the stock price was between $50 and $250.
c. The $100 up to $150 interval has the highest relative frequency, which is about 0.44.

2.26 a. 14
b. 52; 48

2.28 a. The DJIA was more than 26,000 on 44 days in the first half of 2019.
b. The distribution is not symmetric; it is negatively skewed.

2.30 a. 18; 0.99
b. 19; 0.23

2.32 a. 378
b. 46
c. 80
d. 14

2.34 a. 202; 60
b. 0.7030; 0.5588
c. Beer is the popular drink at this bar, followed by wine and then soft drinks. Both men and women are more likely to choose beer over the other two options.

2.36 a. 5; 94
b. 0.25; 0.5417; components constructed during shift 3 seem to be defective at a higher rate.
c. Defect rates seem to be highest in shift 3.

2.38 a. 120; 68
b. 0.1667; 0.32; The data suggest that nonbusiness majors are more likely to study hard, which supports the report.
c. The majority of both business and nonbusiness students do not study hard, but nonbusiness students are more likely to study hard.

2.40 There appears to be a negative relationship between obesity and life expectancy.

2.42 There appears to be no relationship between the returns of A and B, so investing in both would diversify risk.

2.44 a. There appears to be a negative relationship between the price of a car and its age.
 b. There appears to be a negative relationship between the price of a car and its mileage.

2.46 Both countries have a clear and consistent upward trend, but China's begins to stall slightly around 2000. India has slightly higher population growth over the past 40 years.

2.48 This graph does not correctly depict what has happened to company's stock price over this period. Because the vertical axis has been compressed by using an unreasonably high value as an upper limit ($500), the rise in stock price appears dampened.

Chapter 3

3.2 Mean $= -2.67$; median $= -3.5$; mode $= -4$

3.4 Mean $= 18.33$; median $= 20$; the distribution is bimodal: 15 and 20 are the two modes.

3.6 a. 25th percentile: 73.25; 50th percentile: 112; 75th percentile: 142
 b. 20th percentile: 237,275.8; 80th percentile: 825,227

3.8 Mean $= 2.31$; median $= 2.18$

3.10 Mean $= 1,306.94$; median $= 1,287.50$

3.12 a. Mean Food $= 4,416.44$; Mean Travel $= 2,405.27$
 b. Mean food spending for homeowners $= 4,048.90$
 Mean food spending for non-homeowners $= 4,566.70$
 Non-homeowners spend more on food than homeowners
 c. Mean travel spending for homeowners $= 1,960.35$
 Mean travel spending for non-homeowners $= 2,569.05$
 Non-homeowners spend more on travel than homeowners

3.14 a. 101.27
 b. 107.42

3.16 7.72

3.18 a.

	Min	Q1	Median	Q3	Max
Net_Profit	0.20	0.60	0.80	1.30	1.70
Counter_Sales	3.30	4.70	6.10	8.40	10.00
DriveThrough_Sales	2.00	2.50	4.35	7.70	8.40

 b. 50% of net profits were below $800,000 and 50% of net profits were above $800,000.
 c. 25% of counter sales were below $4,700,000 and 75% of counter sales were above $4,700,000; 75% of drive-through sales were below $7,700,000 and 25% of drive-through sales were above $7,700,000.

3.22 a. 18
 b. 4.8
 c. $\sigma^2 = 36.80$
 d. $\sigma = 6.07$

3.24 a. 22
 b. 7.33
 c. $s^2 = 81.2$; $s = 9.01$

3.26 a. Firm A: $s^2 = 162.65$; $s = 12.75$
 Firm B: $s^2 = 173.51$; $s = 13.17$
 b. Firm B's stock price has greater variability as indicated by a higher standard deviation.
 c. Firm A, $CV = 0.22$; Firm B, $CV = 0.24$; Firm B's stock price also has greater relative dispersion indicated by a higher coefficient of variation.

3.28 a. $CV_A = = 0.13$
 b. $CV_B = = 0.14$
 c. Corporation B has a slightly higher coefficient of variation which indicates greater relative dispersion.

3.30. a. Range of household income $= 32,766$; range of house value $= 442,900$
 b. For household income, $MAD_{Income} = 6,834.68$; $s_{Income} = 8,385.91$
 For house value, $MAD_{Value} = 71,738.88$; $s_{Value} = 93,589.10$
 c. The household income and house value have different sample means, so we cannot compare the MAD and standard deviation directly in order to determine which data are more variable. The coefficient variation is the recommended measure to compare the dispersion between the data sets.

3.32 a. Investment B provides a higher return. Investment A provides less risk since it has a smaller standard deviation.
 b. $Sharpe_A = 1.72$; $Sharpe_B = 1.36$. The Sharpe Ratio is higher for investment A which suggests that it provides a higher reward per unit of risk.

3.36 a. Mutual Fund 2 has a higher return over this period ($12.44 > 7.38$); Mutual Fund 1 is riskier as measured by the standard deviation ($35.12 > 28.52$).
 b. $Sharpe_1 = 0.15$; $Sharpe_2 = 0.37$. Mutual Fund 2 had a much higher Sharpe ratio than Mutual Fund 1 which suggests that Mutual Fund 2 had more reward per unit of risk.

3.38 a. At least 75%
 b. At least 89%

3.40 a. At least 75%
 b. At least 89%

3.42 a. 16%
 b. 80 observations

3.44 a. 97.5%
 b. 2.5%

3.50 a. Q1: Approximately 25% of the observations are less than 200; Q3: Approximately 75% of the observations are less than 550.
 b. IQR $= 350$; Limit: $1.5 \times$ IQR $= 525$. Find distances from Q1 $-$ Min $= 75 < 525$ and from Max $-$ Q3 $= 750 > 525$; thus, there is at least one outlier on the right side of the distribution.
 c. The distribution is not symmetric. It appears positively skewed because (1) the median falls left of center in the interquartile range and (2) the right whisker is longer than the left whisker.

3.52 a. At least 75%

b. At least 89%

3.54 a. 68%

b. 2.5%

c. 16%

3.56 a. At least 75%

b. 95%

3.58 a. The boxplot suggests that there are no outliers for the Debt variable.

b. The z-score for the smallest observation is -1.7692 and the z-score for the largest observation is 2.4199. Since the absolute value of both z-scores is less than 3, we conclude that there are no outliers for the Debt variable. This is consistent with the boxplot, which showed no outliers.

3.60 a. $s_{xy} = -12.3$

b. $r_{xy} = \dfrac{s_{xy}}{s_x s_y} = -0.96$; this implies is a strong negative linear relationship between x and y.

3.62 a. $s_{xy} = 631.39$; a positive linear relationship

b. $r_{xy} = 0.45$; a moderate, positive linear relationship

3.64 a. $s_{xy} = 66.79$; a positive linear relationship

b. $r_{xy} = 0.90$; a strong, positive linear relationship

3.66 a. $s_{Income, Value} = 642,995,533.1$; $r_{Income, Value} = 0.82$; the correlation between household income and house values is positive and rather strong.

b. $s_{Income, Foreign} = 30,867.06$; $r_{Income, Foreign} = 0.61$; the correlation between household income and the percentage of the residents who are foreign born is positive and moderate.

c. $s_{Income, NoHS} = -13,232.11$; $r_{Income, NoHS} = -0.46$. The correlation between household income and the percentage of the residents who are without a high school diploma is negative and moderate.

Chapter 4

4.6 a. A union

b. An intersection

4.8 a. Not exhaustive because you may not get any offer

b. Not mutually exclusive because you may get both offers

4.12 a. $2,090/10,000 = 0.209$

b. $245/10,000 = 0.0245$

c. $(2,090 + 2,890)/10,000 = 0.498$

d. No, the probability of the intersection, $290/10,000 \neq 0$

4.18 $P(A) = 0.40$, $P(B) = 0.50$, and $P(A^c \cap B^c) = 0.24$

a. $(A^c|B^c) = \dfrac{0.24}{1 - 0.50} = 0.48$

b. $P(A^c \cup B^c) = (1 - 0.40) + (1 - 0.50) - 0.24 = 0.86$

c. $P(A^c \cap B^c) = 1 - P(A \cup B) = 0.24$; $P(A \cup B) = 0.76$

4.20. Let event O correspond to "students who go to their professor during office hours," and events MI and MA to "minor clarification" and "major clarification;" $P(O) = 0.2$, $P(MI|O) = 0.3$, $P(MA|O) = 0.7$.

a. $P(MI \cap O) = 0.06$

b. $P(MA \cap O) = 0.14$

4.22 Let event A correspond to "Firm raising an alarm," and event F to "Fraudulent Transaction;" $P(A) = 0.05$, $P(A|F) = 0.80$, and $P(F) = 0.01$

$$P(F|A) = \frac{P(F \cap A)}{P(A)} = 0.16.$$

4.24 a. $P(Yes) = \dfrac{4,000 + 5,000 + 8,000 + 4,000}{10,000 + 20,000 + 15,000 + 12,000}$
$= 0.3684$

b. $P(Yes|(NE \text{ or } SE)) = \dfrac{4,000 + 5,000}{10,000 + 20,000} = 0.30$

c. $P(NW|No) = \dfrac{8,000}{6,000 + 15,000 + 7,000 + 8,000}$
$= 0.2222$

d. $P(SW \cap No)$
$= \dfrac{7,000}{10,000 + 20,000 + 15,000 + 12,000}$
$= 0.1228$

4.30 For $i = 1, 2$, let event A_i be "the i-th selected member is in favor of the bonus."

a. $P(A_1 \cap A_2) = \dfrac{10}{15} \times \dfrac{9}{14} = 0.4286$

b. $P(A_1^c \cap A_2^c) = \dfrac{5}{15} \times \dfrac{4}{14} = 0.0952$

4.34 Let event C correspond to "Churn," Y to "Younger," and O to "Older;" $P(C|Y) = 0.12$, $P(C|O) = 0.09$, $P(Y) = 0.62$; $P(O) = 1 - 0.62 = 0.38$

$P(O \cap C) = P(C|O)P(O) = 0.0342$

4.36 Let event S correspond to "Biggest smilers," F to "Biggest frowners," and D to "Divorced;" $P(D|S) = 0.11$ and $P(D|F) = 0.31$.

a. $P(S) = \dfrac{P(S \cap D)}{P(D|S)} = \dfrac{0.02}{0.11} = 0.1818$

b. $P(F \cap D) = P(D|F)P(F) = 0.0775$

4.38 Let event D_i be "the i-th selected mango is damaged".

a. $P(D_1^c) = \dfrac{17}{20} = 0.85$

b. $P(D_1^c \cap D_2^c) = \dfrac{17}{20} \times \dfrac{16}{19} = 0.7158$

c. $P(D_1 \cap D_2) = \dfrac{3}{20} \times \dfrac{2}{19} = 0.0158$

4.40 Let event O correspond to "Optimism about the global economy," U to "Respondents from the U.S.," and A to "Respondents from Asia." We have $P(O) = 0.18$, $P(O|U) = 0.22$, and $P(O|A) = 0.09$.

a. $P(O^c|A) = 1 - P(O|A) = 0.91$

b. $P(O \cap U) = P(O|U)P(U) = 0.0616$

c. $P(A|O) = \dfrac{P(O|A)P(A)}{P(O)} = 0.11$

4.44 a.

Major	Study hard	
	Yes (Y)	No (N)
Business (B)	20	100
Non-business (B^c)	48	102

b. $P(N|B) = \dfrac{100}{120} = 0.8333$

c. $P(Y) = \dfrac{68}{270} = 0.2519$

d. $P(B|Y) = \dfrac{20}{68} = 0.2941$; $P(B^c|Y) = \dfrac{48}{68} = 0.7059$

4.46 a.

Happy	Income		
	Low (L)	Medium (M)	High(H)
No (N)	40	44	37
Yes (Y)	40	66	63

b. $P(Y) = \dfrac{169}{290} = 0.5828$

c. $P(Y|L) = \dfrac{40}{80} = 0.50$; $P(Y|M) = \dfrac{66}{110}$

   $= 0.60$; $P(Y|H) = \dfrac{63}{100} = 0.63$

d. Yes, because $P(Y|L)$, $P(Y|M)$, $P(Y|H)$, and $P(Y)$ are not equal.

4.56 Let event D be "Experience a decline," and event N be "Ratio is negative;" $P(D) = 0.20$, $P(D^c) = 0.80$, $P(N|D) = 0.70$, and $P(N|D^c) = 0.15$; $P(N) = P(N \cap D) + P(N \cap D^c) = 0.26$

$P(D|N) = \dfrac{P(N \cap D)}{P(N)} = 0.54$

4.58 Let $F =$ "Player is fully fit to play," $S =$ "Player is somewhat fit to play," $N =$ "Player is not able to play," and $W =$ "The Lakers win the game."

a. $P(W) = 0.32 + 0.18 + 0.12$

b. $P(F|W) = \dfrac{P(W \cap F)}{P(W)} = 0.52$

4.60 Let A correspond to "U.S. economy performs well" and B to "Asian countries perform well." We have $P(A) = 0.40$; $P(A^c) = 0.60$; $P(B|A) = 0.80$; and $P(B|A^c) = 0.30$.

a. $P(A \cap B) = P(B|A)P(A) = 0.32$

b. $P(B) = P(A \cap B) + P(A^c \cap B) = 0.50$

c. $P(A|B) = \dfrac{P(A \cap B)}{P(B)} = 0.64$

4.62 Let event M correspond to "Men," W to "Women," and H to "Healthy weight" $P(H|W) = 0.365$, $P(H|M) = 0.266$, $P(W) = 0.5052$, $P(M) = 0.4948$

a. $P(H) = P(W \cap H) + P(M \cap H) = 0.3160$

b. $P(W|H) = \dfrac{P(W \cap H)}{P(H)} = 0.5835$

c. $P(M|H) = \dfrac{P(M \cap H)}{P(H)} = 0.4165$

4.64 Let event R correspond to "Republican," D to "Democrat," I to "Independent," and S to "Support marijuana legalization;" $P(R) = 0.27$; $P(D) = 0.30$; $P(I) = 0.43$; $P(S|R) = 0.41$; $P(S|D) = 0.66$; and $P(S|I) = 0.63$

a. $P(S \cap R) = 0.41 \times 0.27 = 0.1107$

b. $P(S \cap D) = 0.66 \times 0.30 = 0.1980$

c. $P(S \cap I) = 0.63 \times 0.43 = 0.2709$

d. $P(S) = 0.1107 + 0.1980 + 0.2709 = 0.5796$

e. $P(R|S) = \dfrac{P(S \cap R)}{P(S)} = 0.1910$

Chapter 5

5.4 a. $P(X \leq 0) = 0.50$

b. $P(X = 50) = P(X \leq 50) - P(X \leq 25) = 0.25$

c. Yes

5.6 a. Discrete

b. Continuous

c. Discrete

d. Continuous

5.10 Let X represent the confidence score.

a. $P(X = 2) = 1 - 0.75 - 0.05 = 0.20$

b. $P(2 \leq X \leq 3) = 1 - 0.75 = 0.20 + 0.05 = 0.25$

5.14 $\mu = 10.75$; $\sigma^2 = 28.19$; $\sigma = 5.31$

5.16 a. $\mu = 0.95$

b. $\sigma = 0.80$

5.22 Let X be the warranty cost; $E(X) = 30$.
Let Y be the total revenue earned by the store; $E(Y) = 3600$.

5.24 Let X be the repair cost if no insurance; $E(X) = 84$; buy insurance because the expected repair cost is greater than the insurance cost.

5.26 $E(X) = -0.70$ million

5.30 a. $P(3 < X < 5) = P(X = 4) = 0.1569$

b. $P(3 < X \leq 5) = P(X \leq 5) - P(X \leq 3) = 0.2160$

c. $P(3 \leq X \leq 5) = P(X \leq 5) - P(X \leq 2) = 0.4828$

5.34 a. $P(X < 2) = P(X \leq 1) = 0.7213$

b. $P(X < 2) = P(X \leq 1) = 0.4580$

5.36 a. $E(X) = 2.58$; $SD(X) = 1.213$

b. $P(X < 2) = P(X \leq 1) = 0.1895$

c. $P(X = 0) = 0.0343$

5.38 a. $P(X > 2) = 1 - P(X \leq 2) = 0.3125$

b. $P(X > 2) = 1 - P(X \leq 2) = 0.5276$

c. $P(X > 2) = 1 - P(X \leq 2) = 0.1362$

5.40 a. $P(X \geq 1) = 1 - P(X = 0) = 0.4375 < 0.50$; statement is not correct.

b. $P(X \geq 1) = 1 - P(X = 0) = 0.5781 > 0.50$; statement is correct.

5.44 a. $P(X = 2) = 0.3747$

b. $P(X = 4) = 0.0677$

c. $E(X) = 51$; $SD(X) = 4.999$

5.48 a. $P(X = 1) = 0.3347$

b. $P(X = 2) = 0.2510$

c. $P(X \geq 2) = 1 - P(X \leq 1) = 0.4422$

5.52 a. $P(X < 14) = P(X \leq 13) = 0.0661$

b. $P(X \geq 20) = 1 - P(X \leq 19) = 0.5297$

c. $P(X = 25) = 0.0446$

d. $P(18 \leq X \leq 23) = P(X \leq 23) - P(X \leq 17) = 0.4905$

5.54 a. $\mu = 360/60 = 6$; $P(X = 2) = 0.0446$

b. $P(X \geq 2) = 1 - P(X \leq 1) = 0.9826$

c. $\mu = 6 \times 10 = 60$; $P(X = 40) = 0.001$

5.56 a. $P(X > 2) = 1 - P(X \leq 2) = 0.3233$

b. $\mu_5 = 2 \times 5 = 10$; $P(X = 6) = 0.0631$

c. $\mu_{180} = 2 \times 3 \times 60 = 360$

5.60 a. $\mu = \dfrac{84}{7} = 12$; $P(8 < X < 12) = P(X \leq 11) - P(X \leq 8) = 0.3066$

b. $\mu = \dfrac{84}{7} \times 5 = 60$; $P(X > 60) = 1 - P(X \leq 59)$
$= 0.5172$

5.64 a. $P(X = 0) = 0.5783$

b. $P(X = 1) = 0.3652$

c. $P(X \leq 1) = 0.9435$

5.68 $P(X \geq 8) = 1 - P(X \leq 7) = 0.0777$
$E(X) = 5$; $SD(X) = 1.7408$

5.70 a. $P(X = 0) = 0.5020$

b. $P(X \geq 1) = 1 - P(X = 0) = 0.4980$

5.72   a. $P(X = 3) = 0.2696$
      b. $P(X \geq 2) = 1 - P(X \leq 1) = 0.7549$

5.76   a. $P(X = 2) = 0.0495$
      b. $P(X = 5) = 0.0000002$
      c. $P(X = 1) = 0.0256$
      d. $0.0000002 \times 0.0256 = 0.00000000512$

Chapter 6

6.2   a. $P(X < 0) = 1 - P(X \geq 0) = 0.30$
     b. $P(X > 2.5) = 0.16$
     c. $P(0 \leq X \leq 4) = 0.70$

6.4   a. $f(x) = 0.0333$
     b. $\mu = 20; \sigma = 8.66$
     c. $P(X > 10) = 0.8325$

6.6.   a. $\mu = 20; \sigma = 5.77$
     b. $f(x) = 0.05; P(X > 22) = 0.4$
     c. $P(15 \leq X \leq 23) = 0.4$

6.8   Let X represent the electricity price
     a. $E(X) = 16$
     b. $f(x) = 0.125; P(X < 15.5) = 0.4375$
     c. $f(x) = 0.125; P(X > 14) = 0.75$

6.12   Let X represent the bloom date; $f(x) = 0.0833$
     a. $P(X > 25) = 0.4167$
     b. $P(X \leq 20) = 0.1667$

6.14   Let X represent the weight of a bag
     a. $E(X) = 11; \sigma = 0.5774$
     b. $f(x) = 0.5; P(X \leq 11) = 0.5$
     c. $P(X \geq 10.5) = 0.75$

6.20   Let X represent the IQ score
     a. $P(84 < X < 116) = 0.6827$
     b. $P(X < 68) = 0.0228$
     c.   Given $P(X > x) = 0.01, x = 137.22$

6.22   Let X represent the points scored
     a. $P(60 < X < 100) = 0.9545$
     b. $P(X > 100) = 0.0228$; about two games $(82 \times 0.0228 = 1.87)$

6.24   Let X represent sleep time on weekdays
     a. $P(X > 8) = 0.0668$
     b. $P(X < 6) = 0.4338$
     c. $P(6 \leq X \leq 8) = 0.4994$

6.26   Let X represent the mpg rating
     a. $P(X \geq 40) = 0.0382$
     b. $P(30 \leq X \leq 35) = 0.4953$
     c.   Given $P(X \leq x) = 0.99, x = 41.94$

6.30   Let X represent the number of weeks to find a job
     a. $P(X > 19) = 0.9332$
     b. $P(X > 19) = 0.0668$
     c. $P(23 \leq X \leq 25) = 0.2417$
     d. $P(23 \leq X \leq 25) = 0.0002$

6.34   Let X represent the exam score
     a. $P(50 \leq X \leq 80) = 0.5328$
     b. $P(20 \leq X \leq 40) = 0.1359$
     c.   Given $P(X \geq x) = 0.15, x = 80.73$
     d.   Given $P(X < x) = 0.10, x = 34.37$

6.36   Let X represent the length of time
     a. $P(X < 2.5) = 0.1056$
     b. $P(X < 2.5) + P(X > 3.5) = 0.2113$
     c.   Given $P(X < x) = 0.01; x = 2.07$

6.40   Let X represent the number of sunny days
     a. $P(X < 200) = 0.2793$
     b. $P(X \geq 266.5) = 0.0031$
     c.   Given $P(X < x) = 0.10, x = 186.07$
     d.   Given $P(X > x) = 0.01; x = 258.23$

6.44   Let X represent the amount spent on St. Patrick's Day.
     a. $P(X > 50) = 0.0205$
     b. $P(X > 50) = 0.0314$
     c.   Women are more likely to spend over \$50.

6.48   Let X represent the time until system fail.
     a. $P(X \leq 10) = 0.1151$
     b.   Expected profit per system $= 271.225$; final answer $= 271,225$

6.52   Let X represent the time between eating mosquitoes.
     a. $\mu_{\text{Poisson}} = 10; \mu_{\text{Exponential}} = 6$
     b. $\lambda = 0.1667; P(X > 15) = 0.0821$
     c. $P(15 \leq X \leq 20) = 0.0464$

6.54   Let X represent the time between car arrivals.
     a. $\mu = 0.0028$
     b. $P\left(X < \dfrac{10}{3600}\right) = 0.6321$

6.58   Let X represent the time for the next speeder.
     a. $\mu_{\text{Poisson}} = 8; \mu_{\text{Exponential}} = 7.5; \lambda = 0.1333;$ $P(X < 10) = 0.7364$
     b. $P(15 \leq X \leq 20) = 0.0659$
     c. $P(X > 25) = 0.0357$

6.62   Let X represent the days between successive crashes.
     a. $\mu = 0.365$
     b. $\lambda = 2.7397$
     c. $P(X \leq 1) = 0.9354$

Chapter 7

7.2   Nonresponse bias due to certain people choosing not to stop at the booth. Selection bias since the booth is only open during the weekend.

7.4   a.   Nonresponse bias if people who respond are systematically different from those who do not respond
     b.   Selection bias since those who frequent the store in the morning are likely to prefer an earlier opening time.
     c.   Selection bias because not everyone reads a newspaper. Nonresponse bias if the people who respond are systematically different from those who do not respond.

7.6   a.   Selection bias because people who go to the beach often go there to walk or exercise and are more likely to follow a consistent walking regimen.
     b.   Nonresponse bias if people who mail back response are systematically different from those who do not.

c. Selection bias because some people may not have access to the website or may not be computer savvy; nonresponse bias because people who choose not to respond may be systematically different from those who do not respond.

d. Selection bias because patients in hospitals are likely ill and may not be capable of walking vigorously three times a week.

7.10 a. $E(\overline{X}) = 80$; $se(\overline{X}) = 1.4$

b. $P(77 \leq \overline{X} \leq 85) = 0.9838$

c. $P(\overline{X} > 84) = 0.0021$

7.14 a. $P(\overline{X} \geq 18) = 0.0142$

b. $P(\overline{X} \geq 17.5) = 0.0022$

c. Janice; her findings are more likely if a representative sample is used.

7.16 a. $E(\overline{X}) = 22$; $se(\overline{X}) = 1.25$. The sample mean has a normal distribution because the population is normally distributed.

b. $P(\overline{X} > 25) = 0.0082$

c. $P(18 \leq \overline{X} \leq 24) = 0.9445$

7.20 a. $P(X > 1{,}000{,}000) = 0.2119$

b. $P(\overline{X} > 1{,}000{,}000) = 0.0548$

7.22 a. $P(X < 90) = 0.2660$

b. $P(\overline{X} < 90) = 0.1056$

c. $[P(X < 90)]^4 = (0.2660)^4 = 0.0050$.

7.26 a. $P(\overline{P} < 0.30) = 0.9014$

b. $p = 0.74$; $P(\overline{P} > 0.75) = 0.3736$

7.34 a. Centerline: $\mu = 20$; UCL = 26; LCL = 14

c. The last two points are outside the upper control limit. There is also an upward trend, suggesting the process is becoming increasingly out of control. The process should be adjusted.

7.36 a. Centerline: $p = 0.34$; UCL = 0.404; LCL = 0.276

b. There are no points outside the control limits, so the process is under control. However, the positive trend suggests that the process may become out of control if the upward trend continues.

7.38 a. Centerline: $\mu = 5.125$; UCL = 5.25; LCL = 5

b. There are no points outside the control limits. It appears that the process is under control, but the positive trend suggests the process may become out of control if the trend continues.

7.40 a. Centerline: $\mu = 94$; UCL = 97.43; LCL = 90.57

b. Kalwant's average speed is out of the control limits on 1 out of 4 of his overs, which rather justifies his coach's concern that he is not very consistent.

7.42 a. Centerline: $p = 0.04$; UCL = = 0.066; LCL =0.014

b. All sample proportions are within the control limits and there is no apparent trend, which suggests that the machine is operating properly.

7.44 a. Centerline: $p = 0.25$; UCL = 0.297; LCL = 0.203

b. 240/750 = 0.32, which is above the upper control limit of 0.297, so the university should be concerned about this.

7.46 a. Centerline: $p = 0.15$; UCL = 0.27; LCL = 0.03

b. 3 out of 6 months were out of the control limits, which is a good justification for why the corporation chose to direct customers away from Country X call centers.

Chapter 8

8.2 a. For 89%, $z_{0.055} = 1.598$

b. For 92%, $z_{0.04} = 1.751$

c. For 96%, $z_{0.02} = 2.054$

8.6 a. $\bar{x} = 78.1$

b. $1.645\dfrac{4.5}{\sqrt{50}} = 1.05$

c. 78.1 ± 1.05 or [77.05, 79.15]

8.10 a. $2.576\dfrac{500}{\sqrt{100}} = 128.79$

b. $7{,}790 \pm 128.79$ or [7,661.21, 7,918.79]

8.14 For 90% confidence interval: [18.81, 21.61]; for 99% confidence level [18.02, 22.40]; the 99% confidence interval is wider.

8.22 a. $2.11\dfrac{9.2}{\sqrt{18}} = 4.58$

b. 12.5 ± 4.58 or [7.92, 17.08]

8.24 a. $2.724\dfrac{10}{\sqrt{36}} = 4.54$

b. 100 ± 4.54 or [95.46, 104.54]

8.26 a. $17.25 \pm 3.499\dfrac{5.95}{\sqrt{8}} = [9.89, 24.61]$

b. The population is normally distributed.

8.28 a. $2.447\dfrac{2.33}{\sqrt{7}} = 2.15$

b. Increase the sample size.

c. 6.6 ± 2.15 or [4.45, 8.75]

8.30 a. Firm A: $18 \pm 4.604\dfrac{20.70}{\sqrt{5}}$ or [−24.62, 60.62].

Firm B: $14.8 \pm 4.604\dfrac{6.50}{\sqrt{5}}$ or [1.42, 28.18].

b. Annual return for each firm has a normal distribution, because the sample size is less than 30.

c. Firm A; it has a higher sample standard deviation.

8.34 $1{,}080 \pm 2.032\dfrac{260}{\sqrt{35}} = [990.69, 1169.31]$; the manager is wrong with the new strategy, since 1200 is not within the 95% confidence interval.

8.36 a. For microeconomics: [68.74, 74.91]

For macroeconomics: [66.16, 74.64]

b. The widths of the two confidence intervals are different because the standard deviations are different.

8.40 a. $0.6 \pm 1.960\sqrt{\dfrac{0.6(1 - 0.6)}{50}} = [0.464, 0.736]$

b. $0.6 \pm 1.960\sqrt{\dfrac{0.6(1 - 0.6)}{200}} = [0.532, 0.668]$;

with larger n, the interval is narrower

8.42 a. $\bar{p} = 0.40$

b. For the 90% confidence interval:

$0.40 \pm 1.645\sqrt{\dfrac{0.40(1 - 0.40)}{100}} = [0.319, 0.481]$

For the 99% confidence interval:

$0.40 \pm 2.576\sqrt{\dfrac{0.40(1 - 0.40)}{100}} = [0.274, 0.526]$

c. Yes, because 0.5 does not fall within the interval.

d. No, because 0.5 falls within the interval.

8.44 $0.05 \pm 1.960 \sqrt{\dfrac{0.05(1 - 0.05)}{400}} = [0.029, 0.071]$

8.46 a. For the 90% confidence interval:

$$0.37 \pm 1.645 \sqrt{\dfrac{0.37(1 - 0.37)}{5,324}} = [0.359, 0.381]$$

b. For the 99% confidence interval:

$$0.37 \pm 2.576 \sqrt{\dfrac{0.37(1 - 0.37)}{5,324}} = [0.353, 0.387]$$

c. The margin of error in part b is greater because it uses a higher confidence level.

8.48 a. $0.44 \pm 1.645 \sqrt{\dfrac{0.44(1 - 0.44)}{1000}} = [0.414, 0.466]$

b. $1.645 \sqrt{\dfrac{0.44(1 - 0.44)}{1000}} = 0.026$

c. $2.576 \sqrt{\dfrac{0.44(1 - 0.44)}{1000}} = 0.040$

8.52 a. $1.960 \sqrt{\dfrac{0.55(1 - 0.55)}{600}} = 0.040$

b. 0.55 ± 0.040 or $[0.510, 0.590]$

c. Increase the sample size.

8.56 $n = 62$

8.58 $n = 24; n = 68$

8.60 $n = 139; n = 62$

8.62 $n = 182$

8.64 a. $n = 102$

b. $n = 40$

c. With higher standard deviation, Fund A needs a higher sample size to achieve the same margin of error.

8.66 a. $n = 50$

b. $n = 139$

8.68 $n = 1,680$

Chapter 9

9.4 a. Incorrect; we never accept the null hypothesis.

b. Correct.

c. Incorrect; we establish a claim only if the null hypothesis is rejected.

d. Correct.

9.6 a. Type I error: incorrectly conclude that conclude mean weight is different from 18 ounces; Type II error: incorrectly conclude that mean weight does not differ from 18 ounces.

b. A Type I error: incorrectly conclude that the stock price increases on more than 60% of the trading days; Type II error: incorrectly conclude that the stock price does not increase on more than 60% of the trading days.

c. Type I error: incorrectly conclude that Americans sleep for less than 7 hours a day; Type II error: incorrectly conclude that Americans do not sleep for less than 7 hours a day.

9.8 a. Type I error: incorrectly conclude that majority of voters support the candidate; Type II error: incorrectly conclude that majority of voters do not support the candidate.

b. Type I error: incorrectly conclude that the average pizza is less than 10 inches; Type II error: incorrectly conclude that the average pizza is not less than 10 inches.

c. Type I error: incorrectly conclude that ibuprofen content in tablet differs from 250 mg; Type II error: incorrectly conclude that that ibuprofen content in tablet does not differ from 250 mg.

9.10 a. Type I error: the new software is purchased even though it does not reduce assembly costs.

b. Type II error: the new software is not purchased even though it reduces assembly costs.

9.12 a. Type I error: the restaurant is incorrectly implicated for using higher fat content.

b. Type II error: the restaurant escapes being implicated for using higher fat content.

9.14 a. Type II error: incorrectly conclude that the diet does not lower the weight by more than 10 pounds.

b. Type I error: incorrectly conclude that the diet will lower the weight by more than 10 pounds.

9.16 a. $z = -2$

b. 0.0455

c. Reject H_0; at the 10% significance level, we conclude that the population mean differs from 100.

9.18 a. $H_0 : \mu \leq 45; H_A : \mu > 45$

b. $z = 1.50$

c. 0.0668

d. We do not reject H_0; at the 5% significance level, we cannot conclude that the population mean is greater than 45.

9.20 $z = 1.4142$; p-value $= 0.0786$; do not reject H_0; at the 5% significance level, we cannot conclude that the population mean is greater than -5.

9.22 $z = -3.5714$; p-value $= 0.0004$; reject H_0; at the 1% significance level, we conclude that population mean differs from -100.

9.26 a. $H_0 : \mu \leq 90; H_A : \mu > 90$

b. $z = 1.5811$; p-value $= 0.0569$

c. Do not reject H_0. At the 1% significance level, the manager's claim is not supported.

9.30 a. $H_0 : \mu = 30; H_A : \mu \neq 30$

b. $z = 2.40$; p-value $= 0.0164$

c. Reject H_0. At the 5% significance level, the average weekly stock price of the home improvement store differs from $30.

9.32 a. $H_0 : \mu \leq 25,000; H_A : \mu > 25,000$

b. $z = 0.5953$; p-value $= 0.2758$

c. Do not reject H_0. At the 10% significance level, the researcher's claim is not supported by the data.

9.34 a. $H_0 : \mu \geq 81.48; H_A : \mu < 81.48$

b. $z = -4.3162$; p-value ≈ 0

c. Reject H_0. At the 1% significance level, the data support the sociologist's belief.

9.40 $H_0:\mu = 16$; $H_A:\mu \ne 16$; $t_{31} = -7.542$; p-value ≈ 0; reject H_0; At the 1% significance level, the population mean differs from 16.

9.42 a. $t_{24} = -2.50$

b. Reject H_0; At the 5% significance level, the population mean is less than -10.

9.46 a. $H_0:\mu \le 5$; $H_A:\mu > 5$

b. The population is normally distributed; $t_{19} = 3.049$; p-value = 0.003

c. Reject H_0. The average waiting time is more than 5 minutes at the 10% level. The manager should hire an additional employee.

9.48 a. $H_0:\mu = 12$; $H_A:\mu \ne 12$

b. Because the sample size is sufficiently large, the sample mean is normally distributed according to Central Limit Theorem.

c. $t_{47} = -1.732$; p-value = 0.090.

d. Do not reject H_0; At the 5% significance level, we cannot conclude that the bottling process has fallen out of adjustment.

9.50 $H_0:\mu \le 6.6$; $H_A:\mu > 6.6$; $t_{35} = 2.7$; reject H_0. At the 5% significance level, the mean increase in home prices in the West is greater than the increase in the Midwest.

9.54 a. $H_0:\mu = 50$; $H_A:\mu \ne 50$

b. $t_{24} = -0.748$; p-value = 0.462

c. Do not reject H_0. At the 5% significance level, we cannot conclude that the average MPG differs from 50.

9.66 a. $z = -0.2955$; p-value = 0.7676

b. $z = 2.0477$; p-value 0.0406

c. $z = 1.0847$; p-value = 0.2781

d. $z = 1.7257$; p-value = 0.0844

9.68 a. $H_0:p = 0.40$; $H_A:p \ne 0.40$

b. Yes, the normality condition that $np \ge 5$ and $n(1 - p) \ge 5$ is satisfied.

c. $z = 1.6330$; p-value = 0.1025.

d. Do not reject H_0. At the 5% significance level, the population proportion is not different from 0.40.

9.70 a. $H_0:p \le 0.65$; $H_A:p > 0.65$

b. Yes, the normality condition that $np \ge 5$ and $n(1 - p) \ge 5$ is satisfied.

c. $z = 2.0755$; p-value = 0.0190.

d. Reject H_0. At the 5% significance level, the population proportion is greater than 0.65.

9.74 a. $H_0:p \le 0.20$; $H_A:p > 0.20$

b. $z = 2.1764$; p-value = 0.0148

c. Reject H_0. At the 5% significance level, the economist's concern is supported by the sample data.

9.80 $H_0:p \le 0.60$; $H_A:p > 0.60$; $z = 1.0351$; p-value = 0.1503; do not reject H_0. At the 1% significance level, the sample evidence does not support the claim that more than 60% of seniors have made serious adjustments to their lifestyle.

9.82 $H_0:p \ge 0.35$; $H_A:p < 0.35$

Case 1: $z = -1.3260$; p-value = 0.0924; do not reject H_0. At the 5% significance level, we cannot conclude that the percentage of Americans who feel that the country is headed in the right direction is below 35%.

Case 2: $z = -1.8752$; p-value = 0.0304; reject H_0. At the 5% significance level, we conclude that the percentage of Americans who feel that the country is headed in the right direction is below 35%.

9.84 $H_0:p \ge 0.20$; $H_A:p < 0.20$; $z = -1.7678$; p-value = 0.0386; reject H_0. At the 5% significance level, we can conclude that the proportion of Americans who do not use the internet is less than 0.20.

9.86 a. $H_0:p = 0.17$; $H_A:p \ne 0.17$

b. $z = 2.0707$; p-value = 0.0384.

c. Reject H_0. At the 5% significance level, the proportion of households in the rural South is not representative of the national proportion.

9.88 a. $H_0:p = 0.50$; $H_A:p \ne 0.50$

b. $z = -2.2627$; p-value = 0.0237

c. Do not reject H_0. At the 1% significance level, we cannot conclude that the proportion of Midwestern households with no emergency savings differs from the national proportion.

Chapter 10

10.4 a. $t_{20} = 1.719$; p-value = 0.051; do not reject H_0. At the 5% significance level, we cannot conclude that μ_1 is greater than μ_2.

b. At the 10% significance level, we conclude that μ_1 is greater than μ_2.

10.8 a. $H_0:\mu_1 - \mu_2 = 0$; $H_A:\mu_1 - \mu_2 \ne 0$

b. $t_9 = -1.667$; p-value = 0.1298

c. Do not reject H_0. At the 10% significance level, we cannot conclude that the population means differ.

10.10 a. $H_0:\mu_1 - \mu_2 \ge 0$; $H_A:\mu_1 - \mu_2 < 0$

b. $z = -5.8081$; p-value = 0 (approximately)

c. Reject H_0. At the 5% significance level, we conclude that there is a "community college penalty" at Lucille's university.

10.14 a. $H_0:\mu_1 - \mu_2 \le 0$; $H_A:\mu_1 - \mu_2 > 0$

b. $t_{16} = 2.145$; p-value = 0.024

c. Reject H_0. At the 5% significance level, we conclude that the mean output rate of the new process exceeds that of the old process.

d. Do not reject H_0. At the 1% significance level, we cannot conclude that the mean output rate of the new process exceeds that of the old process.

10.16 a. $H_0:\mu_1 - \mu_2 = 30$, $H_A:\mu_1 - \mu_2 \ne 30$

b. $t_{54} = 2.219$; p-value = 0.03

c. Reject H_0. At the 10% significance level, the sample data contradicts the claim that it takes 30 days longer to sell SUVs compared to smaller cars.

10.20 a. $H_0:\mu_1 - \mu_2 \le 0$; $H_A:\mu_1 - \mu_2 > 0$

b. $t_{67} = 1.436$; p-value = 0.078

c. We can conclude the mean assembly time using the new method is less than the old method only at the 10% significance level.

10.28 a. $H_0:\mu_D \le 0$; $H_A:\mu_D > 0$

b. $t_{34} = 1.868$; p-value= 0.035

c. Reject H_0. At the 5% significance level, we conclude that there is a positive mean difference.

10.30 a. $H_0:\mu_D = 0$; $H_A:\mu_D \ne 0$

b. -2.10

c. 0.08

d. Reject H_0. The manager's assertion is supported by the data at the 10% significance level.

10.32 a. $H_0:\mu_D = 0$; $H_A:\mu_D \neq 0$

b. −0.859.

c. 0.430.

d. Do not reject H_0. At the 5% significance level, we cannot conclude that the appraisers are inconsistent in their estimates.

10.34 a. $H_0:\mu_D \geq 0$; $H_A:\mu_D < 0$

b. $t_6 = -3.684$; p-value = 0.005

c. Reject H_0. We conclude that the mean difference between new and the existing processing time is less than zero. Yes, there is evidence the new processor is faster than the old processor.

10.40 a. $H_0:\mu_D \geq 0$; $H_A:\mu_D < 0$

b. $t_9 = -1.235$; p-value = 0.124

c. Do not reject H_0. At the 5% significance level, we cannot conclude that the defensive shift is effective in lowering a power hitter's batting average.

10.42 a. $H_0:\mu_D \leq 30$; $H_A:\mu_D > 30$; $t_{39} = 3.932$; p-value = 0 (approximately); reject H_0. At the 5% significance level, we conclude that the mean weight gain of women due to pregnancy is more than 30 pounds.

b. $H_0:\mu_D \leq 35$; $H_A:\mu_D > 35$; $t_{39} = 0.655$; p-value = 0.258; do not reject H_0. At the 5% significance level, we cannot conclude that the mean weight gain of women due to pregnancy is more than 35 pounds.

10.50 a. $H_0:\mu_1 = \mu_2 = \mu_3$; H_A: Not all population means are equal.

b. $F_{(2,21)} = 2.804$; p-value =0.083; do not reject H_0. At the 5% significance level, we cannot conclude that significant differences exist in the average whitening effectiveness of the three detergents.

10.52 a. $H_0:\mu_1 = \mu_2 = \mu_3 = \mu_4$; H_A: Not all population mean incomes are equal.

b. $F_{(3,16)} = 17.07108$; p-value ≈ 0; reject H_0. At the 5% significance level, we can conclude that average incomes differ depending on the recreational sport.

10.54 a. MSTR =2,510,589.667; MSE = 36,379.010; $F_{(3,96)} = 69.012$

b. Reject H_0. At the 1% significance level, we can conclude that the average annual energy costs vary by region.

10.56 a. $H_0:\mu_{Low} = \mu_{Medium} = \mu_{High}$; H_A: Not all population means are equal.

b. Because p-value = 0 (approximately) : reject H_0 at both significance levels. At the 1% and 5% significance levels, we can conclude that the mean fill volumes are not the same for the three pressures.

10.58 $H_0:\mu_1 = \mu_2 = \mu_3$; H_A: Not all population means are equal; p-value = 0 (approximately); reject H_0. At the 5% significance level, we can conclude that the average number of customers that frequent the restaurant differs by weekend day.

10.60 $H_0:\mu_1 = \mu_2 = \mu_3$; H_A: Not all population means are equal; p-value = 0 (approximately); reject H_0.

At the 10% significance level, we can conclude that the average job satisfaction differs by field.

10.62 $H_0:\mu_{Region\ 1} = \mu_{Region\ 2} = \mu_{Region\ 3}$; H_A: Not all population means are equal; p-value = 0 (approximately); reject H_0. At the 5% significance level, we can conclude that the average prices differ by region.

10.64 $H_0:\mu_1 = \mu_2 = \mu_3$; H_A: Not all population means are equal; p-value = 0.020; reject H_0. At the 5% significance level, we can conclude that the average strength of the plywood boards differs by the type of glue used.

10.66 $H_0:\mu_1 = \mu_2 = \mu_3 = \mu_4 = \mu_5 = \mu_6 = \mu_7$; H_A: Not all population means are equal; p-value = 0 (approximately); reject H_0. At the 5% significance level, we can conclude that the average visits to the website differ by day of the week.

Chapter 11

11.2. −0.03 ± 0.082 or [−0.112, 0.052]

Because the interval contains the value 0, we cannot conclude that there is any difference between the population proportions at the 5% significance level.

11.4 a. $z = -0.7543$

b. 0.451

c. Do not reject H_0. We cannot conclude that the population proportions differ at the 5% significance level.

11.10 a. $H_0:p_1 - p_2 \leq 0$; $H_A:p_1 - p_2 > 0$.

b. $z = 5.0916$; p-value = 0 (approximately); reject H_0. At the 5% significance level, the proportion of tulip bulbs that failed from Nursery A is more than the corresponding proportion from Nursery B.

c. $H_0:p_1 - p_2 \leq 0.10$; $H_A:p_1 - p_2 > 0.10$; $z = 1.1905$; p-value = 0.117; do not reject H_0. At the 5% significance level, we cannot conclude that the proportion of tulip bulbs that failed from Nursery A exceeds that from Nursery B by more than 0.10.

11.12. a. $H_0:p_1 - p_2 = 0$; $H_A:p_1 - p_2 \neq 0$

b. $z = -1.1509$; p-value = 0.250

c. Do not reject H_0. At the 5% significant level, we cannot conclude that the proportion of rooms with defects at Seaside is different from the proportion of rooms with defects at Oceanfront.

d. −0.07 ± 0.119 or [−0.189, 0.049]

The confidence interval includes zero which indicates there is no difference between the population proportions.

11.16. a. $H_0:p_1 - p_2 \geq 0$; $H_A:p_1 - p_2 < 0$

b. $z = -1.9988$; p-value = 0.0228

c. Reject H_0. At the 5% significance level, we conclude that the proportion of orders that arrive late with the new supplier is less than the proportion of orders that arrive late with the old supplier.

11.18 $H_0:p_1 - p_2 \leq 0.10$; $H_A:p_1 - p_2 > 0.10$; $z = 2.2052$; p-value = 0.0137; reject H_0. At the 5% significance level, we can conclude that the proportion of patients who see improvement after taking the experimental drug is more than 10 percentage points greater than the proportion of patients who see improvement after taking the placebo.

11.20 a. $H_0: p_1 - p_2 \leq 0.05$; $H_A: p_1 - p_2 > 0.05$

b. $z = 0.4249$; p-value $= 0.3355$

c. Do not reject H_0. At the 5% significance level, we cannot conclude that the proportion of on-time flights at JFK is more than 5 percentage points higher than that of O'Hare.

11.28 a. $H_0: p_1 = p_2 = p_3 = 1/3$; H_A: Not all population proportions are equal to 1/3.

b. $\chi_2^2 = 6.968$; p-value $= 0.031$; reject H_0. At the 5% significance level, the visitor's claim is supported by the sample data.

11.30 $H_0: p_1 = 0.38$, $p_2 = 0.33$, $p_3 = 0.29$; H_A: At least one of the p_i differs from its hypothesized value; $\chi_2^2 = 2.179$; p-value $= 0.336$; do not reject H_0. At the 5% significance level, the researcher cannot conclude that car preferences have changed.

11.32 a. $H_0: p_1 = p_2 = p_3 = p_4 = 0.25$; H_A: At least one p_i differs from 0.25.

b. $\chi_3^2 = 7.720$; p-value $= 0.052$.

c. At the 10% significance level, we conclude that the proportion of bags filled by at least one chute is different than 0.25. At the 5% significance level, we cannot conclude that the proportion of bags filled by at least one chute is different than 0.25.

11.34 $H_O: p_1 = 0.47$, $p_2 = 0.30$, $p_3 = 0.04$, $p_4 = 0.05$, $p_5 = 0.14$; H_A: At least one of the p_i differs from its hypothesized value; $\chi_4^2 = 9.961$; p-value $= 0.041$; reject H_0. At the 5% significance level, we can conclude that the researcher's results are inconsistent with the survey results conducted by Facebook.

11.36 a. $H_0: p_1 = 0.40$, $p_2 = 0.30$, $p_3 = 0.20$, $p_4 = 0.10$; H_A: At least one of the p_i differs from its hypothesized value.

b. $\chi_3^2 = 8.182$; p-value $= 0.042$

c. Do not reject H_0. At the 1% significance level, we cannot conclude that the market shares in 2020 have changed from what they were in 2019.

11.38 H_0: The two categories are independent; H_A: The two categories are dependent; $\chi_6^2 = 1.249$; p-value $= 0.974$; do not reject H_0. At the 1% significance level, we cannot conclude that Category 1 and Category 2 are dependent.

11.42. a. H_0: Vehicle brand and union membership are independent;
H_A: Vehicle brand and union membership are dependent

b. $\chi_1^2 = 14.915$; p-value $= 0.0001$; reject H_0. At the 10% significance level, we conclude that vehicle brand is related to union membership.

c. Given that the p-value is approximately equal to zero, the evidence is strong in favor of rejecting H_0 at any reasonable level of significance. Therefore, the conclusion reached in Part b is not sensitive to the choice of significance level.

11.44 a. H_0: Satisfaction level and age are independent; H_A: Satisfaction level and age are dependent

b. 18.358

c. 0.001

d. Reject H_0. At the 1% significance level, we can conclude that the satisfaction level among the firm's customers is dependent on age.

11.46 H_0: Breakup reasons and one's gender are independent; H_A: Breakup reasons and one's gender are dependent; $\chi_4^2 = 19.463$; p-value $= 0.0006$; reject H_0. At the 1% significance level, we conclude that breakup reason is dependent on one's gender.

11.48. H_0: Delinquency and type of heating are independent; H_A: Delinquency and type of heating are dependent; $\chi_3^2 = 23.82$; p-value $= 0$ (approximately); reject H_0. At the 5% significance level, the sample data suggest that the type of heating that a household uses is dependent on whether the household is delinquent on its bill payment.

11.50 a. H_0: Retirement plan and employee pay group are independent;
H_A: Retirement plan and employee pay group are dependent

b. $\chi_4^2 = 8.217$; p-value $= 0.084$

c. At the 10% significance level, we conclude that the preferred retirement plan and employee pay group are dependent. At the 5% significance level, we cannot conclude that the preferred retirement plan and employee pay group are dependent.

11.52 a. H_0: Days absent and work shift are independent; H_A: Days absent and work shift are dependent

b. $\chi_6^2 = 13.311$; p-value $= 0.038$

c. At the 5% significance level, we conclude that days absent and work shift are dependent at the 5% significance level. At the 1% significance level, we cannot conclude that days absent and work shift are dependent. Our conclusion is sensitive to the choice of significance level.

Chapter 12

12.2 a. $b_1 = -1208.25$; every year the car's predicted price decreases by $1,208.25

b. $\hat{y} = 21187.94 - 1208.25x$

c. $\hat{y} = 15146.69$

12.4 a. $\widehat{GPA} = 0.4256 + 0.0041 GRE$

b. $\widehat{GPA} = 3.35$

12.6 a. $\widehat{Consumption} = 295.6799 + 0.8721$ Disposable Income

b. As disposable income increases by $1, predicted consumption increases by $0.8721

c. $\widehat{Consumption} = \$13,377.72$ billion

12.8 a. $\widehat{Final} = 27.5818 + 0.6774$ Midterm

b. $\widehat{Final} = 81.77$

12.10 a. $\widehat{Watches} = 35.9090 - 0.0261$ Time

b. As the time increases by 1 second, the predicted watches decrease by 0.0261

c. A time of zero seconds is not possible

d. $\widehat{Watches} = 21.57$

12.12 a. As expected for Poverty but not for Income

b. $\hat{y} = 1009.08$

12.16 a. Non-business majors

b. Non-business majors and no MBA

c. No

12.22 a. $\hat{y} = -0.2091 + 0.0875x_1 + 0.1123x_2$

   b. For every additional \$1 million in drive-through sales, predicted net profits increase by \$112,300, holding counter sales constant.

   c. $\hat{y} = 0.7647$

12.24 a. $\widehat{\text{Startups}} = 0.4190 + 0.0087$ Research $+ 0.0517$ Patents $- 0.0194$ Duration

   b. $\widehat{\text{Startups}} = 1.48$

   c. Approximately \$114.94 million

12.36 a. $\widehat{\text{Watches}} = 35.9090 - 0.0261$ Time

   b. $H_0: \beta_1 \geq -0.02; H_A: \beta_1 < -0.02; t_{18} = -2.773$; p-value $= 0.006$; reject H_0. At the 5% level, we conclude that an extra second of Time decreases Watches by more than 0.02.

12.38 a. $\widehat{\text{Cost}} = 14039.1873 + 92.7827$ Temp $+ 446.1406$ Days $- 27.0033$ Tons

   b. $H_0: \beta_1 = \beta_2 = \beta_3 = 0; H_A:$ At least one $\beta_j \neq 0$; p-value $= 0.026$; reject H_0; joint significance at the 10% level.

   c. $H_0: \beta_1 = 0; H_A: \beta_1 \neq 0$; p-value $= 0.011$; reject H_0 at the 10% level

   $H_0: \beta_2 = 0; H_A: \beta_2 \neq 0$; p-value $= 0.549$; do not reject H_0 at the 10% level

   $H_0: \beta_3 = 0; H_A: \beta_3 \neq 0$; p-value $= 0.810$; do not reject H_0 at the 10% level

12.46 a. $\widehat{\text{Salary}} = 62.3383 - 0.9605$ BMI $+ 4.4855$ College

   $H_0: \beta_1 = 0; H_A: \beta_1 \neq 0$; p-value $= 0$ (approx.); reject H_0 at the 5% level

   b. $\widehat{\text{Salary}} = 38.01$ (College); $\widehat{\text{Salary}} = 33.52$ (No College)

12.48 a. $\widehat{\text{Time}} = 0.0357 + 0.0079$ Machine $+ 0.6465$ Manual

   b. $\widehat{\text{Time}} = 14.13$

   c. 85.30%

   d. $H_0: \beta_1 = \beta_2 = \beta_3 = 0; H_A:$ At least one $\beta_j \neq 0$; p-value $= 0$ (approx.); reject H_0 at the 5% level

   Machine parts significant (p-value $= 0.003$); Manual parts significant (p-value $= 0$)

12.52 b. The residual plot suggests changing variability (heteroskedasticity); the estimators are unbiased, but not efficient; the t tests and F test are not valid; use robust standard errors for conducting significance tests.

12.53 b. The residual plot suggests correlated observations (positive serial correlation); the estimators are unbiased but not efficient; the t tests and F test are not valid; use robust standard errors for conducting significance tests.

12.54 The scatterplot suggests a nonlinear relationship; GPA positively related to Hours at lower levels but negatively related to Hours at higher levels.

12.56 a. Perfect multicollinearity (Study + Sleep + Leisure = 24); the proposed model cannot be estimated.

   b. Drop any one of the perfectly multicollinear variable.

12.58 a. Experienced (older) employees are likely to have more variability in salaries.

   b. The residual plot fans out when plotted against experience, suggesting changing variability.

12.60 No issue with correlated observations because the residuals do not show any pattern around the horizontal axis.

Chapter 13

13.4 a. $\widehat{\text{Hours}} = 13.7647 + 4.5144$ Fall $+ 1.6074$ Winter

   $H_0: \beta_j \leq 0$ and $H_A: \beta_j > 0$; for one-tailed tests, the p-values equals 0.0000/2 and 0.0003/2, respectively; reject H_0 at the 5% level; students study more in fall and winter than in spring.

   b. 18.28 (fall); 15.37 (winter); 13.76 (spring)

13.6 a. $\hat{y} = 52.1557 + 0.3354$ Weight $- 7.2916$ White $- 4.0881$ Black $- 6.5697$ Asian

   b. p-value $= 0$ (approx.) for White; the LDL levels differ between white men and Hispanic men at the 5% level.

   c. Use either White or Asian as the reference category

13.14 a. $\widehat{\text{Majority Male}} = 88.57 - 8.57$ Female $- 6.22$ Minority Male $- 18.78$(Female × Minority Male); all variables are significant at the 5% level

   b. 80% (no minority male); 55% (minority male)

13.16 a. $\widehat{\text{Usage}} = 14.9236 + 0.9808$Income $- 42.3267$ Rural $+ 20.4745$ College $+ 49.8701$ (Rural × College)

   The influence of college on the usage of mobile devices differs between rural and urban/suburban dwellers.

   b. 160.64 minutes (rural); 153.10(urban/suburban)

13.18 a. $\widehat{\text{Errors}} = 37.9305 - 1.2814$ Exper $- 7.4241$ Train

   $\widehat{\text{Errors}} = 42.7765 - 1.6991$ Exper $- 23.1111$ Train $+ 0.9785$(Exper × Train)

   b. The second model provides a better fit (higher Adjusted R^2 and significant variables at the 10% level).

   c. 12.46 (10 years); 8.79 (20 years)

   d. Less experienced employees benefit more from the training program (reduced errors) than more experienced employees.

13.26 a. From the scatterplot, crew size of 6 or 7 seems optimal.

   b. Linear model: $\widehat{\text{Jobs}} = 13.0741 + 0.1111$ Crew

   Quadratic model: $\widehat{\text{Jobs}} = 2.1111 + 4.5960$ Crew $- 0.3737$ Crew^2

   The quadratic model provides a better fit because of higher adjusted R^2

   c. $\widehat{\text{Jobs}} = 15.75$

13.28 a. $\widehat{\text{Salary}} = -13434.88 + 2498.50$Age $- 26.01$ Age^2 $- 6995.28$Female $+ 5569$NPS

   b. Maximum at $\dfrac{-2498.50}{2 \times -26.01} = 48.02$

   c. \$84,116 (Female); \$91,111 (Nonfemale)

13.30 a. Linear: $\widehat{\text{Time}} = -14.4886 + 0.7502$Parts

   Quadratic: $\widehat{\text{Time}} = -6.7165 + 0.4476$Parts $+ 0.0025$Parts^2

   b. The predictor variables are significant in both models; the quadratic model is preferred because of higher adjusted R^2.

   c. $\widehat{\text{Time}} = 20.59$

Chapter 14

14.4   a. $MSE = 649.9512$; $MAD = 20.3975$;
        $MAPE = 14.4617\%$; $\hat{y}_{12} = 127.89$

     b. $MSE = 551.5359$; $MAD = 19.9401$;
        $MAPE = 14.0331\%$; $\hat{y}_{12} = 146.06$

     c. Exponential smoothing is preferred.

14.6   a. $MSE = 0.0009$; $MAD = 0.0244$;
        $MAPE = 2.0832\%$ (3-period)

        $MSE = 0.0016$; $MAD = 0.0344$;
        $MAPE = 2.9274\%$ (5-period)

        3-period moving average is preferred; $\hat{y}_{26} = 1.14$

     b. $MSE = 0.0018$; $MAD = 0.0384$;
        $MAPE = 2.8923\%$ ($\alpha = 0.20$)

        $MSE = 0.0010$; $MAD = 0.0276$;
        $MAPE = 2.0791\%$ ($\alpha = 0.40$)

        $MSE = 0.0007$; $MAD = 0.0213$; $MAPE = 1.6115\%$
        ($\alpha = 0.60$)

        $\alpha = 0.60$ is preferred; $\hat{y}_{26} = 1.28$

14.12 a. $\hat{y}_t = 90.4938 + 1.1124t$; positive trend

     b. $\hat{y}_{54} = 150.5647$

14.14 $\hat{y}_t = 746.4615 - 4.0290t - 188.2651 \text{Weekend}$

     Forecast for Monday: $t = 43$, Weekend $= 0$;
     $\hat{y}_t = 573.21$

     Forecast for Saturday: $t = 48$, Weekend $= 1$;
     $\hat{y}_t = 364.80$

14.16 a. $\hat{y}_t = 8624.5136 + 1703.1858d_1 + 4619.0330d_2$
        $+ 1339.3347d_3 + 223.4256t$

        Positive trend; relative to the 4th quarter, the
        revenue is consistently higher in other quartiers

     b. $\hat{y}_{2021:01}(d_1 = 1, d_2 = 0, d_3 = 0, t = 45) = 20381.85$

14.18 The estimated trend coefficient $= 0.2941$;
      $\hat{y}_{2020:01} = 104.82$.

14.22 a. The scatterplot suggests a quadratic model.

     b. Linear: $\hat{y}_t = 219.31 + 1.4378t$; adjusted
        $R^2 = 0.8349$

        Quadratic: $\hat{y}_t = 213.7527 + 3.6607t - 0.1588t^2$;

        adjusted $R^2 = 0.9550$

        The quadratic model is preferred; $\hat{y}_{2018} = 233.88$;
        $\hat{y}_{2019} = 232.94$

14.24 a. Quadratic: $\hat{y}_t = 1983.0652 - 30.4231t + 0.7698t^2$;

        adjusted $R^2 = 0.8976$

        Cubic: $\hat{y}_t = 1969.5755 - 26.7026t + 0.5457t^2 +$

        $0.0036t^3$; adjusted $R^2 = 0.8970$

        The quadratic model is preferred.

     b. $\hat{y}_{41} = 2029.67$

14.26 a. $\hat{y}_t = 241332.1180 - 4024.3036d_1 - 512.1212$

        $d_2 - 10589.2436d_3 + 4219.4278t + 27.9857t^2$

     b. $\hat{y}_{2018:4}(d_1 = 0, d_2 = 0, d_3 = 0, t = 36) = 429501$

14.32 a. $\widehat{\text{Sales}}_t = 17.51 + 0.03(620) - 0.69(9.1) = 29.83$

     b. $\widehat{\text{Sales}}_t = 17.51 + 0.03(700) - 0.69(9.1) = 32.23$

     c. $\widehat{\text{Sales}}_t = 17.51 + 0.03(620) - 0.69(9.5) = 29.56$

        $\widehat{\text{Sales}}_t = 17.51 + 0.03(700) - 0.69(9.5) = 31.96$

14.34 a. Model 1: $\widehat{\text{CPI}}_t = 303.161 - 13.079 \text{Unemp}_{t-1}$;
        adjusted $R^2 = 0.7347$

        Model 2: $\widehat{\text{CPI}}_t = -4.389 + 0.120 \text{Unemp}_{t-1} +$
        1.017CPI_{t-1}; adjusted $R^2 = 0.9867$

     b. Model 2 is preferred; $\widehat{\text{CPI}}_{25} = 258.92$

Chi-square tests
    of contingency table, 302–303
    for independence, 302–307
Classes, 80
Classical probability, 99–100
Clinton, Hillary, 175
CLT. *See* Central limit theorem (CLT)
Clustered column chart, 44–48
Clusters, 177
Cluster sampling, 177
Coefficient of determination (R^2), 327–328
Coefficient of variation, 73–74
College admissions data set, 401
College Scorecard, 313, 336–337
Column chart, 29
    clustered, 44–48
    stacked, 44–48
Complement, of events, 96
Complement rule, 101–102
Conditional probability, 103–104, 119
Confidence coefficient, 204
Confidence intervals, 202–203
    constructing, 203–205, 212–213
    defined, 202
    for differences in means, 258–260
    interpreting, 205
    margin of error, 202–203, 220
    for mean difference, 267–272
    of population mean with known standard deviation, 204
    of population mean with unknown standard deviation, 209–214
    for population proportion, 217–218, 288–289
    precision of, 207
    sample sizes and, 220–222
    two-tailed hypothesis tests, 238–239
    using Excel, 207–208, 213–214
    width of, 205–207
Constants, 179
Constant variability, 345
Construction clothing data, 27, 54
Contingency tables, 43–44, 120, 287, 306
    chi-square test of, 302–303
    defined, 108
    Excel, 45–48
    expected frequencies, 303–305
    probabilities and, 108–110
Continuous probability distributions. *See also* Normal
        distribution
    exponential, 164–166
    uniform, 150–152
Continuous random variables, 122, 124, 150–152
Continuous uniform distribution, 150–152
Continuous variable, 10
Control charts, 192–195
Correlated observations, 347–349
Correlation coefficient
    calculating, 86–87
    defined, 86

population, 86
sample, 86
Covariance
    calculating, 86–87
    defined, 85
    population, 85
    sample, 85
Critical value approach, 234, 253–255
    defined, 253
    four-step procedure using, 254
    rejection region, 253, 254
Cross-sectional data, 5, 6
Cubic trend model, 391–392
Cumulative distribution function, 124, 150, 156, 165
Cumulative frequency distribution, 35–36

D

Data
    big data, 7–9
    cross-sectional, 5, 6
    Internet availability of, 8
    as language of statistics, 4
    standardizing, 158
    structured, 6–7
    time series, 6
    types, 4–9
    unstructured (unmodeled), 7
    on websites, 9
Data preparation
    counting and sorting, 16–18
    data ranges, 19
    missing values, 18
    subsetting, 18–20
Data sets
    college admissions, 401
    house price, 401–402
    tech sales reps, 402
Data visualization, 26
Decision rules
    critical value approach, 234, 254–255
    p-value approach, 234–238
Degrees of freedom (*df*), 210–212
Descriptive statistics, 4
Detection approach, 191
Deterministic *vs.* stochastic relationships, 314
Discrete probability distributions, 124–127
    binomial distribution, 132–134
    discrete uniform distribution, 125
    graphical displays, 125
    hypergeometric, 140–143
    Poisson, 136–138
    properties of, 124–127
Discrete random variables, 122, 124, 150
    expected value of, 129
    summary measures for, 128–130
Discrete uniform distribution, 125
Discrete variables, 10

Dispersion measures, 70–74
  coefficient of variation, 73–74
  Excel calculations, 72–73
  interquartile range, 70–71
  mean absolute deviation, 71–72
  range, 70–71
  standard deviation, 72–73
  variance, 72–73
Dow Jones Industrial Average (DJIA), 11, 12
Dummy variables, 321–323
  interaction variables and, 360–366
  for multiple categories, 356
  significance tests, 360
Dummy variable trap, 356

E

The Economist, 9
Empirical probability, 98–99, 110
Empirical rule, 79–80
Error sum of squares (SSE), 277, 316
ESPN, 9
Estimate, 179
Estimation, 202. *See also* Interval estimates
Estimator, 179, 202
Events
  complement of, 96
  defined, 94
  dependent, 105
  exhaustive, 94–95
  independent, 105
  intersection of, 95, 96
  mutually exclusive, 95
  total probability rule and, 113–116
  union of, 95, 96
Excel
  association measures, 86–87
  bar charts, 30
  binomial distribution, 133–134
  boxplot, 82–83
  central location measures, 63–64
  clustered column chart, 45–48
  confidence intervals, 207–208, 213–214
  contingency table, 45–48
  control charts, 195
  histogram, 38–40
  hypergeometric probabilities, 142–143
  hypothesis test for mean difference, 271–272
  hypothesis testing, 242–243, 262–264
  multiple linear regression model, 323
  one-way ANOVA table, 280–281
  pie charts, 30–32
  Poisson probabilities, 137–138
  residual plot construction, 349
  sampling, 177–178
  simple linear regression model, 318
  stacked column chart, 45–48
  test statistic value calculation, 242–243

Excluded variable, 348
Exhaustive events, 94–95
Expected value, 129
  sample mean, 180–181
  sample proportion, 186–187
Experiment, 94
Explained variation, 327
Exponential distribution, 164–166

F

F distribution, 278–280
Federal Reserve Economic Data, 9
Fidelity, 59, 77
Finite population correction factor, 189
Forbes, 9
Forecasting
  causal models, 395–397
  linear trend model, 386–390
  model selection, 379–380
  monthly housing starts, 398–400
  noncausal, 395
  qualitative, 379
  quantitative, 379
  smoothing techniques, 380–385
  trend models, 386–390
Formulas, Excel, 403
Fortune, 9
Frequency distribution, 28–29
Functions, MS Excel, 404–405

G

Gallup, George, 175
Games of chance, 99
Gender gap, in manager salaries, 355, 366
Globalization, 104
Goodness-of-fit tests
  coefficient of determination, 327–328
  of a contingency table, 302–303
  defined, 295
  expected frequencies, 296
  for multinomial experiment, 294–300
  for regression analysis, 326
  standard error of the estimate, 326–327
  test statistic for, 297–300
Google Finance, 9
Grand mean, 277
Graphical displays
  bar charts, 29
  boxplots, 81–83
  distortions of, 32
  pie charts, 29–32

H

Happiness index data, 9
Histogram, 36–40

Home Depot, 224–225
Hoover, Herbert, 174
House price data, 88–90, 401–402
Hybrid SUVs, efficiency of, 201, 202, 212–213, 218
Hypergeometric distribution, 140–143
    using Excel, 142–143
Hypothesis testing, 202
    average study times, 227, 243–244
    critical value approach, 234, 253–255
    for difference in means, 260–264
    interpreting results, 239
    left-tailed, 229
    for mean difference, 269–272
    null *versus* alternative hypothesis, 228–229
    one-tailed, 229–231
    of population mean, known standard deviation,
        233–239
    of population mean, unknown standard deviation,
        241–243
    of population proportion, 247–248, 289–292
    p-value approach, 234–238
    rejecting/not rejecting null hypothesis, 228–229
    right-tailed, 229
    significance level, 235
    two-tailed, 229–231, 238–239
    Type I and Type II errors, 231–232
    using Excel, 242–243

I

Iced coffee, 173, 189
Imputation strategy, 18
Independence, chi-square test for, 302–307
    contingency table, 302–303
    expected frequencies, 303–305
    test statistics, 305
Independent events, 105
Independent random samples, defined, 258
Indicator variable. *See* Dummy variable
Individual significance, tests of, 331–334
Inferential statistics, 4
In-sample criteria, 379
Interaction effect, 360
Interaction variables, 360–366
    of dummy and numerical variable, 362–366
    with two dummy variables, 360–362
Interquartile range (IQR), 70–71
Intersection, of events, 95, 96
Interval, 202
Interval estimates, 202
Interval scale, 13
Investment decision, 59

J

Johnson & Johnson (J&J), 334–335
Joint probabilities, 102, 110
Joint significance, tests of, 330–331

L

Lagged regression models, 395–397
Landon, Alf, 174, 175
Law of large numbers, 100
Left-tailed hypothesis test, 229
Linear regression model
    deterministic *vs.* stochastic relationships, 314
    multiple linear regression model, 320–323
    simple linear regression model, 314–318
Linear trend model, 386–390
Line chart, 51–54
Literary Digest polls, 174–175
Lower control limit (LCL), 192
Lowe's, 224–225

M

MAD. *See* Mean absolute deviation (MAD)
Marginal probabilities, 110
Margin of error, 202–203, 220
Marijuana legalization support, 118–119, 248
Marital status, 10
Matched-pairs sampling, 267
    mean difference, 267–272
    recognizing, 267–268
Mean, 60–61. *See also* Population mean; Sample mean
    confidence intervals for differences in,
        258–260
    subgroups calculation, 66–67
Mean absolute deviation (MAD), 71–72, 380
Mean absolute percentage error (MAPE), 380
Mean difference
    confidence interval for, 268
    hypothesis test for, 269–272
    matched pairs experiments, 267–268
Mean square error (MSE), 277, 380
Mean square for treatments (MSTR), 277
    between-treatments estimate, 277
    within-treatments estimate, 277–278
Mean-variance analysis, 75–76
Measurement scales, 11–14
    interval, 13
    nominal, 11–12
    ordinal, 12–13
    ratio, 13–14
Median, 61, 63, 65, 67
Method of least squares, 316
Microsoft Excel
    add-ins, 405
        Analysis ToolPak add-ins, 405
        description of, 403
        formulas, 403
        relative/absolute/mixed references, 403–404
Mixed references, Excel, 403–404
Mode, 61–62
Moving average methods, 381–382, 385
MSE. *See* Mean square error (MSE)
MSTR. *See* Mean square for treatments (MSTR)